David Brierley was born in Durban in 1936 and spent his early years in South Africa, Canada and England. After graduating from Oxford he taught in a French *lycée*. He spent fifteen years working in London in advertising agencies before becoming a full-time writer in 1975. His novels have been set all over the world, from behind the former Iron Curtain to the rainforests of Latin America. In 1992 he moved with his wife to France where they now live in a lovingly restored farm cottage.

Praise for David Brierley

'Super-skilled graft of fiction on to history . . . An authentic winner' *Sunday Times*

'If you want espionage in the le Carré class, this is it' *Observer*

'Tough . . . witty . . . in the best tradition of suspense fiction' *New Yorker*

'[The] brilliant description of a damp and cold life after Dubcek makes one want to read it by the fireside; and the paranoia will keep you looking over your shoulder' *Sunday Telegraph*

Also by David Brierley

Big Bear, Little Bear
Shooting Star
Czechmate
One Lives, One Dies
Cold War
Blood Group O
Skorpion's Death
Snowline
On Leaving a Prague Window
The Horizontal Woman

The Cloak-and-Dagger Girl

David Brierley

WARNER BOOKS

A *Warner* Book

First published in Great Britain in 1998
by Little, Brown and Company
This edition published in 1999 by Warner Books

All characters in this publication are fictitious and any resemblance to real persons, living or dead, is purely coincidental.

A CIP catalogue record for this book
is available from the British Library.

ISBN 0 7515 2672 X

Typeset by Palimpsest Book Production Limited,
Polmont, Stirlingshire
Printed and bound in Great Britain by
Mackays of Chatham PLC, Chatham, Kent

Warner Books
A Division of
Little, Brown and Company (UK)
Brettenham House
Lancaster Place
London WC2E 7EN

Horned Viper Lasso Mouth
Basket Arm Two Reeds
&
Mouth Lasso Foot
Stand for Jar Mouth Lasso Folded Cloth
Foot Reed Folded Cloth Lasso Quail Chick Folded Cloth

Chapter 1

The first time Liliana showed herself naked to a man it was on a dessert trolley at the Bucuresti Hotel. It was a December evening in 1989.

The man who emerged from the private dining room had learned the courtier's walk, going backwards, head tucked downwards and sideways. It was a gesture of obeisance, also of protection against any flying glassware. He shut the door on the noise and turned to the ante-room where servants and food and wine waited their turn.

'The comrades have drink taken.'

Liliana knew that. The raised voices, the suggestions that had been made when she passed the platter of goose breast, the pinch marks on her thighs – yes, she was well aware of that.

'They are pigs,' she said.

Standing beside her was Ion, a waiter in early middle age, employed by the hotel, no doubt employed by the Securitate too, but not a bad man. He sucked his breath in and let his eyes dart first to the ceiling light fitting, then to the walls. A large framed portrait of Nicolae Ceausescu hung above a blocked-up fireplace. The dictator, the *conducator*, had his habitual impish grin. He seemed to be listening to their talk. And maybe he was, or one of his underlings.

The man who had backed away from the dining room said, 'More whisky is required. "Fetch Johnnie," they ordered. "Not Commie Johnnie, nigger Johnnie." You may have heard them laughing at the joke. I shall see to that. They are ready for their dessert now. You must take off your clothes.'

With that, he left the room in search of fresh supplies of Johnnie Walker. Liliana stood frozen. She had misheard. Definitely he had said something banal. *Take off the roses.* A bowl of red roses, flown in from Amsterdam, decorated the dining table. She stared after the man, a head waiter of some kind, a political head waiter who came and went to a different routine from the rest of the hotel.

That year of 1989 was the worst of times in Romania though the regime pretended it was the best of times. Posters bearing the same portrait of Ceausescu that watched over this room flooded the countryside. The photograph was subtly airbrushed to make the *conducator* look more youthful, though the result was to make his features look uncommonly like Dylan Thomas on a morning after. The message the posters brought to the populace was that this was the Golden Age of Romania. It must be so because Ceausescu said it. Golden, perhaps, in its promises. Golden, certainly, in its lies.

Liliana turned to Ion. 'What did he say?'

'Didn't you hear?' He glanced away to the closed door against which a glass had just smashed. 'They are impatient for the dessert.' His voice dropped to a mutter, defeating the microphones. 'That's all they've come for, really, the dessert. The booze too, of course. Getting stinking so they can do what they want. "Bring on the *spécialité de la maison*," the Young Pretender shouted. Always a bad sign when he starts speaking French.'

Ion considered the trolley without affection. It was actually two trolleys lashed together and hell to push, its wheels having ideas of their own. It was covered in a tablecloth and had plates temporarily stacked on it. The party had begun with oysters. Some had been eaten. Some had been used as ashtrays. Other were untouched. Ion had warned Liliana not to touch them either. You never knew with the Young Pretender. He had the drunk's sense of humour. He had been known to piss in the oysters – 'season them' he called it – and watch the waiter's face afterwards when he said what he had done. The Young Pretender was the son of Nicolae Ceaucescu so you struggled to keep your face straight and your gorge from rising. Ion began shifting the plates to the floor.

'You better hurry,' Ion said. 'He'll be back with the whisky in a moment.'

'He said . . .' Liliana began, still unbelieving.

'Get your clothes off. The Young Pretender calls it a *bombe surprise.* It's a birthday treat for his friend. Octav, the fat-faced one, in case you're interested who the show's for. You're the *bombe surprise.*'

'No,' Liliana said.

Ion stood up from stacking the plates and took a step towards her. He stood too close so she caught his body odour. There was no soap in the shops and the maids who cleaned the rooms got what soap the guests left.

'Listen,' Ion said. His eyes went away to Nicolae Ceausescu and he leaned even closer. In the airbrushed photo Ceausescu had little ears. But as Ion knew, as the whole of Romania knew, there were often ears behind ears. Liliana found herself holding her breath and counting, which she did at very bad times. 'Listen to me.' Even then he was not quite sure he was safe. If he was spotted whispering, then it must be some secret, some plot, something anti-state. There could be a hidden eye like the hidden ear. So he laid his hand against Liliana's cheek and whispered words of love to her. 'No is not an option. No does not exist. No is not a word that should be in your head tonight.' His eyes flicked towards Ceausescu again. He whispered, 'No has been banned by Himself as an imperialist plot to undermine the Golden Age. So get your clothes off. Just do it.'

The intensity of his whisper shook her. She could still feel his hand on her cheek as if it had burned her skin.

'Please,' she said. She said it as someone begging a favour but Ion took it as if she hadn't understood or wanted reasons.

'Because he is the son of his father. Because of the birthday. Because of the other guests. Because of what could happen to you. You know all that. It is how it is. Who do you think you are?'

Liliana Branoza, 20, student. Correction, ex-student. The fine tradition in Europe that students starved in attics was alive and well in Romania. In Romania students dined on lectures and supped on essays and snacked on books and got drunk on Leninism. What other nourishment did they need? Liliana had been a student with a gift for languages, English and French, but hunger drove her to be a waitress at the hotel. She was hired for her languages, so useful for dealing with foreigners who had been told the Bucuresti was a first-class hotel. In the pasage between kitchen and restaurant there was food to be stolen, chicken wings and bread and butter that the guests pushed to the side of their plates. If she lost her job, she would starve again. Some file in some ministry would record a black mark against her: unreliable, disobedient, puts herself above the demands of the Party.

'What must I do?' she asked. Her voice came from a long way away from her. It was somebody else asking the question, not her.

'Take everything off. Lie here.'

She turned her back to undress. She held her breath as she pulled the uniform up over her head. One thousand and one, one thousand and two, one thousand and three.

'Hurry before he gets back.'

He being the gauleiter of a head waiter, surname Basacopol, first name unknown, gone for fresh supplies of Johnnie Walker. One thousand and four, one thousand and five. She folded her uniform and laid it to rest against the wall. One thousand and six, one thousand and seven. Feeling giddy, she let out her breath and drew another. Her shoes she had kicked off. Now she ranged them beside her uniform. I have never done this for any man, she thought, though Stefan pleaded and Cornel tried with his hands everywhere and Armand swore that his French name was matched by a French ardour that would raise her to fever pitch. One thousand and eight, one thousand and eight, one thousand and eight. She had stuck.

Basacopol, holding litres of Johnnie Walker Black Label in each hand, arrived in the doorway.

'*Totul.*'

She froze. She was in shock. Everything.

'*Totul, totul,*' he said, a dog barking an order. Everything, everything.

It was more than the order. It was the associations. Ceausescu scattered his speeches with *totul*. The Party had done *totul* for the workers. He and Elena had done *totul*. *Totul* was for the best in the Golden Age. Now she must give *totul*.

One thousand and nine, one thousand and ten. She stepped out of her knickers, losing her balance and putting a hand against the wall. She laid the knickers on the uniform. She owned eight pairs of knickers, one for each day of the week and then wash seven pairs while she wore the eighth. On Sunday afternoons. Between the lunchtime and the evening shifts. In cold water. Think how the skin of your fingers gets pinched in the cold water, she ordered. Think how it shrinks and goes white and looks old and unlovely.

One thousand and eleven. There was no man I wanted to do this for, she thought, so I didn't. There is still no man I want to do it for but . . . One thousand and twelve.

'The bra,' Basacopol said. 'Here, I'll do it.'

'Don't touch me.'

She dropped the bra, took a breath and turned round. She was beautiful. She knew it. Stefan and Cornel and Armand had only guessed it from the way her hips swayed and her blouse trembled when she moved. The starvation years had worked wonders, nipping in her waist, slimming the flesh over her ribs so that her breasts stood proud. She looked down and saw to her dismay that her nipples were aroused. She laid an arm across her breasts and a hand over her pubic hair. She was Venus rising out of the sea.

'Christ,' Ion said under his breath, 'they don't deserve it.'

A fresh rebellion seized Liliana. She turned back to pick up her bra and Basacopol said, 'No, you don't. Stretch out on this.'

One thousand and twelve and a quarter, one thousand and twelve and a half. She felt sudden powerful arms round her body and a male hand laid casually on a breast, flattening the nipple. Furious, she turned round to push him away and scratch his eyes or bite or whatever was necessary. But Basacopol was too strong and too determined. He sent her staggering towards the trolley and ordered her to lie down or he personally would pick her up and drop her on it.

She found the breath had been knocked out of her body and she'd lost track of the numbers. She stared at the tablecloth covering the trolley. Cotton, white, standard restaurant issue. A pale yellowish stain was the shape of Australia. I shall lie on Australia, she thought, I shan't be in Romania at all. Those two strange men who are staring my way can't see me because I am on the other side of the world.

'Don't face the wall. Lie on your back. Bloody hell, you look like something on the fishmonger's slab. Kink one leg. Put an arm behind your head. Better.'

This is absolutely not happening to me, she thought. This cannot take place in a so-called first-class hotel in the year of our Lord one thousand nine hundred and eighty-nine, one thousand nine hundred and eighty-nine years and eleven months and six days and twenty-one hours and thirteen minutes and lots of seconds in the Golden Age of Nicolae Ceausescu. But it was happening. Ion, who had only laid a hand on her cheek and not on her body, was wide-eyed at what he had been missing. Basacopol loomed above.

'What are you doing?' she said. 'What's that?'

Basacopol had an aerosol can in his hand. He could be going to kill a fly or write dirty words on a wall. He waved the can above her face. 'It's American,' he said, as if that explained everything. He pressed and white foam appeared from the nozzle. 'It's a cow in a can. Bloody clever those capitalists. You can't get a socialist cow in a can. Or the product of the cow. It's whipped cream.'

He formed a circle round her belly button. He zigzagged at the top of her pubic ruff so that it appeared icicles hung down. He frowned as he got to work on her breasts, covering them with frothy cream so that they became snow-covered hills with little brown peaks.

I shall pray in every church in Bucharest, Liliana promised. I shall light a candle in front of every icon. I shall walk on my knees from the entrance up the aisle to the altar. I shall lick the stones clean with my tongue. Just let me wake up from this nightmare.

She tried closing her eyes to shut out reality but tears stung her eyelids. When she opened them again she found Basacopol stooped over a table with his back to her. He turned round with a candle in his hand.

'Stop crying. It's Comrade Mincu's birthday and he doesn't want to see a weeping woman. Now hold still while I wedge this in.' He forced the candle between her legs, tight up against her crotch. Liliana's body convulsed in a great sob. 'Hold your breath or something, otherwise you'll spill the wax on your thingy and that'll really hurt.'

Saying this Basacopol flicked a lighter to get a flame and touched the wick until the candle was burning.

'Right, open the door,' he ordered Ion. He began pushing the dessert trolley. One wheel was wonky and the trolley slid sideways. 'Hell, you better give me a hand pushing her in. She weighs a bloody ton. What've you been eating? She must have a boyfriend in the kitchen. Mind that doorpost.'

The birthday treat with one red candle bravely burning was wheeled into the private dining room. Six men's faces were turned towards her. She held her breath, as Basacopol had advised, and began counting. First in Romanian. Then in English. Finally, in desperation, in French.

She remembered nothing. Or to be exact, images, sounds and sensations were stored away in her brain, the door closed tight on them, the lock turned and the key thrown away. It was part of the healing process. The wound went deep and needed time to close up. She would bear the scar all her life. Nobody could see it because it was inside, but it was real enough.

It was years before the events came to the surface in her mind and then they floated up in bits and pieces. What she chiefly saw was a face, Octav Mincu's face, saw the rictus of his smile, caught his breath in her nostrils. She would remember that face for ever. As for the rest of Mincu, just darkness. Which was appropriate.

She had perfect recall of being wheeled into that *salon particulier* like a patient going into the operating theatre, naked apart from a light covering of whipped cream, bearing a single lighted birthday candle between her thighs. Silence greeted her entrance, and then there was a roar in her ears, male voices, shouts and laughter, her own heartbeat, her own blood racing, all mixed up and overwhelming her. And then . . . And then . . . And then she was standing in Boulevard Ilie Pintilie, as it used to be called in those pre-democratic times. She wore canvas-topped boots, jeans, a sweater and a raincoat, ill fitting, none of it hers.

The night was black. All nights were black then unless the moon was up. There were no streetlights, no advertising signs, no welcoming cafés, no shop displays, no lights in apartment windows. There were no cars either, though the one source of brightness was the traffic lights at the entrance to Piatsa Victoriei, switching from red to green for a rush hour that never happened.

She could have been standing in a lane in the depths of the country, not in one of the main arteries of a capital of one and a half million people. It was like a city tensed for an air raid. A bus passed. The giant butane gas cylinders on its roof could have been unexploded bombs. Then it was quiet. The only sound was the squelch of boots and shoes. In corners and against walls snow lay packed hard. Elsewhere there was mud that muffled footfalls.

How did I get here? Who brought me? What happened? The questions flooded her brain, filling her with dread. Something awful, something evil, had happened. Her body and her soul felt defiled.

In front of her fireflies danced in the air and brightened on faces as smokers drew on cigarettes. Sometimes two fireflies would meet and stop, swoop and circle. It's a mating ritual, she decided, and found her cheeks were cold with tears. She brushed them away and began walking.

One, two, three, four, she counted her footsteps.

A firefly with a male voice asked a question and she quickened her pace.

Five, six, seven, eight. She marched to a drumbeat only she could hear.

Chapter 2

Liliana was seriously shaken, no doubt of it. Her voice on the telephone was half an octave higher than usual but only half as loud.

'It's you? Gabriela, you? Not some answering machine? Gabsi?'

'When the Dips come in the door they want to see a live smiling face above a live moving body.' Using her off-duty voice, halfway beween a laugh and a scold. 'The Dips can't chat up a machine. Curdle their breakfast. What is it?'

There was silence.

'Lili? Liliana? Are you there?'

'Can you get away?'

'Now? Course not. I'm on until five. What's the matter? BBW chasing you again?'

BBW was Liliana's boss. They weren't his initials. The Big Bad Wolf was Gabriela's name for him.

'I've got to see you. I've seen him.'

See you/seen him confused Gabriela for a moment. 'Take it from the beginning. Where are you?'

'International Trade Fair. Listen, I have to go. There are some Americans waiting.'

'Hold on. You want to see me because you've seen him. Who is he?'

'Not on the telephone,' Liliana said. 'I can hear whistling.'

'It's a painter. They're redecorating the reception. Royal blue in honour of the Queen, off-white for her daughters-in-law.'

'And he's whistling?'

'He whistles all day. He can whistle with a cigarette in his mouth. He can whistle while he cleans his teeth.'

Liliana wasn't satisfied. In the old days the Securitate tapped all telephones. It was routine. Everybody knew and expected it. Nobody talked of anything secret or important or rebellious or liberal or scandalous or dangerous. So there was no point in tapping the telephones but the Securitate had continued to listen in. Maybe they still did, though now they called themselves the RIS. They used to tap the British embassy lines. And maybe they still did.

'We've got to meet,' Liliana said.

'Where?'

'The café on Piatsa Romana. Seven o'clock.'

'Lili, I have a . . .'

But the telephone had gone dead.

It was the autumn of 1995. The equinox had passed but the days continued warm and sunny as if summer could last for ever and winter snow was an ugly rumour put about by Bulgarians.

They sat outside with tubs of greenery to protect them from the traffic. Their table was the very latest in Italian plastic with a central hole for a sun umbrella advertising Riccadonna vermouth, though the umbrellas had been taken inside. The chairs were made for neat Latin bottoms and the German couple at a neighbouring table seemed cramped and uncomfortable, shifting their haunches from side to side as they spooned up pre-dinner ice creams.

'Lili, I thought you said seven.'

'The Americans were demanding.'

'Demanding what?'

But Liliana was looking away at the Germans and beyond to the people walking along the pavement and didn't reply. A waiter sauntered over and flicked at their table with a cloth.

'What'll it be, ladies?'

Liliana continued staring at passing couples and students and tourists. Gabriela thought she wasn't seeing them at all and her gaze seemed fixed on something more distant.

'Lili, you look . . .' She was going to say shaken. But if you are shaken, you don't need someone telling you. 'Exhausted. It's the demanding Americans. You better have whisky.'

Liliana nodded and then shuddered at some thought. 'I'll have coffee.'

Shaken definitely. Just seen a ghost, Gabriela decided. Ghosts don't exist. Well, just dug up a corpse then. Something dead and buried had come back and thrown a scare into her. She had wanted to talk and now held back. That must have been some scare. They were friends since university where they had both been learning English. They used to sit next to each other in the library so they could try out new words on each other. 'Hey, Lili, what does "tit" mean?'

'A tit is a small songbird, Gabsi, I think a *pitsigoi*.'

'Why has this woman got birds under her sweater, Lili? Is it to keep them warm? The English are a strange people.'

Is she going to tell me? Gabriela wondered. Sometimes you could be bursting with news and then hold back. To share a secret or a discovery or an idea was to hand it to someone else and risk losing it. When they were at university they chatted about everything, about the boys they knew and passed on to each other and what they did and what they said. 'Cornel said he would die if he didn't touch my beautiful *pitsigoi*,' Gabriela reported and they both giggled. Gabriela went to bed with Armand.

'Did his ardour raise you to fever pitch?'

'He was finished before I started and then he snored.'

'We shouldn't waste our *pitsigoi* on boys who are only practising,' Liliana said, 'we should be generous with a man who's learned it all.'

Gabriela wasn't so sure. 'Armand was right about one thing: a shared bed is a warmer bed.'

They formed the *Pitsigoi Club*: with the two of them that made four members. *Pitsigoi* was their very own code.

The waiter brought their coffee. He seemed inclined to linger, liking the look of two young women, one so bright and eager, the other so distressed. Surely his services would suit one or the other. Gabriela glowered and he retreated. Then, to get Liliana to focus on present things, she said, 'I think that German woman is wasting her *pitsigoi* on her man.'

Liliana gazed at her friend as if she was mad. In swift succession her lips twitched in a smile and she looked as if she was going to burst out sobbing.

'He came up to me at the Trade Fair,' Liliana said, launching straight into it. '"You got something special for me?" He's got this face that looks as if it's been stuffed and when he opens his mouth in a smile it's really just to stuff more inside it. That's what he does – stuff himself. Stuff himself with food, with whisky, with money, with cars, with houses, with women.'

With *pitsigoi*, Gabriela said. But wisely only to herself. The mood wasn't for joking.

'What is this Trade Fair?' Gabriela asked.

'Called The Open Eye. Nothing to do with opticians. There are glasses on offer but they're funny glasses for seeing at night. They turn everything pale blue. Israelis make them. I don't know what they are in Hebrew. Everything's written and spoken in English and priced in dollars. There are binoculars that can see round corners, sort of bend the light, I swear it. All sorts of video equipment, cameras in cigarette lighters, fancy lenses, television sets with cameras inside that shoot through the screen at whoever's watching. There's a mirror that fixes the image when you press the button. And then there's the military stuff.' Liliana's voice seemed to slow right down. She was stirring her coffee, round and round the spoon went, round and round. 'Sniperscopes, nightscopes, laser targetting, underwater cameras on frogmen's helmets, computer-controlled aiming for anti-tank launchers. And then there are some stalls – they call them stalls but they're front desks on patches of fake grass with mobile offices behind – with names but nothing on display and no photos or descriptions. If you don't know what they're selling, don't bother to ask.'

She stopped suddenly and looked at her coffee. There was a puddle in the saucer so she picked it up and sipped it dry.

'Sounds like the spying and killing fair to me,' Gabriela said. Her mind skipped to the one or two snippets she'd heard at the embassy and the man who'd flown in from London. 'Mr Royston Cox, my dear, to see the Assistant Commercial Attaché.' Yes well, everyone knew that commerce was more of a sideline for Andrew Crake. 'Why are you there?'

'It's not spying and killing, it's security. Personal security, national security. That's what they say. Swear it on their mothers' graves.'

'They should swear it on the graves of the people who get killed,' Gabriela retorted, and asked again, 'So what are you there for?'

Liliana picked up her cup and sipped from that. Between sips she said, 'I'm on loan from the Foreign Ministry. For my languages.'

For your *pitsigoi* too, Gabriela said, but again to herself. Laughs were definitely out with Lili. She had become too earnest for her own good.

'Then this man wanted to know if you had something special for him. He didn't mean infra-red cameras, I take it.'

'He meant me.'

Liliana frowned at the dregs in her cup. Gabriela didn't so much as twitch a nostril, waiting.

'He'd forgotten me, of course. It was years ago and I never meant anything. An evening's entertainment. A birthday present. Do you believe in hell?'

'Well,' Gabriela said cautiously.

'Satan will have to stoke up a whole extra boiler for him.'

Then, inexplicably, her mouth snapped shut and her lips thinned as she pressed them together so no word could escape.

'What had he done that was so awful?'

But the words couldn't get out.

There was a period of a year when Liliana had simply disappeared. She'd left university and gone to the Bucuresti Hotel. She had kept in touch with Gabriela, smuggling her a ham sandwich or a squashed piece of cake. Then suddenly she was gone. Afterwards she said she'd gone to Constantsa, down on the Black Sea. A string of concrete holiday hotels with names like Sunny Sands, Riviera, Blue Lagoon stretched down the coast and her languages would have landed her a summer job. But the winter? Constantsa had a bit of old town on a short promontory with a pleasure marina on one side and Romania's deep-sea harbour on the other. Bangladeshi and Arab sailors huddling into thin jackets wandered through the harbour area looking for sleaze and a matelot's idea of a good run ashore. What had Liliana done there? She never talked about it, no more than she talked about what drove her to go there.

Still Liliana found it difficult to say what he had done. To talk about it, to think about it, was to relive it. But she looked across at the German couple and checked where the waiter was and began. It didn't come easily. 'Nicolae Ceausescu was executed. Shot. Elena too. Nicu Ceausescu got twenty years in prison. But the others . . .'

The others, well, Gabriela knew as everybody knew that the revolution had been a magician's trick. The apparatchiks, the Party bosses, the fat cats, the chiefs of all kinds had disappeared in a puff of smoke only to emerge as glossy and powerful as before. The old networks resurfaced. The same hands pulled the levers, made the phone calls, signed the contracts, did the deals, pocketed the loot. They bought their half-million dollar apartments on Boulevard Unirii. The apartment blocks were ten storeys high and clad in marble with Roman columns and fake temples on the roofs and a sideways view of what Ceausescu intended to be the palace for his dynasty. Others had stayed put where they'd always been in the leafy diplomatic suburb, so handy for national day parties at the Swedish or German or Dutch embassies.

'His name was Octav Mincu,' Liliana got out. Her chest hurt when she spoke his name and her voice turned guttural. She closed her eyes and saw his face above hers, puffing up like a balloon as it lowered towards her, his eyes glittery but seeing nothing, his lips parted and the corners turned up. The image disintegrated, flew apart in fragments like a shellburst.

Gabriela had moved her chair to be able to put an arm round Liliana's shoulders.

'It's all right,' she crooned, 'you're safe, you don't have to worry about this Mincu.'

'He had the same glittery eyes. It's because his cheeks are like . . . I don't know, Gabsi . . . like slices of pumpkin. He was talking to some colleague, walking past, when something registered, my presence. He just turned and said, "Hello. Have you got anything special on offer? We could discuss it over dinner." No social chat, no getting to know me. The kind of girl he wants to pick up must fall for the direct line. I couldn't speak or move so he shrugged and moved off. After a few steps he turned and saw me watching and he nodded and went on. Nodded, as if – yes, I've got her interested. I know, I absolutely know, he'll be back tomorrow and will come to find me. If he touches me . . .'

'It's all right,' Gabriela said again and hugged her body tight, being her sister, her mother, her lover all in one. 'He can't do anything. He can't touch you.' Gabriela touched her, smoothing her hair until Liliana gave a jerk.

'Gabsi, why is he staring?'

'Who?'

'The waiter. He's just standing inside the door and staring.'

'That's what waiters do. They're on their feet all day, handing out glasses or clearing dishes, and when they're not doing that they stare.'

'Why me?'

'He's not staring at you. Not specially. You, me, the Germans, his daydreams, his vacant head, he's looking at anything.'

'He might remember me from the Bucuresti. He's too young to be Ion.'

'Who was Ion?'

'He told me I couldn't say No.'

'Some boyfriend you spurned?'

Liliana got abruptly to her feet and stumbled out into the night. Gabriela looked at her hunched shoulders retreating, put money on the table and went after her.

'Lili, stop. Just stop running away from it, whatever it is.'

Gabriela had to skip round in front to stop Liliana.

'First we've got to find a telephone. There's a party I was meant to go to but it doesn't matter. A lot of musicians and they only want me because I speak English and I'm young and female and free.'

Gabriela used a telephone on a wall, facing Liliana to make sure she didn't bolt. Liliana had her hand to her mouth, her eyes flicking from face to face. Then they began to walk, with Gabriela's arm round her shoulders, holding her upright, keeping her from falling to pieces.

Liliana talked. It had been pressed down for nearly six years and now it was released and came to the surface. Her words stank in her own nostrils. They were like bubbles of gas made by rotting vegetation at the bottom of a pond, rising and breaking the oily surface. They walked in the dark but it wasn't the darkness of Ceausescu's Golden Age. Traffic, streetlamps, shop windows – Ceausescu had forbidden them all. One forty-watt bulb per household had been the rule and the city had been black as if aliens had carried the population off. They walked aimlessly and by chance found themselves opposite the Bucuresti Hotel where a commissionaire in a beige uniform was flagging a taxi. Liliana stopped and stared in silence. She pointed to a window on the first floor to the right of the entrance. The façade was anonymous, the windows all alike. She hesitated.

'There, I think. On a dessert trolley. Covered in a capitalist cow's cream.'

And a lighted candle between her thighs. The candle

was important. She talked about it. And the Young Pretender, who was drunk. Another woman was pushed into the room, maybe a maid though Liliana thought not, because she inspected each man in turn and raised her eyebrows at Liliana with the candle and the cream and didn't look scared. The Young Pretender tore her blouse open and lifted her skirt and backed her against the table but still she wasn't scared. After all the booze the Young Pretender was impotent and contented himself with messing about with her. Liliana was so frightened she lay frozen on the trolley and counted thousands and thousands.

'I read that the Nazis used to make partisans watch hangings while they waited their turn. It was like that.'

Overwhelmed by the memories, Liliana broke away and ran down the street. Gabriela caught her up and hugged her tight. They walked a block like that while Liliana gasped for air. She drew a lungful and talked again.

'Everybody was looking at Mincu. It was his birthday party. I remember the Young Pretender trying to sing "*Bon anniversaire*". The same as the English "Happy Birthday to you", yes? You know? But he couldn't even manage that, forgot the tune. He called for more whisky and got everyone to sing and they drank toasts to Mincu with the fat smile on his face and they smashed their glasses against the wall and then it began for me.'

Gabriela had a flat out beyond Nord station and that's where they went. The building had been thrown up during the Golden Age and it had been a slum from the start. The cement walls were streaked, an ominous crack started at ground level and was working its way up, a board by the entrance announced it was Bloc 19. Inside was like a succession of caves, the rooms small, the ceilings low. Gabriela's flat was an entrance like a broom cupboard, a bedroom, a tiny sitting room with a cooking corner, and a shower room. It had been intended for a family of four, troglodytes presumably. She was planning to move out and join a friend who worked at the Italian embassy as soon as the friend kicked out her lover who had developed an interest elsewhere.

Gabriela was going to offer whisky until she remembered how Liliana had shuddered at the idea. There was a bottle of vodka and they sat with it on the table between them. After the first gulp, Liliana didn't touch it. The vodka was called Rasputin so maybe that put her off. Lights on? Lights off? Which was better for confession? A small lamp on the bookcase provided intimacy.

Liliana talked. Sometimes she talked loudly and angrily. Sometimes so softly Gabriela missed it. A parked car outside the building had an alarm that was set off by every passing bus and then Liliana was silent until the alarm had run its course.

Liliana didn't cry as she talked. At most she would give a choked gulp as she filled her lungs with air. Her eyes would screw up as if she'd got shampoo in them but they stayed dry. Crying was in the past. She talked of what had happened in that private dining room, she talked of finding herself in Boulevard Ilie Pintilie, she talked of what happened in the time in between.

'Even now I can't remember all of it.'

Maybe that was for the best, Gabriela thought and refilled her own glass. There are mistakes we make and don't want to remember but should, to learn. There are bad times we don't want to remember but maybe should, to appreciate how things have got better. But there are other events too terrible and maybe it's better they stay buried. One shouldn't have to relive them.

'And it is this same Octav Mincu who wants you to have dinner?'

'Yes.'

'He hasn't even changed his name?'

'Why should he? Who'll do anything about something that happened six years ago? What evidence is there? Who would back up my story? What's my word against his? He's rich, he's powerful, he has connections, he has a whole network from the past who would support him, lie for him, say how I willingly took part in their fun just like that whore had. Who was I? A drop-out from university, a waitress who was known to steal food. What am I now? An interpreter, a girl who gets asked to dinner. A nobody.'

'Don't say that,' Gabriela said, gripping her forearm. 'You are what you think you are. Respect yourself.' The laughter had long gone from her voice and the scolding had turned serious.

They kept quiet while the car alarm blared. Someone should do something about the car. The owner didn't care. He lived in a flat at the back. Set fire to the car, give it something to shout about.

When the alarm switched off, Gabriela said, 'I think you should have dinner with him.'

Liliana went very still. She seemed to have stopped breathing.

'Lili? Lili?'

'I couldn't.'

Gabriela went behind Liliana and pulled her upright. She held her by the shoulders so their eyes were very close. Unblinking, they stared at each other.

'You can.'

When Liliana parted her lips to protest Gabriela leaned closer and kissed her full on the mouth as sometimes they used to after they had spent too long over their books. To come alive again, Gabriela used to say, to rejoin the human race.

Now she said to Liliana, 'Forget justice. Have you thought of revenge?'

'I can't,' Liliana whispered.

'Can't?' Gabriela was beside herself with anger. A man like that, she'd put a knife under the pillow and when he climbed into bed she'd slice his balls off. She shook Liliana before letting her go.

Liliana's head was a turmoil of awful images. They were from the past but they were very vivid to her. The images were jumbled, sometimes her own legs or breasts, sometimes some unknown hand, or Mincu's face, his grin, other faces, eyes wide and glittery, a candle. There was a soundtrack from a crazy film, laughter, grunts, shouts, a scream, a hand against a cheek.

'I'll be with you,' Gabriela said. 'Not at the same table but close.'

'Gabsi,' Liliana whispered, 'please.'

Then she remembered Ion saying: *No is not an option. No does not exist. No is not a word that should be in your head.*

Chapter 3

Mr Royston Cox, asking for the Assistant Commercial Attaché, had called Gabriela *my dear.* You're going to find yourself in deep doo-doo one day, certain colleagues had cautioned, younger ones who took their language and opinions from across the Atlantic. What? Cox had looked innocent and bewildered. He said he'd never yet come across a pretty girl who didn't respond to a smile and a friendly word. *Silly cow,* well it stood to reason that would get a frosty reception. But *my dear* . . .

Thus Mr Royston Cox.

It was the day after Liliana Branoza had spilled her dark secrets to Gabriela. The weather continued balmy, though light cirrus very high up gave a slight haze to the sunshine. This was the tail of a complex system that had covered Europe from the Shetlands to the Dalmatian coast. Its rain had already been dumped. The day would be blessed and Cox enjoyed walking the streets.

He took coffee with a certain Professor of Psycholinguistics. Cox recalled the time when Tudor Harasteanu had been struggling with translating 'phonological component' and 'morphophenomenal rules' into Romanian. He had been struggling, too, with the attentions of the Securitate who were sure this must be anti-state activity. Between these struggles he had found time and space and courage to get together with certain students whose fathers – high Party functionaries – were careless enough to gossip. Yasser Arafat had visited Bucharest and boasted of a PLO plan to assassinate King Hussein. Having gathered together bits and pieces about this plot and feeling rash one evening, Harasteanu had bumped into a diplomat outside the US embassy. He thrust a document into the startled man's pocket while Securitate goons looked on and one sharply ordered him to watch where he was going.

'Ah yes,' Cox reminisced, 'we've known bad times but good times too.'

'When you brought me coffee.'

In the Golden Age, coffee had disappeared. Cox used to come with a supply from London, Turkish coffee. Out of habit, and as a farewell gift, he had today.

'Every conqueror leaves some trace,' Harasteanu said as he waited for the little pot to come to the boil for the third time, 'except I cannot think of a single thing the Russians have left behind.'

From there Cox walked to have a chat with an old priest who in former times had been known in London as Saint Peter, actual name Petr. Cox had once had a meeting with him in a confessional. The priest, in defiance of his calling, had repeated certain things that had been confessed to him. Petr had gone virtually blind and he pressed his hands to Cox's face 'just to make sure the moustache is in place'.

Cox walked once more, smiling benignly at girls he passed. Mostly they smiled back because Cox had the kind of smile that brought a response.

They're not *girls*, his critics warned him. They're *women*. *Girls* is an insult, as if they've never grown up, have brains the size of peas, need patting on the head and asking what their boyfriends do for a living. Cox considered this and said, Well, sometimes I'm called *Roy boy* and I don't feel demeaned. Not even at my age.

Outside the Athenaeum was a family of gypsies. Spying the foreigner, four of the children besieged him, clawed at him while he thrust his hand firmly in the pocket with his loose change. A girl of about ten kept saying in English, 'I love you, I love you.' Cox smiled his smile and they followed him, Pied Piper-like, to the entrance of La Boema, but no further. This was a restaurant chosen by Lucas Jaeger because of its distance from the American embassy. Tables were laid on the pavement with the usual tubs of greenery to protect diners from the attention of gypsy children. Cox went inside. Palm trees in outsize pots soared but their plastic fronds would never burst through the ceiling. The walls were tropical blue and even in the middle of the day small spotlights cast shafts of sunlight slashed by the palm fronds. But Jaeger had retreated even further, into a small back room at a corner table.

'Roy, a pleasure, an honour, sir, welcome to the whorehouse of the Middle East.' Jaeger was big, his belly, his hands, his voice. He didn't look like a secret warrior.

'At my age, Lucas, a whorehouse madam simply yawns.'

'Your age? Holy mackerel, Roy. Think on old Abraham in the Good Book. Centuries old and he has two virgins in bed to warm him up.'

It was King David and he made do with one, Cox didn't tell him. This was Lucas Jaeger's party.

'Here we are,' Jaeger said as a waitress in a leather mini-skirt handed over menus like small books. He opened his but looked over the top at the neat buttocks and perfect legs as they moved away. 'Well, what's it going to be? Caviar? Fancy that? Caviar hit the spot?'

Cox had eaten caviar in Warsaw and caviar in Budapest. 'Perhaps not today. I'm caviared out, to be honest.' He ran his finger down the hors d'oeuvre page. 'Cuttlefish salad . . . They're the little fellows, right? Little squid?'

'Squid aren't kosher.'

'I didn't know you were Jewish.'

'With squid I'm Jewish,' Jaeger said.

The waitress with the pert backside and front to match stood at the table and smiled back at Cox while she waited to write their orders on a pad. Jaeger followed her with hungry eyes when she left. 'The best dishes aren't on the menu here.'

'Sweet girl,' Cox agreed and remembered how he mustn't call her a girl. What was Lucas's view?

'Hell no, better be careful,' Jaeger warned. 'Else the feminazis will come and cut your tackle off. Girl is not politically correct.'

'But, Lucas, with our experience of the world, do we think politics is correct?'

And so it goes, another meal for Queen and country. An army marches on its stomach. Cox does too. Jaeger on several stomachs. He ordered a tuna steak followed by 'a real one'. They talked of this and that, the mood in Washington and London.

'Now hear this. They're going to create a whole new apparatus,' Jaeger confided in a monumental whisper, his fork poised in mid-air. 'They are not happy with us spooks. No sir. They want new ones, squeaky clean, no taint of failure on them. They are going to be posted all over the world with bona fide commercial cover. The great idea is that these guys are going to be trading for real and their spying they'll fit in in their off-duty hours. Roy, they are going to be right here, my town, for God's sake, doing whatever their business cover is. Buying up the Romanian tomato crop. So . . .' He took a big draught of white wine to soothe his pain. 'So what happens when the tomato growers in California and Florida hear of that? Importing Romanian tomatoes. Oh no, not when the tomato growers' lobby gets to work, with the California congressmen shoving and the Florida guys heaving. So the Romanian tomato crop will be dumped at give-away prices in some Third World slum, gift of Uncle Sam, ruin the Third World tomato growers, lose the American tax-payer a mountain of money. Am I right? Or am I out of my noodle?'

'Your noodle looks in fine fettle to me.'

'That's not the end.' Jaeger carved another chunk of tuna. 'Then what happens? The grateful Romanian tomato growers, the trade ministry chiefs, the lawyers who drew up the contracts, the airline that flew the cargo, they all want to socialize with our great hero. Tennis Sunday afternoon. Opera Saturday, poor guy. Sorry, no can do, no socializing, weekends are the only time he has left for spying. Holy mackerel.' Jaeger shook his head and stuffed in his tuna.

'The world gets crazier every day,' Cox said.

'Screwier, Roy, screwier,' Jaeger said, as if correcting him. He shook his head. 'Now I hear you're quitting. Don't blame you. Got the right idea. Dickybirds tell me you're having yourself some kind of farewell tour.'

'Not much you don't hear,' Cox said, his smile wide and his ears wide open for hints behind the words.

'Roy's last hurrah, I'm told. *That*'ll be the day. When they come to lay Roy in his pine box – middle of next century, I reckon – he'll be peeping through a knothole in the wood. Told them so.'

'Just checking on the tomato crop.'

'I heard Hungary and Poland. Where else?'

'Prague beckons. Brno too.'

'Moscow?'

'I was satellites only. Never had to deal direct with the Soviets, thank Bog.'

'Bog?'

Cox pointed at the ceiling. 'Old fellow upstairs. All-seeing, all-knowing, all-powerful, all-merciful. In this case His mercy was sparing me Russians.'

The waitress cleared their plates. Cox beamed at her. 'Delicious, dear.'

'No serious purpose to the tour?'

'Saying goodbye is serious. Saying thank you is serious. What would people think if I just disappeared? Sent to the British Siberia for unknown crimes? Can't just vanish leaving a bad smell in Bucharest. I did vanish once. Did you ever hear? Before your time.'

'Tell.'

Their steaks arrived. Jaeger thought white wine was fine with tuna, but steak called for red. The waitress opened the wine, poured their glasses and left the bottle on a serving trolley.

'They never put the bottle on the table,' Jaeger said. 'Used to drive me crazy. Still, if it's her bending over to fill my glass, I don't object. Now tell.'

'It was back in the mid-eighties,' Cox said, easing himself back in his chair. 'The Golden Age. Old Nick in full flow. His people spying on everyone. "Never buy technology from foreigners when you can steal it," was what he used to say. Spying on Texas Instruments,' he pointed a finger at Jaeger before jabbing it at himself, 'spying on the British Aerospace Corporation. They'd been wanting blueprints of the Harrier for ages. Simply years. So I had come to Bucharest to talk to one or two people to see if they had penetrated BAC.' Cox paused, giving a reminiscent smile. 'My last field trip before I was grounded. I was blown, though I hadn't known it when I flew in. It was the second morning, while I was having breakfast, that I heard the first tinkle. The waiter was too attentive, always hovering, not serving anyone else, actually asking if I would be in for lunch. Waiters simply didn't do that, not here at any rate. Too eager, wanting to impress his bosses. Then walking down the street, stopping outside the bookshop in Calea Victoriei, window packed with Old Nick's books.

His speeches, his thoughts, his ghost-written articles. I remember counting them. Thirty-nine volumes. Whole forests had given up their lives to his greater ego. And I remember watching reflections in the window of two men on the opposite side of the road, stopping, waiting for me, then continuing at my pace. At the corner when I turned to check for traffic, two more behind me. So I was blown. And I thought whatever it is one thinks at such moments. Oh shit. Don't panic. Help, someone get me out. And fighting the desire to start running down the street. Happened to you?' he asked to give himself time to eat a mouthful.

'Only with Erica. Erica was my first wife. She spied a bit but she only ever hired one gumshoe to check on me.' He glowered at the meat on his fork. 'And you got out? Vanished?'

'Well yes, I did. I was fortunate to spot an empty taxi because taxis didn't cruise. I told the driver "*Gara*", and hopped in. "*Gara de Nord*," I repeated to make sure he'd got it. Out of the rear window I saw a Dacia, grey one, behind. It was still there at the station. Paid off my driver and went in. Dreadful place. Queues everywhere. Posters of Old Nick watching. Slogans for Peace. I joined some queue or other. Don't know what it was. I spotted two Securitate goons coming in. They stood out because they weren't dressed in rags. One held back to watch me, the other hurried off to telephone or round up some back-up. So I looked at my watch, big arm movement so it would be noticed, leaned out to estimate the length of the queue, muttered, "The hell with it" as I decided against waiting. I marched out – down to one tag now – and went to the taxi rank and said loud enough to be overheard: Intercontinental Hotel. I saw the Securitate chap turn away and run back inside the station. So . . .'

Cox ate a mouthful, just to keep the suspense going.

'I'm not a linguist. Too many languages to learn. Bits and bobs is all I've got. But I said to the driver, *Benzina*? Tank was pretty full so I decided to change my destination. The Securitate thugs would wait at the Intercontinental and I reckoned it would be half an hour before they cottoned on I wasn't coming and another half an hour before they reported this and the search started. By then I'd be way beyond the city limits. I persuaded the driver with the help of the sight of some dollars to drive me all the way to Giurgiu. Fast, I said, quick as you can. He looked blank. *Vite*, I tried and he twigged. *Rapid*, he said, so we agreed on that. He did it in about an hour, good going, and I thought I was still just about ahead of the game. Giurgiu was the usual frontier nonsense, flags and guns and striped pole. Romanian officials wanted to know where my luggage was and I said I was only going for the day. One day in Bulgaria was quite enough for anyone, thank you very much, I said. The English-speaking officer translated and all their scowls turned to grins. Then they grew friendly and the officer wanted to practise his English. When the *conducator* visited London, had he really slept at the Queen's Palace? Why didn't Diana put on some weight up top? And I'm grinning back at them and looking at my passport still in the officer's hand and wondering what to do if I hear the telephone ringing. At last he handed the passport back. All right, see you this evening and I'm on my way. After that the Bulgarians were easy. Where was my visa? Then I must pay double: once for the visa, the second time for their pockets. I picked up a bus to Sofia. I reckoned I was safe there until the next day when I could fly home. Romanians weren't lovey-dovey with a load of Slavs.'

Jaeger was so moved he leaned over himself to get the bottle to top up their glasses.

'Holy mackerel, Roy,' he breathed and shook his head in admiration. 'One of the true legends. Those tomato merchants could never pull something like that.'

*   *   *

'The Americans know nothing,' Cox said.

'You can't be certain,' Crake said.

'Nothing,' Cox repeated. 'I am certain.'

It was just gone three-thirty. Cox had refused, gracefully, all offers from Jaeger of liqueurs and brandies. He'd had his hand shaken, his back slapped, his hand shaken again with instructions to go well and be on his guard against the tomato merchants in life. He had gone at his own pace with the sun warm on his cheeks, the very model of a chap of advancing years enjoying an afternoon stroll, should anyone be watching. Then he had pulled up short at the sight of the gorgeous baroque villa where George Enescu had lived, and seemingly on impulse had gone in.

The composer's life was laid out in glass cabinets: musical scores, batons, playbills, photographs. A woman in a caretaker's black dress had sat herself on a hard wooden chair just outside the door and pretended not to keep them in view. She didn't understand English. Cox had already found that out.

'They'll hear about it,' Crake said.

'Not if we're careful. Not if we're quick. Damn it all, it's our side of the Atlantic, our boys at risk. It's not a US playground. Well, is it? Why should they take an interest?'

Crake knew that wasn't quite right and gave the rejoinder: 'Because they want to run the world. Before they had to share it with the Russkies. Now they want to do it all.'

'They'll learn.'

'They'll come in like they always do, too many of them, too many organizations, too many mouths to feed, too many budgets to justify. They'll say their interests are involved, their companies at risk. They mean their profits but they won't say it. They'll talk about geo-political factors, about . . .'

Cox let the voice trail on. He stood before a tailor's dummy clothed in evening dress, once worn by the great composer when conducting his first triumph, *The Romanian Poem.* He reached a hand towards the lapel. Hearing a noise behind him Cox turned to see the woman in the black dress standing up for a better view. *It's all right, my dear,* he said with his smile. They strolled. No other visitors disturbed them.

'Didn't Jaeger ask why you'd come?'

'But he already knows. My farewell concert tour. As many last nights as Caruso. I ate specially with his colleagues in Budapest and Warsaw – which was beyond the call of duty. No shadow of suspicion attaches to my visit here.'

Cox stopped before another glass cabinet, stooping to peer at one of Enescu's scores. It was dedicated to Yehudi Menuhin '*en grande affection*'. He gave a little grunt as he stood upright.

'When I retire I shall open a spy's museum. The umbrella the Bulgarians killed Markov with. A microdot on a full stop. An architect's plan of the Lubyanka. A pistol disguised as a camera. A camera disguised as a pistol. A signals pad with *en grande discrétion* written in invisible ink. A cloak. A dagger.'

Crake was not sure how to take this flight of fancy. He gave a small smile and cleared his throat.

'Now what's new about Chummy?' Cox asked. 'The latest dirt.'

Chummy was his all-purpose cover name for the villain of the moment. The latest dirt, as he put it, was to do with his activities now the Trade Fair was in full swing. The Open Eye, Crake said, winked a bit at under-the-counter deals. Big players had come to town and Chummy was chummy with them. A good time was being had by all. Dinners, casinos, girls – Bucharest was a long way from the dark, cold, dour, silent city of the Golden Age.

'The whorehouse of the Middle East,' Cox murmured.

'Jaeger's phrase. Never considered it as the Middle East somehow. All that Parisian architecture, Haussmann style.'

'Istanbul's just over the horizon.'

Istanbul had never been in Cox's territory and he'd never gone there. Its past had repelled him. Sultan Ibrahim having his harem of 280 concubines put into sacks, weighted with stones, rowed out into the Bosphorus and tossed into the water. Its Golden Age, he supposed.

'The fleshpots first, the business after, that's Chummy's style, is it? Or t'other way round?'

'Fleshpots first, during and after,' Crake told him. 'He goes to the Fair, he talks, he smiles. I've been there, stood ten feet from him and listened in. Chit-chat. Any luck at the Golden Horseshoe last night? What have you done with that gorgeous assistant you brought with you? He's playing the field. Germans, French, British, Americans. But the real business, the money, the verbal contracts, the handshakes on deals, all that is well away from spying ears.'

They knew no more than Cox had heard in London. Then it had been rumours, hints, after-hours telephone calls from concerned executives. The arms-to-Iraq scandals, the Scott enquiry, the axe hovering above certain necks had thrown a scare into some. Action had been decreed but play it very discreet, Roy boy, very low-key or things could turn ugly. Better not even be thought operational at all. Make it a social swing through old stamping grounds.

'And we still have no access?'

They were in another room. The caretaker had had to move her chair to keep them in sight. What did she do if there was more than one party? Cox stopped in front of a photograph of a woman, young, dark hair close cropped, one kiss curl on her forehead.

Crake hadn't replied. Cox asked again: 'Any way of getting closer?'

'We may have found a way in,' Crake said. 'It's possible.'

'I say, was this Enescu's wife? Looks quite a girl, very modern.'

'I said we may have access, just possibly.'

'I heard. I'm waiting.'

'She's an amateur.'

'Lord preserve us.'

'I said *just possibly* because she's reluctant. Strong motivation but holding back. She unburdened her soul last night to one of the embassy staff who passed it on to me.'

Cox stopped his examination of the photo to look at Crake.

'But you're on your own at the embassy. No team, no regulars.'

'It's more in the way of a personal relationship.' Crake, despite himself, felt the blood warming his cheeks.

Cox was not pleased. He stared at Crake who apparently gossiped out of hours.

'This personal relationship,' Cox said. 'Who is she?'

'Receptionist at the embassy.'

Cox remembered. Good-looking girl. *My dear.*

'And you share everything?'

Bed, secrets, gossip. It wasn't so much a question as a statement. Cox went back to studying the photo of the young woman while Crake gave a résumé of Liliana's traumatic past and troubled present. No doubt about it, Enescu's wife had been an attractive woman, Cox thought with part of his mind as he noted Crake's report. Look how boldly her eyes stare back. Then, damn strange thing, you think the eyes have moved – perhaps through disappointment – to something more interesting behind you. It could be your shadow that draws her, in her imagination seeing something more intriguing.

'Hang on a mo,' Cox said, interrupting the flow. 'She said Chummy has done what?'

'Picked her up. Asked her out.'

'And she refused?'

'No. Not in so many words. Too shocked to answer. It's what I said: she's holding back.'

'Sensitive girl, is she? Not wanting to face Chummy across a dinner table?'

'Shocked. I said shocked.'

Shock, yes. Shock gave way to withdrawal or to determination, never could be certain which. Did she have it in her to act?

He took a final look at Enescu's wife. Her mouth was serious but as he glanced away he could swear her lips perked upwards: fooled you.

Cox had returned to his hotel and put his feet up. Too old for this kind of caper, he told himself. I should be put out to grass at the training school imparting my wisdom to the next generation. What I did during the hols. Tales of derring-do from the Cold War. Boys all agog. Girls too now. 'They'll come in droves to listen to the Orange Pippin.' Jenny made a joke of it while she pressed him to take early retirement. Well, she was the one who retired early, last March, a mercifully swift exit with a brain tumour. Widowers only had themselves to consider, their vanity. When something like this came up, what was needed was someone 'with a safe pair of hands'. The Chief's cliché. Not someone who put his hands on the embassy's receptionist. No tomato merchants either.

It was towards six. He might have rested his eyes for a few moments when the telephone on the bedside table rang. It was Crake.

'Chummy has invited her for dinner tonight,' Crake said.

'Tonight? And?'

'She said yes.'

Chapter 4

In the autumn of 1995 La Premiera still had the reputation for the best food in Bucharest.

'You've never been?' Mincu had said in some surprise. 'Then you shall have it. You'll love the place. Everybody goes there. Where do you live? I'll pick you up.'

'No,' Liliana had said.

'Do you say no a lot?' Mincu's smile was open and honest. Of course there wasn't a hint of anything behind his smile.

La Premiera is at the back of the National Theatre, 'within clapping distance', people say. If you come by car or taxi you go along University Boulevard then up a narrow alley. Liliana came by metro and then on foot, skirting the Intercontinental and following a path round the National Theatre. She stopped. Here it was as dark as during the Golden Age and she glanced round for fireflies swooping in the air and listened for a man's voice asking where she was going. To my fate, she answered. She peered into the blackness hard against the walls but the darkest shadows were in her memory. She took a deep breath and held it.

Count your blessings, Gabsi had said. A thousand and one, a thousand and two, a thousand and three. Big C is dead. Elena is dead. Nicu is in prison. The past is the past. Think of revenge.

Except the past wasn't dead. She was going to dine with it. And Gabsi hadn't told her how she was going to get her revenge.

Liliana walked on again, crossing the windows that gave into the kitchen, then into the glow from La Premiera's terrace. First she passed the terrace that could be used for private parties, then the open-air bar, then the grand terrace with lights chasing away the darkness and tubs of greenery and a pianist who played 'The Very Thought of You' and smiled at her. It was a professional smile from a man who could smile all night but it was better than Mincu's smile which was a liar's smile.

Insist on La Premiera, Gabriela had said, say you've always wanted to eat at the Premiera, say it's the Premiera or nothing. If you say so, Gabsi. I do say so because it's expensive and you won't be hidden away in some back room, you'll be right out in the open, you'll be safe. All right, Gabsi. Gabriela had taken her by the shoulders and looked into her eyes, not at all liking this docility. There should be steel and fire. Hate him, Gabriela had whispered as if it was a lover's secret, you must hate him. She kissed Liliana's lips to pass on strength to her.

And there he was, this object of hate, a dozen steps away, bending over a table with four people but ignoring three of them. A woman with a lot of blonde hair and a mouth that stayed open even when she wasn't speaking was looking up at him with big eyes. Then she was talking, exuberant, her right hand moving so the bracelets on her wrist caught the light and sparkled. Mincu straightened up, laughing and, laying a hand on her shoulder, turned and saw Liliana. He gave half a wave to the blonde woman in farewell and came to greet Liliana.

'Wonderful woman,' he said. 'International marketing

consultant, dining out some Canadian investors. Really knows how things work. Brilliant. I'll have to get together with her one day, work out a deal. Good evening, Liliana, and welcome. You're looking wonderful.'

He was smiling at her. She looked at the cheeks that bulged, at the eyes that took you apart, at the lips that twitched up in anticipation of private delights.

'What's her name?' Liliana said, her first words to him. Her voice seemed to come from a long way off, it was so thin.

'Name?' Mincu was puzzled. 'Whose?'

'She speaks English. She has many commercial contacts. She could be useful to me.'

Mincu seemed to have overlooked entirely that Liliana worked. She was the evening's fun. 'Rona Dragusin,' he said.

Mincu escorted her himself to their table while the head waiter hovered and smiled, pulled out Liliana's chair and smiled some more. She sat down but Mincu turned away to greet two men by the railing. Liliana looked at him and then at the candle the head waiter had lit. But she wouldn't let herself look round the terrace. Instead she watched Mincu's hands that moved in the air with such grace. They were hands that could press and pull and claw at human flesh. She had to hold her breath.

Mincu sat down and said casually, 'Champagne be all right?' Not waiting for an answer he beckoned a passing waiter and gave the order. 'They have wonderful stuff here. None of the Sovietski Shampanski we choked on. You'll like it.'

Is that an order? She was prepared to hate it, spit in the glass, tip it on the floor. When the wine was poured, Mincu raised his glass and looked at her over the rim like any Hollywood seducer. 'Here's to a wonderful evening.' *Wonderful* seemed to be his word. Liliana sipped, Liliana liked, Liliana drained the glass. His eyes were taking this in. They were eyes that measured, calculated, hungered, demanded everything. The eyes were fingers, touching, possessing.

'Caviar?' he suggested, not bothering with the menu. 'Unlike the champagne, the caviar is Russian. They have Beluga. Yes, I think caviar.'

But Liliana opened her menu and stared at it. Don't let him steamroller you, Gabriela had said. Don't get into the pattern of agreeing to everything he suggests or you'll find yourself back at his place for a nightcap and Frank Sinatra crooning on the hi-fi.

'I prefer smoked salmon,' she announced. The boldness of her voice surprised her. Thank you, champagne.

What can I talk about? Liliana had asked.

Don't worry, Lili. He'll do the talking. He likes to talk about himself. It's a subject of absorbing interest to him.

Then you do know him?

Of course, Gabriela had said. I've never met him but I know him. There is Mincu in every man. I have the bruises and fingerprints to prove it.

'Liliana, Liliana, such a beautiful name. Like poetry. Or music, a bell chiming.'

Liliana regarded this full-frontal charm offensive with grave eyes. He smiled.

'Does it ever get shortened? Lili, perhaps?'

'No.'

'Or Liana?'

'No.'

'Lianas, you know, those climbing vines they have in the jungle? Have you ever seen the jungle, real steaming jungle? I don't mean what they have in the hothouse at the Botanical Gardens. I was in Brazil last year. Listen.'

He laid a hand on hers. To help her listen. Petrified, she stared at the hand. It was the most powerful hand she'd ever met. It could order champagne, sign cheques for millions, draw up contracts to blow up the world. It could hold a glass or a fork. It could hold a breast. It could descend under his own body to wipe away his own filth. The hand obsessed her. What was he saying?

He was telling Liliana about his visit to Brazil. To Rio naturally, for the carnival and the *cariocas*. São Paulo, for business. Then to Manaus and on by private jet into the jungle for more business, though he didn't say what. He'd seen very strange things, Indians in the jungle, small men, women with naked breasts – and here his eyes dropped as if he was measuring her against those Amazonian breasts – huge trees draped with lianas, Liliana, monkeys and parakeets and jaguars. There were odd religions, people worshipping jungle spirits, even worshipping the devil, and all sorts of African-Christian mumbo-jumbo called – he had made a point of getting someone to write down the names – Candomble and Umbanda. Isn't Umbanda wonderful? Can't you hear the jungle tom-toms beating? Then before he flew back home he had a weekend on the coast at Olinda, sand and hot sun and lobsters and palm trees. Paradise while Romania shivered. 'You'd really enjoy that.'

He smiled at her. His hand, still on hers, gave a little squeeze before reaching for his glass. Had she been offered a trip with him? She said, 'Excuse me, I must just go inside a minute.'

She threaded her way between the tables, past the great international marketing consultant and the man Mincu said was the reporter for the BBC and other business associates he'd waved to and the man in his dinner jacket with a carnation in the buttonhole who smiled at her and played 'These Foolish Things' on his white piano. Inside in the Ladies' room where she had come to splash water on her face to take some of the heat out of it she found some butterfly-brain had scrawled on the mirror with lipstick in a mixture of English and Romanian: *Hands off your pitsigoi!*

Returning to the terrace she found Mincu was standing at a long table with a dozen people, his hand resting at ease on the shoulder of a woman whose make-up and hair and low-cut dress showed stubborn resistance to advancing years. Liliana allowed herself her first look to the end of the terrace to what were called the 'ethnic' tables, not so well lit, no gleaming white tablecloths, no candles. If you were American or British or French or Japanese or Korean, if you had dollar bills or an expense account, if you had connections or were a big enough crook, you never got to sit at these tables. Your eyes avoided them completely. The sort of Romanians who sat there were of no use to you.

So Liliana only gave these four tables the swiftest glance. Two men having coffee and an earnest discussion. A man with a beer reading a newspaper. Two young women, one brunette, one blonde, in eye-catching dresses seeing whose eyes they could catch. Another woman of Liliana's age with a much older man with grey hair crinkled like a winter sea and a grey moustache. The man seemed to glare at her and frown so she looked away.

For Cox this was a first sight of Liliana, her looks and her bearing. It was her vulnerability that struck him. He wasn't prepared for such fragility. Was that the attraction for Mincu? A beauty that looked as if it would come apart in his hands? She was Gabriela's friend but without her spirit. He wondered, quite simply, if she was going to be able to last the evening, let alone do what he asked her.

No, he'd told Gabriela, I won't meet Liliana beforehand. We have to know whether she can stand being near Mincu first. You've told her she must think of revenge. She can have her revenge but it will be doing what I ask her to: through gaining Mincu's confidence.

'Didn't you tell her not to look at us?' Cox muttered. 'She must only have eyes for him.'

'We're invisible. Don't worry.'

'I have to worry. It's part of the job description. If I wasn't worried, I wouldn't be in Bucharest.'

'People who sit at the ethnic tables are invisible. We don't exist. It was the same under Big C. Ordinary people were invisible. Ordinary people didn't exist, so we needed no clothes, no food, no light, no heat. Big C existed. Elena existed. Nicu existed. Valentin half existed.'

'Who was Valentin?'

'The elder son. Zoia half existed too. She was the daughter and they both rebelled. Party bosses – they existed until they did something wrong. Then they ceased to exist.'

Congratulations, Cox told her in his mind. The history of Romania during the Golden Age in one hundred words or fewer, using one side of the paper only. Marks will be deducted for spelling mistakes and slovenly writing. Additional marks will be given for brevity, wit and spirit. And Gabriela had spirit. Cox had realized that in their first hurried meeting. She bubbled with spirit. Give her to me for this evening, Cox had told Crake, and you can have her for the rest of the night. He wouldn't say no to the rest of the night himself.

He fixed on Liliana again. Her hands lay on the table and she stared down as if she couldn't think what to do with them. It was going to be a problem, he could see, giving her the stomach for this. Gabriela had the spirit but Liliana had the access.

'Who's he with now? Do you know?'

Mincu still stood talking at the long table.

'I see Italians,' Gabriela said as if playing I-spy-with-my-little-eye. 'The Ambassador is at the head of the table.'

Mincu was drawing something out of his pocket. He did it slowly, talking all the time like a magician diverting attention, favouring one of the ladies with a smile. It was a packet of cigarettes he produced and took one, the cigarette jiggling between his lips while he talked. He lit it with a gold lighter. Lighter and packet were returned to his jacket pocket. Kent, Cox registered. In the rest of the former communist bloc it might be Marlboro but in Romania it was Kent that had always been the favoured brand, smuggled in, almost a second currency. In ancient Greece the custom had been to place a coin in the dead man's mouth. Cox supposed it was to pay Charon who ferried you across the Styx. In Romania, during the Golden Age, a packet of Kent cigarettes was put on the corpse's chest.

While Cox's attention had been on the business with the cigarettes, a gypsy boy of about ten had sidled up the steps to the terrace. He carried a basket of roses, single blooms with the stems wrapped in foil. He was offering them to a table by the balustrade when a waiter caught hold of his arm. Mincu turned, saying something. He peeled notes off a wad he took from the inside pocket of his jacket. He was too far off for Cox to be certain how much he gave the boy, thirty thousand lei he thought. Mincu scooped the entire contents of the basket up and presented them to the woman he'd been smiling at. She laughed and raised both hands in an operatic gesture of mock horror. Mincu, catching one of the hands, raised it to his lips.

'Mrs Ambassador,' Gabriela said.

Mincu, having second thoughts, plucked a single bloom from the bunch and returned to his table. Food had been brought – perhaps that was why he returned – though Cox had been too diverted by the Kent cigarettes and the basket of roses to have noticed it. Fish. A fish each. Mincu put the rose, its stem tipped with foil, into a glass of mineral water. He began on his fish, filleting one side, eating a mouthful, talking, drinking wine. He seems to do everything at once, Cox thought, and wondered if he tapped his feet as well to keep time. Liliana took a mouthful, a small one, and chewed it so grudgingly it was like watching a film in slow motion.

Mincu was showing his charm again. He used to take what he wanted, Cox decided, and now he has to work for it. Mincu talked, Mincu smiled, Mincu leaned in closer, Mincu must have told a joke because he laughed. But Liliana didn't laugh, Liliana didn't smile, Liliana ate a little and talked less. While he watched, Cox listened with part of his mind to Gabriela.

'That is bad man. Everybody knows he is bad man. And Liliana is good woman. Why do you make her do this? She has a white face. She wants to be sick or maybe cry or run away. She doesn't want to have dinner with bad man. Her memories are no good for her appetite. If he touches her again, I think Liliana will scream.'

Then she's going to scream, Cox decided, because Mincu was one of nature's touchers. Meanwhile Cox willed her to look at her dinner companion, to melt just a little because . . .

A scene so sudden and melodramatic killed the thought. Mincu was talking. He laid down his knife and fork, plucked the rose out of the water glass and held it out. Liliana looked from her plate to the flower and at last to Mincu's face. She seemed to ask a question. Cox could see her expression, how her eyebrows rose. Mincu not only answered, he pressed the rose forward so it nestled against her left breast. Like a swift exchange across the tennis net she spoke, he spoke, she slapped his face. Mincu lunged to grab her, knocking over a wine glass, but she was already out of reach. She stood up, banging over her chair, making the table rock, and while Mincu bent forward in a fresh effort to get hold of her, she half ran past the Italian Ambassador's table, bringing a brief lull in the flow of their talk.

'Oh lord, oh pray,' Cox said under his breath.

Liliana disappeared inside the restaurant. Gabriela moved to follow her until Cox put a hand on her arm. Mincu was standing, in half a mind to follow inside to continue their scene. Abruptly he got his wad of money out, tossed a number of notes on the table, strode past the pianist who played 'Ain't Misbehaving' and stormed out down the steps into the Bucharest night.

I'm a fool, Cox told himself, and there's no fool like an old fool. It's time someone put a bullet in my head. A kindness really. I rushed into doing something without preparation. It seemed like an unlocked door to Mincu's business so I opened the door and stepped boldly forward into free fall. Lesson number one: do not use amateurs. Lesson number two: do not use people who haven't been told what they're supposed to do. Lesson number three: if you haven't learned your lessons by now, put things right damn fast.

'Go and fetch her. Be as quick as you can.'

Liliana hadn't been crying. Some hurts go too deep for that. But she seemed to hyperventilate and then not let the breath out and Cox was afraid she might faint.

'We're getting away from here,' he said. Too many bad memories were plaguing her. Better away from the bustle and the piano and the staring waiters and the BBC man who had cast a long look before going back to his dinner. 'Give her an arm,' he told Gabriela, pushing the two of them ahead. He smiled his most confiding smile to the Italian Ambassador's wife who had half risen. 'Had something of a shock. Be all right in half a tick. Touch of the *così fan tuttes.*' He edged his way behind her chair and was free. '*Prego.*' Now he was passing the pianist who played 'The Night They Invented Champagne', and they beamed at each other. Then, with Liliana clinging to the rail, they were down the steps onto the pavement. The terrace stood above them, its balustrade, its lights, its bar, its chatter and laughter, its music. 'Like a liner cruising off into the night,' he said. 'Jenny made me go on a cruise once.' They were moving off, or possibly La Premiera was sailing away into the night. 'Jenny was my wife,' he explained. 'She always wanted to cruise the Caribbean. Steel bands and rum punch. Told her you could get that at the Notting Hill carnival and still have change from a fiver. She wasn't impressed.' With this inconsequential chatter as a diversion they passed out of sight of the restaurant.

Liliana stopped, looking all round her.

'My dear, you're safe. He's gone. Went off in a Mercedes half the length of the restaurant.'

Liliana asked Gabriela a question.

'Mr Cox,' she replied.

'Afraid I don't speak your language, but if it's my name you're asking you can call me Roy. If you like.'

Liliana spoke again in Romanian. Gabriela answered in English.

'I prefer not to be interpreter. That's what you are. You speak English perfectly. That's what Mr Cox is, English.'

'So why is he here? Why are you with him? Why were you watching?' Suddenly furious – which Cox took as an encouraging sign of spirit – she fired off another question in Romanian.

Gabriela said, 'Liliana asks if you were the one who made her meet Mincu.'

'My dear,' Cox began and got no further.

'Yes or no.' She'd spun back on Cox.

'My dear, let me—'

'Why don't you give me a simple answer? It is because you are another trickster like that man.' Her eyes caught the light from a streetlamp, the whites of them seeming to spark at him. 'Why don't you answer?'

'Because you won't let me. When I was a boy and lost my temper my mother told me I should hold my breath and count to ten.'

'Ten! I've been holding my breath and counting for years. Thousands. Millions.'

'The initial idea was Gabriela's. She was urging revenge on you. Being an opportunist I joined the enterprise. So if you feel angry, be angry at us both. I apologise. I'm not sorry but I apologise for the distress you feel. I'm not sorry because I need you and your help. If you'll indulge me just a little, I'll explain why you are so very important to me and a lot of other people, and how your help will strike a blow against Mr Octav Mincu. Come, I can see a bench over there.'

Acting the courtly old man, which was the cover that came most naturally to him these days, Cox smoothed over Liliana's spat of anger. It bubbled just below the surface but for the moment she was quiet. A gentleman, he offered his arm to her. She didn't take it but she walked at his side.

They were at the front of the National Theatre where a small patch of grass was criss-crossed with town planner's concrete paths. For the weary a concrete bench was placed with its back to the theatre and with the traffic of Boulevard Balescu in front. There'd been a student demonstration earlier in the evening and groups lingered on the pavement, reluctant to acknowledge the excitement was over. Old Nick would have sent the boys with truncheons in. That would have got them hopping.

He began formally, introducing himself. 'My name is

Royston Cox and I work for a department of the British government.'

'What department is this? Don't go on hiding things from me.'

Gabriela stirred as if to tell her friend to shut up and listen. Cox lifted his hand a fraction to quieten her. He'd placed himself in the middle of the bench so that the two women would be separated. No more asides in Romanian, thank you very much. He sat close beside Liliana, aligning himself with her, but looking straight ahead. Out of the corner of his eye he saw how she fixed on him. He could feel the tension in her, her intensity, like a sexual charge. She was roused, battle bright. Mincu was her enemy. But if she couldn't attack Mincu, she'd lash out at whoever was near. Such as himself.

'It's a department of the Foreign Office I work for. Here is identification.' He produced his wallet. He had credit cards, a medical insurance card, a kidney donor card, a press card describing him as Freelance and the one he handed her that had the royal crest and the words 'Foreign Office' and a photo. She reached to take it then snatched her hand back. 'The red stripe means I have clearance for confidential work. On the back is a magnetic strip that opens locks to certain back rooms in Whitehall. Actually, though, I work in an ugly modern building south of the river. We call it the Glasshouse. You know what a glasshouse is?'

'Of course.' Liliana was impatient. She wasn't sitting on a bench in the centre of Bucharest to be tested on her knowledge of English. Nonetheless she obliged: 'Where you English grow plants that need heat. Tomatoes. Also . . . also certain jungle plants.'

'Ah yes. But it has another meaning. A prison, a military one. At the back of the Glasshouse where we drive down to the garage someone has put up a notice: *No rest for the wicked.* The British sense of humour, you see. Maybe we who are always toiling are the wicked ones. But I like to think that it is our job to hunt down the wicked ones, of which the world has a plentiful supply. You had dinner with one, a very wicked one indeed.'

Her whole body jerked towards him. 'Are you telling me you are a spy?' He had been expecting her interest, her understanding, her sympathy. Her reaction was quite different. 'You make me part of your plots without asking my permission? Make me have dinner with Mincu? Make me go into danger with this wicked man without warning me? Is that a spy's morals?'

'Well,' Cox said, 'it's not a word I use myself. My wife used to say I was a cloak-and-dagger man. Bit of a romantic, she meant, going out of fashion. The last of the type. They don't let us in any more.'

'I know nothing about your cloak and your dagger. You are a spy. You made me have dinner with Mincu and sat there frowning, spying on us. You have some game to play with Mincu, then you do it. Don't make me suffer. Do your own spying.'

And with that she bolted with Gabriela in pursuit.

Cox kept their heads in view until they disappeared down the steps into the subway under University Square. When he followed ten seconds later there was no sign of them. Hamburger and pizza restaurants were crowded, a tape shop blared rock music, tables had been set up selling bread rolls and chewing gum and plastic combs and single cigarettes, old women squatted on the steps begging, boys hawked baskets of apples. He was jostled by two men. The Middle East starts here, he thought, clamping a hand to the pocket where he kept the wallet with his identity as a cloak-and-dagger man. Liliana's spy. But of Liliana and Gabriela there was no trace. A board showed the way to the metro. He went down a corridor, fumbled with 100 lei coins for the turnstile and heard a train coming in. On the platform he saw them again, Gabriela apparently in furious mood. He ran down the steps and as the doors started to close squeezed into the first carriage.

Am I wrong? A stubborn old fool? No, she does have spirit, as much as Gabriela. Anger has given it to her. She just needs to have her anger refocused.

At the next station he got out and walked along the platform, ducking his head to look through the windows. They were in the third carriage, both silent now. A truce. There were touches of colour high up on Liliana's cheeks. The glow of battle. He stood with them while the train rumbled through the tunnel.

'Leave me in peace,' Liliana said. Her eyes darted at him and away. 'Please,' she added.

'Ah you see, I shan't be in peace,' Cox said. 'It's not what I'm paid for.'

'I'm not paid for it either.'

'I could, of course, offer you money. But that would be an insult to you. It would be like buying you for what you've suffered in the past.'

'You know nothing of what I've suffered.'

Cox decided not to answer that one. Later. For the moment he concentrated on himself.

'And when people say it's what I'm paid for, I think to be honest I'd do it even if I weren't being paid.'

Seeing a pair of old women staring, Cox favoured them with his smile. It's all right, my dears, I'm not pestering the young ladies. We're all good platonic chums. Though he knew quite well that what he was trying to do was seduce Liliana, stroke her until she consented to do what she was reluctant to.

The metro in Moscow is buried deep, Stalin having been persuaded it could double as an air raid shelter. The metro in Bucharest, by contrast, lies just below the surface. Old Nick had ordered it built in a hurry during the Golden Age. Instead of tunnelling they had dug what amounted to a deep ditch, taking away the spoil in battered old trucks, causing a chaos of closed roads and mud, and finally roofing over and resurfacing it. As the three of them gripped a rail and swayed he was reminded of trams in another European capital and felt himself being carried back over the years.

'Mine is not a profession one chooses to go into,' he said. 'More it is a job that chooses you.'

Liliana stared at him. 'You are not making yourself plain, Mr Cox.'

Mr Cox, not Roy. Well, she was a generation, a generation and a half younger than he. Yet looking at her, at her dark hair and dark eyes and lips that looked pursed for a kiss, he felt . . . No, not love, it was that sad longing we call nostalgia. He wasn't in Bucharest with Liliana, he was in Budapest with Ilona. Even the names were similar. The train was carrying him back across the years.

'And really,' he said, 'I got in by accident. It was in 1956, long before you were born. I remember it as a blissful summer. I'd just finished university. I'd wandered round Europe looking for adventures and ended up in Hungary. And stayed. Stayed through the autumn. There was a girl, of course. She was a second cousin or a great-niece of Imre Nagy, something like that. I always thought Nagy was a reluctant reformer but to Ilona he was a hero. Going to kick the Ivans out and introduce an uncorrupted form of socialism. Ilona was an idealist. A romantic, part of her appeal. That and . . . well, the red in my bed.'

An old man has a lifetime's stories to tell. He had her full attention so he told her.

Chapter 5

'My name is Ilona,' she said. She gave her second name as well but it fought its way round Cox's head and he couldn't untangle it. Later she told him that Hungarian was one of the Finno-Ugric group and related to the Ostyak and Vogul languages and he had no reason to doubt her. When he told her his own name she said, 'Roy? Roy? That comes from French and means King. We don't want any kings here. I shall call you Cox.'

'It's Royston, actually.'

'Royston? Roys-town? A whole town of kings?' Her black eyes flashed a warning and so they settled for Ilona and Cox. Her father spoke seven languages. He is some kind of professor? He is a painter. A famous artist? Should I have heard of him? He paints houses. He used to be a journalist but he got something wrong with his brain. Cox was full of sympathy. His brain kept having incorrect thoughts, she explained.

'Naturally I shall do better than my father. Not in housepainting – which is dull. Nor in journalism – which is frivolous. But in languages. Already I have,' and she counted them on her fingers, 'Hungarian for my mother tongue, German for our history, French for its arrogance, Italian for its decadence, Russian because we had to learn it at school, American to speak to the imperialists, English to speak to you.'

'American is the same as English,' Cox objected.

'Don't be stupid, Cox. Fag in English is a slave at the schools of the ruling classes. Fag in American is homosexual. That makes American and English different languages, though I think there is much homosexuality among the English ruling classes. Are you homosexual, Cox?' She frowned at him.

'Great scott, no.'

'Good.'

Cox blinked. There was a silence while he digested the unexpected lurch their talk had taken. Then he smiled. She continued frowning but maybe it wasn't at him but at the situation in Budapest. They had met on the street where life, love and death were all to be found. Cox had stood next to her, impertinently close in Ilona's opinion and she had frowned and said something and found out he was English. They were part of a crowd listening to a fiery speaker, mostly students at first, plus some professors with untamed hair. There was a statue of Petőfi who long ago had been a poet as well as a nationalist leader. After the First World War Poland had had a concert pianist as leader. In Europe, Cox knew, they ordered things differently. They were unruly but they were cultured. Who did Britain have as its leader? Anthony Eden, *Sir* Anthony Eden, one of the English ruling classes who had been beaten as a fag and in turn had beaten other fags and now wanted to relive his adolescence by beating the Arabs in Egypt.

'What is he saying?'

'He is urging solidarity with the Poles. They have won reforms, you see, so we should have them too. Only we cannot say that openly. But the Poles are our fraternal socialist allies so we can proclaim our solidarity with them. Do I not speak English well?'

'Perfectly,' Cox said. Indeed, what he could see of her was all perfection: her dark hair, her flashing eyes, her intensity which was so exhilarating compared with the vapid creatures his mother trawled in front of him, her promising breasts, her frank and bold nature.

The crowd moved off and marched across the Chain Bridge to the Buda side and filled the square by the Foreign Ministry. Cox and Ilona kept side by side.

'You see those aerials?' Ilona was pointing at the roof. 'That is how they receive their orders from Moscow. We shall tear them down.'

'There are soldiers guarding the building.'

'Not now, Cox. When we have triumphed. When we have the real revolution and true socialism is introduced we shall take orders from no one. That man who is speaking, he is demanding free elections and the Soviet troops to return home and the political prisoners to be free. Isn't that marvellous?'

But Cox was watching the soldiers, how their fingers were curled in the trigger guards of their weapons.

The crowd had grown a hundred thousand strong, office and factory workers, housewives with shopping bags, actors, pastrycooks, waiters, dentists who abandoned their patients, market traders, road sweepers, postmen, a nation. They marched again, across Magrit Bridge to Lajos Kossuth Square. The lights blazed from the upper windows of Parliament but underneath in the shadow of its walls stood more men in uniform.

'Those are AVO,' Ilona said. For a moment she seemed distracted. AVO were the worst. When she said the word again – 'AVO' – her voice was venomous. AVO were the security police. The ones who wore plain clothes were the most loathed of all: interrogators, torturers, murderers.

Chanting had begun. 'We want Nagy, we want Nagy.'

'Imre Nagy is my great-uncle,' Ilona said. Or she might

have said second cousin. He only had the movement of her lips to go by, the words themselves being swallowed in the roar of voices. Nagy appeared on a balcony and made a sort of speech before the lights in the square were switched off. But the crowd rolled up newspapers and lit them and made torches. The flames didn't last long but it was a defiant and joyous gesture to Cox. We have lived in the dark long enough, the torches said, and now we shall make our own light.

Ilona had taken possession of Cox's arm now, dragging him away. 'We must go to the radio station. It's under siege. They are refusing to broadcast the people's demands. Hurry.'

Mihaly Pollack Square was already jammed, the crowd chanting. The radio station was like a giant wedding cake built of grey stone and on the roof was a frieze of AVO armed with rifles and several machine guns aimed down at the crowd. In a side street stood trucks of reinforcements and it was rumoured that tanks had been sent for. The doors of the radio station remained closed and a wooden gate protected the entrance. The director of the radio was a woman built like a brick wall, by name Benke, a Stalinist to her fingertips. But she made a bizarre concession: a deputation would be allowed to shin up a drainpipe onto the balcony and through a window into her office. She made another concession: that their manifesto would be broadcast.

'Isn't that fantastic?' Ilona swung round on Cox and gave him a hug. For solidarity, for friendship, for warmth, for their very own October revolution, for whatever was in the air that night. They watched electricians appearing on the balcony, unreeling flex and fixing up loudspeakers. Finally an announcer appeared and the crowd fell silent. He read from a sheet of paper, each demand being greeted by a roar of approval until abruptly the roars turned to anger as people in flats across the square shouted that the radio was still playing music and this was just a trick.

The crowd began shoulder-charging the wooden gate. On a street beside the radio building water cannons were aimed at the crowd. The first cobbles were prised up and thrown. Then a squad of soldiers handed their weapons over and that was the spark: a volley of rifle fire from the roof was aimed at the sky as a warning. Fresh rounds were loaded and the rifles were aimed down. A pair of ambulances flying the red flag used on emergency calls arrived to carry away casualties. The leading ambulance swerved to avoid running someone down and crashed into a gatepost. Its rear doors broke open to reveal four crates loaded with guns. The driver fled, his white coat splitting open to reveal his AVO uniform.

This is the twenty-third day of October in the year 1956, Cox told himself. He glanced at his watch. The time is eight minutes past nine. Detail was important. Memorize everything because nothing will ever be the same again. He had just seen his first man killed. The AVO on the roof had stopped aiming at the stars and shot instead into the thickest part of the crowd where students held high the Hungarian flag with a gaping hole in its centre where the Party symbol had been hacked out with a knife. Memorize these screams, he told himself. Remember the thuds the bullets make as they hit flesh and bones, more a feeling that passed through close-packed bodies than a sound. Memorize the screams of fear as a detachment of AVO charge out of the building, bayonets fixed on their rifles, stabbing at chests and stomachs. Memorize the taint of tear gas and how they wrap a scarf round the canister and hurl it back through gaping windows. Memorize the sound of voices lifting over the apartment blocks as the whole city erupts. Memorize how the conscript soldiers are grinning and shaking hands and being kissed as they join the crowd. Memorize the smoke billowing from windows and the flicker of flames playing on the ceilings and the smashing of glass and the wailing and the slush of mud and blood and vomit and the bonfire of propaganda leaflets and single rifle shots and the stammer of automatic weapons.

Commit to memory and then make use of it.

The Astoria Hotel was where Fleet Street's finest were holed up. Some turned up their coat collars to venture out, coming back thoughtful or wide-eyed or worried according to temperament. 'Jesus, it's like the bleeding Polish cavalry charging the sodding Panzers, except these boys haven't even got horses,' opined one of the tabloids. 'They should send for Bem,' said a quality Sunday with historical vision.

'Who's Bem when he's at home?'

'General who fought for Hungarian independence. Pole, actually. It was 1848. Wasn't successful, mind, but the Hungarians put up a statue to him.'

And some covered events from the Astoria's bar.

'That was no cock-eyed squaddie with a pea-shooter. That was a tank. What they got, then? T63s? T54s?'

'Yes,' said the barman, not knowing.

'Jesus wept. Same again. Make it a proper double this time, generous with the wrist. Understand double?'

'Yes,' said the barman.

I am blessed by nature in the width genes, Lovelace liked to say, but not in the height genes. Imagine me stretched out to the height of the common herd and everything would be hunky-dory. And don't fret, I'm absolutely hunky-dory in other departments, darlin'.

'Christ, look what the wind blew in. You look like you've been at a Guy Fawkes party gone wrong. You English?'

'Yes,' Cox said. 'That is, *I* am.'

'And she ain't, if I take your meaning. Nice work if you can get it.'

'Are you a journalist? Ilona said this was where a lot of the journalists were staying.'

'Smart lass. The rest of the pack hired a cab or two to view the action. Me, I have a bit of a problem with my eyes.' He pointed to spectacles as thick as the bottom of wine bottles. 'So I let the action come to me. Name's Rex Lovelace. Rexie to you, darlin'.'

Ilona did not count Latin among her languages so she allowed her hand to be shaken. 'Why do you call me *darling*? We have met for the first time.'

'Darlin', my pet, ducks, sweetheart, my fancy, love, sugar, poppet, whatever you like. Talking of which, what'll you have? Same as me? Make them doubles, Paddy. Understand double? I always call barmen Paddy unless they're Irish. Your Irish are very sensitive about that.'

That night and every night Lovelace bought drinks until the day that Soviet tanks shot holes in the Astoria's walls and the barman disappeared. Lovelace explained his business philosophy. Expenses were divided into three to diddle the accounts scrooges: there was *Entertainment* which was grudged to a certain limit, there was *Buying sources*, and there was *Reciprocity* which was when he had to buy a round because someone else had bought a round. 'Bottoms up,' he said and drank. 'And you've truly never heard of Rex Lovelace? Never read Rexie? Perhaps you don't take my rag. That would explain it.' In the street of shame, he said, his rag was known as the *Daily Wretch*. Or maybe it was *Daily Retch*. He never spelled it.

From outside came the sound of gunfire, shouts, running feet. Lovelace cocked his head to it. 'Things are warming up. Excuse me, I've got to give the *Wretch* a bell.'

'Actually,' Cox said, 'that's why we came looking for

the press. We were at the storming of the radio station. I thought an eye-witness account of that might be worth a bit.'

'Well,' Lovelace said, easing himself back into his chair, 'well now. Our lad in the thick of it. Young British hero leads assault on Red radio. Local beauty praises his courage.'

'I didn't say *leads*.'

'No, I did. Listen, old son,' a quick glance at his watch, 'I've got ten minutes before my latest late deadline. Just time for another while you tell me about it. Don't worry, I'll see you right with the loot.'

'Do I like Mr Lovelace?' Ilona asked of herself. 'I do not think so.'

'It's not a question of liking,' Cox said, giving that writhe of the shoulders of an embarrassed Englishman. 'He's useful. The money's useful. As a contact he's useful.' Cox, puzzled about his life's career pattern, had developed an ambition to work for a newspaper. It was just that the idea of starting on the *Hemel Hempstead Gazette* didn't appeal.

'But he's a looter. We are making history and he thinks of loot.'

'Ah now, you've got that wrong. I'll give you a lesson in demotic English.'

He was going to explain about loot and seeing a man about a dog and aiming Percy at the porcelain and mud in your eye but she interrupted. 'Where are you staying, Cox?'

They were standing outside the Astoria in Muzeum Street. He made a vague gesture into the night.

'At the youth hostel.'

'I do not think that is safe. You must come with me. You will stay in my parents' flat.' She linked her arm through his. 'My parents are away,' she added as if further encouragement were needed. 'My uncle died so they have gone to Eger. I think they will not be able to get back. Maybe not for some time. Are you virgin?'

The pavement rocked under his feet to sudden gunfire. Or maybe it was all inside him.

'Well no, actually. I'm not promiscuous or anything of that sort but at university, you know, there were parties and things.' He seemed to have run out of words. He felt her hold on his arm tighten.

'It is good you are not virgin. I am virgin. Until tonight I am virgin. But tonight I shall become free woman. You will show me.'

Free woman? Cox wasn't certain this was correct usage but now was not the time for English lessons.

Later, in her no longer virginal bed, she asked to the face close beside hers on the pillow, 'Do you love me, Cox?'

'Yes, oh yes.' Cox from his limited experience knew this was what girls wanted to hear. And what Cox wanted to do was go back to the beginning and do it all again.

'I do not think so. I think,' and her hand crept its way down his belly, 'you want to do this so you say you love me. It's all right. I wanted to do this too. Tonight I am free woman, do you understand? I am free Hungarian woman. But there is fighting we must do. We are like soldiers and maybe . . .'

She didn't say what the maybe was but it lodged in Cox's memory like a pebble in his shoe. In a single movement she swung her legs away, rose out of the bed and walked to the narrow dormer window. She looked first at the sky to see if the stars watched over them and then down to the city. They could hear single rifle shots and what sounded like cheering.

'People are making the revolution,' she said, 'and we are making love.'

Her voice was flat. Was she disapproving?

'Come back to bed, darling.'

'Don't call me that. He did. He is frivolous. It means nothing.'

'Ilona, come back to bed.'

'First I want to give you something. It is something to remember me by. In case.'

'In case what?'

But she didn't seem to have heard. She had switched on a little lamp on the table against the wall under the poster of Lenin and was searching among her books. She found a pencil and pad. Naked, she sat on the edge of the bed with the pad on her knees. 'I write you a poem.'

She tore the page off the pad and handed it to Cox. He turned to lie on his elbow and hold the paper towards the lamp. She had printed carefully, as if for a child:

Akarhattalak,
de nem szerethettelek.

He said, 'I don't understand it.'

'Of course not.'

'What does it mean?'

'You must find out.'

He stared at the words. All those consonants, they seemed like the stutter of a machine gun. 'It almost rhymes,' he said. Not knowing what else to say he added, 'It's very short. I know, like a *haiku*,' he finished in a stroke of inspiration.

'Sometimes life almost rhymes – like tonight. And life is very short.'

Later, much later, when he was in London he found the page jammed in a jacket pocket. She must have put it there. So one morning he went to the Westminster Reference Library and struggled with dictionaries and grammars, for Hungarian has both suffixes and prefixes. As far as he could decipher what she had written was:

I could have wanted thee,
but I could not have loved thee.

That night the statue of Stalin that stood halfway up György Dosza Avenue was toppled. Of all the symbols of Soviet bondage, this was the most hated. Like the man himself, the statue was monstrous. 'We should have heard it crash from here. He was ten metres tall, made of bronze.' Stalin's fall rang out like a huge bell striking the hour of freedom. Cox rehearsed the simile in his mind. Would Lovelace use it? Cox hadn't actually heard Stalin's statue tumble: he and Ilona had been too involved with each other. Ilona was angry they had missed it.

'Cox, you must get dressed at once. We will join the people.'

Cox lay on his side watching her body disappear inside clothes.

'Get up now. We are making the revolution today.'

Cox got out of bed, shivering in the cold. There was no heating. When he tried a light switch, there was no electricity. Ilona was inspecting him, her eyes travelling down his body.

'This morning you are—'

But she didn't finish. Somewhere not far away there was the booming of a tank's cannon.

'Hurry, Cox, we have work to do.'

When they went outside it seemed at first that the city had been evacuated. Then they realized the people had gone to war. They stood in doorways, peeped slyly from windows, ran to shelter behind trees where they could watch for danger. Ilona selected a young man, possibly a student, to question. She told Cox, 'He says the government has invited the Soviet tanks in to crush the people.'

'Perhaps they didn't need an invitation,' Cox said. 'Perhaps they were coming anyway.'

'Then they must go. We shall make them.'

It's the Red Army, he screamed at her. They've got bloody tanks. What have you got in your hands? Nothing. But he only screamed inside his head. He felt a tightening in his gut and his head seemed to shrink down inside his coat. Fear. It had paralyzed even his voice.

Lovelace could have spent the entire day in the bar of the Astoria. He could have spent the whole time since they had met the evening before. He had the deliberation – sobriety even – of a man who had been drinking a long time.

'Greetings. Good evening. Welcome. What'll it be? Same as mine? Two similars, Paddy, and make them doubles. Where's your popsy? Not run off, I trust. My word, you're doing yourself well there, old son.'

'She's fighting,' Cox said. 'I was fighting too. I just slipped away to come and tell you.'

Cox had almost said *report to you*, as if Lovelace was some kind of superior officer.

'Fighting? The veteran of the radio station grapples with Russki tanks? Tell Rexie.'

'Did your paper use the piece you phoned in last night?'

'My dear chap, place of honour just under the masthead. Proprietor Lord Muckit. Price twopence. Then *Derring-do in the city of hopes – young VC's story*. As told to yours truly.'

'VC?'

'Very Courageous.' The barman brought their drinks. Lovelace raised his glass and clinked Cox's. 'Confusion to the French. In this case it is the Russkies who are the French. Now tell.'

Cox did. It was a tale that a hundred or a thousand or ten thousand others in the city could have told: dodging trouble in the morning, meeting other people, lunching on a loaf of bread from a bakery that was miraculously working, then coming across a tank parked near the steps to Keleti station. One of their group had two bottles filled with petrol and with rags round the necks. A match to one rag brought an instant roaring flame. It was suicide if you weren't quick. The man tossed the bottle and the tank was engulfed in fire: the petrol bomb, oil spills, grease in the tracks, debris under the engine cover. Any minute the fuel tank would go up. The hatch popped open but the flames stopped the crew escaping. The man tossed the second petrol bomb and Cox could still hear the Russians.

'They screamed and screamed.'

Cox was staring at his untouched glass. Not a VC, more SS. Scared shitless.

'Christ,' said Lovelace. 'More. More details. More colour. Did the crowd sing the national anthem? Or cheer? What did your girl do? Didn't hide, I bet. Did she kiss the hero? I can see that: *Kiss of death for the Russkies, kiss of freedom for the heroes.*'

But Cox couldn't remember. His head ached from the screams.

'Maybe they danced? You know, link arms, do some kind of crazy Hungarian folk dance round the burning tank?'

Cox shook his head. The screams kept banging from one side of his skull to the other.

'I've got to describe this to our readers. Something to make their breakfast cereal go snap, crackle and pop. This funeral pyre—'

'They screamed and screamed,' Cox interrupted him. 'And then they stopped.'

Tram lines had been torn up to form barricades in the

street. The regular police and the army were on the side of the people. Their armouries were thrown open, rifles passed out. Cox wore a red, green and white armband to show his allegiance. Against them were the AVO and the Soviet forces. The battles were tiny and vicious. Sometimes a tank blasted open a building. Sometimes an AVO was flushed out and killed. At night Cox and Ilona exulted together in bed. Life and love, danger and freedom, tumult and silence, bonfires of Party cards and propaganda leaflets and posters and red stars, shouts in the streets and whispers in bed.

'I love you, Ilona.'

'No,' she said. 'I am a woman, you are a man, we live in danger, we hold each other. That is what it is.'

But he did love her. She shouldn't try to take it away from him. Was she acting cynical? Trying to strengthen herself, be tougher, be braver, not agree to tenderness? He couldn't understand. Finding her mysterious, admiring her courage and iron will, he loved her more.

A thousand Soviet tanks had been sent into the city, but on the first day no infantry to flush out the buildings. The operation had been mounted too swiftly for that. Then Russian soldiers came and fighting grew bloodier. When Cox tried to meet Lovelace he found a dozen tanks at the junction of the streets where the Astoria was, a gaping hole in its wall and men with red stars on their uniforms. The next evening the soldiers had vanished and the tanks had moved elsewhere. The bar was a shambles but Lovelace sat with a bottle of whisky in the foyer.

'I just stayed in my room. I had company.' He lifted the bottle of Dewar's White Label. 'Cheers. Could soon be time for a tactical withdrawal. Her Majesty's gracious representative will oblige. He probably takes the *Wretch* for the footmen. Besides Lord Muckit flogged him at Harrow. Tell me, what've you seen?'

Cox was ashen-faced. First he told of the miracle of the Soviet tanks, how festooned with Hungarian flags and with women and children riding on them like floats in a carnival they had gone to join the demonstration in Kossuth Square.

'Kids on tanks! I love it. More.'

A huge crowd had gathered outside Parliament, chanting, singing, when uniformed figures on a rooftop opened fire. AVO shooting at their own citizens. The crowd stampeded but the streets leading from the square were jammed and bodies kept falling. Hundreds. Four hundred, six hundred. Well, it seemed like that. Ilona and Cox had got away and Cox had come to the Astoria.

'Where's your girl? Rexie wants to interview her.'

'Gone to her parents' flat. She's dead beat.'

'Oh yes.'

And for all of what Ilona dismissed as his frivolity, those eyes behind their thick glasses seemed to penetrate right inside Cox. No shamming, those eyes said, no mumbled half-truths. I know.

Suddenly the Russians were leaving. Ilona heard the news on the radio and translated. 'Their officers are meeting our officers. They're going. They're actually going, Cox. We've won!' She kissed him with passion, her tongue wriggling in his mouth. 'Maybe I love you after all.' She laughed and skipped away when he tried to grab her.

But of course they hadn't won. The Russians weren't going home. They had withdrawn to put Stalin together again, taller and more monstrous than ever, before they returned. The tanks had rolled across the Soviet frontier in their thousands. The infantry came in their tens of thousands, Mongolian troops, according to the legend, who understood neither Hungarian nor Russian and couldn't be pleaded with. They invaded the city in the hour before dawn, wrenching Ilona and Cox out of sleep. When Ilona switched on the radio it was the voice of Imre Nagy they heard. It sounded mournful, betrayed, defeated, not full of Churchillian defiance.

'What is he saying?'

'Saying?' She looked wildly at Cox, then pointed at the window, at the city outside. 'That is what he is saying.'

They heard the roar of artillery, the screech of tank tracks over cobbles.

'He is saying that he informs the whole world that the Soviet Union is invading. What good is that? He is useless.'

'I thought you said he was your uncle. Or a cousin. Something. A godfather.'

She glared. 'A godfather? Don't be frivolous, Cox.'

'Perhaps the Americans will help. Perhaps the British . . .' But the British government was preoccupied with its own invasion.

On the street men with rifles were running. 'Where are they going?'

'They say the Kilian barracks are under siege.'

'I must find Lovelace. He'll have more news.'

She glared at him again. 'They're fighting at the Kilian barracks. There's a tunnel under the road to the Corvin cinema. They're handing out rifles.'

It needed more than rifles, Cox understood. It called for planes and tanks and artillery from the West. A crash of falling masonry jerked his head round. When he turned back, she had vanished. He looked inside doorways, peered through windows, shouted up staircases.

'Ilona! Ilona!'

Muzeum Avenue was patrolled by tanks. Cox could see the Astoria Hotel with its smashed windows and gaping wall. Was Lovelace still there? Hiding in his room?

He ran doubled up across the street when there was a big enough gap between the tanks and clambered over rubble into the foyer. He shouted out for Lovelace and nobody answered. He climbed stairs and shouted again. He climbed higher and opened doors at random. In one a man lay stretched out on the bed. Cox thought he was dead. He was so painfully thin, emaciated, he could have starved to death.

The corpse heaved over to face Cox. 'Lovelace? The fat Brit? That guy?'

'Do you know where he is?'

'Sure, gone home to mommy,' the man said. 'He drank the bar dry and said there was no point in staying. He's probably at Buck House by now. Early cocktails.'

A tattoo of gunfire away to the east was answered by a salvo close at hand. The walls shook and a little plaster dust drifted down. Cox crossed to the window. Sunlight lit up the smoke of a hundred fires. He saw a tank roll over a makeshift barricade of tram lines.

'Will he make it?'

'Our Rexie? Oh sure. His kind always do. We were the last here. The fat Brit and the lanky Yank. I should've got out too, only I fell down. Too much juice. Made the mistake of trying to keep up with Lovelace. I guess I'll just lie here a while and think happy thoughts. No point in going out and getting my ass shot off. You see, I hid something from the fat man. My reserve supply.' He pulled a bottle from under the covers.

'You're a journalist as well?'

'Like little old sexy Rexie, you mean?' The thin face relaxed in a seraphic smile. 'Could be, son. Could be.'

Chapter 6

Cox found himself outside on the pavement with Liliana and Gabriela to each side of him. Had he really told them all that? So many details of his first love? Enough anyhow. A first love is precious and some of the memories are so precious, so deeply buried, that it is not a question of concealment but of their coming to light slowly. *I could have wanted thee, but I could not have loved thee.* And she had wanted him, desperately, as if she'd known that time was short. He remembered that first night and how she had clung to him in bed, her hands pulling their naked bodies together, urging him to get inside her, to be done with the formalities and delights of foreplay, time enough for the preliminaries afterwards. That night she had become a woman. She was a virgin and as he entered her she cried out. It wasn't a cry of pain, more the shout of someone going into battle. Well, he'd only had that thought later, reliving the thrill of their lovemaking while the Budapest night had its own cries and battles. How thin Ilona had been, her stomach flat, her hip bones like two bookends, her breasts prominent because of the lack of flesh over her ribs, her nipples as tiny as orange pips and as hard. These were things – so little but so important to the young Cox, so precious to the old Cox's memory – that he hadn't told Liliana now.

They seemed to have been walking up and down, but for how long he couldn't say. In his mind he'd been walking the streets of Budapest. They were in a part of the city he didn't know. To one side was a metro sign and he remembered starting his story on the train under the disapproving stare of some old women.

'A curious detail, a postscript really.' He was conscious of having been silent with his memories and he needed to get talking again. 'Imre Nagy, who had some connection to Ilona, was flown here. I don't mean Bucharest but to Romania. He had been the focus of resistance so the Russians bundled him and a few others into a plane and got them out of sight. He was taken to somewhere in the Carpathians.'

'People go there for skiing,' Gabriela said.

'Ah well, Nagy and the others would have had a different view of it. Do you know, I've forgotten whether they were thrown into a concrete prison or Dracula's castle. One of the Hungarians said to Nagy, "So there you are – Kafka was a realist after all."'

Neither of the women smiled. Perhaps, Cox admitted, black humour didn't appeal to Romanians. Black humour had been ordinary life.

'Afterwards, they shot Nagy.' He added, to show he wasn't frivolous, 'Murderous thugs.'

'Your girl,' Gabriela said. 'Did you see her again?'

'No.'

'What happened to her?'

Cox raised a hand. 'Maybe she survived. Maybe . . .' He let the hand drop. 'She was set on being a hero. She had the determination and the courage. If she couldn't be a hero, then a martyr.'

'Didn't you try to find her?'

'It was chaotic. And murderous. *Sauve qui peut.*'

'Later. Didn't you make enquiries?'

'Would that have been doing her any favours? The hard-liners were back in charge and turning the screws. Someone from the West asking for her – that would have been the last thing she needed. You know how it was.'

'So you got out.'

Her tone had been censorious. *Men,* she seemed to imply, they plunder our bodies, take what they want, spin us a tale, and abandon us. He wasn't about to dispute this and treated it as a straightforward question. 'The embassy was impossible. Couldn't get near it. So I walked and got lifts and hid in barns. There's a lake on the border the Austrians call Neusiedl, the Hungarians something else. Very shallow. Used by fishermen and duck hunters. I found a skiff hidden in the reeds . . .' He shrugged as if it had been a normal day's picnic, but he'd seen people arrested, heard the sound of shooting.

'You said,' Liliana had been quiet for a time, 'that you didn't choose your job, it chose you.'

Gabriela stirred as if this was an area that Liliana shouldn't pry into. Cox understood it was sometimes necessary to expose yourself to gain another's trust.

'Well yes. It was about three weeks before I reached home. My parents' home, that is. There was a note to call such-and-such a number. My mother had written it. *Message from Lovelace, call WHItehall 1000, ask for Fortescue.* My mother had added: *Sounds queer to me. Queer* in the fifties would be *gay* now. If she'd meant *strange,* my mother would have written *rum.* Oh good, I thought, the loot. Of course it wasn't that, and Fortescue – if that was his name – wasn't a journalist. He suggested lunch. His club in St James's had no name outside and I had to ask a policeman. Over sherry he said, "Heard a lot about you, Cox, well done, splendid, quite the hero." I said, "I think Lovelace was laying it on a bit thick." "Chaps like him always do. Justifies their expenses." Over soup he said, "Was it frightening?" "I was terrified," I said. "Ah, right," he said, "but you kept going. Splendid. That's what I like to hear." Over the fish he said, "Kill anyone at all?" I said, "I don't think so, sir, actually." "Not even a little bit? But you were there when some of the baddies got topped?" "Hard to avoid." "Didn't faint?" "No." "Splendid." Over lamb cutlets and frozen peas he said, "What did you think of that journalist chappie?" I said, "Well, sir, he didn't seem much of a newshound. He didn't go out much. I gave him stories. I saw a couple of others talk to him. Otherwise he spent his time in the bar." "Goes with the job," Fortescue said. Over cheese he said, "What are you planning to do now?" "I've got no plans really." "Bit of a loose end, eh?" Over dessert he said, "Excuse me, I've got to see a man about a dog." He came back and we had coffee. He said, "Look here, Cox, I've been jolly favourably impressed. Now there are one or two chaps I'd like you to meet." So that is how it was. That was how they set about recruiting in the old days.'

And Cox had gone from St James's to a building in Queen Anne's Gate where their headquarters was. A much classier place than the Glasshouse, though there was a concrete block at the rear where less classy things went on.

It was time to move things forward. They'd stopped in front of an open gateway to what looked like a builder's yard but there were metal tables and chairs set out on the cracked paving. Despite the hour the air continued balmy and people sat drinking and smoking. A smell of charcoal-grilled meat hung in the air.

'Bulgarians,' Gabriela announced and waved a dismissive hand. 'Look at them! Aristocrats all!'

Cox caught her wrist. 'My dear, I'd like you to leave us now. There are things I want to discuss with Liliana.'

'I don't . . .' Liliana began. Whatever she didn't, she kept to herself. She bit it back, quite literally biting her lip while giving her friend an imploring look.

'I think Liliana needs me,' Gabriela said. 'We have no secrets. We share everything.'

'Not this,' Cox said. He still had hold of her wrist and squeezed it. 'You talked of Liliana's revenge. It's hers alone.'

'But she's worried that—'

'She's not a young girl,' Cox said more sharply. 'She's grown up enough to deal with her own worry. You run along to that nice Mr Crake or he'll be thinking we've eloped. Go on now.'

Gabriela said something to Liliana and hugged her tight. Cox watched as if worried that Liliana would run off with her friend. He saw them embrace, how Gabriela kissed Liliana full on the mouth, and wondered uselessly what 'sharing everything' meant. Gabriela left in the direction of the metro entrance, slowly at first, then faster as if eager to reach her lover. Cox laid a hand under Liliana's elbow to direct her to one of the small round tables. A middle-aged woman with an apron round her middle and her hair wrapped in a scarf came up and wiped the table with a rag.

'We'll have coffee,' Cox said, deciding for them both. 'I don't know how you like it.'

'It'll be Turkish,' Liliana said and ordered.

'I'll have a brandy to wash it down.' With Turkish, he always seemed to get a mouthful of sediment. *Waiter, waiter, this coffee tastes like mud,* he thought foolishly. *It should do, sir, it was ground this morning.* He looked round again at the courtyard which the taverna had colonized, at its sprawling grape vine, the string of naked light bulbs, geraniums in cans painted white, tables and chairs that wouldn't stand straight. The noise from the city was shut out. I've left

Bucharest, Cox thought, I'm in some Balkan village before the war. Which war? The first war of the twentieth century? The one to come?

Liliana was perched on the edge of her chair. Her hands in her lap held on to each other, to stop their shaking or for comfort. She was staring at Cox as if afraid he would spring at her. She looked so taut that something might snap in her at any moment and she would bolt.

'Don't jump ship,' Cox said. 'Just listen to what I have to say. There's no danger in listening, is there?'

Her hands sprang apart and she swept a strand of hair off her forehead. Then the hands clung together again. Her lips moved.

'What did you say?' Cox asked.

She whispered but loud enough for him to hear this time. 'You don't understand.'

'Oh, I think I do. Not in the way you understand – in here, inside, with your emotions. But from all the experience of my life, the suffering I have witnessed, the pain I've felt, the cruelties, injustice, heartlessness and just plain indifference to the desperation in other people's lives . . .' He came to a halt, uncertain where the rhetoric was taking him. 'People talk of priests having a vocation. I don't put myself so high. But sometimes when things have been very bad, when our adversaries have seemed to gain in strength, when our own political masters have shown neither courage nor morality, when the future has seemed bleak, I've said the reason I chose the path of my life – or it chose me – was that I could do *something* to make the world a better place. No great triumph, but a small step forward. My wife used to call it my Mr Valiant-for-truth role, that I fought alone against all the evils in the world – though I assure you I never saw myself as a hero like that. Other times she said I was Sisyphus, condemned to heave this big boulder up the hill only to have it roll to the bottom and have to start again. You know about Sisyphus? He was being punished for all his misdeeds. So what have I done that was so very wrong, I would ask, that my labour never ends? And bless her, she would reply: You care too much. So, Liliana, I don't know in every detail what you suffered but I do care most deeply. I think that if you were to help me to destroy Octav Mincu you would also be helping yourself. Revenge is what Gabriela called it. I would call it justice. But my wife always said I was old fashioned.'

It was a speech he made, though it was delivered in a low voice. He had spoken at length to make her listen. And instead of revenge he had talked of justice because she was of an age to be idealistic and believe the world was perfectable. There is a sort of dependence that develops in the listener which he was counting on. Her eyes were fixed on his face and then they jumped over his shoulder. Had he lost her? No, it was just the arrival of the Bulgarian woman with a tray: two little cups of coffee, two tumblers of water and a glass of what she called *koniak*, which would have made the French livid. Cox's throat was not so much dry as sore. He supposed it was from tension and he drank half the water. He could see the hands on Liliana's lap. Her right hand was gripping the index finger of her left hand and twisting it as if she could unscrew it and set it free.

'So,' he said, as if they had reached a point together and the only way was forward. He leaned across the table and laid a hand on her arm, to have contact, to show concern, perhaps to let strength flow into her. Her hands were at once still.

So, he said again, but to himself. What do I tell her? The truth? Which truth? Which speculation? Do I tell her we are on the brink of war? For the third time this century the leaders of Europe will bring their vaunted civilization crashing down round their ears, cities consumed by fire, millions of lives blown away. Some said the war had already started in what used to be Jugoslavia. It was possible, always possible. Never understimate mankind's love of destruction. Is that what she would believe, act on? Liliana, he could say, the Germans are arming the Croats. The Russian nationalists are breathing fire in defence of the Serbs, their fellow Slavs. Muslim volunteers from Iran and Afghanistan are already in Bosnia. The United Nations is toothless. The Americans blow hot and cold. And Mincu rubs his hands and makes contact with the Serbs, the Muslims, the Croats. Well, gentlemen, what do you need? I can get you missiles, artillery, mines, tanks. You want helicopter gunships? Russian, maybe? Field-tested in Afghanistan and Chechnya? No problem.

Mincu, he decided, would be the kind who said *No problem.*

She was speaking again but she'd lifted a hand to her mouth as if to stop the words coming out. He had to bend forward to catch what she said. 'What has he done to you that is so terrible?'

'Not to me,' Cox said. 'Not to me personally.'

'But it concerns you enough to bring you here, to try to trap me.'

'Not trap, persuade.'

She lowered her hand to speak more urgently. 'Why? Why?'

'Because he is a monster. He is more than bad, he is evil. I make a distinction. A bad man will do bad things but he will do them to you as an individual. An evil man is a wholesaler of bad things, not just to you or me, to unknown people, to whole unseen classes or tribes or categories. Or to luckless people who wandered too close. A terrorist bomber is evil in a minor way. Mincu has a grander vision. You've seen him at your Trade Fair, possibly interpreted for him, know the kind he does business with. Except, of course, the evil deals he conducts behind shut doors. That is where I need your help: to get behind those doors because he accepts you, he trusts you. In short, I need you to grow close to him.'

Liliana made a noise in her throat which Cox chose to take as a question.

'You want to know the details?' He took a sip of coffee, which he found too sweet. He followed it with a sip of brandy and felt the inside of his mouth pucker. 'It is to do with Jugoslavia. Or the former Jugoslavia. And the warring factions. Mincu has been offering weapons to anybody who is interested. Well, arms dealers are promiscuous. They say that money has no colour, except possibly the colour of blood. Only they don't call them weapons, they say *matériel*. Sounds classier in French, not something for blowing people up. But weapons is what they are and offering them round means that eventually we get to hear of it. There are meant to be sanctions in force but no one seems to be running short of guns. They even closed Timisoara airport to stop smuggling over the border. It's made no difference. The border leaks like an old barn in the rain. Mincu has a menu. He's like a head waiter standing at your shoulder and running through the day's dishes. Stinger rocket launchers? Shoot down the other side's helicopters? No problem. The CIA gave them to the *mujahaddin* to kick the Soviets out of Afghanistan and Mincu can get those. At a price. Naturally. Mincu does nothing for nothing. If Stingers are a bit too pricey, how about rifles? Mincu can do you Kalashnikovs and offers a choice: Czech made or Russian made. Sniperscopes – well, you've seen those at the Fair. Maybe you're more ambitious. There are hi-tech Gatling guns, fire something like three thousand rounds a minute. Or those dinky little Uzis. Or anti-tank guns, also good against apartment blocks. Latest in Russian shells that spread a carpet of gas over half an acre and then ignite it. South African artillery, very long range, very accurate, tested in Angola. Radar. APCs. Fragmentation grenades. Oh, the list goes on, the list goes on. The head waiter murmurs and asks your pleasure. Then the head waiter ducks down low to whisper in your ear because what he is about to offer is very special and it's for your ears only.'

Liliana had bent closer over the table. Her face looked ghostly pale, her eyes round and dark, her mouth so tightly closed that her lips had vanished. Was she going to faint? Vomit? Cox would have offered her his brandy but someone had drunk it. He looked round and found the dumpy woman staring at them. He held up the empty glass in one hand and two fingers of the other hand. She nodded, then cackled with laughter and said something to a man who puffed at a little barbecue with bellows. She knows I'm making a pitch, Cox realized, she's just mistaking what I want Liliana to do. The woman arrived with two glasses and a bottle. She poured out the brandy, then added another shot into Liliana's glass for courage. Cox picked up a glass and made Liliana do the same. The spirit still burned his mouth and had a strange aftertaste, like the exhaust of a diesel engine. Cox was aware of men at neighbouring tables, arguing over tumblers of wine and plates of meatballs from the grill. If the wine matched the men's appearance it would be rough. There were shouts and two men jumped up, knocking over their chairs, pushing each other in the chest. Then they fell on each other's necks, pals again. Cox thought of his contact at the American embassy: The Middle East begins here. Then once again the outside world was banished and Cox saw only the pale moon of Liliana's face. And the ghostly echo of another face, Mincu's, smiling.

'The *spécialité de la maison* is not on offer to everyone. It's not like the other hardware, churned out by a dozen countries, a glut on the market, cheap provided you pay cash. No, Mincu's special costs a fair bit of cash. Because it's tricky to acquire. Because there are certain greedy middle men to pay off. Because even in a world that's lost its innocence this still commands horror. Chemical weapons. Canisters you can drop from planes or toss out of the back of trucks as you accelerate away, and the poison spreads wherever the wind blows, an invisible cloud of death gathering up everything in its path, man, woman, child, dog, camel, chicken, friend, enemy, it's not choosy. Which is where we – my masters and I – start running scared. Because Mincu has been talking to Serbs, to Muslims, to Croats, testing the water, seeing what interest there is, what price the market will bear. Now, my concern is not solely humanitarian. You see, there are British troops in there wearing blue berets, French troops too, Italians, even the Germans are signing up. But the British troops are my particular concern because, you understand, it is the British government that employs me. I do not like the idea of British troops being gassed. It might not be deliberate. It might simply be that they were in the wrong place when the wind changed. No matter. I shall do everything in my power to remove the danger. If I cannot get your help, I shall find another way. But I hope very much that you will consent to help.'

Liliana didn't speak, didn't move, didn't show any emotion. Cox felt mounting anxiety. Everybody found the idea of chemical weapons abhorrent and reaction to the idea of their use was automatic. But she simply sat while the men at the other tables grew rowdier and the dumpy waitress who brought another bottle pinched their cheeks and batted away fumbling hands. I've spoken too long, Cox thought. She's listening to a lecture. But how else was he to bring her on board?

'One complication is the origin of the goods,' Cox said, resuming his lecture. 'Any second-year chemistry student from university could probably cook something up for you. It takes little more than chlorine, bleach and ammonia and you're in business. But what he is touting, we think, is the nerve agent Sarin – what the crazies let loose in the Tokyo metro.' Liliana shivered. The evening was cooling and a breeze had sprung up. She clamped her arms across her breasts and leaned over the table. 'We hear it's available from stock, as it were. One possibility is that it came from Iraq, though how it slipped out is not explained. Or from one of the republics of the former Soviet Union – after all, they had forty thousand tons of various chemical weapons and they need hard currency. China, North Korea, they do it. Possibly, possibly . . .' His voice had dropped right down and then it stopped.

Liliana had begun to rock, back and forward, back and forward. If she'd had a baby clasped in her arms she could have been rocking it to sleep. But still she didn't speak. He watched her steady movement. Perhaps not cradling a baby. He'd seen old women in grief rocking like that. Palestinians. Or had they been Israeli? He hesitated because he'd come to the heart of the matter. Everything else was out in the open: arms trader, touting for business, nasty piece of work. But now Cox was treading on treacherous ground. This was conjecture, a secret fear.

'Possibly,' he got going again, 'the stuff comes from America. The American government is firm in its condemnation of chemical weapons. They are committed to destroying their stockpiles, either burning them or rendering them neutral by chemical action. That is official. No doubting it. However, there is more than one centre of power in the United States. Washington gives its orders but others go their own way. For instance it could be criminals who have got hold of a supply. Say the mafia. They have moved on from drugs to other areas and supplying weapons would be a profitable area for them.' He paused again. 'It could even be some maverick branch of the American establishment that has its own ideas. We simply don't know but we need to find out. And if you were on the inside . . .'

'But why me?'

'Because you are reluctant, because Mincu frightens you, because he has chosen to pursue you and not the other way round. In short, you are the least likely person, beyond suspicion.'

Liliana shivered again. Perhaps it was the fitful wind, a reminder that Bucharest's harsh winter was tiptoeing closer. Perhaps at last it was horror of chemical weapons. Or fear of what he was asking of her.

'What would you have me do?'

'Not a lot. But it's something that only someone close to him can do.'

'In what way close?'

Cox frowned at his brandy glass and she jumped on his hesitation.

'I'm not sleeping with him. I couldn't.'

'I'm not asking you to. If he's pressing you hard, make an excuse. A woman always can.' He meant she could protest it was the wrong time of the month but didn't feel able to say that to her. 'But you have to be in his confidence. To know who he is talking to, if possible to help him. His English is serviceable but not fluent, his French non-existent. With luck he'll ask you to interpret. But only if he feels sure of you. What we need are the facts. What precisely is he offering? What is its origin? Who is buying? What route does he propose for delivery? What associates are involved? How is payment to be made?'

'So much.'

'I won't be greedy. Who is supplying it is most important. Names. That will be enough. We'll be able to stop the trade and I promise you Mincu will be destroyed too. You'll see justice.'

'Revenge,' she murmured.

Sometimes the unlikeliest people became heroes. A person would go to meet a blackmailer with a microphone under his clothes. Or her clothes. Or allow himself to be kidnapped. Or would ring the doorbell of a house where terrorists were holed up. Or would ask an armed robber for a light and distract his attention. A woman would walk through an unlit park where a rapist lurked. Or let herself be picked up in a bar and taken home. Or let herself be taken out to dinner at La Premiera and then apologise sweetly the next day for running away.

'I understand now,' Liliana said. 'All that tale of love and war in Hungary. It was to show me the way, give me a role model. I'm your Ilona, aren't I?' She pushed back the hair that had fallen over her face as if she wanted to see him more clearly. 'And this,' she gestured at the table with the cups and the brandy glasses and then round at the rest of the courtyard, 'this is our attic bedroom. Now I'm being sent off to battle.'

Cox was uncomfortable. If she wasn't one hundred per cent right, she was close enough. He gave a grunt – yes or no or don't try to analyse me.

Liliana got to her feet. 'Excuse me.'

'Where are you going?'

She nodded towards a crooked home-made sign that said *Toaleta*, with an arrow pointing to a passageway round the side of the taverna. He watched as she crossed the courtyard, went close to the dumpy waitress to exchange some confidence. The woman laughed and patted her cheek, and then Liliana disappeared in the direction of the arrow.

The nightmare is – he remembered his Chief's words – the real bugger is that it could even be the CIA supplying the stuff. His Chief had unscrewed the cap of The Famous Grouse and poured them both generous measures. They were alone in his corner office. The view was of Lambeth and Streatham and, if the smog allowed, part of Croydon. His Chief swirled the whisky in his glass and stared into it. You see, he said, no American ground troops are at risk. This was before the Dayton agreement brought the US infantry in. The Agency has lost its direction in the post-communist world, he went on. Some within it might just want to cultivate a charmer like Mincu to make use of him later in other dirty little wars. Like they cuddled up to Saddam because he was whipping the Iranians. Then came Kuwait and Bush decided to show he wasn't a wimp. The Americans took chemical weapons to the Gulf just in case Saddam was mad enough to try to use them. War is chaos. It wouldn't be too difficult for mavericks within the Agency to have got their hands on a supply. If by any chance the Cousins – a distant branch, say second cousins twice removed – are in the business of supplying nasties, we're in a mess. Actually, Roy, you sniffing them out would personally be in a tricky spot.

In his Chief's language a tricky spot was next door to being dead. Little wonder he raised his glass but frowned into it.

'But . . . has it happened? Or is it just another crazy conspiracy theory? They'd do a deal with Mincu. Money of course, but also a squeeze. Do this or else. We have to know, have to,' his Chief had said. 'So I want you to find out if there's anything in it. You've got to take off your shoes and tiptoe. Peep through the curtains but don't be seen, don't set off any alarms. Roy's grand farewell tour, dinner with old chums, crack a bottle or two, tears as the old war-horse goes out to grass. And just happening to end up in Bucharest. So, that's the American connection, if it exists. Cheers.' Finally he'd drunk from his glass of Scotch.

On the wall above the cabinet where he kept the whisky bottle was what looked like a framed sampler. The Chief told enquirers it was a quotation from Sun Tzu, a fourth-century BC Chinese general: *Be so subtle that you are invisible. Be so mysterious that you are intangible. Then you will control your rival's fate.*

His Chief had downed the Scotch at a gulp and made a face. 'What would our Cousins say? That's the scenario. Let's have another.'

Cox watched as a man got up from a table by the wall and took the same route as Liliana had towards the toilet. Three minutes went by, five. Neither Liliana nor the man who'd followed her came back. Cox got slowly to his feet, aware of eyes on him. Two men who'd been arm-wrestling and groaning or shouting in triumph fell silent. Cox made his way to where the waitress was jamming empty bottles in a blue plastic crate.

'The young lady? The mademoiselle? Where did she go?'

The woman straightened up and put a hand on her hip. She raised an eyebrow at him.

'The girl I was with.'

'*Domnisoara?*'

'Liliana.'

'*Da, domnisoara.*'

A lot more followed, Bulgarian or Romanian Cox had no idea. But he understood the emphatic gesture of her arm: gone off, done a runner, made her escape. This dumpy creature with wisps of hair escaping her headscarf and ankle socks and a greasy apron and a gold tooth seemed quite fierce with him, then she made a moue and patted his cheek. Cox took a wad of currency from his jacket pocket and then wished he hadn't. A lot of eyes were still on him. She selected four notes, pulled open her blouse and seemed deliberately to give Cox a sight of her breast as she tucked the notes inside her bra. As Cox turned to go she waggled her hips at him. A little laughter from one of the tables died away to silence. It's because I'm a foreigner, he told himself, nothing more.

Don't hurry, don't be conspicuous, just go where the arrow is pointing. The taverna building was to one side, a wall to the other, and what light there was came from a dim bulb right at the end of the passageway. Someone with an aerosol can had sprayed the word SEX on the wall with the 'S' the wrong way round. No fool like an old fool, he reminded himself. He'd come with no back-up, no watcher, no one to check the back way out, look out for trouble. It was too risky to bring someone from London, he'd decided, might start gossip. First impressions were that Crake wasn't the man for the job. If he used local talent there would be the chance that word would filter through to Mincu.

He came to the door marked *Toaleta* – there was only one for men and women – and called out her name, and again more loudly. He rapped on the plywood panel. He pushed the door open. He was greeted by a smell, nothing more. He sighed and continued down the passageway. The further he walked, the more it looked like an alley. Hearing movement he stopped at once. He stared ahead where the dismal light only emphasized the shadows. Flying solo is all very well, he told himself, but it's a young man's game. The sound came from behind him and he whirled to face the danger. A cat leaped onto the wall and down the far side.

His pulse was beating faster and he felt that same soreness in his throat. When he raised a hand to soothe the ache he felt it tremble. I'm ill, he told himself, in for a dose of flu. But he knew it wasn't that.

Chapter 7

Cox was back in the Capitol Hotel, the same hotel he'd stayed in the last time he was in Bucharest and had had to beat a retreat to the Bulgarian border. The Capitol was built in the style of a Parisian *grand magasin* and boasted it had been the haunt of artists and musicians and writers, though in the Golden Age these dangerous spirits had been mostly banished. He was staying here for nostalgia, also to observe what changes had been made in the new Romania. The Capitol was being refurbished. One had to step over rolls of new carpet in the corridor. But in his bathroom the shower still dripped all night the way it used to.

He sat on the bed while he waited for the telephone to be answered. Time to sleep, he thought, time to call it the end of a long day. He counted the rings. Four, five. Are they in bed? Well, of course. But he meant: was he disturbing a particularly tender moment? Eight, nine.

'*Buna.*'

Somehow he assumed it would be Crake who answered and for a moment he was at a loss.

'*Buna,*' the voice repeated. '*Alo.* Hello.'

'I wasn't expecting you,' Cox said, though there was no reason not to. 'Is he there? Can I speak to him?'

'Oh, Mr Cox. No, he's not here. He's out.'

'Out?' Cox looked at his watch: a few minutes before one. He doubted that diplomatic bunfights went on so long in Bucharest. Private dinner? Crake hadn't mentioned he had an invitation. 'He left you alone?'

'He wasn't here when I returned.' Gabriela paused but Cox said nothing. 'Sometimes he likes to visit a casino.' As if she could sense Cox's frown she added, 'He doesn't gamble much. He watches the floor show and has a drink. He says he likes to see what people are in town. Americans, Italians.'

And Arabs. The Middle East begins here. In Old Nick's day Yasser Arafat used to fly in. There was, he had been told, a clandestine film of him enjoying himself. Perhaps an Iraqi or two found their way here now. Middle men.

'Our little bird has flown,' Cox said.

'What?'

She seemed nonplussed without a name being spoken. In the old days when all telephones were routinely tapped, it had been the custom to use nicknames or descriptions or roundabout ways of describing someone without using a name. Gabriela must be out of practice.

'We had a drink and I talked to her and then she made an excuse and vanished.'

'I should have stayed. I would have told her what to do.'

'I've tried her flat. She doesn't answer the phone.'

'I know where she is. I think I do. I take you to her and we tell her she's got to do what you want, it's necessary for her revenge.'

'It's too much for her.'

'She's a strong person. At the moment her strength is against you. We change her mind and then her strength works for you. Don't worry – she is strong.'

He supposed she meant stubborn.

'Where are you?' Gabriela asked.

'At my hotel.'

'I come now. Then we go to see her. I know where she goes.'

Cox ran a hand over his eyes. It wasn't so much the lack of sleep. It was the sense that he was stumbling through fog, following someone elusive. They would enter a wood where the fog was less dense. As he hurried forward to make contact, the figure stepped behind an old oak. He reached the tree, looked behind the trunk and no one was there.

Liliana kept slipping away from him. He should have let her go but his judgement was clouded by tiredness. Like any seducer, he only wanted her the more.

Cox had a natural distaste for waiting on street corners. People who wanted to be noticed did it: currency touts in leather jackets, policemen in uniform, that sort. Also tarts on their beat, he said to himself, and walked from the corner to the hotel entrance and back again. He caught sight of his reflection in the plate glass of the lobby. He had picked up his raincoat because of the night chill, draping it round his shoulders so it fell almost to his ankles in black folds. You wear it like a cloak, Jenny used to say, so where's your dagger? Turning again, the coat swirled. A bat, he thought, a huge bat, a vampire, off to suck her blood. Beyond his reflection, by the reception desk, the security guard was staring back at him. One-thirty in the morning, waiting to be picked up, he knows I'm up to no good. And he's jealous. Cox turned again and his reflection marched with him.

The taxi came down Calea Victoriei from the north. Its headlights bounced over the rough patch where the road had been dug up so that it seemed to flash a signal to him. Gabriela's face was a pale moon at the window. She shifted across the seat to make room for him.

'You looked like Batman standing there,' she said. 'You have seen the movie?'

'I've heard of it.'

'So I am your Robin,' she said, laughing. She seemed delighted at the notion and put a hand under his arm to squeeze it. It is the Latin blood in her, Cox decided. They pride themselves on their Roman origins and despise plodding Slavs. She is a girl who could bring a plaster saint to life, but she had already taken her hand back and was leaning forward to speak to the driver. 'I tell him it is an emergency.' The taxi turned the corner with a squeal from its tyres, accelerating down the hill past some establishment where cars were parked with their wheels up on the kerb. There was a uniformed man at the door, and neon lights in the shape of a top hat above the entrance. There was a sign but they went too fast for Cox to read the name.

'Casino,' Gabriela said. 'There are many here now.'

'Has Mr Crake come home?'

'No. It does not matter. I see him tomorrow.'

'He won't worry you're not there?'

A passing streetlamp showed a small frown puckering her pretty face. 'There is no reason. I don't live there. I have my own flat.' She looked out of her window and then turned back to Cox, deciding she should make a statement concerning her modern attitude in such matters. 'Sometimes I sleep there, sometimes I don't. Sometimes I go out by myself. I go dancing. I like dancing very much and Mr Crake doesn't. When I go dancing I meet people of my own age. You know? Boys. Mr Crake is older. You say mature. One day I will be mature too. But now I like very much to meet boys. A boy my age is more eager. You understand?' She turned her whole body on the seat to give him her full attention. 'You are shocked maybe? Why shouldn't I like young man? I like you too.' She smiled and put out a hand, lightly touching his knee. 'You are my uncle. You call me "my dear" and don't tell me what I must not do.'

'You don't go to the casino with Mr Crake?'

'It's boring. He has a drink. He plays a little baccarat or roulette. He talks to some people. He looks at the girls on the stage when they kick their legs.' She made a ho-hum yawn and patted her hand over it. 'Does that interest you? Girls wearing feathers and they turn their backs and go wiggle-wiggle. Do you like to watch?'

'I don't care for it much. What's the point?'

'You are right. Watch but do not touch. What is the point? One time I go with him and there is striptease. She is called Miss Non-Stop. Why? When she has taken all her clothes off then she has to stop. Nothing more. What is the point?'

She leaned across him and he thought he was going to be kissed but it was to speak to the driver.

'We are nearly there. I tell him to stop now. You have money for the taxi? Give it to me, I will pay him.'

The taxi had stopped outside a Chinese restaurant which seemed closed. The chairs were up on all the tables except for one where two Chinese men sat playing cards. It seemed to be a game where the winner was the one who slapped down his cards the hardest.

'Not there,' Gabriela said. 'Come.'

The street was cobbled with tram tracks in the centre. The rails gleamed in the lamplight as they disappeared round a corner. From their mad taxi-dash, Cox thought the station lay in that direction. Across the road dogs behind a fence began barking. There was a pack of them, half a dozen at least, guard dogs for a car repair yard. Gabriela took Cox's arm and they walked beside iron railings that protected a patch of grass. A gate led them down a path to the darkened hulk of a church.

'This is the church of St Peter and St Paul,' Gabriela said, 'I think.' Her voice was much calmer now. 'For Liliana this is a special place. She comes here when she is troubled in her head. I know this for a fact and this is why I bring you here tonight.'

'You say it's a special church?'

'No, I mean for her it is special. When she have that trouble with Mincu before – you know – and she is wandering in the streets afterwards and thinking: What shall I do? Where do I go? Shall I kill myself? She sees this church and the door is not locked and she goes in. I am not religious but Liliana says this church speaks to her. What does it say? I ask. She says that if I believed then I would know what it says. Tell me anyway, I beg. So she tells me it says I am the life and the road and if you walk along my road I will hold your hand. Oh, I say. To me it sounds dull but I don't tell Lili I would prefer Petr or Stefan to hold my hand. She would not laugh, she would frown. In the old days she would laugh. She has become very serious.'

The door was not locked but it needed Cox's shoulder to shove it open. It made a noise like a broom sweeping the floor. Gabriela passed in front of him and when he let the door go it swung shut. The church was not completely dark. A small bulb fixed to a pillar gave a yellowish glow. A sand tray on a table had four or five candles burning even at this hour of the night.

For a moment everything was still. Cox tried to grasp what the church said to Liliana. Peace? Divine grace? Salvation and eternal life? Love – he doubted it. Forgiveness – certainly not.

Cox took another step forward and realized why the door had made a noise like a broom sweeping. The floor was carpeted. His eyes were adjusting to the gloom so he could see that the walls were painted with geometric patterns in shades of brown and mustardy yellow. Raising his eyes he saw a cupola with what might have been figures painted round it. He could make out nothing of them except for the gleam of their gilt haloes.

'Is she here?' Cox asked. 'Liliana, are you here?'

'Lili, don't hide,' Gabriela said in English. 'Lili,' she trilled. She added something in Romanian. 'I tell her you are not angry that she ran away. I tell her she must not be like a timid mouse and hide under a chair.' She gave a giggle before turning serious again. 'You are not angry, are you? Me, I am very angry with her even though I love her.'

'I want to know you are all right,' Cox said. 'Liliana? We are concerned for you, that's all.' He spoke straight down the nave and his voice echoed. He turned and said her name again and his voice was muffled. He saw a statue in a niche with candles burning in front of it. St Peter or St Paul, he supposed. Who had lit the candles? His eye was caught by the pulpit, set high against the wall with spiral steps to reach it and an eagle, gilded, with spread wings to hold the holy book. He thought of climbing the steps which would show him the whole church but then he saw Gabriela with a piece of paper in her hand.

'She has been here.'

Gabriela stood by a table covered with an oilcloth. There was an offertory box and underneath was tucked a sheaf of papers. There were pages torn from a school exercise book, old bills, the inside of a cigarette packet and a picture postcard of an Orthodox dignitary, the Patriarch of Antioch the Great and All the East.

'You sit here on this bench and write out a prayer,' Gabriela explained. 'You put it under this box then you put money in the box so God pays attention. Many people come and do it. Old women mostly. They pray for their daughters to be good girls. They pray for their dead husbands. Liliana also. She tells me she does it. "Does God listen?" I asked her. "Does God make your dreams come true?" "He will in His own time." "Lili," I said, "can He give you back what has been taken away from you?" "I don't ask for that." "What do you ask for?" Then she shakes her head. "That is between my soul and God."' Gabriela waved the paper in her hand. 'Now we find out what she prays for.'

Gabriela took the sheet of paper over to the statue of St Peter or St Paul and held it under a candle. Her brow furrowed as she read and she gave a little grunt. 'I translate it for you. It is not long, which pleases me, because her writing is not good. There was no candle on that table so she writes it in the dark, I think. "O Mary." That is how she begins. She does not want to ask God directly. She wants someone to plead for her. "O Mary, blessed mother of Jesus, you know I should be a virgin like you. You are pure as I am pure in my heart."' Gabriela pointed to the paper. 'There is a word here I do not know in English. Something like *ask*. So. "Ask God the Holy Father to give me the strength to do what I must do. When I have done it then I shall give thanks here every day. I write you this message, also I say many prayers so you will hear me."'

That is why she comes here, Cox understood. For strength. To carry on each day. What I wanted her to do was too much so she came here for the strength to do it. He knew he should feel shame at listening to her private prayer but he felt only relief. 'Where is she now?'

'Maybe now she goes home. Tomorrow she will speak to you again, I think. See how she signs her name? She writes it very clearly so the Virgin Mary will know who to help.'

'She's written something after her name.'

This was even more of a scrawl than the rest of the prayer, as if it was done in haste or done against her will. Gabriela twisted the paper to catch the best light from the candle. 'She has written: "I light this candle in place of the candle that was put out."'

They were standing in the churchyard. The dogs across the street were hurling curses at them again. Nobody appeared at a window to see what the trouble was. Who would try to burgle a place with so many dogs?

Ask God the Holy Father to give me the strength to do what I must do. Cox supposed the word Gabriela couldn't translate was something like *intercede.* She had written out her prayer and lit her candle and presumably – some time after he had tried telephoning – she had returned to her flat.

Prayer, he thought. Prayer as a last resort. Prayer to change an uncaring world. Prayer to make a miracle happen. Prayer to stop the inevitable. Prayer as thanks. Prayer to cure the uncurable. Prayer to alter someone else's behaviour or bring rain or move mountains. These were the kind of prayers true believers offered up. Prayers to change God's mind, or at least jog His memory. Cox's life, if it had had any central core, had been a struggle to find some rational way in a world that seemed bent on the irrational. Prayers like these were a cry in the dark.

But a prayer to change yourself was in a different class. It was an affirmation of your ability. It was concentrating on the possible. It was striving with all your being to triumph over difficulty. It was saying: If I want to, I can.

'You want to go to her flat?' Gabriela asked. 'I take you there. Then I tell her she is a bad girl for running away and you say you forgive her. You call her *my dear.* Maybe she cries a little.'

Gabriela had the whole scene set out in her mind. She was a woman who thrived on drama.

Cox looked at his watch. 'She's gone to sleep. She has the right idea.' In his mind he put himself to bed. A few hours. Later, when he'd eaten the Capitol's breakfast of ham and salami and white cheese, he'd be strong enough to face Liliana. Better without Gabriela. Three cars passed in a bunch, their tyres thrumming over the cobbles. There was a whole world outside the churchyard but for a moment he turned back to look at the dark wooden door. Liliana had come here after, as Gabriela put it, her trouble with Mincu. Now there would be more trouble with Mincu.

He turned back to Gabriela. 'My dear, you've been very helpful. The only thing I don't understand is that bit at the end of her prayer. After she'd signed her name she wrote something about the candle that was put out. What's that? A symbolic candle?'

Gabriela began to walk towards the gate. There was a new hesitation to her and Cox understood he'd touched on something painful. But painful for Gabriela or for her friend?

She seemed to reach some kind of resolution and faced Cox again. 'Remember I told you how she was taken away in his car to some big house? This was during the time when the communists were in power. At this house Mincu raped her while other men held her down. Then these men had their turn. There were three of them. Three plus Mincu. This I know because Liliana told me. I held her in my arms because she was shaking so much, and I stroked her hair, and she was able to bring the words out. Like a confession. It was as if it was she who had done something wrong. She told me that before the rape she was in a private dining room at a hotel where there were important people. They were making some kind of a party. It was here it began. The terrible time. The rape was bad but there was also the humiliation. You want to understand how she feels, there is something you must see. A proof. Come.'

Cox felt a deep reluctance. Perhaps it was the atmosphere of the churchyard in the small hours that was draining his courage. Did he want to have proof of Liliana's trauma? Wasn't its effect on her enough? Or couldn't it wait?

'Now?'

She put her arm through his. 'It is only possible at night. This is secret, also dangerous. Come. We find a telephone.'

Chapter 8

To every journey, its own flavour. The ride from the Capitol Hotel to the church had been like a dash to a party, in high spirits, swift. Gabriela had been eager to get to Liliana, to scold her, to embrace her. But the next stage seemed suddenly fraught with difficulties and to be slow. First there was the telephone to be found. The station was best, Gabriela said. Also there would be taxis there. It was a good ten minutes' walk while neither talked. The streets were deserted except for a pair of police in a car who watched them while their radio was tuned to a pop station.

'That way they can't be called to arrest anybody,' Gabriela said.

The telephone was outside the station. It took an age to be answered and Gabriela had to talk and talk, to plead, it sounded, and when it was over she appeared glum.

'Yes,' she said, 'is fixed.'

'What is? What are you showing me?'

'You'll see.'

Getting a taxi was another problem. There were no trains at this hour so the taxis had vanished. Only one was parked outside the entrance to the booking hall, but with no driver. Boldly Gabriela opened the door and beat a tattoo on the horn. When the driver appeared he was surly, seemingly reluctant to take them.

'He says he is not on duty. I think he is looking for woman.'

Gabriela entered into negotiations.

'I tell him you pay extra so he agrees.'

There was none of the helter-skelter speed of the earlier journey. Gabriela stared out of the window in silence. I'm not her uncle, Cox thought, I'm her lover and we've had a tiff. They passed the church they'd been in half an hour before and kept moving towards the centre of the city.

'Driver, why are you going so slowly?' Cox asked in a loud voice. The driver made no reply. Satisfied he understood no English, Cox said to Gabriela, 'Tell me one thing. You said it was dangerous. I want to know what danger I'll be in.'

She opened her mouth and hesitated. Perhaps she was going to tell him not to talk. She looked at the mirror but the driver's eyes were on the road, not on them. 'In the old days, in the time of Big C, to know a secret was a dangerous thing. It was safer to have one hand over your eyes and one hand over your ear.' She mimicked this. 'Otherwise . . . they come and try to get the secret out of your head. Now you are going to be shown a secret. Nothing can take this knowledge away from you. Yes?'

Cox nodded his head.

'Except one thing. If you are dead.'

'Give him eight thousand,' Gabriela said.

Cox had been given notes of five hundred lei in exchange for his pounds – a wad as thick as a brick – and he counted out the money. The driver counted it out a second time and began a rambling complaint. Gabriela spoke sharply to him and slammed the door.

'I tell him you are a big policeman from America

and if he makes trouble you report him to your colleagues here.'

Cox watched the taxi accelerate away with more speed than it had shown on its journey. He waited until it had turned the corner with its squeal of tyres. Ahead of them was a massive and ugly building, like the hulk of a vanished civilization. Which it was. Not the barbaric one that had just crumbled, an earlier one. The street lighting had turned its stone the colour of overcooked liver.

'Where are we?'

She answered a rather different question. 'We must go down here.'

She led him down a passage tucked between a low building with a curious glass roof and the stolid block. Was it a ministry? A prison? The head office of an insurance company?

'What is it?' he asked her, putting a hand on her arm to slow her.

'Hurry,' she said. 'He said there was a security check at half past three.'

'Gabriela, I—'

'It is the Museum of National History. Also Archaeology.'

'What you have to show me is here?'

'Yes.'

'And it is dangerous?'

'Stop asking questions please. We must be as quiet as cats.'

She walked ahead of him. He stood still, looking after her. She was deliberately refusing to tell him, knowing a secret is more compelling than the same thing in the open.

She turned and said, 'Hurry please. If we are late he will refuse to show us. He didn't want to. I had to persuade him.'

'Money?' She was free with his money.

'Something else.' Her voice was low. She turned aside. 'I do it for Liliana.'

She didn't say she did it for me, Cox noted. Perhaps that was an oversight. She didn't say she did it for any wider reason, for the good of humanity, for the future of the world. Her concern was personal. For Liliana. Cox accepted this. Now she was making an impatient gesture. He turned up the collar of his black raincoat, though it hadn't grown suddenly colder and they would be going inside shortly. Camouflage, he supposed, hiding his face, damn fool. He followed after her, minding where he placed his feet. My second dark alley of the night, he thought. I should be used to it. I shouldn't feel the patter of my heart.

The alley turned a right angle and swelled into a little yard at the back of the museum. There was a big dumpbin for rubbish. How do they get a rubbish lorry in here? They didn't. The bin had wheels. There was a stand for bicycles though he'd never noticed any cyclists in Bucharest. It's natural selection. The successful ones go on to cars; the unsuccessful ones are killed by the Bucharest drivers. There were no lights in the area, no gates, no security cameras that he could see. In time, they'll come in time.

There were double doors into the building, tall and wide enough to back a lorry in. Then they must get a lorry in the yard. Looking back he saw that what appeared a solid wall had in fact a gate in it. He turned his attention to the massive doors of the building again. Inset was a smaller door, human size. Gabriela rested her fingers on the handle.

'He said he would unlock the door for us. He said we should just come in and be quiet.'

She spoke as if they were unruly children who had to be taught how to behave. And perhaps they were. Cox asked, 'Are there microphones?'

'Maybe. There used to be microphones everywhere. Maybe no one has taken them out of here.'

'So who would be listening?'

'Mr Cox, why do you have so many questions when I don't have the answers?'

The door hinges needed oil. They passed inside and Gabriela closed the door. It was very black.

'Do you have a cigarette lighter maybe?'

'I have this.'

From his raincoat pocket Cox brought out a thin torch. He twisted its head to switch it on, twisted further to narrow the beam and shone round them. It was a delivery bay with a raised platform for unloading from the back of a lorry. Steps led up.

'Now we must climb.'

'Where to?'

'Up,' she said.

'He's up there?'

'Yes.'

'Where?'

She gestured with her head. 'Up, up, until we can climb no higher.'

'You have come here before?' She didn't answer so he tried a different question. 'Who are we going to see?'

'Come.'

She started up the steps. Cox moved the beam away so she was plunged into darkness.

'Tell me his name.'

'Vasile,' she said. 'Now hurry.'

'Vasile? Vasile who? What is his surname?'

'Sadoveanu. No more questions. We shall be too late.'

'So, Vasile Sadoveanu.' He had found out something.

'But I think you do not call him by name. I think that he does not like that you know it.'

Cox joined her up on the delivery platform. With his

little flashlight showing the way they went through a door into a storeroom. Here were wooden crates, stacks of old weapons, rusty swords and muskets and armour, open boxes of pottery shards, the skeleton of what looked like a pony, urns, plumed helmets, flint arrowheads, Cox wasn't certain what else. The air was filled with dust and decay and a lingering hint of tobacco smoke as if someone had just passed this way. They picked their way through this jumble and the next door led to a large workshop. There were tables laid with a jigsaw of broken pottery being reassembled, paintings being cleaned, shields being refurbished. The workshop had a glass wall and beyond that was the museum proper. A little light came in through tall windows looking onto the street so Cox doused the torch. They went into the entrance hall, vast, empty, with a ceiling high enough for a giraffe. Gabriela clutched the empty sleeve of his coat, leaned close and whispered in his ear.

'You want to pay, the window is over there.'

She giggled.

Nerves, he told himself.

'I think we are not really here, so there is no need to pay.'

They turned away from the deserted cashier's office, walked the length of the hall and turned to go up a grand staircase. They passed out of sight of the windows and Cox switched on the torch again. The staircase was wide enough for two duchesses in ball gowns to have walked abreast but Gabriela went a step or two in front. It took two flights of stairs to reach the first-floor landing. Cox heard running water and flashing his torch round saw the door to the men's lavatory ajar. Was someone in there? In the dark? He thought of his hotel shower. It was some piece of plumbing that leaked all night. Doors of opaque glass led to galleries of exhibits. His torch caught a gleam of metal down a corridor. A vintage car had found its last parking place. It was built like an old hansom cab where the driver sat outside. How did it get up the stairs?

'No, this way,' Gabriela urged, tugging at his sleeve.

They climbed again and at the next landing she took him down a passageway to a narrower flight of stairs. What looked like a metal hurdle with a No Entry traffic sign on it normally blocked the way. Some thoughtful person had dragged the hurdle aside to leave room for them to pass. They climbed the stairs and were faced by a closed door.

'Normally this is locked,' she said. 'He tells me that only the director of the museum has a key. But Vasile also gets key. It is a secret place and Vasile knows many secret men. So Vasile has unlocked the door for us.'

Cox wanted to know more of these 'secret men' but Gabriela tugged on his sleeve again and he entered the secret place.

'In the old days,' she said in a whisper, 'when the communists were in power, this was a special exhibition. Called Homage to Ceausescu. It is many rooms. We must pass through them all. Nine rooms, ten rooms, I think.'

Pointing the torch at one wall he saw it was covered in photographs: Ceausescu reading a speech, Ceausescu cutting a tape, Ceausescu reviewing the troops, Ceausescu receiving bouquets from little girls, Ceausescu waving at the top of aircraft steps, Ceausescu at the controls of a train, Ceausescu in a motorcade, Ceausescu casting a vote. For Ceausescu. The face had the chubby charm of Dylan Thomas, the same pouting lips, but it was altogether tougher, the face of a brawler, and with eyes that slid sideways looking out for trouble.

Without pausing they passed through the next room and the next room and the next room. In flashes of light the display cabinets showed glimpses of gifts from a grateful nation: glasses, vases, china, plaques, scrolls, urns, trays, ceremonial keys.

Overwhelmed, Cox could only ask, 'Why?'

'Why? Because nobody knows what to do with it. So is like Pharoah's tomb. Maybe in a thousand years they open it up and like you they ask: Why? They cannot give it away, they cannot sell it, because maybe secret believers get hold of it, make a shrine.'

'They could destroy it.'

She whispered in his ear. 'They say there are some in the government who do not want to destroy it.'

Once again he wondered if there were microphones.

The next room was devoted to chains of office, diplomas, medals and decorations from foreign governments. There was the Légion d'Honneur with the certificate signed by a shaky de Gaulle. Ceausescu was a university professor in Malta, Islamabad and Beirut. He was an Honorary Citizen of the State of Texas. Dead dictators had loved him – Marcos and the Shah of Iran. Royals had counted him an intimate – Juan Carlos, Margareta, Olav, Juliana, Baudoin, Hussein, Hassan. Cox was transfixed by the Order of the Bath bestowed by Queen Elizabeth. What treat had he imagined was in store?

'Through here,' Gabriela said.

Here were gifts of state, gathered in several rooms. Silverware, robes, urns, dinner services, candlesticks, decanters, swords, a machete from the communist party of El Salvador, tablecloths, a teddy bear – his torch illuminated them all.

'My God!' An elephant was charging out of the wall at him, the gift of Mozambique. Or at least it was the front half of the elephant, stuffed, a taxidermist's nightmare. Its ears flapped, its trunk was raised. It should be trumpeting as it charged. It was silent, wary of microphones.

His torch passed over and went back to more grotesquerie, the figure of a man, stuffed. He was standing directly in the path of the charging elephant, upright and unafraid, a gun in his outstretched hand. The figure was close enough for Cox to see the whites of its eyes shining in his torchlight. The eyes blinked.

'*Stai.*'

Cox stayed very still. The man had a flashlight of his own which he raised. Cox thought he would remember for ever the click it made as he switched it on, like the cocking of a rifle. There was a pause while the man played the beam over his face, briefly over Gabriela, then back to him again, doing a tour of his body from head to toe. No point in my little torch, Cox reasoned, I'm outgunned. He slipped it back in his coat. This brought an immediate shout from the man.

'He says, Keep your hands away from your pockets.' Gabriela's voice had risen a tone.

Cox supposed this was Vasile Sadoveanu but he couldn't ask. He wasn't supposed to know the man's name. But that was nonsense because now he heard Gabriela address him by name and the man replying. The man gestured with his flashlight to come forward. Cox did so and found himself being prodded in the back with the pistol, go on, go on. They went in a procession: Cox first with the gun always pressed close, Vasile next with his flashlight picking out the way, Gabriela in the rear. They passed through another room of official gifts, an amphora encrusted with seashells, a huge devil mask, a scale model of a military aircraft. One of ours, one of theirs? Dear Lord, wasn't it a Harrier? But by then they'd passed through into an office beyond the exhibition rooms. Vasile closed the door and pressed the light switch. There was a neon tube suspended on two metal struts from the ceiling and it stammered into life.

So here we are, Cox thought, one old and jumpy spy, one trollop from the British embassy, one man with a pistol. Cox inspected him: twenty-five or so, dressed in lumpy jeans and a grey cardigan zipped almost to the neck, a face of that pallor that Jenny would have called unhealthy, an unheroic body but who needs a body like Atlas when he holds a gun. Without the gun, a nobody.

Vasile spoke and Gabriela translated. 'He wants you to keep very still. I think it is wise you do this. He is very nervous.'

Cox thought it was wise too. Vasile came closer to pat down Cox's body. He did it one-handed because he still held the pistol. Now is the time I could take him, Cox knew, if I was quarter of a century younger and faster and prepared to chance it. The pistol was close enough to grab. Vasile patted down his chest, then a sleeve of the coat which he found empty. He spoke sharply, Gabriela giggled and Vasile rounded on her. Oh so easy, even now, to knock the gun aside.

Gabriela said, 'He asks if you lose your arm in the war?'

'What war is that? I may be old but I'm not ancient. Does he speak English? No? Well, tell him I'm taking my coat off and then he can see I have two arms.'

It was baboons that counted one, two, three, many. Obviously Vasile estimated age on the same principle: twenty years old, twenty-five, thirty, one foot in the grave. Vasile had abandoned any attempt to check Cox for concealed weapons as if in taking off his coat he'd shown he was unarmed. Cox looked round the small room. There were microphones in the museum after all for here were the loudspeakers. This was the control room where the regime's agents had been able to listen in. Did someone drop an unguarded remark such as: Life was better under King Carol; or Comrade Ceausescu is getting a belly as big as Mussolini's. There was a desk with a white telephone and a black telephone, tape recorders in banks, a TV monitor, a video player, a tearsheet from a magazine of Marilyn with her skirt billowing up, and tacked to the wall a postcard of the Statue of Liberty.

'So we're here,' Cox said. 'What for? What is he? Some sort of spook?'

'Spook?' she asked.

'What does he do?'

'He is nightwatchman.'

'I thought you said there was a security patrol.'

'That is to make sure he is awake.'

'And you've been up here before? You knew the way?' Cox had noticed a settee in one corner and his glance went that way. Gabriela didn't reply. *I had to persuade him* she'd said. With money? *Something else.* Vasile had some material to show that would make Cox understand Liliana. Cox had been offered too much bogus intelligence in his time. First find out that your source is genuine. 'So what is he? Watchman, I know. But his background.'

'I cannot tell you. He would understand and then it would be very bad. But I think when you see what he has, you will guess.'

There seemed a flaw in logic here. If he would know Vasile's background from looking at his material, wouldn't that be as bad as telling him? Perhaps not. Vasile could say he'd bought it or found it by chance. Whatever it was. Looking at Vasile again, Cox revised his idea of his age: twenty-seven or twenty-eight, maybe thirty. So what had he been doing when Ceausescu was alive?

Vasile spoke. Gabriela said, 'He wants to know if he should show you the material? Is it agreed?'

Cox looked at her. Unless he was mistaken, Vasile would only show the material in exchange for Gabriela. For her favours. It was grotesque, incredible. It was the corruption of the old regime carried forward into the new. To Cox it was the dirtiest trade of his life. He muttered, 'I can't agree it. Only you can say yes.'

She stared at him.

'Well damn it, it's not the kind of deal you can ask me to make. If it is what I imagine it is. It's like something out of the dark ages. You must think the world of Liliana even to consider it. With him . . .' Well, Cox supposed with anyone but with Vasile in particular. Pale as a silverfish, Jenny would have said, unhealthy mind in an unhealthy body, needs a good day's tramp in the country. The notion was sick. He was about to say No; let's get out into the fresh air; but Gabriela made up her mind. She snapped an order at Vasile and then went to stand beside him as if this was a slave auction and she'd just been bought.

The Middle East starts here. Oh Lord, oh pray, he thought. But then his mind had other things to focus on.

The material that Vasile had to offer came from a cardboard carton that had Chinese characters on one side, English words on the other. *Dried Milk Powder,* Cox read, *Product of the People's Republic of China.* There was a picture of a red cow with a bucket under its udder. Vasile tipped the carton onto the desk and a number of bulky brown envelopes slid out. Selecting one, he removed a videocassette which he inserted into the player.

So it's the movies, Cox thought, lowering himself onto the settee. The springs protested under his weight. What would it be like with two bodies? He found out as Gabriela sat herself beside him. She looked subdued, as well she might. She knew what the videotape showed. Home movies I have seen shot by tourists, by students, by businessmen, by air crew. They contact the police on their return to Britain, or the Foreign Office, or their MP. We're about to win the Cold War for our side, they used to claim, with the amazing footage we've shot. Despite the process of selection Cox had had to see a few. The façade of the KGB building in Voronezh with a scowling guard who waved an angry arm. A slow-moving shot of a deserted platform in a closed U'bahn station in East Berlin with emphasis on an unguarded exit. The Black Sea fleet on the horizon shot from a cruise liner approaching Odessa – was it waves or camera shake that made the silhouettes shiver and dip so much?

No one spoke. Voyeurs are silent pleasure-seekers, locked in their own fantasies. But Cox had no fantasy. He could not imagine what he would see. Liliana had been raped. He knew that. Mincu had done it, others too. This was something else. What more could have been done to her?

The lights weren't dimmed. I should prefer to view this in the dark, please, so I don't have to witness the expression on Gabriela's face, or on Vasile's face, or have my own face naked to them. But now the monitor was switched on and the tape was running. Vasile spoke a few words.

'There is no sound,' Gabriela said. 'He wants you to know that normally there was sound but on this occasion the machinery didn't work.'

'Normally? You mean they made a habit of this?'

Gabriela didn't answer. She sat forward to get closer to the screen, to the figure that suddenly appeared.

At first Cox didn't recognize it was Liliana. It was an overhead shot, he guessed from a concealed ceiling-mounted camera, of a table covered in plates, glasses, bottles and a bowl of flowers. There were men round the table, half a dozen, maybe eight, but now he wasn't looking at the men because he was put in mind of an operating theatre with the patient being wheeled in on a trolley. This patient lay on top of the sheet. The trolley advanced sideways towards the table, like a crab, and the camera angle was from above and behind her so that she glided silently into the picture. First her feet, then her shins, her knees, her thighs. He realized now she was naked. It was mysterious because of the absence of a soundtrack but he could see men's mouths open. They were shouting. In silence. Banging the table with spoons. In silence. Smashing glasses. In silence.

Cox leaned forward on the settee, feeling an awful sense of vertigo. He was falling into that room, becoming part of it. It was the jeering faces, the open mouths, the lack of sound. He was right there and he had gone deaf.

But what was this? Between her legs, against her crotch, was a lighted candle. It was dark in colour – the tape was mono so he couldn't tell if it was red or blue or black. It could have been a Christmas decoration, pubic hairs were holly, and there was what looked like a band of snow. Round her navel a circle of more snow. Now her breasts appeared, ski-slopes of snow with darkish rocks at their tips.

The face was turned away from the camera but then it flopped over. Liliana's face, Liliana's eyes tight closed, Liliana's lips moving. She wasn't speaking aloud. Cox was certain it was silent mouthing, a prayer for deliverance, for it to be finished, for oblivion.

Oh Lord, oh pray. Like Liliana his lips moved. In silence.

He switched his attention to Mincu who grinned at his friends, then dipped a finger in the snow on the slope of a breast and stuck it in his mouth. He was a grubby boy in a pastry shop swiping a meringue for a dare. There was no special lighting for the camera but even so Cox could make out the sheen of sweat on Mincu's face. Drink in part, sex even more.

Mist seemed to drift over Liliana's body. It was a stream

of cigar smoke blown by the man nearest the camera with his back turned. It seemed his own private game for he bent closer to blow some more. The candle's flame guttered in the draught, a drop of hot wax splashed on her thigh and Liliana jerked. One of the two men who'd wheeled her in grasped her ankles, the other pressed down on her shoulders.

There was laughter. Cox could see the open mouths and shaking shoulders. Here, in the room with the three voyeurs, it was silent and tense.

Then the man at the head of the table struggled to his feet. Was it – could it possibly be – Ceausescu's son Nicu? His face was ravaged, his hair messed. From the stiffening of Gabriela's body Cox understood that the climax was approaching. What had gone before was cruel; this would go beyond that to humiliation.

This man was probably the drunkest because it took him two or three attempts before he got upright on the dining table. He stood uncertainly among the dishes, knocking over a bottle, putting a foot in the bowl of roses. He was fiddling with his clothing, he was unzipping the flies of his trousers. Oh Lord, was he going to rape her in full view of his drunken cronies and the camera and Cox? No. No, it wasn't that. He was urinating. Everything which he had drunk came in a steady stream as he washed away the snow from the slope of one of her breasts, standing on the edge of the table, straining to direct his aim, lurching and tumbling to the floor.

Oh Lord, oh pray. It was what Jenny used to say. What use are swear words, she argued, which are so used they no longer shock? At bad moments I have my own.

These were bad moments, the worst.

Now the other men pushed back their chairs and jostled to join the sport. It was Mincu who was in the middle, Mincu the birthday boy, Mincu whose idea it was to aim at the candle to try to douse the flame. Liliana's mouth opened in a silent scream so one of the men aimed at that. Liliana was thrashing so wildly that the two waiters had difficulty controlling her. The man who'd been smoking the cigar tossed it away and stood above Liliana, pressing down on her breasts, subduing her as if she'd been an epileptic convulsing in a fit. Cox was suddenly off the settee and bending close to the monitor, rubbing his hand across the screen as if it was dusty and he wanted to clean it or as if he wanted to take part in the humiliation of Liliana. Gabriela was shouting something at him and Vasile was roaring in a kind of laughter but Cox's stare was riveted on the action.

Now the waiters were rolling Liliana up in the white tablecloth, muffling her thrashing as if with a strait-jacket. Liliana was trussed, Liliana was gift-wrapped. Mincu was shouting an order and Liliana was lifted up and carried from the room with Mincu punching the air like a victorious athlete and shouting something to his friends as he left the room in pursuit of his birthday present, the man who'd been smoking the cigar tagging on behind.

Cox was kneeling in front of the screen. The tape was still running, showing drinking and laughing. Cox said, 'Go back. Run it again from that time they started pissing.'

'You're disgusting,' Gabriela said. She was on her feet, lashing out with her shoe at him. 'You are worse than any of them . . .'

Vasile was laughing and laughing, gleeful at the effect the tape had had. He pressed the rewind button to run the show again.

Cox looked up at Gabriela. He ignored her kicks completely. He spoke in a voice of such monumental quietness that she stopped kicking. 'Who else has seen this tape? The three of us. Anybody else? Mr Crake, for instance? Some of your friends?'

'I don't know,' she said.

'Ask him. Ask this oaf who has seen it.'

Gabriela did. 'He says only him and you and me.'

'Nobody else?

'He says only us.'

The tape was running again. Here was the scramble up onto the table. Here was the yellow rain. Here was Liliana's violent shaking. Here was her body being held down. Here was Liliana being rolled inside the white cloth. Here was Liliana borne out of the room, Mincu in pursuit, one of his friends following in haste as if they had business to do together.

Cox got to his feet. He seemed to stare at nothing or perhaps he peered at the abyss inside his own head.

'Enough,' he said. He'd seen enough, more than he'd dreamed of.

Suddenly there was no time for anything, no time to ask questions or discuss possibilities. Vasile was urging them to hurry, to get out now because of the security patrol.

'I thought they only checked to see he was awake.'

'Sometimes they do more, they search a bit.'

'It's a big museum. We could conceal ourselves.'

'Maybe they bring dogs,' Gabriela said. 'The dogs smell you out.'

To Cox's ear that reason had a desperation to it. Gabriela didn't want to stay. But nor, certainly, did Vasile want them to. The descent through the museum was done swiftly with Vasile's flashlight showing the way. They went out through the loading bay and Cox turned to face Vasile.

'Tell him I want—'

The door was slammed and they heard the lock click.

'We must hurry,' she said. 'We mustn't be found here.'

Cox agreed. They mustn't be found there.

When they were in Calea Victoriei again Cox stopped

her. The river lay some way down the gentle slope to the left, his hotel a short walk away to the right. The street was empty, not a late-night gambler, not a cat, not a shadow. The night seemed darker than before.

'My dear,' Cox began and stopped. No more avuncular tone. 'Gabriela, are you listening?'

'Of course.'

'Not of course. Really listening. Pay attention to what I say. I want to thank you for showing me that tape. No, don't get angry. It was very terrible and it made me understand – even feel – what Liliana is going through. But it is more than that, much more, more than you can guess. Gabriela, it is late now and we both need to sleep. Tomorrow – later today – there are questions I must put. But not here. Now promise me this: you must tell no one about that tape. Tell no one we have seen it. Tell no one it even exists. You were absolutely right when you said it was a secret. But it is a more dangerous secret than you thought.'

'Of course.'

'Not *of course*. This is serious. Say *Yes, Mr Cox, I shall say nothing about it to anyone*.'

She repeated it.

'That tape is more dangerous than you can imagine,' he warned a second time.

Headlights were approaching from the direction of the river so they turned away and began strolling like any other couple late at night. Cox offered his arm and just for a moment thought she wasn't going to take it. They walked together the four, five blocks to Cox's hotel. He pressed her hand tight against his side so she wouldn't leave him. He wanted her for protection – a man walking late at night with a pretty girl goes unremarked. For Cox felt something he hadn't for years: he felt frightened. They stopped outside the Capitol Hotel where the security guard would be sure to notice the reason for his outing.

'After we've had some sleep then,' he said.

She nodded. Then to his surprise and secret delight she reached up to place a kiss on his cheek.

For a time sleep wouldn't come. He had visions of a candle's guttering flame, convulsing limbs and the face of the man who followed Mincu out of the room.

There was the sound of voices and slamming car doors in the street below where a casino's lights blinked. Cox got up to sit in a chair by the open window. Why should a man go to a casino if he didn't gamble much? He has a drink, she'd said, speaks to one or two people, watches the floorshow, sees who has come to town. Part of the job, Cox supposed. As it had been with Rex Lovelace.

A light rain began falling. He closed the window and went back to bed.

Did he bet with his own money? Was it a legitimate expense? Did the Treasury demand his winnings? He would ask Gabriela when he saw her later on. He remembered the security guard's conspiratorial wink as he walked through the hotel lobby. Cox rather thought he might have patted Gabriela's rump when he left her.

He slept.

Chapter 9

Her Britannic Majesty's embassy was in Michelet Street which, leading nowhere in particular, was blessedly free of through traffic. At its eastern end was a small garden which was favoured by teenagers from the nearby school. They stood in groups, boys and girls apart, except for one girl with long blonde hair who had attached herself to a gang of four boys. The Gabriela of tomorrow, Cox thought.

The nighttime rain had cleared and the sun shone from an unblemished sky. The shower had cooled the air. The little garden was planted with chestnut trees and the first yellowing leaves were scattered on the paving stones. Conkers had the gleam of army boots on parade. There were four benches and Cox had chosen one on the west side. What could be more natural than for a man to seek out a place in the sun? He was freshly shaved and wore a pale grey suit with a cornflower blue tie and altogether looked the picture of a man of advancing years enjoying his ease. His face wore an indulgent smile as he regarded the youngsters through half-closed eyes. But those eyes flicked to the junction where Michelet Street meets Lupu Street when a pedestrian appeared. Over the dinner table at La Premiera last night, in the waiting period before Liliana and Mincu got together, he'd quizzed Gabriela about Crake. For instance, how did he cope with Bucharest drivers who take their style from Ben Hur? *He always walks to the embassy,* Gabriela had said. *It takes him fifteen minutes, maybe twenty. He says it is his constitutional. I thought constitution was to do with government.* Ah, Cox had said, but he works for the government, you see.

So here he was, a little before nine, waiting to have a quiet word with Crake. No offices, no telephones, no walls, no colleagues, no lovers. Just the two of them, two men on a bench enjoying autumn sunshine and chatting about everyday things, children, football, why women cross their arms when they take off a sweater whereas a man simply hauls it over his head. This garden was on the direct route to Crake's apartment. So he was puzzled when it was Gabriela he saw, walking fast, on her own, her blonde hair bobbing in the sun.

Cox could have got to his feet and reached her in ten seconds. But there is something furtive about whispering in a pretty girl's ear in the street. A whisper draws the world's attention because everyone wants to know a secret.

'Gabriela.'

She was startled.

'Mr Cox, why are you here?'

'Perhaps I have been taking my constitutional. Have you a moment to sit with me?'

'Ow,' she wailed, 'I will be late.'

'I shall explain to the *grosse légume* that it is my fault.'

'What is *grosse légume,* please?'

'I'm sorry. Of course it is Liliana who has the French. The French say the big vegetable. We say the big cheese. Your boss. The ambassador if it comes to that. Talking of Liliana, how is she today? Have you spoken to her?'

'I had no time.'

Despite having no time she settled next to Cox who

shifted sideways a little to give her extra room, also to be able to look at her without twisting round.

'I must see Liliana again. I telephoned but there was no answer. It was too early for the Trade Fair so where's she got to?'

'Maybe she goes to church to send another message to God.'

'You make her sound very religious.'

'She likes to sit there. She says she knows peace.'

'The peace that passeth all understanding.'

'What does that mean, please?'

'The big things in life are mysteries. Why we are what we are. Why we do what we do. Why we have the capacity for good but like Mincu do evil. She goes there and talks to that part of herself which is also part of God. That is what I believe. It eases her spirit. It gives her peace of mind. It gives her strength. You said she was a strong person.'

She was frowning. 'She will need a lot of strength to do what you ask her. Maybe one message to the Virgin Mary does not give her enough.'

Cox made a mental note. 'And Mr Crake? Where is he this morning? Isn't this the route he takes to the embassy?'

Her face cleared. She was of the generation younger than Cox's who found religion embarrassing to talk about but sex simple and natural. She laid a hand on his. 'Mr Cox, you are my very good uncle so I can tell you everything. Sometimes I sleep with Mr Crake, sometimes I sleep in my own place. Last night, after I leave you, I don't want to be alone. Those pictures we watch, yes? So I go to Mr Crake's apartment and he has come back. But you see, in the morning after I sleep with him, he says we must walk separately to the embassy. He takes different route from me. The first time I ask him, "Why is this, Panda?" When we are alone he likes me to call him Panda. "Are you ashamed

I sleep with you? I am Romanian woman, I am good for sleeping, but not good the English know. Is that it, Panda?" He gets cross then and just says it is better.'

'My dear,' Cox said. She had taken her hand away to make sharp jabbing gestures in the air. He took hold of it in both his hands. 'Mr Crake is being a gentleman. He is considering your reputation, which is very right and proper of him.'

'You think so?'

'Most assuredly,' he said, mentally crossing his fingers at the lie. 'I want to see him but not at the embassy. I'll telephone him later.' Another mental note. First Liliana before she went to work, then Crake. 'Also I want to study the tape again.' She made no response so he didn't press her. 'Will you tell me now about Vasile?'

He let go of her hand and it flew to her face, rubbing a cheek. The hand dropped and she looked at her wristwatch.

'Don't worry,' he said, 'if you're late and there's any trouble, I'll explain.'

'What do you want me to tell you?'

'What was he? You said I could guess when I saw what he had. I prefer to *know* who I'm dealing with rather than guess.'

Gabriela looked round, at the teenagers, at an old man who was hitting the fallen conkers with his walking stick, at a woman on the next bench who had two skeins of different-coloured wool she was twisting together into one ball. Beyond the woman was a curious statue of naked children that Cox had not liked to study too closely.

'You know there used to be Securitate in Romania,' Gabriela said.

'He worked for them?'

'It was separate department really. Its initials were DGTO. You heard of them?'

'Tell me about them. What do the initials stand for?'

'Directia Generala de Technica Operativa. Securitate were everywhere, in every office, in every factory, in every hotel, in every school, in every park. Maybe that woman would be Securitate. Maybe me. But the others, DGTO, they were even more secret because they stole people's lives silently. You understand what I mean? Their job was technical operations.'

'Such as?' Cox asked, though he knew the answer. He just wanted her to get the habit of telling him.

'They listen on telephones, open letters, put microphones in taxis, put cameras in bedrooms. That is what he did.'

'You mean cameras in bedrooms?'

'Elena Ceausescu liked very much to watch such films. Vasile told me he had films of many people, of government ministers, of their wives, of capitalist businessmen, of ambassadors, of foreign leaders. With their lovers, mistresses, sometimes boys. It was his job to take these pictures to Elena. I said, Surely not you, you are too young, they get someone more senior to take such things. He agreed that was so, but once he went with the Chief of the Department, General Ovidiu Somebody, and Elena afterwards insisted that he bring the tapes, only Vasile, not the General who was fat and spat when he talked. Sometimes Elena made him stay with her while she watched. She would grow red in the face and make rude remarks. Look at that whore, look at what she is doing, look at her pretty mouth, such disgusting things. Sometimes she would be drinking. Vasile says she used to ask him: Would you like to do these things? It is disgusting but it is not uninteresting. He was afraid she was going to order him to take his clothes off. Maybe he did take his clothes off. Maybe he is lying.' She put a hand through her hair, frowning. 'Anyway the tape you saw he could not show her because of who was in it.

You saw him on the table. You recognized him, I think. Show that to Elena, she would have killed Vasile. So Vasile keeps it. Others also. He wants me to watch them with him. That is what he asks me to do last night.'

'A real charmer.'

'You think such a man is charming?' She glowered at him.

'My dear, a little joke. Sometimes the English say the opposite of what they mean. It stops them being too earnest.' Or maybe it stopped them facing reality.

She thought about this. 'Is true. Is why Panda calls me sometimes "old girl". If I am old girl, I tell him, then you are grandfather.'

'How did you meet Vasile?'

'I went to dance and he was there. He was not dancing, he was looking. That is what he likes to do. I talk to him so . . .' She shrugged. That's how life is. 'Now I go.'

Cox thought for a moment she was going to kiss him on the cheek again but she raised a hand, said, '*Ciao*', and was gone.

To leave the little public garden, he had to walk past the piece of statuary. There was a fountain that didn't work and a rock topped by a pillar with three pre-pubescent children clambering up. They were naked. One boy was looking saucily over his shoulder at the naked girl scrambling up after him. She was holding a fish and gazing longingly at him. The third figure, another naked boy, was looking at a frog that was pursuing him. He was lifting his foot out of the way and his face showed some alarm, though Cox guessed that if he bent down to kiss the frog it would turn into a naked pre-pubescent princess.

Elena Ceausescu must have ordered its creation. Inspired by the bedroom romps that Vasile had filmed. It was her idea to give the frog the face of Yasser Arafat.

He'd had to walk all round this bizarre statue, as if he was inspecting it, was drawn to it. As he reached the pavement he looked back and saw the woman had lain her skeins of wool on her lap to stare after him. Disapproving? Searching for a kindred spirit?

He hurried away. St Peter and St Paul, I'm coming.

But he hurried more cautiously as he approached the church. It was down Calea Grivitei, he had worked out on his map. He walked fast at first, then slowly when he saw its spire appear on the right-hand side of the road. He had just learned that Vasile had been in a branch of Romania's old security apparatus. This had spread like a stain throughout society and like a stain it was difficult to get out. Vasile might have chums who would be interested in an Englishman who looked at videos of orgies back in the Golden Age but was more interested in the faces than the bodies.

He strolled, a middle-aged gentleman showing interest in all facets of the new Romania. He peered into a bakery at the selection of rolls in the window, seeing what reflections there were in the glass. The Chinese restaurant was still closed and nobody played cards. He frowned at the shop with its stock of retread tyres spilling out of the door – who would buy a used tyre from a Romanian driver? He was fascinated by a tailor, so fascinated he turned abruptly back to have another look. The man was hunched over an old treadle sewing machine. Trousers hung from rails at the back and the side. Only trousers, no jackets. His concentration on the stitching was ferocious until he finished the seam, lifted his eyes to the Coca-Cola poster on the wall and was refreshed. Cox swung round at the sound of a tram. Number 52, curses, don't want that. He looked both ways, left, right, left, right again. Satisfied it was safe, he crossed the street. He passed a group of gypsy children playing a form of hopscotch on the cracked paving. They were barefoot. It's their traditional costume, and he smiled benignly on them.

There was a service in progress. Cox could hear the monotone voice of the priest as soon as he walked through the gate in the fence. Today this was manned by an old fellow who got off a little stool, wrestled with the catch and waited for a coin or two. This is the Middle East, Cox reminded himself, and one acquires merit by giving alms.

He slipped inside the church and stood to one side against the wall. It was almost as dark as it had been during the night. Beams of sun like spotlights came through tiny windows. One of the beams lit up a display of tracts. A crone dressed in black was in charge of these pamphlets and Cox considered buying one, to show good will, not to stand out as a gawper. There was one on mission work in Africa. Another looked like an appeal for drought relief with three figures isolated in the middle of a parched and cracked landscape. But when he looked closer he saw it was a warning against homosexuality and he knew he would stand out even more with that in his hand.

Orthodox services had always been a mystery to him. They seemed not to be conducted for the glory of God, nor for the spiritual refreshment of the congregation, but for the benefit of the priest. Catholic priests could look ascetic or well nourished. Anglican priests could look fatuous or anguished. But this man droned and droned and then lifted his head, gazing not down the nave at the congregation but up at the cupola. He was like a man listening for a birdcall or a far-off shout. Then he returned to reading aloud from a book held open by a young accolyte. The congregation was a dozen strong, one man and the rest women of middle age and above. And Liliana.

Cox let his gaze wander round the church and then

return to her. Gabriela's hair was so startling in its brightness and Liliana's hair was dark, black really. With her head bowed, Cox had overlooked her at first. She was writing, writing, writing. Another prayer, Gabriela had said. It looked like her last will and testament. Once she looked up, straight at Cox, but seemed not to see him. He had the feeling he didn't exist. Perhaps he didn't for her. She was off somewhere else in her mind. He tried to put himself inside that mind and couldn't. Is she speaking to God? To the statue of a crucified Christ with blood trickling from a crown of thorns? To Gabriela who kisses her on the mouth?

Perhaps – Cox had an unnerving thought – she's writing a farewell note like someone going away on a wartime mission. 'I have been called to do my duty in a foreign place. There may be some danger involved so if . . .' That sort.

Or she's writing lines like a punishment at school. *I light this candle in place of the one that went out. I light this candle . . .*

Tired of useless speculations he went outside into the churchyard.

'You were waiting for me,' Liliana said.

'Yes.'

'How did you know I would be in this church?'

'I didn't, but I had no better idea of where to look.'

'I mean, how did you know about this church?'

'I came last night with Gabriela. She said it was a place where you sought peace.'

'Peace, yes.'

'Also strength.'

They walked past the car breaker's yard where the dogs were tussling over a large bone and paid them no attention. Cox led the way down the road towards the station. He remembered a café from last night and they found a table in the sun with a view of a wooden hut which sold bus tickets to Turkey.

'Do you want coffee?' she asked as the waiter stood by their sides. She ordered without waiting for Cox's reply. 'I think it is too early in the day for you to drink brandy.'

He smiled at her, thinking it was a joke, but her frown suggested it was a reproach. You English can no longer be serious about the world, her look said. You have lost your empire and your direction in life and adopt a frivolous attitude. Which was definitely not the case, Cox felt. He knitted his brows and brushed a fleck of dirt from the front of his jacket. He frowned more: the summery paleness of his suit and the jauntiness of his tie were at odds with this new earnestness.

Her eyes were levelled on him. They were dark eyes, he knew that, dark Romanian eyes that matched her hair. He'd never put much store by the notion that eyes were the windows of the soul. Conmen's eyes didn't say: do not trust me. Murderers' eyes didn't say: watch your back. Philby's eyes hadn't said: I am a traitor. But now looking at those eyes he could see worlds within. He saw hints of the ordeal that had battered her, wounds that had never healed but been hidden away. He fancied he could see more, see her country's history in the darkness, all the struggles as people were ordered to march with Hitler one day, about turn and march with Stalin the next. It took steel to stand firm in such turbulence. In a last fantasy he imagined he could see beyond Liliana, beyond Romania, all the way to Ilona. Ilona had had that resolution before she went out to fight, to be a martyr.

Cox drew a deep breath. It was lack of sleep, he told himself, that caused his brain to jump so much. I'm English, I'm a pragmatist, theories are castles in the air that vanish with the next breeze. That's *nonsense* about seeing Romania's history in her eyes.

'The Trade Fair opens in an hour,' Liliana said. 'You know where it is? On the road towards Otopeni. The airport, you know. So I must leave very soon to catch the bus. And when I get to the Fair I shall meet Mincu. Oh, not at once. He won't be waiting for me. But he will come out into the hall about lunchtime, make his way between the stands. He will speak to people, lay his hand on their arm. He likes to touch people. Men, also. I think he touches men to feel the muscles under their sleeves. The women . . . So he will see me. What do I do then, Mr Cox? You have come from London specially. You are going to give me a gun? Is that why you were waiting for me? It would not be Christian to give me the gun inside the church so you stay outside. You give me the gun now under the table. I shoot him. He is dead. That is what you want, isn't it?'

'I've brought no gun. I certainly wouldn't ask you to do that. I wish – fervently – that Mincu was not alive but it is not my job to kill people.'

'You employ others to do it, I think.'

The talk seemed sliding in a direction Cox did not want. He waited a moment too long to deny it and she made an impatient gesture.

'I understand,' she said. 'You do not employ women to do that kind of work. Women are good for another sort of thing. Is that what you want me for?'

'Me?' Cox was indignant. 'Do you think I came to Bucharest to find a woman?'

'No, I mean you want me to sleep with Mincu. You came to Bucharest, you found out about me and now you want me to seduce Mincu. No, *seduce* is the wrong word. Submit to him. Again.'

'I most certainly do not.'

Cox could feel the anger swelling in him. He knew – he

knew as a fact from interrogation sessions – that when you accuse someone of something and the person grows angry in denial, then you've hit a sensitive spot. When you're angry, his mother had said, count to ten. I've been counting all my life, thousands, millions, Liliana had retorted. But at this moment the waiter brought their coffee and by the time he had given a token wipe to the table and put the cups down, Cox had his feelings under control again.

'You are to be an intelligence gatherer, that is all. Not a Mata Hari. It is just as I told you last night before you slipped away. We need to know the precise nature of the weapons he is offering and how he is getting hold of them. We need names. That is the absolute requirement. Are there any Americans in the background? Or Russians? Are there any English?'

She nodded: that was what he had asked of her. He thought of her writing the prayer for strength which was really a means of instilling discipline into herself. He thought of her lighting a candle. He thought of another candle being doused in a shower of piss. He thought of the faces of the men in that room. She nodded again and he decided this time she was agreeing so he hastened on.

'You don't have to do this.'

She looked surprised. 'Then why are you here?'

'I'm here to tell you that if you say no, that you cannot help, I shall understand.'

There was confusion on her face. She had been steeling herself, offering prayers, lighting candles and now she was told the fixture might be called off. 'Explain please.'

Two men had taken the next table so Cox leaned closer and lowered his voice.

'It's a lot I'm asking, too much really. You are not one of us. If anything happened to you my Chief would say I was criminally insane to have used you. You have no training, just to take the most obvious objection. You have signed no contract. We haven't broached the subject of payment – though rest assured we shall be generous. But the fundamental objection is that you are an amateur. Paradoxically it is also your greatest attraction. You are so obviously not involved in this kind of work that it makes you above suspicion. Mincu sees you – unfortunately – as a desirable woman. He has no other thought about you.'

He looked in her face as if he were asking for her forgiveness. Her eyes were two dark points, fixed on him, waiting for an end to his excuses.

'The man is a rogue in his business, a rat in his private life. He is a rapist. He has vile habits. He is violent. He is a killer by proxy – and could be a murderer in fact. I have come across smilers like him before. What you are being asked to do is dangerous. If you want to say no, this is the time to say it. I shall not think the worse of you. There will be no taint of cowardice. No one will ever know that you declined. No one will even know that you were considered.'

Her eyes waited, knowing he hadn't finished.

'You are a volunteer. The best and strongest people are the ones who volunteer. But once you volunteer there can be no backing off. No running away whatever the provocation.'

He wondered if he should say more: about the importance of what she would find out, the lives she would save, the revenge she would achieve. He decided it was better left unsaid.

'That is all,' Cox said. There was silence. They had both forgotten their coffee and paid no attention to the traffic or the people at other tables. They were like lovers intent on each other. 'What do you say?'

'Yes.'

Cox went to a restaurant that served pizza. A board above

the counter showed garishly photographed specialities. He ordered a pizza Constantsa which turned out to have tomato paste, some flakes of fish and pickled gherkins.

He thought again of their leave-taking. He had looked round for the waiter to pay the bill and Liliana had said, 'You have been doing this work for a long time. Nearly forty years, yes?'

He had turned back to her. 'Yes.'

'You have seen many bad things in your time. Maybe you have done some yourself that you are not proud of. Your face . . . Sometimes it looks more than tired. It is as if there are things in the past that you do not like to think about. Now, of course, since 1989 the world has changed. All the old battles are finished. Instead we shall have new struggles, new enemies.'

Cox said, 'The Chinese maintain that the normal state of mankind is war. Peace is an unnatural interlude. On that pessimistic view, yes, there will always be an adversary.'

'But I think soon you will retire. What will you do with your days? Fish? Do you like to catch trout? Play golf? I do not think they will let you write your memoirs.'

'Jenny used to say that when I had the time I should buy a ruined windmill somewhere along the coast in Suffolk and restore it to working order. I would create something beautiful and useful. As a bonus the labour would be therapeutic, it would stop me thinking too much about the past.'

'Perhaps you should think, Mr Cox. The old demons are dead and new ones are straining to be born. Perhaps you should think how to change human nature. That would be a really useful service. Then all spies would be out of a job.'

She had walked away to catch her bus to the Fair and the inevitable meeting with Mincu. He watched her, his cloak-and-dagger girl. The further she walked, the younger she looked. Old men always sent the young out to fight their wars.

Chapter 10

In purely operational terms Cox now had an agent, even if the professional virgins of the personnel department hadn't vetted her. It was grudgingly agreed that a controller in the field could hire local talent where necessary but the virgins insisted on being told.

Old boy, they said, supposing you bought a bullet in some back alley one night. There might be a dozen claimants for pay and expenses and widow's pensions and God knows what else. We need to know who is genuine and who are the jokers. Remember Peterson. Dreadful business.

Ah yes, Peterson. On any miserable day in February, when the sky pressed down on the roofs in London, when taxi drivers ignored your wave but not the puddles, when the police cars wailed for another bomb scare, Cox could remember Peterson and smile. It had happened in El Salvador during the bad time. Some trigger-happy *muchachos* in a car had shot up the British embassy so it had closed down. The only British presence in the country was an honorary consul, a fine old fellow everyone called Chip. The Glasshouse, needing to provide intelligence, had sent Peterson. For a year he sent reports, quite good ones since he got it all from the reporters he met at the bar of the Camino Real hotel, as it turned out. But his expenses told another tale of a downtown office under cover of being a garment exporter plus a girl for the front office, meals with influential contacts, trips to Santa Ana and to Chalatenango when the road was open, informants in the army and the Treasury Police plus brave souls from the guerilla side who passed through army checkpoints to make certain that Western governments knew their hopes and aims. Then Peterson disappeared during a visit to San Miguel. The FLMN got him, people said, or the army. He was asking too many questions in the line of duty. Questions were dangerous. Poor old Peterson. He was missed at the bar of the Camino Real. Someone thought of starting a collection but not knowing who to send it to they held a wake and drank it.

Then the claimants started. They visited old Chip who could do nothing but pass it all on to London: bills for rent overdue on the office and a reinforced villa in the Zona Rosa, the unpaid instalments for the Toyota Celicia, the office receptionist's back pay and money in lieu of notice, no fewer than seven men and one woman who claimed various fees and expenses. Much of this, it was believed, had already been paid but London had no proof. It was paid again. Thirty-five thousand dollars were handed over. Then a woman appeared – embarrassingly – at the Glasshouse claiming a gratuity and a widow's pension. No one had known Peterson was married – he certainly hadn't taken his wife with him – but she had the certificate to prove it. And how about our two boys? Their schooling? Fees were negotiated.

It might have ended there if the following year, taking a winter holiday and passing through the Osa peninsula in Costa Rica, one of the professional virgins of the vetting department hadn't run into Peterson enjoying a Saturday night out in Puerto Jimenez. He'd set himself up very nicely in a ménage à trois with his wife and the receptionist from the Salvador office. The boys were due out for their Easter holidays. He was breeding horses. On Sundays he played baseball for the *gringos* against the *ticos.* Peterson had planned well. There was nothing the Glasshouse could do because Costa Rica has a policy of asylum to all, with no extradition.

Peterson for Director General, Cox thought. Then we can all retire and enjoy our creature comforts in some tropical hideaway.

Hey-ho, the current Director-General, his Chief, was made of sterner stuff.

'Hello, Chief, I'm calling from my hotel in Bucharest.'

Meaning, an open line, no security, no names.

'I understand. You're making progress?'

'Yes. I have access to Chummy. I will put her name on a piece on paper and send it to London, your eyes only.'

A pause here. Cox imagined the Chief swivelling his chair to stare out at the sky. A local agent, female, recruited. The vetting department not to be informed at this time. Embassy facilities not being used.

'I take it things are hotting up.'

'Warmish.'

'Is the transatlantic scenario working out?'

'Chief, I'm thinking the danger lies more on our side.'

'And it is a danger?'

'I believe yes. Danger of two kinds. Physical. Well, Chummy is a nasty piece of work. Also danger of a political nature.'

Another pause for consideration. Now he would have transferred his gaze to the sampler with the thoughts of Sun Tzu.

'I'm sending you some back-up,' his Chief said. 'They won't be London people. They're Munich-based so no one will gossip. You don't have to use them but you need to know they're there. And I want you to find a safe house with a telephone we can talk on. Hear me?'

The line went dead as if the Chief had put the telephone down swiftly, in anger. But Cox didn't think so. It was just his way. The Chief didn't hold with goodbyes. Saying goodbye was like saying you'd never meet again.

The British Council, being cultural, did not have such a good address as the embassy. Only half a kilometre separated the buildings but in spirit it was a whole cocktail circuit away. Cox had walked, passing the embassy. Its railings had display cabinets celebrating British Women of Today. Not Thatcher, she was Yesterday. Cox was uplifted by the Speaker of the House of Commons, the first female black QC, the first ordained woman priest, a sprinter, an equestrienne.

The British Council was celebrating a successful young British novelist. Well, youngish. He had been flown out, housed at the Dobranti Hotel round the corner, wined and dined, and delivered his talk the previous evening. A poster announced its subject: The Yuppie as anti-hero. Cox found himself gatecrashing a small reception. The sound of cups clinking on saucers could be heard. An eager young Indian at the door asked to see his invitation, 'If it is convenient, sir.' Cox patted his pockets.

'Do you know, I don't think it is convenient. I seem to have left mine behind. Do you think if I promise not to eat too many cucumber sandwiches you could possibly let me squeeze in?'

Doubt replaced eagerness on the young man's face. But Cox's invincible smile plus his undoubted English accent won him entry.

A couple of dozen or so guests stood with cups, making the kind of mid-afternoon chat that tea allows. A woman wearing a Romanian peasant blouse swung round on Cox's entry. She had a long face with hair fluffed out at the sides perhaps to soften its lines.

'Hello, I'm Angela. And you are . . . ?'

'Cox. Royston Cox.'

'Were you present last night? Wasn't he wonderful?'

With her long face and her long drawn-out vowels Cox was irresistibly reminded of a horse. No invitation, no sugar lumps either. She tossed her head back towards a group of people presumably surrounding the great man.

'Alas,' Cox said, 'a press of engagements . . .'

'He was absolutely right about the shift from working-class heroes to moneyed parvenus showing the cultural shift of the 'eighties. Spot on. But the 'nineties? What about now? The "dreadful decade" – wonderful phrase. Never mind *fin de siècle*, more *fin de civilisation*, if you ask me. Isn't it *disgraceful* the way the tabloids have been hounding him?'

'Again, alas, I seemed to have missed that.'

'What? Mr Cox, how can that be possible?'

'I have to travel rather a lot, you see.'

'Well, it's an absolute scandal, let me tell you. Literally *hounding* him because of his last publisher's advance. Well, I mean, I know half a million does sound rather a lot when you consider the absolute *pittance* people work for here and the ragged children in the villages and those poor orphans. But *they* said – the papers – *they* said it made him one of the people he was so critical of. And then that business with his mistress – such a *passé* term – and what they insist on calling "romps" on Hampstead Heath, and how he needs the money to pay for her breast implants. I mean, honestly. Isn't it wicked?'

'Breast implants? I've never really considered—'

'Mr Cox, *you* are wicked. You are trying to provoke me. I mean the hypocrisy of the gutter press. Fish wrappers, I call them. And you missed all this? Only good thing was it pushed the Royals off the front page. Of course I don't read that kind of paper myself but it's been hard to avoid all the fuss. Where have you been hiding? A monastery?'

'Oh, abroad.'

'Abroad? Well, I suppose this is abroad when you think about it. You're an academic of some kind? Are you really Professor Cox and modestly hiding your light under a whatnot?'

'Afraid not. It's plain Mister. A gritty businessman. Exports.'

'Exporting is *fun*, right? Didn't Macmillan say that? And the UK exports simply tons of books, no one has any idea.'

'I do machine tools.'

'I beg yours?'

'Stuff for heavy industry.'

'What, widgets and spigots and things?'

'Ah, but on a Brobdingnagian scale.'

She blinked a couple of times. Her eyes seemed to glaze over, then shift beyond Cox's right shoulder. 'How absolutely fascinating. Do excuse me. I've just . . . you know . . . got to circulate.'

Cox took stock. The knot of people surrounded a man so short that only the top half of his head was visible. He had a high forehead allowing plenty of space to develop great thoughts. Beyond him was what Cox was looking for. A sign on a door said Reading Room. Cox made towards it, a hand half raised in salute as if he recognized someone. He closed the door softly and stood with his back to it as if he had entered a dangerous place. What he saw was unalarming, little different from a room in the Enescu house. Bookshelves lined two walls. A table had four hard chairs for serious students. A noticeboard advertised various BBC publications, the programme at the National Theatre in

London, English conversation classes, videos of *Henry V* for hire and an English-owned villa in Cyprus available for summer rentals. A long table under the window had a slew of periodicals plus a week-old *Sunday Times.* The smell was the dusty one that books give off after a hot dry summer. The sounds from the party next door were muted. He listened for, but couldn't catch, Angela's bray.

He started with the *Sunday Times,* giving close attention to the business section. He shuffled through the magazines. The demise of *Punch* would surely be felt here. He was turning the pages of *Country Life* when the door opened. It was Angela, one arm raised to protect her breasts under the peasant blouse, her long face drawn in disapproval.

'Mr Cox, you are here under false pretences. I have checked the list. No exporters of heavy machinery were invited. Only persons of *cultural* merit were asked. The British taxpayer is footing the bill and we can't go lavishing hospitality on every Tom, Dick and Harry.'

'Admirable policy.' Cox beamed at her. 'But I haven't so much as pinched a cup of tea, though I am parched. I came to browse through these. Being abroad so much I have been missing out.'

He held up the magazine with its photographs of a dance at some country house. Young men in dinner jackets were draped over the banisters of a wide staircase. Young women in flouncy evening dress spread themselves on its steps. Cox doubted they had a thought or generous impulse between the lot of them. And these were meant to be the cream of the society he was sworn to protect. Hey-ho. But Angela took it quite otherwise. She looked from the magazine to Cox.

'Heavy machinery, you said?'

'It pays the bills. I have a little place in Shropshire, Ludlow way. Dry Rot Hall I call it.'

'Ludlow? You must know the Fernleys then?'

'Only *of* them, I'm afraid. My wife kept up much more with the county. Being abroad so much I simply haven't been able to. Sadly Jenny was taken from me last year. Jenny was my wife.'

'Taken? I'm *so* sorry.' She opened a cupboard and pointed at a stack of back numbers. 'We have loads more going back yonks, practically to the Middle Ages. Don't know why we hoard them. Maybe they're a little link with England and we can't bear to cut the umbilical whatnot. It's nostalgia, actually. Myself, I *love* a good wallow in nostalgia. Why don't you have a rummage and I'll bring you that cup of tea. Milk and no sugar, am I right?'

So it was that twenty minutes' search produced the photo that Cox wanted. Angela, displaced county girl with the face rather like a horse, brought him his tea and returned to the guests. He could hear her voice raised in horror at the *squillions*, honestly, being squandered on Covent Garden though naturally she adored the opera. She seemed safely launched. Cox laid the magazine flat on the table. With his penknife he removed the page, folded it twice and slipped it in his pocket.

'Do you know,' Cox said in his most affable tone, 'that during the Golden Age Old Nick had this grand plan for wiring the whole country. I've heard a figure of ten million microphones, though God knows where he'd have found all the people to monitor them. It wasn't just offices and factories and blocks of workers' flats. Everyone expected that. Outdoors as well. The lamp posts, the trees, the rose bushes, all would have microphones to pick up passing chat. It might be innocent, it might be an imperialist plot. He called it his "opinion poll". A fine piece of Orwellian double-speak.'

Crake, at his side, nodded. If Cox wanted to burble on, so be it. They were strolling through Cismigiu Park. To one side were beds of exhausted flowers and thickets of bushes and what might be picturesque ruins. To the other side a meandering piece of water with a couple of lethargic ducks. An outdoor café was a resting place for women with bags of shopping.

'Even the park benches were to have microphones.' Cox stopped, bent to peer underneath and straightened. 'Here's one he overlooked.'

They sat. A row of iron chairs further down the path was taken by mothers with babies and old men enjoying the afternoon sun. The bench was in the shade and had been empty. There were the distant shouts of children and the steady scratch of a rake on gravel.

'Good of you to spare the time,' Cox said.

'You're the man from London.'

Cox considered the terseness of this reply. Indeed, he was the man from London. Still, it showed a lack of grace, resentment of the man from head office who had arrived and taken over. Or a lack of sleep. Dark rings under the eyes marked the nighttime player, the gambler, the lover. Well, the frequenter of casinos. Gabriela said he didn't bet much.

'What's the latest on Chummy?' Cox asked.

'Gone quiet.'

'Quiet? What does that mean?'

'I went along to the Open Eye around lunchtime. You know, the Trade Fair. Just to have another peek at him, see who he was talking to. Mincu wasn't there.'

'Did you ask for him?'

'In an off-handed way. I'm not a probationer, you know. Spoke to a pansy young man at the reception desk, said I had a message for Mincu and he said – the pansy – that Mincu hadn't been in. Or he hadn't seen him at any rate. So, he's out of town or he's got a bit of business in hand that he's conducting away from the bright lights.'

'You saw Liliana?'

'Saw her. Kept clear of her naturally.'

'She's working for us now. I saw her this morning again. She agreed.'

Crake looked away down the path to where a mother was dragging a small boy by the wrist. The boy held an empty cone and was bawling at the loss of his ice cream. Crake turned back and looked at Cox.

'Could be dangerous. Mincu doesn't keep to the Queensberry Rules, you know.'

'I know. She knows. She knows better than either of us. The man raped her. His buddies did too. I found out there's a tape of that evening, not of the actual rape but before it. She starkers, on a dessert trolley, covered in white goo, with a lighted candle stuck between her thighs. It's an image I can't get out of my mind. It was like a sacrifice, some warlock ritual. Chummy and the other lovelies are peeing on her. I understand some people get their kicks that way. No accounting for the sexual beast, is there? You knew about this? The tape?'

'No.'

'I thought Gabriela might have told you. We saw it together last night and after we parted she went to you.'

Crake was frowning. He shook his head.

Cox carried on. 'You said yesterday that Liliana had the motivation but was too shocked to agree to anything. The motivation has won through. She is going to try to get close to Chummy so she can dig up some names. As you say, dangerous. I want to have a tracker put on her.'

'Tracker?' said Crake, as if he didn't know what Cox meant.

'Tiny transmitter so we can keep track of her movements. Smaller the better. One she can slip inside her bra, if she wears such a thing.'

'No can do.'

'You don't have anything like that? Not in the office safe? Not at home?'

'No, I told you.'

Definitely a lack of grace today. Exasperated, Cox said, 'Well, get hold of one. You can do that. This is your city. You have your sources. If the worst comes to the worst, go to Jaeger. The Americans and the Russians are the same: they adore gadgets. Spin him a yarn about keeping tabs on some big tomato merchants.'

'Tomato merchants?'

'Private joke. You know Jaeger? He'll cooperate. He's a little in awe of us – the last in the world who is. Thinks we're all the Scarlet Pimpernel.' Cox took a moment to start again in a more serious tone. 'Look, this could get very nasty. We need to know where she is.'

'I'll do my best.'

'Where does Chummy live?'

'He has one of those millionaire flats just off Unirii Boulevard. I can get you the address.'

'Anything else? A quiet hunting lodge somewhere? A love nest? Some retreat his old nanny looks after?'

'It's not like England, you know. You don't just look up under Mincu in the phone book. He could have the use of a dozen places, a hundred. They help each other, the people who were the top dogs in the old regime. Remember Lord Lucan? When he disappeared after the murder his friends simply clammed up. Same here. Spot of rape? Pissing on Liliana? That's nothing – they pissed on the whole country.' Crake paused a bit and took a breath. 'I'll make enquiries.'

'There's one other thing.'

'Yes?'

'I'm not being prurient – at least I don't think I am – but I want to study that tape I saw last night again. There was a face I recognised. Chap seemed to be joining in the fun. When Liliana was trussed and carried away, this chap followed after Chummy. At best he was indulging in nasty things. But since he was at Chummy's birthday party he obviously had close contacts with the old regime that we didn't seem to know about. Careless. Or if you are a conspiracy theorist, sinister.'

'Or the Lord Lucan syndrome.'

Cox inclined his head. 'I just wonder if he's in town at the moment. Maybe staying with Chummy, maybe at a hotel. The Intercontinental, for instance. Or the Bucuresti, for old time's sake.'

'Got a name, has he? I'll have to have that. Or a photo.'

Cox had a photo in his pocket but he wanted to keep that. With the toe of his shoe he scratched a name in the gravel. Crake leant forward to read it. The woman with the bawling boy had reached their bench. The boy, his attention caught by the strange adult scuffing the path, stopped crying to stare. His mother, too, turned her head. Cox wiped the gravel smooth with his shoe.

Crake murmured something under his breath. Cox thought he caught the word, 'Christ.'

'Quite so,' Cox said. 'Puts a different complexion on things.'

Confined to the bench, Crake had grown tense. Cox noted the stiffness of his shoulders and the way a hand would scratch a cheek, then clasp a knee, then burrow under an armpit. He had the pent-up energy of a boy. Cox supposed he was thirty-two or thirty-three, wanting more seniority than he had, more steps up the ladder, more power.

Cox said, 'Shall we . . .'

He hadn't even finished before Crake was on his feet, anticipating what he had been going to say. They turned away from the mother dragging the boy. He had thrown away the cone and was sucking his thumb, half turned to watch the two men.

'This is your first solo posting?' Cox asked.

'Yes.'

'How long have you been here?'

'Eighteen months, a bit less. I came the year before last in the spring. There was a month's handover with Jensen. He was taking early retirement. That's what Bucharest is, really. A backwater. A pre-retirement post.'

'You're lucky to be here,' Cox said with unexpected force. 'Damned lucky to be in the right place at the right time. It's the same with spies as it is with Generals. Remember what Napoleon said? He wanted lucky Generals. It's a priceless asset.'

Crake said nothing. They were on a circular route through an overgrown rock garden. Rockeries always put Cox in mind of bomb sites and Berlin because even twenty years after the end of the war there had been bomb sites. Some were because of disputed land titles. Others because ownership rested with the Soviet-sector authorities.

'I was about your age,' Cox said. 'It was my third foreign tour. First had been Oslo, quite normal, a Nato country posting. Then Vienna. Then Berlin. The Wall had been up four years and Berlin was an exciting place for those in our kind of work. No doubt of it. Not a backwater. Friends of my intake said how lucky I was. That word again. Berlin had allure, glamour, intrigue, plots, informers, assassins, smugglers, old Nazis, neo-Nazis, mercenaries, blackmailers, escape artists, forgers, the lot. It had double agents, triple agents, agents who'd turned so often they were too confused to know who they were meant to be deceiving. Berlin was *Baerlein*, the little bear. Berlin was its own honeypot where the bear put in its paw.'

Cox stopped. I'm a garrulous old fool, he thought. That's his opinion. He's the fool. Won't listen, won't learn.

'I want to tell you about my luck,' Cox said. 'I was nobody important in the Berlin station, just one of the ragtag collection who handled signals, took night shifts, welfared the occasional agent and for a treat could have a run on the other side of the Wall when there was a spot of messenger work to do. Sounds a bit like your backwater except for the undeniable smell of danger. Which is what we like, afterwards at any rate. What, perhaps, you have been missing.'

As they walked, Cox talked. His look became inward, a hint of a smile sometimes lifted the corners of his mouth.

Chapter 11

This happened in 1965, Cox said.

As he talked, they moved slowly through the rockery, round and round, like prisoners in the exercise yard.

'Much like your tour here, I had been in Berlin for about a year and a half. My immediate superior was a man called Knowler. He was fanatical about cricket, so being in Berlin was a particular penance. The British army occupying force organized a match on summer weekends but that didn't satisfy Knowler. He used to bring copies of *Wisden* to work and he could quote county scores and batting averages with ease. Mysteriously he always seemed to have work reasons for being in London at the time of the Lord's Test, though he usually returned to Berlin in a black mood because there was something of a tradition of England losing the Lord's Test.

'Where was I?

'Yes, a morning in May. This is a good month nearly everywhere with the long days and the blossom and the fresh greenery on the trees. Rather less so in Berlin, I felt. The huge old lime trees had been destroyed in the war or chopped up as firewood in the bitter winters that followed, and the young trees that had been planted didn't hide enough of the dreadful buildings that were springing up.

'Knowler was crossing to the other side of the Wall for a meeting with an agent and he wanted me to come. He told me I should trail behind him, watch his back, because the last crossing he made he had the suspicion he was being followed. Nothing definite, just a face he thought he saw more than once. Or not. But Berlin was the jungle and you ignored suspicions at your peril. We were going to do the crossing into the Eastern sector by U'bahn. I was to travel in the same coach but well away from him. I was to hang back to see who followed, if anybody.

'The U'bahn ran mainly in the Western part of the city and was controlled by West Berlin. The S-bahn, the elevated railway, ran in both halves but was controlled by the communist authorities so it was a point of honour for Westerners not to use it. The U'bahn crossed under the Wall and passed through a couple of ghost stations. The train went slowly through them without stopping. The platforms were dimly lit and each had a couple of armed Volkspolizei to ensure the train didn't make an unscheduled halt and someone slip out.

'At Friedrichstrasse Knowler got out. But so did dozens of others so how could I tell if anyone was following him? We climbed the stairs separately and went into the immigration hall to fill in the forms. There was one queue for West German citizens, one for foreigners. The big difference was that the Germans carried shopping bags with a decent ham or Kasseler or a chocolate cake to take to family or friends.

'I was the fourth person behind Knowler in the queue. You'd think we were going into prison – which in a sense I suppose we were – because nobody talked, nobody made eye contact. I looked round but nobody met my gaze. No one was obviously observing Knowler. He dawdled going out of the building so that I wouldn't be far behind. He began walking away from the entrance about thirty metres ahead of me. Still nobody taking an interest. He walked to the corner where a car pulled up and Knowler got in. So far, so according to plan. He was going to Köpenick and my orders were to get a taxi to a place nearby his rendezvous, just to watch over him.

'I looked round and a taxi pulled in to the kerb. The driver seemed to be leaning across to hear where I wanted to go but you never say that out in the street where you can be overheard. I opened the door to get in the back just as a man straightened up from crouching behind the driver's seat. I found myself looking into a gun.

'Many things flash through your mind at a moment like this. How could I have been so stupid as to walk into a trap? Wasn't his face familiar from the U'bahn carriage? Or the queue? Or a café on the Ku'damm? Is it a real pistol or a replica? But his voice was low and urgent.

'"Do not run. Do not shout. Please do not make any theatre. It will be better for all of us. Get in at once please."

'Two things. He spoke English so he knew what I was or at least my nationality. The second thing was that *please.* When did the East German lovelies take to polite pleading? And he was German, I was positive, not Russian. Though what difference that made in my confused state I do not know. They were as close – to use the Chinese expression – as lips and teeth.

'In Köpenick Knowler was going to the Müggelsee, a pleasure lake popular with East Berliners. Here he would meet his agent and go for a row. In the middle of the lake, it was felt, they could talk and make any exchanges. My orders had been to amble along the shore, eat an ice cream, enjoy the sun and keep my eyes open. At first the taxi followed the same route towards Müggelsee but then we peeled off following the sign to Schönefeld airport and I wondered whether I was being kidnapped and being flown to Moscow. I would end up tomorrow on the front pages of the world's press as a Western spy and provocateur. A mug shot. I was the mug.

'My kidnapper broke in on these wild speculations. "The taxi belongs to my cousin who understands no English. He is a man you can trust. It has a microphone but he has switched it off. It is most important I speak to you, Herr Koch. I work for the Ministry for State Security and I wish to spy for you. I apologise for the gun. It was necessary. I put it away now. In any case the gun was from the last war and it has no bullets. Please."

'It is everyone's dream to be selected by someone in an important position in the opposing side. You, he says, are the only one I can trust and give my secrets to. But, oh a thousand buts. He knew my name, or its German equivalent, close enough. He knew who I worked for. He must know what I was doing in East Berlin so therefore he had been following both Knowler and me. The sweat was crawling down my chest and standing out on my forehead. When I wiped my face the man said, "I am sorry it is so hot in the car but it is dangerous to speak with the windows open." I don't think he was being sarcastic or gently covering up my bad attack of nerves. He was genuinely concerned that someone whom he had appointed his saviour – or his country's saviour – should not be inconvenienced.

'Anyone in their right senses would have been issuing vigorous protests. I should have demanded to be let down, denounced him as a kidnapper of an innocent tourist. I would like to say I had an instinct about him right from the start but I might have been simply rash. I was disoriented at that period of my life because Jenny had returned to England. It's not easy being the wife of a spy. His hours are long. His work is secret. He can be away all night and offer no explanation that can be checked.

Recently there had arrived at the Station a Scottish lass who caught everybody's eye. And . . . well, that's neither here nor there. Anyway Jenny had been gone three months and I was a little lightheaded. Or maybe it was that luck which I stress is so important. Anyway I decided – if it was anything so rational as a decision – to trust him.

'We didn't go to Schönefeld. The taxi simply drove on the road out, turned round and drove back while my abductor – I dubbed him Heinz – talked. He was not heroic in build: I have a vague memory of a roundish, featureless face, spectacles, receding hair. No *Supermensch*. Pointing the pistol at me had been the rashest act of his life. He said his work in the MfS was nothing important, just the records department. Nothing important! Why, he had access to all manner of secrets but he meant he hadn't a grand title or a high-wire job. Just a backroom boy, a humble toiler, and doubtless looked down upon by his superiors, unreformed *Junkers* to a man.

'His country needed to be saved, of that he had no doubt. He said that at first he had been a great believer in the socialist experiment because it appeared such a clean break with Germany's recent past. By degrees he had come to see it was a false dawn for the redemption of humanity. The rulers were hypocrites. They professed the highest ideals, they lauded the triumph of the proletariat, they preached the equality of all men – but they had their large cars and their servants and special shops and country estates and the sort of food that no ordinary worker had ever seen.

'"Also, Herr Koch, in their hearts they despise me. I am a Jew, you see, my mother was one of the survivors. I have read certain reports of the help my government is giving to Egypt, the instruction in interrogation techniques, the military cooperation for the destruction of Israel. They are training certain elite units of the Egyptian army. I know of two Generals and two Colonels who have been loaned. Of tanks, of artillery, of amphibious warfare. I tell you their names."

'He had given me a motive but I think it was more complicated than he said. I think he felt guilty that his mother had survived and that she had borne him. But I had no time to speculate on what she might have done and why he might want revenge on the German officer class. I was desperately trying to remember everything he was telling me.

'"You see, Herr Koch, I trust you to make good use of the information I give you."

'"How do you know my name?" It was close enough.

'"This is the important secret I have to tell you. There is a traitor working in your Berlin office. He has passed over the names and photographs of all functionaries. I knew you were coming today. Obviously you would use a passport in a different name but I knew what you looked like."

'I might have lost consciousness at this point. I don't mean that I fainted, just that my brain was overloaded and my thinking paralyzed. The danger on the wrong side of the Wall, the gun, the kidnapping, names of East German officers, and now this. We had been quarter of an hour together and my whole life was violently shaken.

'"Who is the traitor?"

'"I do not know yet. His name has not been on the papers I see. My grading is low, you see. I shall try to find out but it is difficult for me."

'"And dangerous?"

'He looked at me but didn't reply. Or at least not directly. What he said was, "You must tell no one about me, Herr Koch. If it is suspected there is a Western agent in my Ministry, then they become ruthless. They ask questions. They look at duty lists, see who is in the building when it is most empty. We have a certain machine made in the West. The name of the machine is Xerox. It is very unusual in our world to have such a machine. We must sign a book when we use it. They will see my name in the book and ask why I have been using it. This is why."

'From inside his jacket he produced a manila envelope and took out a dozen sheets of photocopy paper. In those days the machines were cumbersome and the print they made was shadowy and imperfect. The material was not earthshattering. In fact it was the sort of chickenfeed that would be fed to a gullible person to entrap him. I knew that. There was a departmental breakdown showing regional and technical responsibilities. His long pale finger pointed to the heading Travel. "That means kidnapping of persons in the West." Another sheet was a list of fellow travellers in the Italian Foreign Ministry. There was a schedule for a visit of KGB officers from Moscow. There was a programme of seminars for agents based in Central America. Then I stopped at one sheet of paper and read it and reread it. It was for the "liquidation" of an East German journalist posted to Prague for "proven imperialist contacts". I checked the date.

'"But this is for tomorrow. If he is one of ours, he must be warned. He can take refuge in—"

'"It would be most unwise, Herr Koch. If the man is warned it will start the very hunt for a suspect here that I am frightened of. When his death is reported, you will know what I bring you is real."

'The knowledge of the man's death within twenty-four hours was dreadful. It haunted me for weeks after. If I had acted decisively I could have saved that man's life – and he was someone who was working for the West. But I did nothing. Nothing. Except two days later I did ask our Station in Prague and yes, an East German journalist had been reported murdered. Then, as if I was eager for details, they said there was an unconfirmed report that he had been garotted.

'We were less than an hour together – he could not risk being away from his Ministry for longer. But when he dropped me at a corner of the Alex I was as exhausted as if I'd done five rounds in the boxing ring. My mind was in turmoil. Was it all an entrapment of some kind? He had shown me a photocopy of a directive from the Glasshouse to Berlin Station marked Top Secret. This wasn't in fact very secret at all but the fact of its being in East German hands was damning. If it wasn't a forgery. I found myself anticipating next day when the "liquidation" in Prague would verify everything.

'But before that could happen I found myself in dreadful trouble at the Station. Knowler returned furious that I had not been watching his back. He barked an order down the telephone, summoning me to his office. It had the usual dispiriting government-issue furniture. The only redeeming feature was the shelf with its row of *Wisdens*, yellow covers like a blaze of sun.

'Knowler demanded to know what I had been up to. Why had I not come to the Müggelsee? Had I not been able to find a taxi? There was something about the way he fed me that excuse that alerted me. So I said I'd got a taxi but it had broken down en route and I hadn't been able to get another. He nodded and thought and nodded again. "All right," he said, "you got a taxi. Too bloody right you did. I saw you. I turned round to check and there you were with the taxi door open. Who was the person in the back who greeted you? I saw him speak and then I saw you get in. Where did you go with him?" I wasn't prepared for this. I did the only thing I could and said I had full answers to everything but I would only be prepared to give them to the Station Head. Knowler hated me for that. But since I insisted there was nothing he could do.

'The Station Head was a man called Crofts. He had just reached forty – what is called early middle age – but had been fighting hard against his years. He was perfectly groomed, like a thrusting young business executive. He had sharp little eyes that never wavered from my face while I told him about being picked up, about who the contact was, about the fact that our Berlin Station employed a double agent. "It could be anyone," I said. "It could be Knowler which is why I couldn't tell him."

'Crofts pursed his lips in thought, then said, "I see. Does this man from their Ministry – your source – have a name we can check?"

'"I call him Heinz?"

'"Source Heinz? Is that some kind of joke? Heinz Sauce?"

'Crofts was not known for his sense of humour. I said, "He hasn't told me his name."

'"Have you arranged the next meeting?"

'"He will telephone me."

'"You were absolutely right to tell nobody. It would only start speculation and that's bad for morale. And it would warn him. But keep me informed. Is that understood?"

'There was no direct telephone link between the two halves of the city. It had to be routed via West Germany. Of course the calls were monitored but Heinz and I had agreed a code. So it was that three days later just as I was leaving for work I got a call at my flat.

'"Is Sigrid there?"

'"Not until later."

'"I must see Sigrid today. Tell her at one o'clock."

'I did the crossing just before midday, using a different identity from the previous visit. I took my time coming out of the Friedrichstrasse station entrance, searching in my pockets for a handkerchief, blowing my nose, looking left and right. Well, the usual routine, you know. I walked to

Unter den Linden and strolled east, gazing at the buildings, the model tourist, sometimes turning right round for a view of the Brandenberg Gate. I seemed clear. So I went through the Alexanderplatz to a dire department store which had an open space round one side and at its back. Stalls sold food of a proletarian standard. I bought an *Eisbein* and a half litre of beer. The glass still bore the last customer's fingerprints. I sat at an outdoor table, ate and drank slowly, waited. A man sat beside me. He leaned closer and said in a low voice, "*Bitte, Ich hätte gern der Mostrich.*" I pushed the bowl towards him. It's a fact: that when you're in badland every man is an Indian brave after your scalp. Why had he chosen to sit at the seat next to me? Plenty of others were free. Company, maybe. He began to complain about the Berliners' way of talking: why should mustard be *Mostrich*, not *Senf*? I was busying myself with a mouthful of pig's trotter so I could only grunt. He took that as being unfriendly and shut up. Heinz didn't show.

'We had agreed a fallback. An hour and a half later I was back in Unter den Linden standing in front of Neue Wache staring at the soldiers on sentry duty. Heinz said that as a Western tourist I would attract no attention waiting here. The sentries were doing the goosestep. The whole of Berlin has echoes for me, I suppose from boyhood and hearing news broadcasts on the wireless of thousand bomber raids. But those soldiers with their high boots cracking down on the paving – I could hear Hitler's march through the capitals of Europe.

'"If you will walk a little, Herr Koch," said a voice behind me in German, "towards the Rathaus and then on to Karl-Marx-Allee, I will follow and observe. Do not look round, please."

'He said *bitte* but I remembered his *please*. I crossed Unter den Linden and passed the Old Library with its curved front, which Berliners call the Chest of Drawers.

I strolled and inspected the red brick of the Town Hall. I don't remember if Berliners have a name for that. But on my left was the TV Tower and that they call the Tele-Asparagus. So to Karl-Marx-Allee, never once looking behind me. This is very broad. The authorities said it was so they could use it for parades celebrating the triumph of socialism. Berliners knew it was so tanks could manoeuvre in case of an uprising.

'"Herr Koch," he said, falling into step beside me, "have you been careless? Have you been speaking about me? You are friends with a Scottish lady, I have read. Maybe boasting to her?'

'"Why are you asking?"

'"There is activity in my Ministry. They suspect something."

'Well, we all know that with agents paranoia is normal. I said, "It can't be me. You're imagining things. Have you been questioned?"

'"It's not like that. But there are men I have not seen before. They are asking to see papers and registers. I passed two of them in the corridor. They stopped talking and their heads turned."

'"Heinz, if they are strangers, they don't know you. Of course they stopped talking. That is absolutely normal."

'"Nothing is normal when your life is in danger."

'When I looked at him I thought his cheeks were a little greyer, his thinning hair a little more lank. A worried agent is a liability. Taking precautions is what we are all trained to do. Jumping at shadows simply draws attention to yourself.

'"For a time it would be better if we did not meet," I said. "We'll give things time to calm down."

'Meaning you.

'"You are right," he said. "But I had to see you today. I have brought you something of great importance. It is the proof of the double agent in your bureau."

'He was carrying a twice-folded newspaper under his arm like a field marshal's baton, though otherwise he looked most unwarlike. His elbow squeezed the newspaper tighter so I knew where the proof was. I had turned over and over in my mind which of us might be the traitor and my thoughts had always returned to Knowler. He'd asked me to watch his back but that could be by way of an alibi. I would be on the lakeshore, he would be in the boat, and I could never tell in which direction papers were passed. A photograph? Was that the proof? A tape?

'Heinz looked both ways along the pavement. Fear seemed to have consumed him. He said, "You must take it to the very highest level in London. They will denounce it as a trick, something produced by forgers. So I have included something else to show my *bona fides*, as they say. I give you the identity of a highly placed traitor in the West, one of our most valued sources."

'He turned aside. There was a rubbish bin on a post and in it he dumped the copy of *Neues Deutschland*. My last view of him was as he crossed the road, how fearful he seemed of the traffic. I spent five minutes with that bin under my eye until I was satisfied it was safe to retrieve the newspaper. Even so I half expected a shout or running feet or a hand on my shoulder. His fear had infected me. Nothing.

'There were scribbles in the margin of the front page. With a black ballpoint pen someone had drawn a tulip – or it might have been a claret glass – and a starburst and a squirrel with its tail arched. In the middle of the doodles a neat hand had written: *This will tell you who it is.* Not the little drawings, something inside. I found a café and ordered a beer and opened the newspaper and closed it swiftly. The waitress must have thought me an alcoholic. When the beer came I lifted the glass and my hand was shaking. Inside I had glimpsed a photograph cut out of a

West German newspaper, also the photocopy of a signal sent from the Glasshouse in London.

'Oh dear, oh pray.

'To be in East Berlin and to be carrying secrets like that. My only thought was to reach the comparative safety of the Western half of the city. Two crossing points were available for non-Germans: the Friedrichstrasse station and Checkpoint Charlie. By now I was closer to Charlie so that is where I headed. The city was deserted in the vicinity of the checkpoint as if its inhabitants had been carried off by the Black Death. There was even a U'bahn station near by but the East Germans had closed it and the entrance had padlocks on its gate. I went into the immigration hut.

'At the desk I was confronted by a harridan of a Border Control officer, truly monstrous, with dark suspicious eyes in a bloated face like a potato. She looked at the visa card inserted into my passport, then into my face. She spoke sharply to me in German. I pretended not to understand because sometimes you can pick up things. At the corner of my eye I could see the two *Grepos* – the Border Police – stiffen and shift the weapons in their hands. "You cannot cross back," she said in a harsh English. I was estimating my chances of making a run for it. At Checkpoint Charlie it would mean doing a zigzag through the barriers. Their orders are to shoot and they would have ample time to put a bullet or two in my back and let me bleed to death while the American soldiers on the other side spoke into their radios but did nothing to help. She said, "You entered by Friedrichstrasse. You must leave by the same route." Of course. But I had been so eager to get out I had forgotten.

'This was a Thursday afternoon. Back at the Station I pleaded a sudden family crisis. On Friday I took a BEA flight out for a long weekend in London. From Heathrow I phoned the Chief. I had to go through an exhausting procedure with secretaries and deputies and controllers and to each I said: "It is to do with the security of the Service. For the Chief's ears only." They could probably hear the planes taking off and landing in the background so I kept my eye on the people hovering nearby. Heinz's paranoia had been infectious. Eventually I got to him and arranged a meeting in a pub in Holland Park Avenue. I said it had to be one-to-one.

'Something about my insistence must have impressed him because he came alone. Most unusual. I was watching from across the street. The place was two-thirds empty and he sat at a little table in a corner. He'd got himself a glass of sherry. I remember that because I think it's a dangerous drink to order in a pub. You're served dishwater. I got myself a whisky and joined him. He said "Cheers," and continued watching me over the glass as he drank.

'I told him about going into East Berlin as a watcher for Knowler, about being picked up, the taxi, the gun, the lot. I told him about Source Heinz and his warning. Then I gave him the signal from the Glasshouse to the Berlin Station which Heinz had passed to me the previous day. It was classified: *Head of Station. Eyes Only. Decipher Yourself.* There was no higher rating. Only Crofts, the Head of Station, would have seen it. Only Crofts could have passed it to the East Germans.

'He read it. He must have read it more than once. He turned the paper over but the back was blank.

'"A photocopy," he said.

'"Well yes."

'"You've been conned, duped. Crofts has been in the Service for nearly twenty years. He's been in Berlin five. He's been a thorn in their flesh."

'"True," I said. "But with respect, if they wanted to neutralize him they had a choice: discredit him or recruit him."

'"You're the victim of a dirty trick. The East Germans have a whole department devoted to nothing else."

'All this was as Heinz had forecast. So then I produced the newspaper cutting he'd given me. It was a photo of the West German Chancellor on a visit to Strasbourg, being given a symbolic embrace by the French President. Heinz's black ballpoint pen had drawn an arrow pointing to the man at the Chancellor's shoulder. The face was clearly recognizable and from the files in the Berlin Station I had identified him.

'"That is the man who runs the Chancellor's political office," I said. "He is an East German spy. They wouldn't give up such a priceless asset just to discredit Crofts."

'The Chief held these two pieces of paper, one in his left hand, one in his right. For a long time he contemplated them in silence before tucking them away in an inside pocket. "You're in London for the weekend? We'll see what they have to say about this in Bonn. You're to lie low, see no one, say nothing."

'I decided that seeing no one couldn't apply to my wife. I took a taxi to Swiss Cottage and Jenny and I had a rapprochement, quite an energetic one. On Monday morning when I put in an appearance at the Glasshouse I was summoned by the Chief. In his office he had the European Controller and the Director of Operations. Both men still had that look of bereavement on their faces when it has been proved how badly misplaced their trust has been.

'The German security police had been to question the Chancellor's political secretary. I sometimes wonder if he knew he was in danger of being exposed because he was uncommonly quick with his pill. A miniature camera, a code pad, the usual paraphernalia were discovered.

'"So yesterday evening," the Chief said, "a detachment of British military police went, on my orders, to our Head of Station's apartment in Berlin. He was having what could be called a tryst with a *Mädchen* whom they described as blonde and voluptuous. She was German, but their German not ours. She protested her innocence but the documents in her bag proved the opposite." The Chief sighed. "I suppose they'll arrest one of ours and we'll have to do a swop."

'So there we are. Of course I wasn't promoted to take Crofts's place but I was marked as a chap with a certain flair, a coming man. But the truth is I was the one who had been outside the U'bahn station at the right time. I'd simply been lucky.'

Chapter 12

How many times did they do the circuit of the rock garden? A dozen? Twenty? Always telling the story of my life, Cox thought. Jaeger, Liliana, Crake. Or part of my life, the part that would be useful. It brought Liliana round. But Crake?

'You know, I met Jensen once, your predecessor here,' Cox said. 'Long ago. It was some refresher course we were both on. Thin face he had. Hair so pale it was almost white.'

'It had grown completely white by the time I met him,' Crake said. 'He'd grown a beard too. Old Father William, that's how I thought of him.'

'There was more to him than you think. He'd lived illegally in Tallin for two years. Got out on a fishing boat when the local lovelies tumbled to him. His mother was a Dane, his father Scottish. He'd taken his mother's name. One evening we'd had a noggin or two so I asked him about that. He said his parents never got officially married, that was one thing. Another thing was his father used to fly into a drunken Glaswegian rage of a Saturday night and he had no wish to be reminded of him. So, Jensen. Did he ever talk about his time in Tallin?'

'Not to me.'

'City was founded by Danes. I wonder if that's why they sent him there.'

They had walked into an area enclosed by a hedge run wild where eight or ten permanent chess tables were set up. A crowd of men sat and played or stood and offered loud advice. This wasn't Slav chess, all cerebral. This was Latin temperament chess, noisy mayhem. Cox touched Crake's arm to turn him and spoke directly to his face.

'Listen, it is not a backwater here. This business is highly sensitive. Your being here is like my being outside the U'bahn station at just the right time. A stroke of luck. It'll give you a heave several steps up the ladder. You do see that, don't you?'

But there was uproar at one of the tables. One player swept all the pieces off the board and jumped up, shouting. Bystanders held him back from assaulting his opponent.

Cox said, 'Why do they put reports of chess matches in the sports section of the papers? It's war.'

Had Crake understood how fortunate he was or not? The moment for reading his expression was lost.

Gabriela greeted him with a kiss. It was no more than a peck on the cheek but it pleased Cox.

'"I am going to see my uncle," I told Maria at the embassy. "I must leave now so please take my place." "Some uncle," she said, "you are smiling too much."' And Gabriela smiled at Cox. 'You are my good uncle. You are not like my bad uncle.'

'What bad uncle is this?' Cox asked.

'My Uncle Maximillian. When I was a girl, not yet a full woman, maybe thirteen, he comes to my room to say goodnight and he puts his hand, you know, here.' She touched a breast. 'He said, "My, you are getting a big girl." He sat down on the edge of the bed. Then I had to climb over him, which I think my uncle enjoyed, so I can kneel beside the bed. "I must say my prayers. Uncle Maximillian, will you kneel beside me?" He is so surprised he kneels at my side, very close. I take his hand and he squeezes it because he thinks this is a good game. "Dear Lord, make me a good girl, pure in my heart and my body. And make Uncle Maximillian a good man." Then my aunt comes to the door and asks what we are doing. I said, "I am praying that Uncle Maximillian's hand becomes good." He never came to say goodnight to me again.'

It was rush hour and the bus was packed. When it lurched round a corner Gabriela was pressed close to him. That is the breast that Uncle Maximillian felt, Cox thought, and it is Gabriela pressing against me not the other way round. Otherwise she might start a loud prayer.

She said, 'We get down here, Mr Cox.'

A dozen people got off the bus with them. When they had scattered to their homes Cox was able to enjoy the prospect to the full. Identical buildings lined both sides of the street, concrete that was grey in the early evening light, light grey walls with dark grey streaks where the weather had stained it. The windows were squares, which Cox found curious.

'This way.'

She led him across the road and up two steps into one of the buildings. A sign outside announced it was Bloc 8. Pure poetry. In Britain it would have been called after a Labour politician, safely dead, or a doughty colonial freedom fighter, though that had its drawbacks. In Liverpool he had seen a pair of council workers with a ladder against the wall of Winnie Mandela Hall. They were painting over the first word.

Inside the entrance to Bloc 8 there was a noticeboard. In the old days it would have had exhortations for *Pace* and *Familia* and reassurance that this was truly the Golden Age, never mind the evidence of your eyes to the contrary. Now it had a poster for a pop concert. The group was called The Dead Devils.

'They are very famous,' Gabriela said. 'They are Romanian. When they had Romanian name, nobody heard of them. Now they are The Dead Devils everybody hears of them.'

'And now I have.'

'Come,' she said.

They climbed stairs that were too narrow for two abreast. On the first floor they turned left down a short corridor that was lit by the window at the end. Cox had a strong feeling of walking back into the recent past, a time when lights were forbidden and it was a crime to heat your home above 10°. Gabriela had a key from her bag already in her hand and unlocked a door. Cox went into a sort of cubbyhole that did for an entrance hall. It had two closed doors and one open one. They passed through the open door into the living room-cum-kitchen. His eyes lifted automatically. In the former Iron Curtain countries you judged a person not just by the size of the room but by the height of the ceiling. The lower the ceiling, the lower on the social scale. No wasted space, no wasted fuel heating it. This ceiling was very low. It explained the square windows that had puzzled him. Windows of a normal shape would have reached nearly to the floor.

'Will this be all right, Mr Cox?'

He had asked her for a safe house – actually he had said somewhere quieter away from curious eyes in the hotel, and she had understood. Inwardly he shuddered, but it would only be for a few days. Others had had to contemplate a life here. Still did in the other flats.

'This will do very well, Gabriela. Who did you say it belonged to?'

She hadn't. She didn't now. 'It's all right. No one will disturb you. Not until Monday anyway.'

Until Monday, Cox thought. And she has a key. And

seems at home here, watching her struggle with the window that had stuck on its rusted metal frame, then pick up two cushions that for some reason were lying on the rug. Cox looked round the room. A man's place, a bachelor's place. A shelf of books with the garish covers publishers believe attract thriller readers. In Romanian mostly. But *The Day of the Jackal* and *The Guns of Navarone* in English. A copy of *Time*, a fortnight old. On a narrow little sideboard – everything had to be cramped – a bottle of Grant's Standfast Whisky marked Duty Free – For Export Only. Grouped round the bottle were a gold and black lacquered plate of a Buddhist temple, a sampan done in seashells, a coconut carved to resemble a squatting monkey. A traveller then. His eyes rested a moment on a little foil packet that contained a cologne-impregnated towelette. Tarom, he read. Aircrew. Out on the furthest reaches of the network, the eastern route by the evidence of the souvenirs. Who came first, Crake or this man? Did she run her men in tandem? More than two?

'I may want to use the telephone,' Cox said. 'Will it be all right if I stick some dollars under it?'

She pursed her lips before smiling. 'Don't do that. Coming here will be our secret.'

Bet I'm not the only one she shares this particular secret with, Cox thought. Regular little minx. That uncle was only a shade too soon.

'And the key,' Cox said patiently, 'for getting in and out. Because you won't be here.'

Gabriela gave him the key, though her face was a little troubled at its loss.

'You can have it back for Monday,' he reassured her. 'Don't worry. Now is it too early to ring Vasile? I don't know where he is in his day. He's awake, had his breakfast?'

She sighed. 'All right. I telephone him.'

There was a settee which would take two people and

she huddled herself into a corner of that to do her telephoning. Cox prowled the room, peering from the window down to the street and up to the sky. He ran his eyes along the row of books again. He picked up an empty cup where the dregs of coffee had dried and took it to the sink. When he came back Gabriela was talking to Vasile. Her head was bowed low with the telephone so he couldn't see her face but her right hand was clenched into a fist and was raised to defend her breasts. It seemed another negotiation, like last night. It drained the spirit out of her so that when she had finished speaking she held the phone away from her and took a deep breath before she spoke to Cox.

'I fix it. We can go tonight. He says at eleven o'clock.'

'Good girl.'

'Vasile wants to know why you want to see it again.'

'What did you tell him?'

'I tell him not to be stupid. Why does he think you want to see it.'

'So I'm just another pervert.'

'I'm sorry. What else can I say?'

'It's all right. I don't care what he thinks. It's better he should think that. Thank you for doing it. I'll meet you at a quarter to eleven on the corner near the hotel. Now be off with you.'

He was in time to stop himself patting her on the rump, otherwise she would have had to pray for his hand.

Cox toured his safe flat. In the bedroom there was a double bed that took up most of the room. A small hanging wardrobe contained a suit, three leisure jackets and an airline uniform, presumably a spare. From the lack of pseudo-military splendour he assumed the man was a cabin steward. A shower room was windowless and dank.

He returned to the main room and dialled the Glasshouse, the telephone which blinked on his Chief's desk.

'Who's about to spoil my weekend?'

'There are no weekends where I am,' Cox said. 'Weekends are for the lazy. I am looking forward to the New Year when I become officially lazy and draw my pension.'

'Ah,' said his Chief. 'But we might decide your talents were too rare to be lost to us. What's new?'

'I have a safe house. Well, it's a rabbit hutch in a workers' block. Also, it's only safeish. Who knows? Telephones, walls, neighbours – this is Romania and Dracula never dies. Want my number?' Without waiting for a reply, he rattled off, 'Alpha gamma zita gamma epsilon kappa delta.'

The Greek alphabet was the most primitive of codes, letter for number. A sixth former could crack it in four seconds, but only on playback. Otherwise it went too quickly and any chance listener picking it up live wouldn't be able to write it down.

'These two friends who're coming in from Munich,' Cox said, 'are they muscular friends?'

'Yes.'

'Tell them to stay in the Nord Hotel. Stay in the background. Not to make contact.'

There was silence in London. Silence has many different sounds, Cox thought. The silence of fear, wondering who is listening at the other end of the telephone. The silence of disillusion, knowing that nothing anyone says can put things right. The silence of lovers, with a secret breath in your ear. The silence of disapproval.

'Chief, how many secret-service men were guarding Kennedy in Dallas that day?'

Sometimes protection simply drew attention to you. Cox knew that.

'I had a heart-to-heart with our man today. He's out of place here. Maybe he should find another line of work altogether but certainly Bucharest doesn't suit him. It could be woman trouble. She is – how shall I put it – flying from nest to nest. Queers a man's judgement, that does.'

'More?'

'There is a certain videotape I've seen. I'm going to see it again tonight. I want to buy it. If he won't sell, I'll have to steal it. Politically it is sensitive. We should have it in our keeping. When you've seen it, you may want to request a meeting with the Prime Minister.'

'You said sensitive?'

'Yes.'

'Explain.'

'Dynamite. That's all I'll say for the moment.'

'More?'

Cox wanted to ask questions. He wanted to know if there was any news about the chemical weapons, who the supplier was, who Mincu talked to when he left the Fair. He wanted to know what diplomatic momentum there was with Bosnia and the Serbs. He wanted to know if Washington was taking a serious interest at last. Because once the Americans took a serious interest that would prompt desperate moves in the war zone and here. Mincu sniffing his best chance would close a swift deal and by the end of next week the chemical weapons would be in place. But his Chief would have told him.

'Not for now.'

'Good. Keep me informed.'

He was gone and Cox was alone again in a flat where the fading daylight had a prison greyness and the rooms were designed like cells.

Cox was lying on the bed, on top, just to rest his eyes for a bit because he had had little sleep last night. The pillow smelled faintly, a feminine fragrance, not after-shave or haircream. Rest his brain too because it had a tendency to run a bit too fast these days and then slump in exhaustion.

He remembered being in the Chief's office earlier in the year. It was the close of the day and late spring sunshine was slanting in through the windows. They had a glass of Scotch apiece. The Chief had had a wearying afternoon fighting the warriors of the Treasury. He had come back angry. 'They're not pruning, they're hacking.' By the second whisky he was in a more philosophic mood.

'An Intelligence Service is like a hothouse plant. You have to water it,' he raised his glass, 'and feed it if you want it to flower. Why don't they understand?'

'Careful, they're all weekend gardeners,' Cox had said. 'To encourage it to go on blooming, it's also necessary to dead-head it. They know that.'

The Chief said nothing but smiled. They shared the same sense of humour.

Cox turned his face on the pillow. The fragrance came to him again and he recognized it. It was the scent Gabriela wore.

Liliana came when it had grown quite dark. Cox was wakened by her knock and was still a little muzzy as he opened the front door.

'My dear,' he greeted her.

Do I embrace her or not? He had forgotten the terms they were on. With Gabriela no such problem, but Liliana was not Gabriela. She solved his dilemma by sailing past him into the living room. Hello, she knows the way, she's been here before. Then he decided he was trying to be too clever. The living room door was open and she had simply walked straight in. He followed her and was perhaps unwisely beaming when she turned to face him.

'Mr Cox, I have several important questions to ask you.'

'Yes? What is the subject?'

'Men.'

He let his smile change to a look of concern with his eyebrows raised. Then he lowered his eyebrows and became grave because he could see it had been a difficult day. Was he the cause? Some other man? Mincu? She was scowling at him. He was not her good uncle.

'I work for the Foreign Ministry,' she began. Her dark hair had fallen in front of her face. She put a hand up to sweep it aside so she had a clear view of Cox. 'I am an interpreter. Not a translator which is more relaxed, more reflective I might say, because a translator can sit back in her chair or his chair and consider at leisure how to write something. Or can reach for a dictionary to find the exact word. No. For me it must be all here,' she touched her temple, 'and now.'

Cox's spirits sank. She was laying the foundation for a lengthy complaint.

'I must be alert. I must think quickly when someone addresses me. "Hi, young lady." "Good afternoon, Mr Tirrell, how can I help you?" I see his name from his badge. "Call me Bill," he says. "I come from Dallas and we don't hold with surnames. No time for them." "All right, Mr Bill." "That's neat." Then he says, "Don't you ever smile? First thing in the morning when I wake up I like to see a smiling face on the pillow beside me. Kind of sets me up for the day. It's what I really miss here. What do you say, honey? Like to smile for me?" Well, Mr Cox, what do I reply? You have two seconds.'

Her eyes fixed on him. Some people only hear if they look at you, Cox knew. He didn't hesitate. 'You tell him, "That's just what my husband says."'

She considered that and nodded. 'Very good. Then I have another man. Or maybe he is two men put inside one skin. He has eaten many sausages and drunk many litres of beer in his life. Also at lunch. I can smell it. He says to me, "*Guten tag.*" I explain to him I do not speak German, alas, only French and English and of course Romanian. "I have a problem," he says. "What is it?" "I am a stranger here. I only arrived in Bucharest yesterday and I do not know your address. Where do you live?" Well, Mr Cox?'

Her eyes still rested on him, listened to him. She was measuring him, not his height but his trustworthiness. No English frivolity, please. You must be serious, Mr Cox, or I do not go further with you.

'You tell him, "With my husband."'

She nodded. 'All right. And another man, he comes up behind me so I am not prepared for him and he says, "Why did you run away from me last night?" She seemed to have come to a full stop, her face, her breathing, her hands and, Cox suspected, her brain. Like a rabbit caught in the headlights. Then her brain began to send out orders. She took a deep breath, she squared her shoulders, and these two actions parted her jacket and thrust her breasts forward under her blouse. 'I turned to face him.'

Cox found his own breathing had stopped while he waited for her.

'He was smiling. There are many smiles, Mr Cox. Smiles of happiness, of love, of complicity, of good nature, of not understanding. But Mincu's smile is none of these. No. His smile means, I am going to eat you up. I said, "I am very sorry. I felt suddenly faint. I won't run away again."'

'What a girl you are! That's wonderful.'

'Don't say that. Don't say "wonderful". He keeps saying that. *Minunat.* Some woman he meets is *minunat.* Some crazy Brazilian religion is *minunat.* The evening is *minunat.* My hair, the food. It is all the same to him. Everything in his life must be *minunat* or else it is cut out and thrown away.'

Liliana turned at last, letting him escape her eyes and

her anger. She was filling a kettle at the sink and putting it on one of the rings of the bachelor's little cooker. Once again Cox wondered if she was at home here or simply showing a woman's competence.

'I make some coffee, if I can find it. When Gabriela tells me where to meet you she says I must look after you because you are a good man and you are alone.'

Cox wondered whether 'looking after' meant more than coffee in Gabriela's language. He went to the open window, looking down to the street, both left and right. He'd most likely have the habit all the rest of his days. There was a burst of traffic released by a light somewhere, then nothing. A man and a woman walked down the opposite pavement, paused in front of a shop window with a display of table lamps. Had lamps been permitted during the Golden Age? Ordinary people didn't exist, Gabriela said, so they didn't need light. The couple moved on and Cox came away from the window. Liliana had made instant coffee and Cox wanted to slip some of the duty-free whisky into it but he remembered her strictures on alcohol.

'He asked why you ran away,' Cox said, 'you apologised, what next?'

'He said we should start again. We should pretend that last night never happened. He said he could not offer me dinner tonight because of certain commitments. But tomorrow . . . He paused, seemed to be considering. He said tomorrow he would be having a small party to celebrate the end of the Fair. People he had met. He said he would like me to come to that. He said there would be Belgians and French and English there so I could help entertain them. Would I come? I said yes and he said *Minunat.*'

'Where is this party? At the Fair? In a restaurant? His house?'

'He didn't say.'

'It would be a tremendous coup to see the guest list.'

'You think he makes a list of people like that? I shall see.'

'I must know where you're going. It's for your own protection. I can't be with you but I can be close.' Saying this, he realized how little faith he had in Crake acquiring a tracker.

She had chosen to sit in the two-seater settee. It would be crowding her to sit beside her. She needed space after having Mincu so close. Cox turned one of the four chairs jammed into a small square table to face her.

'Thank you for what you are doing. Have I said that stongly enough? It is important and it is brave.'

'Brave?' She considered the word then to Cox's surprise she said, 'Come sit beside me.' When he had lowered herself onto the settee she took one of his hands and laid her own out on it, palm to palm, fingers to fingers. Her skin felt dry and a little rough. 'Put your other hand on top of mine so that you can transmit to me some bravery.' For all that she was an interpreter, English was a language she had learned from textbooks.

'Tell me again why it is important. Sometimes I forget and see only Mincu the man and his smile and don't connect him with anything evil except what he did to me.'

For most people that would be enough. But Liliana was not most people. He laid it out simply, with no decoration. 'He has got hold of a supply of chemical weapons – but we don't know who from or by what route. He is offering them to anybody in Bosnia who is willing to pay. Maybe it will be the Bosnian Serbs who are killed, maybe the Muslims, or the Croats. He doesn't care. The wind changes and it could drift over French or British or Italian troops who are there trying to do the impossible. Soldiers, civilians, children – again he doesn't care. If we can find out the supplier, we can stop it.'

'He is a relic. Mincu, I mean. He is left over from the last regime. As you say, he doesn't care. When I was at university I had a friend, a boy of my own age. One day he took a pot of white paint and a brush and began to write on the wall of the administration block. Do your students do that in England?'

'Often.'

'L-I he splashed on the wall in big letters. One of the bureaucrats looking out of the window saw him. B-E-R. The bureaucrat had telephoned the police. They were very quick. They came in a car with a siren. My friend must have heard but didn't run away. T-A. Three policemen came up and stood behind him. My friend didn't stop. He went on. T-E. Then he put down his paintpot and his brush and turned to face the police. "Can you read?" I think my friend was very brave.'

'Or very desperate.'

'Mr Cox, they can be the same thing. By now half a dozen other students had come but they stood back. Maybe they weren't feeling so desperate that day. They heard the oldest policeman say, "Take him over there and break his arms, both of them." That is what they did. They dragged him to the corner of the building and broke his arms against the stonework. None of us ever forgot that. Those police were part of our university education. They taught us you must go on asking for freedom even if it means your bones get broken. Your bones will mend and you can struggle again. *Libertate.* You have to keep painting it on walls and shouting it in the street. You must pray for strength and courage. You mustn't despair. Otherwise everything will be *minunat* for the Mincus of the world.'

Cox had nothing he could say. The language of outrage and pity had been debased. Politicians seized on tragedy for their own ends. Protest had become a profession. He held her hand in both his and kept quiet.

At last she said, 'I hate him very much. You can have no idea.'

She doesn't know about the tape, Cox understood. She doesn't know I have seen her naked and something of what happened to her. He was glad Gabriela hadn't told her.

'Are you staying here?' Her voice had withdrawn from him. She was tired. Mincu had frightened her, disgusted her, angered her. Cox was the ringmaster who urged her on. But she had had enough.

'My clothes are still at the hotel. I'll sleep there. No, it could be I'll want to telephone from here late tonight so I'll sleep here.' He shrugged. 'I haven't decided.'

'I shall write down the number.'

Chapter 13

The waitresses wore cheongsams of jade green and black. The slit on the right side of the skirt went up midway between knee and hip. Their long black hair was drawn up into a topknot. Their lips were painted a garish pink. Their eyes were slanted and lifted at the corners, which Cox found curious. It must be a trick of make-up, he decided, because the women weren't Chinese but Romanian. But a fat Chinese woman guarded the till and the sound of Chinese voices lifted through the serving hatch from the kitchen.

Coming people, the Chinese, so it was said. Some clever historian had pointed out that the centre of civilization always shifted west. First China, then Mesopotamia, Egypt, Greece, Rome, Spain, Britain, America. Russia had geared itself up to dispute the succession with America. It had got itself an empire and armed forces to match and satraps came to the Kremlin bearing tribute. But Russia was on the wrong side of the Atlantic, so its empire crumbled and the prize had slipped out of its grasp. Now America was faltering, Japan was constipated on its own economic success, so it was China's turn again in the coming millennium.

Well, that was the chap's theory, Cox thought as he

picked at his duck with ginger. Here China was running the restaurant while local girls waited on table. A parrot in a cage surveyed the room, seemed not to like what it saw and said so. Customers had instructed it in half a dozen languages. *Gott in Himmel*, it screamed. *Bog off*, it muttered in upper-class disdain. A television set on a shelf high on the wall showed a Chinese video. A girl in a skimpy leotard did dreamy exercises to plinking music. Legs apart, she bent first to the left foot, then to the right. Her movements were slow so you appreciated a glimpse of her breasts as she leaned towards the camera. And in China will they be watching a video of a naked girl on a dessert trolley with a lighted candle stuck between her thighs?

Later, when he came to think about it, to close his eyes and take a deep breath and thank any gods that were listening, later Cox decided that the thing about greatness applied also to luck. Some are born lucky, some wear their cotton socks out in pursuit of luck, and others have luck once or twice in their lives fall on them out of heaven. He'd been lucky to be outside the U'bahn station in East Berlin when Heinz had kidnapped him. He was lucky now as he approached the Capitol hotel.

The sky had clouded over. This kept the evening balmy but there seemed to be a smell of rain somewhere coming on the breeze. Though he hadn't needed his raincoat all day, now he sniffed the air and thought he might just slip upstairs to collect it. But he was late following a dispute over the bill and Gabriela was standing on the streetcorner. Like a tart on parade swinging her handbag of tricks and treats, Cox thought. Sheer luck kept him out of the hotel.

'My dear, I'm late and you've been hanging around.' Cox held both arms wide. He thought better about embracing her. It was scarcely five hours ago that they'd parted.

There was no doubt about it: Gabriela was a most attractive woman. She was blonde and that had always had a certain allure for Cox. He could feel the bad uncle stirring in him. 'Blame the confounded restaurant I was in. Tried to charge me for the parrot's food.'

'Why is that man staring at us?' Gabriela's face had closed up in a scowl.

'Which man is this?'

'In the hotel. In the entrance lobby.'

Turning, Cox saw the top half of the night security guard behind the plate glass. The figure was ghostly grey, a ghost that pulled back and vanished. Like the Cheshire Cat on a bad day, the frown faded last.

'He was most assuredly not staring at me,' Cox said, though instinct cautioned him otherwise. 'You were the attraction. Come, we mustn't disappoint Vasile.'

She tucked her hand inside his elbow as they crossed the street. Four youths in blue denim uniform approached, fell silent, and after they'd gone by they joked and laughed among themselves. They're saying: there's no fool like an old fool. They passed an antique shop whose window was packed with chipped china and ormolu clocks and lockets and other Victoriana that had been stuffed under the bed during the Golden Age.

'You're quiet,' he said.

'We go to see Vasile,' she answered.

Maybe it was that.

They approached the museum. Its bulk blocked out the sky above them as they took the alley. The blackness seemed more intense ahead. Good place for muggers. Good place for lovers with no room to go to, a knee-trembler in the friendly darkness. They reached the yard at the back. Cox looked up to see if any window showed a light but saw nothing except a hazy piece of moon quickly hidden by clouds.

'Said he'd leave the door unlocked, did he?' Cox asked.

'Yes.'

'Well, it's more than unlocked. It's open.'

The massive double doors were closed but the pedestrian door inset into them stood ajar. Cox took the little torch from his pocket, narrowed its focus to a beam which he played first round the yard, then on the door. He found a place where the old wood had been splintered, a groove that gleamed in his torchlight. He didn't like it, didn't like it at all.

'Someone has used a chisel on it, or a heavy screwdriver, or a tyre lever. Something to force it.'

'Mr Cox, I don't think we go in there.'

Cox hesitated then he did go in there, just a step, far enough to play his torch over the floor and round the platform of the loading bay. He turned the torch towards Gabriela who had lifted a hand to her cheek.

'I'm afraid,' she said.

'Gabriela, I am fifty-nine and three-quarters. There have been several times in the past that I have been afraid and being absolutely frank with you this is another of them. The door should not be open. The door should not have been forced. Certainly Vasile didn't do that.' Why am I being so long-winded? Because I am trying to talk my fear down. 'Listen, being afraid is a part of my life. Well, on occasions. But it's not part of yours. Do you want to wait here while I go to see Vasile?'

'Oh Mr Cox, I am too afraid to wait here by myself.'

'All right, we shall drag ourselves upstairs like naughty children who've been sent to bed without any supper.'

Her eyes clung to him and her frown didn't relent at his attempt to lighten the atmosphere. She took a small step inside and Cox knew just how she felt: a step into a minefield. He played the torch on the stairway to light them up. We've done this before, he thought, we could do it a second time in the dark like blind people. Except one never knew if the darkness didn't hide some devil. They passed through the storeroom and entered the workshop. There was a clatter from behind one of the worktables.

'What is that?' She gripped his arm. She spoke first in Romanian, then in English. 'Who is there?'

Why is she speaking English? For my benefit? Cox decided she was just scared and would have stammered it out in Sanskrit if she knew the language. 'It was me. I knocked something off the table.'

'Mr Cox, please do not knock things. It makes my heart knock.' She grabbed his free hand and Cox in his confusion thought she was lifting his hand to feel where her heart beat beneath the bad uncle's breast. But she was gripping his hand for comfort. He switched the torch round until he discovered a pottery shard on the floor. They went into the entrance hall that was higher, longer and darker than before. It was a cathedral in the middle of the night or Victoria station during a bomb scare. They began the trek down the length of the hall. Their footsteps echoed, or was it other people's?

'Mr Cox, why was that door open?'

'Good question.'

'Did Vasile do it? Did somebody not shut it when he leave?'

'Keep asking.' Here were more questions: Did someone come in and not shut it? And was now standing behind a pillar, watching, waiting? He tried to think down memory lane for other times when he had been frightened. Every time was different. Every time felt the same. Why do I do it? Why go on? Why not turn round and tiptoe out? Why me? As always he could never think of the answers. Or none that satisfied him.

They began climbing the stairs. There were more stairs than last time just as the hall had been longer and the night darker. The stairs went on and on, right up to the stars, to heaven. At a landing the torch showed a chair jammed against the wall. That hadn't been there before. He was sure of it.

'Are you quite determined you don't want to wait here? Someone's put out a chair for you. Let me go up by myself.'

She had never loosened her grip on his hand. Now she squeezed harder. 'I would have a complete heart attack.'

They reached the floor of homage to Ceausescu. With difficulty Cox prised his hand from hers. 'In case I have to use it,' he said. The torch picked out the gleam of silver, the twinkle of cut glass. The display cabinets had a patina of dust. No fingerprints showed. The certificates were as mysterious as papyrus scrolls found in the pharoahs' tombs. In 2995 archaeologists would puzzle over the code: Honorary Citizen, Fresno, California. In his racing brain he imagined revisionist historians claiming that honour was only due to the noblest and most worthy, so Ceausescu must have been the wisest and best of rulers. See, he was also a professor at Yucatan university, an economics professor because he had made his country so rich it had a Golden Age.

'Mr Cox, do you hear something? Why have you stopped?'

'Just checking.'

The torch made a tour of the final rooms. Hello, tusker, still charging. Hello, teddy, why were you called after Roosevelt? Some day you must tell me. If there is a some day. Good grief, a sombrero to shade half of Mexico. But no man standing upright and pointing a gun. On, more slowly now. Amphora, model of the Harrier.

The door to the office was shut. Stepping close and putting his ear to it Cox heard a voice, one male voice chattering, a second voice joining it. Now a third voice breaking in, a woman's voice, and there was laughter.

Gabriela was beside him, leaning on him, her head cocked to the door. She whispered, 'Is radio.'

'So who's listening?'

Her head still cocked she said, 'I think Radio Contact.'

'Contacting who? The security patrol?'

The voices stopped.

'Contact is name of the radio station. Music, advertisements, weather, your luck today from the stars.'

There were guitar chords, thunderous, no discernible tune. A radio station. Of course. Vasile, in his eyrie, played the radio when the videos palled. From time to time he made a round of the building, polishing doorknobs. A couple of times a night the mobile security boys called on him. Why the hell is the door to the loading bay open, they'd demand. Well, I was upstairs waiting to hear my horoscope.

The radio played but there was no movement and no more voices. What legitimate reason do I have for being in the museum in the middle of the night? None, Cox told himself. What reason could I have for knocking? None. Loosening Gabriela's hand, which had battened on his arm again, he turned the handle. With his shoulder against the wood he eased the door open a crack, then further until he could see across to the banks of tape recorders, then as wide as the door would go so that the whole scene was laid out in front of him. There was just too much to absorb in one sweeping look of the office.

Sudden and violent death takes people in different and sometimes surprising ways. Gabriela didn't scream or vomit or run or burst into tears. She actually pushed past Cox to bend over the body of Vasile who was in the chair by the desk. His ankles were crossed and he slumped sideways. His grey cardigan was bloodstained all down the front. His eyes were open. His mouth was open but Cox thought it was in shock and not in a scream. His pistol lay on the floor not too far from his right hand. But it had not been suicide.

'Mr Cox, he is dead, I think.' She spoke in a matter-of-fact voice.

Cox stood beside her. There was no need to check for a pulse or for breathing. Vasile was most certainly dead, shot in the chest. Cox put his mouth to her ear. 'Don't speak.' She shouldn't have spoken out loud, not in English, and especially not giving his name. He glanced at the tape recorders. None was working that he could see, but this was Romania and Vasile had only been one of the army of secret watchers and listeners.

Every murder room is a murder story. It is not just a whodunnit but a howdunnit and a whydunnit. Cox was not a detective. Scene of the crime experts had a training he had never received. But his brain wasn't paralysed. He could piece together the sequence of events.

The murderer or murderers – and for no rational reason Cox favoured more than one – had come uninvited. They had had to break in at the loading bay. They had known to climb the stairs right to the top, known where Vasile's hideyhole was. They were acquaintances, they had been here before or they had been told the way.

The radio was playing so this covered their footsteps, their whispers. The door burst open and Vasile reacted. It wasn't eleven o'clock when Cox and Gabriela were due. An unexpected arrival is a potential enemy. He may only have been a technician but he'd still been part of the security apparatus. He had a pistol – where? A desk drawer was open. With the pistol in his hand, he went forward a couple of paces and was shot. No, he stumbled forward after he was shot. He fell to the floor where the stain spread over the rug. Hands dragged him to sit in the chair. A lot of blood had flowed. Artery severed. Death was not instantaneous but it was fairly quick. They had shot him but they hadn't intended to. They had shot him because—

Cox lifted the pistol, smelled the barrel and slipped the pistol into his pocket.

They had shot him because he had fired first. He hadn't wounded anyone because there was no trail of bloodstains towards the door. Somewhere in the woodwork or the walls would be the bullet that Vasile had fired. They had shot him in self-defence because he was dangerous. They had shot him before they had a chance to speak to him, to ask questions. The proof of that lay all around. The office was a mess. Papers tossed, files opened, cabinet doors gaping. But above all videotapes inspected, dumped, thrown away. They had known what they were coming for but they couldn't find it because they had killed Vasile before he could tell them. They would most likely have killed him afterwards but to have shot him first was a blunder. Hence the chaos and possibly the failure.

He should have gloves. He used a handkerchief so he wouldn't leave fingerprints. He picked up a videotape. The title had been written on a sticker. *Violeta la Berlin.* It could have been a movie. He picked up another and beckoned Gabriela with a finger.

'What does this say?'

'*The Spanish ambassador's wife with her driver.*'

'And this?'

'It is Yasser Arafat doing something.'

They stood close to each other, whispering in each other's ear the sins and secrets that Vasile had recorded. Another tape and another and another. He dropped a couple into his pocket. So where was the tape of Liliana on the dessert trolley? They might have found it and left. That was always a possibility.

He stood by a heap of discarded tapes, handkerchief in hand like a man waiting for a sneeze that won't come. Did they? Didn't they? They hadn't made a thorough search, which might take a day. They hadn't lifted the floorboards or dismantled the furniture and no more did Cox intend to. The books had not been examined. The pages of one might have been cut to provide a nest for the tape. Maybe they had . . . His eyes did a slow tour and stopped. A green light shone on the videoplayer. It was a small light, dull, easy to overlook. He crossed the room, pressed the eject button and a boxed tape slid out. Gabriela came to look.

'*Girl with candle in her* . . . It is not a word I know in English. It is a bad word.'

The tape had been inserted ready for viewing. They had not thought to look.

They stood at the end of the alley where it meets Calea Victoriei. Gabriela was behind Cox and they both hugged the wall of the museum. I'm a great supporter of museums, officer, Cox rehearsed to an imaginary policeman. If I don't hold it up it will come tumbling down, another lost civilization. A corpse in there, you say? Not surprised in the least. Museums are full of the dead.

A couple of students passed, talking loudly. A car came in a tearing hurry. Its headlights disappeared and seconds later they heard the sound of tyres and the hollow tinny sound as it met another car in an equal hurry. Silence, then a woman howling. Cox took Gabriela's wrist and led her in the other direction.

The worst thing in the field, Cox considered, was to stagnate. To have nothing happen. To lie on your bed staring at the ceiling, waiting. To imagine every little thing that could go wrong, from dropping the piece of paper with the vital address to being held up by a military parade while you're running for the airport. To brood, to play what-if, to ponder absurdly if maybe you should be working for the other side. None of which had applied to him in the last forty-eight hours. And now was no time to start stagnating. So act.

They had drawn abreast of a shopping arcade, deserted. Act now. Abruptly he turned on Gabriela, shoved her so that she stumbled, grabbed an arm to haul her to her feet, dragged her into the arcade. She yelped once, in pain or fright or plain surprise. He swung her round, pinning her to the wall by both shoulders. She took a breath. Her mouth opened as if to scream so he released one shoulder and gripped her jaw. She whimpered. Did she think she was victim to some sexual assault as he put his face close to hers?

'Now it's confession time.'

'Mr Cox.' She stopped.

'Yes?'

'I don't know what you mean.' Her voice was a mumble because he gripped her jaw so fiercely.

'Don't play games with me. Vasile is dead, murdered. The killers were looking for this.' He slapped a pocket and jammed his hand back on her jaw. 'Three people knew where the videotape was. Vasile himself, me, you. We can discount me. Would Vasile have told people? Boasted a bit about the lurid scene of the naked girl with a lighted candle? Yes, he might. But I don't happen to believe it. There were a couple of dozen other tapes where the sex was probably right out in the open. Ministers doing it. Ambassadors' wives doing it. Foreign politicians doing it with girls or boys carefully provided. Stuff that was more explicit. He might have shot his mouth off about that. But the tape of Liliana? I don't think so. And especially not now.'

'Please,' she said.

'Please? What does that mean?'

'You are hurting me.'

'You know what I was told when I did my training all

those years ago? It's good to feel pain; it shows you're still alive.'

She said nothing.

'Not me,' Cox said. 'Not Vasile. Which leaves you.'

She was silent.

'Which leaves you. You hear me? You understand? I told no one. I don't believe Vasile did. Who did you tell? Which little friend? Showing off a bit? Trying to rouse someone? Who was it? You didn't even tell Liliana but you've told someone. Who, Gabriela?'

He let go of her jaw, confident she wouldn't scream. He gripped both shoulders, forcing his thumbs into her flesh. The nerves placed just under the shoulders can send shocks like electricity down the arms to the wrists and she cried out.

'Who?'

'Panda,' she whispered. 'Stop it, please.'

'Who?'

'Mr Crake.'

Oh dear, oh pray. Crake. Bloody Andrew Crake. Suffering Jesus. His mind raced back to Cismigiu Park where he'd told Crake what he'd seen, and with whom, but not where.

'When did you tell him? Come on, I'm waiting.'

She wouldn't say so he let go of her shoulders and grabbed fistfuls of her hair. He jerked her head back so hard she cried out again.

'After work. I went from the embassy to his apartment. He was there. He said he was doing secret work and he needed to get hold of the tape. He said I mustn't tell you because some things were secret even from you.'

'He said that, did he? By God.'

He could see there were tears on her cheeks. Because he'd treated her roughly. Because of the murder. Because she couldn't understand the world that Crake lived in. Because the confusion inside her frightened her.

'Now listen to what I have to tell you,' Cox said. 'You mustn't go home. Not his home, not your home. They want the tape. They failed with Vasile so they'll start on you. Whoever they are. You know what happened to Liliana but that is *nothing* compared to what they could do to you. Rape? Most likely. But rape would be the easy part. You'd tell them I had taken the tape because you'd be desperate for them to stop. But they wouldn't stop. You'd beg them, you'd plead, you'd swear you didn't know where I was but they wouldn't believe you. They'd go on. You're a woman and they'd have their ways. Your very worst nightmares come true.' He paused. That should scare her. The unknown had its own power. She'd try one horror after another and believe there were even worse ones she couldn't begin to think of. 'Now, have you got a good friend, not embassy, someone Crake doesn't know?'

She nodded.

'Man? Woman? A man would be better. He'll take you to bed and get your mind off it. Girlfriend will want to gossip and find out what's wrong. Got a man you can go to at this time of night? Not that airline chap's place, Crake may know you go there on the sly. Write down the telephone number for me.'

He stuffed the piece of paper in an inside pocket. She wiped away her tears with the back of a hand. She looked in Cox's eyes and let out a sharp breath. It was something he couldn't place, not a sob, not a laugh, a choked piece of emotion. He'd hurt her and then he'd stopped. She wasn't angry about the pain. She seemed to accept it.

'Are you going to the hotel?' she asked.

Cox thought about it, how he'd intended getting his coat but hadn't wanted to waste time. He thought of the night security guard's frown and how the man had stepped back out of sight. Gone was his conspiratorial grin and the wink at Gabriela's presence. Chap had been got at, nobbled, bought, threatened. Maybe he was a thug from the Golden Age, letting a pal go up to search Cox's room and settle down to wait. It was luck that had kept Cox away.

'No, I'm not going to the hotel because I think they're waiting for me. Nor that flat you found for me.'

'How can I get in touch with you?'

'You can't. Only I can get in touch with you. It's my protection. Are you frightened?'

'Yes. Oh yes.'

'That's good. Stay frightened and you've a better chance of not being hurt.'

He walked her to the end of the arcade. To the left was the museum and beyond it the street curved out of sight. A car was parked on the bend. Cox could just make out the word *Politie* on the side. Two men in uniform questioned a man and a woman. The man made operatic sweeps with both arms. The woman had her hands raised to her face. They were the accident victims. Satisfied, he gave his attention back to Gabriela.

'Off you go.'

'Oh Mr Cox, I think I will be much safer if I stay with you.'

She reached out to him. His jacket was unbuttoned and she rested her hand on his shirt. Her touch was light but he could feel each of her fingertips pressing his chest. She flattened her hand so that the palm rested on him. He could feel its warmth.

'Gabriela, go. I have things to do. Go on, be off with you.'

She left him. After half a dozen steps she turned her head to look back at him.

'Gabriela, I'm your good uncle. Remember?'

Cox watched her figure grow smaller until the night swallowed her. I'm growing old, he thought, old.

Chapter 14

Standing on the doorstep Cox shivered, not because of the night air but because of the conviction he was reliving an episode in the past. He was in Prague, in one of the villas tucked in among the trees below Hradcany castle. Just such a villa as this, with a fancy colonnade and stuccoed walls and a big fir tree like the one to his left that darkened the whole garden. Mirek's wife had answered his ring and said, when she recognized who it was, 'They've taken him away.' She shut the door in his face. The episode had taken ten seconds, and he'd made the journey from London specially. He thought of ringing the bell again and asking for details but with the memory of her closed and hostile face he didn't bother. He turned and set out on the walk through the shadows, his nostrils straining for the aroma of the Marlboro the secret police favoured.

I've been too long in the job, he told himself, I remember too much.

He looked back to the street, left, right, left again, for all the world like some smooth-chinned probationer on a training run, scared more of the assessor who might be watching than of any enemy. He looked right again, this time not for an assessor's benefit but his own. The trees were densely leafed, the streetlamps few, the shadows black, but he thought there was no one there. In the shadow of the big fir tree – well, he couldn't tell. At last he pressed the bell. Some instinct made him glance up. The windows had shutters. One pair of shutters was open a crack and he saw the paleness of a face, which vanished. Or he thought he saw it. Or his imagination was jumping. The fanlight suddenly glowed. Somebody was coming. He heard the lock turn.

A woman of thirty-something opened the door. She was heavily pregnant and one hand clutched a housecoat closed over her belly. Disconcerted, Cox stumbled over his words. 'Hara . . . Harasteanu? Tudor?'

She spoke a few words in a low voice, gave a grave smile and shut the door in his face.

The smile Cox was returning drained away. Had she understood? Had she said Tudor was out? Or worse, as Mirek's wife had? Had he come to the wrong house? But a blue and white number plate – souvenir of some visit to France – was screwed to the wall. It was the right house.

Cox had to wait outside a couple of minutes. When the door was opened again, Cox looked past the man's shoulder into the hallway. And the man, knowing it was Cox and that he had come unannounced and it was long past midnight, looked out into the shadows of the street.

'Why didn't you come in?' Tudor asked.

'I came alone,' Cox said, choosing to answer a different question.

'Yes,' Tudor said. 'Of course.'

'I know it's late.'

'Please,' Tudor said, putting out a hand not so much to shake Cox's hand as to usher him in. He closed the door with one final look down the street and locked it. The pregnant woman stood at the foot of the stairs. When Cox had called in the previous day – no, it was the day before now – there had been no sign of her. Cox assumed she was

Tudor's wife, though she must be twenty years younger. Seeing Cox stare at her, Tudor said, 'This is Magda.'

Tudor led the way down a short passage. Cox, following, was aware of the flip-flop of loose slippers behind him. All three went into Tudor's study. The unwise frowned at the busts of Lenin and Marx, the photos of Stalin smiling and Beria wondering who to execute and whose wife to give a tumble. There was a grainy blow-up of Lenin haranguing a crowd and pointing to a glorious future over their heads. Another showed the Romanian wartime leader Antonescu, who had sent troops to help the Nazis at the siege of Stalingrad. But this photo was of a haggard Antonescu taken at his trial in 1946 before he was shot. There was a montage of photos of the Ceausescus, Old Nick and Elena, accepting bouquets from little girls and being greeted by President Carter in Washington. 'This is the museum,' Tudor would explain, 'where we put the safely dead.' Also, such a rogue's gallery had provided some protection when the Securitate had paid their visits.

Tudor had chosen to come here rather than the sitting-room, Cox guessed, because he knew this was not a social visit. But he shouldn't have brought Magda. The room was furnished for work, a dark wood desk standing on bear's paws, bookshelves, a chaise longue where Tudor might stretch out in those moments of weariness known to all intellectuals. It was Magda who took the chaise longue. A padded stool was pushed close to it. Tudor sat there. Which left Cox only the chair behind the desk. Cox pulled the chair away and as he sat he saw Tudor staring at his shoes, which were mud-spattered.

'I walked. I didn't want to risk a taxi. They might question the drivers.'

'They.' Tudor's eyes lifted from the shoes to meet Cox's eyes. 'You understand now. It's not over. When you came before I did warn you.'

'You did. I thought you were exaggerating.'

'I said it was still the same old pack running things, just shuffled a little. Not so brutal, maybe.'

Cox thought of Vasile's body but said nothing. His eyes turned towards Magda.

'Oh, Magda doesn't understand English,' Tudor said smiling. 'Do you?'

'No,' she said, smiling back at him.

Cox was baffled. Perhaps she'd said *Nu*. Or Tudor meant she understood but would forget. He was hardly reassured. He pointed to the ceiling and walls.

Tudor said, 'After our apology of a revolution I went to the American embassy and asked for someone to come to check the walls. They protested they weren't in that line of business so I reminded them of certain favours I had done for them in the past. They sent a man – this is funny – with ears as big as Mickey Mouse. Did his ears grow with the job? "I'm the resident bugger," he said. He did what he called a sweep and found six transmitters. Six. I was flattered. It is safe to speak now.'

If Jaeger had been involved, Cox would not put it past him to have slipped in a little something of his own.

'I need to use the telephone,' Cox said.

'Well, if you must. You run the risk. Would you trust a telephone in England? Even your royal family has been caught out.'

He gave Magda a hand to help her up and they left Cox alone. He pulled the chair close to the desk and waited for a few moments, his eyes closed. Lordy, I'm tired. I must get some sleep. Later.

He dialled Liliana's number. Sorry to wake you from your beauty sleep, he told her in his mind. I would have called earlier but the first telephone was occupied and the second wouldn't work. He counted the rings. Two, three. She said she'd been counting all her life. Thousands, millions. Four, five. Answer, damn it. Perhaps she's not asleep. Perhaps she's in bed but otherwise occupied. Some nice boy. Or girl. Mincu might have put her off men for life. Seven, eight, wherever I'd got to. Answer, Liliana, pick up the telephone and speak to me. I don't want you to go any further. I want you to stop. It's gone murderous.

Then he stopped counting. He let the telephone ring and ring. She's in a passionate clinch. She's in the bath. She's on the floor, dead. She's been abducted. The telephone was clamped to his ear, his fingers ached from gripping it. Now it had stopped ringing. She'd picked up her receiver. No, he had gone deaf to its trill.

He hung up. She's safe or she's in hazard and there's nothing to be done. I should never have involved her. I have broken the iron rule: do not use an amateur. The amateur has no training, has not signed up and taken the Queen's shilling. The amateur has not been warned of the dangers and thrilled to them. But Liliana had volunteered. All right, he had given her a nudge. But she had wanted to go ahead. It wasn't for him to dictate to her. She had her own agenda, as they said nowadays.

With his eyes closed he saw Liliana's face, intense, a little disapproving. The voice he heard wasn't hers. He thought it might be Jenny's, his wife's voice. Jenny could be censorious. His conscience, he had thought of her. That girl is seriously disturbed. You *inveigled* her. Jenny made it sound like seduction. But sometimes your conscience says one thing, necessity says something else. What nonsense, Jenny would retort, there is always another way. Otherwise there is no moral difference between us and the other side.

He sighed, as he had often sighed, because Jenny had not had to do the job. He picked up the telephone again. Yes, high time I got out, he thought as he punched in the numbers, I used to be able to hide behind the necessity of fighting the great evil. But the evil has crumbled so where is my excuse now? This time the number he dialled didn't ring at all. There was silence and then 'Greensleeves' played softly. Cox identified himself and waited until he heard his Chief's voice.

'You have important news?'

Meaning – Cox interpreted – I trust you are not disturbing my evening for a trifle. In the background was the sound of voices, male and female, suddenly cut off as if a door had been closed. It was still the dinner party hour back in Kensington. A different world.

'A murder,' Cox said.

'Anybody I know?'

'Who did it? Or had it done to him?' Cox queried.

'Either.'

'Mincu's cronies did it. Our man pointed the finger at the murderee. He was a nobody. Dregs. Former Securitate. I doubt even his own mother will mourn him, if he ever had such a human genesis.'

There was the briefest of pauses before his Chief said with great deliberation: 'Our man, you say? Our very own chap?'

'He found out about a piece of evidence. He's our man in name only. His loyalty belongs elsewhere. Result: one corpse. I have the evidence still.'

'Should I alert H.E.? Have our man locked up?'

'I've chewed that over. It's the old routine: I know he's bad but he doesn't know I know. It gives me an edge.'

His Chief didn't speak but hummed a bit of tuneless nonsense. It was his way of saying: I'm here and I'm pondering what you've told me. Finally he said, 'They're making progress in Dayton. The Americans are finally getting involved and this is concentrating the minds of the warring tribes. If they have minds. If the Americans do put troops on the ground in ex-Jugo, they'll make damn certain Mincu doesn't supply chemical weapons to anybody.'

'It could be too late. Mincu has something planned this weekend.'

Mincu wanted Liliana present. Not just because she was pretty. He wanted her to interpret. And afterwards? She'd know too much.

'This evidence,' his Chief said, 'does it damn Mincu?'

'In a different context. But it's important because it involves someone from London.'

'An important someone?'

'Yes. I have a video showing him caught up in dirty games. Well, a game is not how she'd see it. Awful stuff.'

'I ought to be told. Suppose something happens to you.'

'This is an open line.'

'A clue.'

This was against all rules of security. But his Chief had a point: something might happen to him.

'You did Latin at school?'

'Yes.'

'Julius Caesar?'

'*Gallia est omnis divisa in partes tres.* It was beaten into me.'

'Classicists change their minds, like all experts. Pronunciation, now. I was taught to say V as W.'

'So was I.'

'All right. Do you remember this bit? *Veni, vidi . . .*' It came out as *Weni, widi . . .* He left the third word hanging. 'Got him?'

'Good God! Him?'

'Him. His smarmy smile, his greedy eyes, his lizard tongue slipping over his lips. Him.'

There was silence. His Chief was too disturbed even to hum. In the silence Cox imagined he could hear breathing.

* * *

Yes, him. Wix, known as Wicky in the Westminster corridors. Known to his cronies as Wicked. Sir Terence Wix. Can you be knighted for wicked behaviour? Why not. You can be knighted for damn near everything else.

Cox sat slumped in the chair behind Tudor's desk. There was an oyster shell between the telephone and a stone jar of different-coloured pens. He held the shell in the palm of his hand. Mother of pearl, beautiful name. But this was spoiled by a blackish smear as if someone had stubbed out a cigarette. He'd never seen Tudor smoke. Perhaps Securitate on an unsocial call.

His Chief had asked if there was any doubt it was Wix on the videotape. None, Cox had told him. Doing what? Party to an abduction, possible participant in a rape. Even if the charge of rape was Wix's word against Liliana's, the tape was damning enough. One more scandal to a government that seemed to wallow in sleaze. The PM will have to be told, Cox had said. When you give me the evidence, his Chief replied. Don't lose it. Don't fall under a bus. Cox understood him to mean: Don't get pushed under.

What a cesspool he was poking into. Cox sighed. The door opened and Tudor reappeared. He brought a bottle of brandy, as if he knew Cox would be in need. Magda came behind carrying a tray with little cups and a Turkish coffee pot, an antique, a real beauty.

'Finished with the telephone calls?'

'For the moment.' Cox wondered if there was an extension in the kitchen and what Tudor's breathing sounded like. Tudor poured two snifters of brandy and handed one to him.

'Courage, my friend.'

The men drank. Magda poured coffee for them and stretched out on the chaise longue again. She drank nothing herself.

Tudor said, 'You used to bring me coffee – do you

remember? – from the Algerian Coffee Store. It said it on the package: Algerian Coffee Store, Old Compton Street, Soho, London W1. You cannot imagine how exotic that was to me. Soho. Romance, mystery.'

'It's mostly porno places now. The Algerian shop still holds on.'

'I had to remove the coffee from its bag, of course. Too dangerous.'

'Oh dear, oh pray. I never thought.'

'But it was an opportunity. I didn't waste the bag. There was a history professor at the university, a real pig, an informer, Party man. What you call a creep, I think. I dropped the Algerian Coffee Store bag in his waste basket. He got into the most terrible trouble for undeclared contact with an imperialist.'

Tudor Harasteanu, Professor of Psycholinguistics, was showing a fresh side of himself. He had always had courage, or daring. But he had never been relaxed enough with Cox to show his mischievous streak.

'Those were the days,' Cox said. 'We knew what we were fighting for. We knew it was a just struggle. Now . . .' He sighed. I must stop sighing, he thought, I sound petulant. Tudor kept silent as if encouraging some confession, so Cox went on, 'Sorry, old friend, it's just that tonight I have been rubbing my nose in the past and it stinks. The present is rotten. And the future . . . Who believes in the future any more?'

'Romanians do. Romanians have to. When we have nothing to eat, nothing to buy, no freedom, then your true Romanian believes in the future. Since he believes that things cannot get worse, he is both an optimist and a pessimist at the same time. When you have nothing, then the future must be better. Ceausescu was the most Romanian of all. He said it was the beginning of the Golden Age and things would get better and better. He was a super-optimist. Me, I was a super-pessimist. I scratched the Golden Age with a thumbnail and found there was dull metal underneath. Cheers,' he said, raising his glass again. 'To the future.'

They drank again. Cox's glass was empty and Tudor refilled it.

'To all our futures,' Tudor said, but they didn't drink this time.

This is what it's like in war, Cox thought, waiting until the hour for action, drinking to fill in the time, talking to fill in the emptiness inside, then silence.

'Look at Magda,' Tudor said suddenly. 'Isn't she beautiful?'

The woman, knowing she was being talked about, smiled.

Tudor rested his hand on her belly. 'Come and feel this. Come on. Forget your British reserve.'

Cox crossed the room, knelt and laid his hand on the mound wrapped in the housecoat. He felt movement, a new life stirring. Magda's dark eyes were steady on his face.

'Harasteanu – my family name – you could translate roughly as Gift of the Stars. What you feel is my gift to Magda. That is the future you are touching. Whatever it is you are doing, it is to make that child's future better. It is why I helped you in the past. Still help you.'

Making the child's future better, Cox wasn't sure. Just stopping it from becoming terrible, he'd go for that. He crossed to the window, opened the shutters a crack to peer out. In case there were hobgoblins out there. He turned back into the room, pointing at the bookshelves.

'Does that video player work?'

'Yes.'

'I picked up a couple of tapes tonight. I'm not at all certain they're of use but I'm interested. I'm just going by the initials.' He took one of the videos out of his pocket and handed it to Tudor.

'*Meeting between KGB and CIA – December 13th,*' Tudor read.

'See, it was the initials that caught my eye.'

'It doesn't say what year.'

'No.'

'Who made the tapes?'

For an answer Cox pointed at the walls and the ceiling.

'Ah, my friends,' Tudor said. 'Let us see what they caught.'

Tudor inserted the cartridge and they settled to watch.

Chapter 15

On either side were five-storey concrete blocks of flats but this house was single-storey and old. So old, Dorina used to joke, that staircases hadn't yet been invented which was why there was no upper floor. A wooden verandah down one side was decaying. A grape vine was trained along it, if trained was the word. The vine sagged, Dorina said, like a middle-aged breast.

'Who the devil is it?' Dorina asked through the letter flap. 'Who the hell is hammering on the door at this hour? Holy bum, you'll waken the bats.'

'Liliana.'

'Liliana? Which Liliana is this? Liliana the cripple? Liliana the whore? Liliana the queen of Azerbaijan?'

Liliana didn't reply, not knowing what Liliana she was.

'What do you want? Are you in trouble?'

'Yes.'

'It's the middle of the night. Trouble can wait until it's light.'

'Let me in.'

'Middle of the night trouble . . . You should take more care.'

The door opened the width of a pair of eyes. The vine blocked out most of the light from the streetlamp and the eyes were suspicious.

'You.' The eyes probed behind Liliana's shoulders. 'Liliana the trouble. Are you alone?'

'Yes,' Liliana said. 'Dorina, let me in.'

The door opened on rusty protesting hinges. My burglar alarm, Dorina called it, as if burglars couldn't just as well hop over the windowsill. Dorina was wearing a nightdress and had put a raincoat on top. The raincoat was unbuttoned but held together by a belt that was tied rather than buckled. The door opened straight into the bungalow's main room which was part sitting room, part consulting room, part dispensary, and all mess.

'Well, come in if you're coming.'

But Liliana was already stepping inside. The door was pushed shut and locked. Dorina wore felted slippers and she shuffled to a table to switch on a lamp. Liliana had seen the room before during the hours of daylight. Then it had appeared grey and chaotic like a secondhand shop in Constantsa where penniless sailors on a run ashore had parted with their belongings for a little ready cash. Now it was a place of shadows and movement as three or four cats prowled and hissed at the newcomer. The table was draped with oilcloth where forgotten cigarettes had burned holes. Orange peel had curled as it dried. A cup, a smudged glass, a clock with bells on top to sound the alarm, a straggly vest or was it a bandage, a plate of walnut shells, a jam jar holding a single pencil, a small chrome frame of the kind that displays a photo of a loved one but held instead a packet that once contained nasturtium seeds. A chaise longue – no boudouir piece, this – was covered in cracked polythene sheeting. Shelves held a few books, an empty bottle of Albanian brandy, a skull sectioned with a phrenologist's claims to Memory, Creativity, Courage, Willpower, and many jars of powders, roots, leaves, dried insects and unknowable objects. Unknowable but not unimaginable. When she had launched herself on the works of Shakespeare Liliana had had a stab of recognition in *Macbeth*: Eye of newt and toe of frog, Wool of bat and tongue of dog.

'So, Liliana, you are a girl in trouble again. Once is carelessness, once is bad luck, once is a mistake. But twice—'

'It wasn't any of that,' Liliana interrupted. 'You're stupid to say that.' The harshness in her voice surprised them both and for a moment there was silence. Then by a kind of dreadful attraction the eyes of both were drawn to the chaise longue with its insanitary plastic cover where the old woman had induced an abortion. For a moment the despair and degradation and terror she had felt threatened to swamp Liliana. She took a deep breath and swung back to Dorina. 'I told you it wasn't like that. What care should I have taken? Tell me how I should have prepared myself. You think I'm like the others who come to you?'

Dorina was muttering to herself. Liliana caught a word or two: rude, hot tempered.

'I came once for that.' Liliana stabbed a finger at the chaise longue. 'I came afterwards some times for that.' The finger accused the jars of herbal medicines. 'People said – good friends of mine said – you would put me together again, heal me, make the pain melt and the memories go. They didn't say you would take my money and give me a lecture whenever you saw me. Now the pain has come back and the memories burn me and I have come for help. There is no trouble down there, it is all up here. Do you understand?'

Exhausted, Liliana flung herself on a chair. With a screech a cat leapt to the floor. The anger had subsided but it could come back at any moment. She could feel it like a tensed spring inside her. Dorina had lifted an arm to her face as if to shield it from the heat of the words. She gripped the sleeve of her raincoat between her teeth.

Liliana looked away and her eyes rested on a battered record player. Dorina had put a record on before she got to work. Liliana remembered. Beethoven's Ninth. The last movement. Schiller's *Ode to Joy* but Dorina didn't see the irony. She chose it for the voices which drowned any cry from a distraught girl having her trouble terminated.

Dorina was muttering again. Horrible, she said. Or maybe it was ungrateful. As any Romanian will tell you, through clenched teeth even *love* and *hate* sound much the same. Should Liliana feel gratitude? During the Golden Age Dorina had made a steady if precarious living. There had been no contraception, no abortion. Another of Ceausescu's grandiose plans had been to breed more Romanians. Married women had regular medical inspections. Why aren't you pregnant? Isn't your husband up to it? Get a new man. A girl in trouble, as Dorina put it, had to suffer one way or another.

Dorina tore the sleeve from her face. Her lips twitched up. As a smile it would convince no one. 'Do you want wine?'

Liliana shook her head. Dorina the drunk, some had called her. Dorina the dregs, others said. And I put my life in her hands, Liliana thought. Now someone else's life.

Dorina opened a cupboard door and brought out an anonymous bottle. She poured a half tumbler, drank it and put the bottle away. She burped and the smell of plum brandy wafted over Liliana. With new courage in her veins she swung on Liliana.

'Well, what do you want?'

'Something from one of those jars. Or maybe from a jar you keep hidden in a closet. One of the men who raped me – the leader of the pack – has come into my life again.'

'Yes, get on with it.'

'I have to go to his house later today. He has no memory of what he did to me. Maybe he's done it to many women.

A woman is just a vessel that he fills. He says there is work he wants me to do. He has become more powerful than ever, one of our new secret rulers, rich and influential, beyond the reach of the law. Simply put, he deals in death. That is his work. After the work, he will think of pleasure. Me.'

'Yes? And?'

'I said he'd come into my life again. I want him out of it.'

There was a pause. Dorina cocked her head and frowned, chewing over these words. A cat went to the door, miaowing to be let out, and was ignored. Liliana leaned forward as if she was going to share a secret.

'You will give me something. I'll tell him it is a love potion, make him very strong. Or it could be I just slip it in his whisky while he is distracted. That would be safer, not arouse suspicion. But what I want – really, desperately want – is for him to look in my face as he is dying and know that I did it.'

When she had finished speaking, Liliana fixed her eyes on Dorina. The eyes were steady and bright. They didn't beg or threaten, they commanded obedience. They showed the strength that Gabriela had talked of. This thing has been done to me and that thing and the other thing. Now this is the consequence, now it is time to redress the balance. You will give me the powder or the liquid and I will punish the man. When I kill him it will be for every woman who has been humiliated, tortured, raped. Call it revenge, call it justice. I'm not concerned with words, only with the act.

Dorina opened her mouth wide but her voice was only a whisper. 'Holy bum. And you said you were a girl in trouble.'

'So you would let me in. You would understand that.'

'It is not you, it's the man who is in trouble.'

Liliana simply stared. She'd said all she had to say.

Only an hour before the telephone had rung and she had lifted the receiver and it was Mincu. He was close, in her ear. He was closer, inside her head.

'Are you in bed? Are you alone?'

He didn't even give his name. He had that arrogance.

'What do you want?'

'Apart from the Taj Mahal as a summer cottage and the best chef in Paris and scoring the winning goal in the European Cup and the keys to Fort Knox, there is one thing I really want. Can't you guess?'

Liliana's hand had trembled, her wrist ached to smash the receiver down but somehow her muscles had lost their strength. Why had he rung? Was he obsessed, drunk, playing some foolish game? He was smiling as he spoke. She could tell he was. It wasn't a smile for her. It was for himself. In his millionaire's flat on the other side of town. With a glass of whisky to hand and music playing. She could hear an aria. He was listening to *Carmen*.

'The little party I planned has turned out to have a serious side to it. I'll need all your language skills.'

'I only have English and French. You know that.'

'Indeed I do and that'll be enough.' Then he'd told her what her duties would be and how she must be charming to everybody. He'd had another drink of whisky and told her more. He could be boasting to her a bit. Or he just wanted to keep her at the other end of the telephone, imagining her lying with her dark hair spread over the pillow. He said, 'I've decided to use my country house. Afterwards we can relax. Now I—'

'I must go,' she broke in.

'Go? Go where?'

She dropped the phone in its cradle and stared at it. Its cord gradually returned to its normal shape. It coiled itself like a snake. When the telephone rang again she hadn't answered. She had counted the rings. Ten eleven twelve. Who would have thought he had so much patience. Or he was angry at being cut off.

She was standing on the corner. She was waiting for the lights to tell her she could cross. There was no traffic to speak of but old habits died hard. During the Golden Age you did not cross against a red light. Police, in or out of uniform, would lay a hand on your shoulder. Against the law. Break a minor law and you were on a slippery slope. Next you'd be stealing crusts of bread, breaking wind on May Day, not getting pregnant, planning the overthrow of the People's Socialist Republic. Cross against the light and you were a dissident in the making, a closet imperialist, an agent provocateur testing the vigilance of the people's protectors.

Liliana lifted her arm and turned her wrist. The street lighting killed the luminosity of her watch face but wasn't strong enough to tell the time by. Life's predicament made simple. An approaching car stopped even though the traffic light was in its favour. Driver, male, puffy face, balding. He beckoned with a finger. She bent to peer in. He gave her a grin and mouthed something. Furious, she banged a fist on his roof and walked round the back of the car. Angry in his turn, he opened his door and swung his legs out.

'Don't.' She spat the word at him. 'Lay a finger on me and I'll kill you.'

Where had it come from – the sudden fierceness, tough resolve, the reckless disregard of the odds? The man hesitated, and was lost.

'What are you flagging me down for if you don't mean it?' With his libido thwarted, his tone turned petulant. He stood up, took a step towards her but not a big one. She jabbed a finger at him like a pistol and he stopped.

'Don't,' she repeated. She listened to the sound of her voice in her head, its forcefulness, its command. No need to go further, say she was a karate black belt, she could break his neck, anything. One word turned him to stone. She crossed the road as a cruising police car approached. Halfway along the block she swung back. Two officers had got out and the man was trying to explain why he was standing in the road beside his car while the lights turned red-green-red, waving his arms, pointing in her direction. She walked on, turning into a side-street. Strada Witing, she read on the wall, and hurried on. I can do it, she told herself, I have the power, I am afraid of no man. Ahead of her was the hulk of the Nord railway station.

She passed through an encampment of street people, a whole village it seemed. Mostly they were children, teenagers, but some as young as seven or eight. Several wore sweatshirts emblazoned Adidas, the gift of a German charity. They squatted on the ground, smoking. Or lay against the wall, rolled in newspapers, sleeping. One couple, a boy and a girl of perhaps fourteen, had covered their bodies with a flattened cardboard carton which moved rhythmically in an act of love. Or an act of desperation. A teenage mother had a baby clamped to one breast. A man beside her had draped an arm round her shoulders, his hand fondling the other breast. He was a much older man. The baby's father? The girl's father?

Two men stood under a lamppost that didn't work. They shared a cigarette. Its tip brightened each face in turn. The cigarette passed between them, a firefly. She remembered other fireflies and a man's voice, an echo down the years. He was asking her a question, asking if she wanted to, wanted to, wanted to . . . Her body remembered how it had ached, every part of it, every muscle, every pore, every opening. Lovely lady, do you want to, want to . . . Something. She remembered counting her footsteps. One step, two steps, three steps, four, five steps, six steps, seven steps, more. And more. And more. How many steps had she taken? A million? A zillion?

She'd almost reached the end of the journey. One more big step. Then she could stop counting. Soon.

It was an act of will to light the candles, remembering that other candle and how the hot wax had burned her thighs. A candle for Peter, a candle for Paul. She carried the candles and Paul's candle trembled so much a little molten wax spilled on the tender white flesh of her inner wrist. But it did not sting like the wax on her thighs. She could feel that still. She crossed to the statue of the Virgin Mary and planted the candles in the sandtray.

By day the church was half dark as if in mourning. By night, in contrast, what you noticed was the light of the candles. Liliana walked towards the altar and her shadow pranced ahead of her, climbing the brown and mustard wall. Some current of air bent the flames so that her shadow swayed. Her head seemed hunched down as she weaved left and right. She was a soldier caught in an ambush, ducking bullets as she ran for cover.

Under the cupola she looked up. The frieze of figures was invisible. She imagined she saw the gilt of their haloes but in truth saw nothing. A sound made her swing round. She'd heard a muffled cough, a shoe scuffing the carpet, the thump of a heavy body sinking onto a chair. She saw nobody, just her own shadow drunkenly leaning against the wall.

She climbed the spiral steps to the pulpit set high against the north wall. The church was laid out before her like the field of battle to a general. Peter, the rock on which the church was built, roll over and crush my enemy. Paul, no lover of women, redeem yourself and support me in my endeavour. She thought she heard the sound again, like a footfall, but if anyone was there he had to be lost in the shadows. She could see no one, not a fellow sufferer, not a boy from the street village, not the disappointed driver of the car, not the old man who kept watch by day over the church gate. She was alone.

She descended, lit another candle from the ones that burned in front of the Virgin and carried it to the table covered with an oilcloth. A pad was lying there, as if it had been laid out for her use. It wasn't some cheap school exercise book but good quality writing paper. Imported, she noted. Basildon Bond, cousin of James. She opened it and found the first page had been written on. *Father of Fathers, Why at this crisis in my life have You abandoned me? What have I done that so offends You? Is it* But here the writing stopped. A woman's hand, Liliana thought. A rich woman who simply got up and walked away, not bothering to take the pad with her. She had suddenly lost her faith, or suddenly been ashamed of some act, or suddenly been overwhelmed by the futility of trying to alter what she had already done. A mark on the paper could have been caused by a tear. Did the rich weep like other people? Didn't they employ others to cry for them?

Turning to a new page, Liliana sat poised with a pen in her hand. Father of Fathers. Oh Paul. Hear me, Peter. Sweet Virgin Mary, mother sublime, chosen one to bear God's son. Help me in the greatest test of my life. But no, she didn't need any divine help. She had the resolve, the strength, the iron inside her already.

Dear Mr Cox, she wrote and laid down the pen. What could she write? Her thoughts went skipping away from her.

Why did the English start a letter like that? The familiar *Dear* and the formal *Mr* together? It showed a confusion, a split in the English character, a fault line. The French, perplexed, said the English were perfidious. The Americans believed they were cynical, professing a civilizing mission while they stole other nations' land. The Germans dismissed them as not serious, dilettanti, an enemy they always trounced except for the final battle. Mr Cox, how did he see himself?

She took up the pen again. *As an Englishman, Mr Cox, do you consider yourself to be severely practical or wildly romantic? Or both shoved inside the same skin? Think of the muddle you display when you write Dear Mr Bank Manager (who is making me bankrupt). Or how about Dear Mr Hitler – I do not know my exact address though it says Arbeit Macht Frei over the gates. Would you say Dear Mr Attila, or should it be Mr Hun?*

She stopped again, read the sentences she had written and tore the page from the pad. It's because it's the middle of the night and I haven't slept, it's because Mincu has whispered in my ear, it's because I have visited Dorina and told that driver I would kill him and walked through that village of the damned, it's because it's the night before Agincourt. She crossed to the statue of the Virgin Mary and held the paper to a candle flame. She dropped it into the sandtray and watched it burn.

Returning to the table, she bent to the pad once more. Catching sight of movement in the corner of her eye, she glanced behind her. The last flickering flame of the letter made her shadow shift on the wall. It made her look a hunchback. Or Atlas with the weight of the world on his shoulders. Yes. But I am strong enough.

Dear Mr Cox, she wrote again.

I am worried about you. First I tried telephoning you at the flat where I saw you and you held my hand and transmitted courage to me. I think you have been successful in doing that. When you did not answer the telephone I tried to contact you at the Capitol Hotel. The man I spoke to was very brusque, demanding my name and where I was telephoning from. Where were you, Mr Cox? Why did he ask these questions? I think it was most impertinent.

On she wrote, sometimes lifting her head to gaze up at the pulpit and the gilded eagle with its wings spread for a flight it would never make.

Chapter 16

It had gone three in the morning. Magda had disappeared to bed. Tudor had withdrawn, possibly to the kitchen. Cox heard the sound of footsteps approaching up the short path to the front door, then the bell. He peeped through the gap in the shutters. There was no back-up loitering in the shadows that he could see. There'd been no sound of a car either. Lucas Jaeger had parked it some way down the street, like the good scout he was.

Cox let him in. Jaeger raised his hand in a Red Indian salute but neither spoke. Cox led the way down the passage into Tudor's museum.

'Jesus Christ, who lives here?' Jaeger said, taking in Marx, Stalin *et al.*

'A friend.'

'A friendly friend?'

'I've known him since the old days. One of us.'

'Cover then,' Jaeger said, patting Lenin on the head, then inspecting his fingers for dust. 'So what is it you couldn't speak of over the phone?' Jaeger's face had pouches and shadows and the grim set of a man who knew that to be called out at three in the morning was bad news. He fixed steady and none too friendly eyes on

Cox. 'I thought you were doing a farewell lunch tour of Europe.'

'Cover,' said Cox.

'Cover? Oh, Roy's still the boy. Cover, right to the end. You are retiring, aren't you, turning in your star, going to spend your days pruning roses?'

'Growing tomatoes, Lucas. I'll be a tomato merchant.'

'Holy mackerel.' Jaeger didn't laugh but a little of the tension went out of him and his eyes released Cox. 'I smell brandy.'

'There's a bottle on the floor by the chaise longue.'

With a grunt Jaeger bent to scoop up the bottle and the snifter beside it. 'Second hand,' he said. 'What the hell. Alcohol kills the bugs.' He poured and drank. 'So. Here we are. Yes indeed. What do we do now? Play Scrabble? You got some girls lined up?'

'There are girls involved. One in particular. She's part of it. She's in trouble.'

'Oh boy. You're in town – what is it? Forty-eight hours? Seventy-two hours? Already a girl in trouble. That old-world charm gets them every time.'

But Cox wasn't playing and there was something of an awkward silence, which Jaeger broke.

'OK, what is it? Shoot.'

'Got a couple of videotapes for you to see.'

'Dirty movies.'

'Got one of those too. These ones look dull but I think you'll be . . . Well, I don't quite know what you'll be.' Riveted, appalled, hangdog, suspicious – Cox shook his head. 'Better do a bit more of that, my advice.' He pointed to the brandy bottle.

Jaeger lowered his bulk into the chair by the desk, one big fist holding onto the bottle for support. Cox pulled the padded stool away from the chaise longue and squatted on that. The video began. There was no introduction, no titles. It was a shot taken from overhead of what looked like a dining table. Three men sat on one side, two men faced them.

'It's stolen,' Jaeger said, meaning the recording was done clandestinely.

'It dates from a few years back. 1989. It was their big industry then, bugging and filming. December '89, around the middle. Interesting times, Lucas. We were privileged to live through them, even to play a little part. We held our breath and couldn't quite believe it was happening. It was like the retreat from Moscow except it was the Russians who were doing the retreating. Poland had shown the way. Hungary and Czecho had broken free. The Berlin Wall came down. Which left Romania, if one ignores jokes like Albania and Bulgaria. That's when this was filmed, just before the revolution here.'

Jaeger was deaf to this potted history. He leaned forward, his belly spilling over the desk, concentrating on what the men talked about. His brows drew together. 'Funny accents. Going quick too.' He was reluctant to say he couldn't follow. 'Who are they? Just a minute. It was the accent that fooled me. It's Romanian they're speaking, right? What's it about? Come on, Roy, stop the fan dance.'

'Well, you've got your Russians and then you've got your fellow countrymen. The three on the other side of the table who look like Wall Street brokers are the Russkies. Good suits, neat hair, gold Rolexes. The pair who look like Moscow heavies are American. Lumpy suits, corner barbershop hairstyles. Confusing, I agree. Maybe it's cover.'

Jaeger didn't rise. 'You're going to tell me who they are.'

'They're KGB and CIA. It says that on the label. Recognize anyone?'

'No.' Jaeger was frowning. They listened half a minute in silence. Jaeger muttered like an adulterer in a confessional, 'Mid-December 1989 but they're talking about what's going to happen. I just heard the big Russian guy say "post-Ceausescu".'

'Correct.'

The word triggered Jaeger's anger, as if he resented being put to some kind of test. 'It's the middle of the fucking night. Stop playing games, Cox. Are you going to tell me?'

'Wait.' Cox raised a hand. 'There's a good bit coming up. You're going to be fascinated.'

Silence again while they watched and listened. A tray on the table held a carafe and half a dozen glasses. One of the Russians poured and drank and said something. There was a little laughter.

'So what was that? Something about vodka?'

But Jaeger didn't press for an answer. The shadow of an approaching figure moved across the backs of the two Americans. A man with cropped grey hair stood beside them a moment before pulling out a chair and sitting down. He nodded across the table to the Russians. 'Gentlemen,' he said. Inclining his head to the American next to him, he said, 'They all speak English?'

'You bet,' said one of the Russians.

An American said, 'Fred was at the embassy in DC. Alex and Yuri at the mission to the UN.'

'Fred? They're taking over our names now?' The older American shrugged and turned so that for the first time his face was in profile. 'OK, let's get the show on the road.'

'Holy mackerel,' Jaeger said, his voice a hoarse whisper, 'that's McAllister.'

Cox said nothing but now he had a name.

'He's like God's right boot in the Agency. Or was. Used to kick the shit out of sinners. Why didn't you tell me?' His voice had grown to a shout. 'You're playing games again.' Jaeger's anger came flooding back. He made an abrupt sweep of his hand, knocking into the brandy bottle, then gripping it as if it was a spar and he was a sailor lost in a heaving sea. 'Be quiet,' he ordered, though Cox wasn't speaking. His attention was fixed on the screen where McAllister was talking.

'Fred, Alex, Yuri, pleased to make your acquaintance. Glad to have you aboard. You can call me Tex.'

'Tex!' Jaeger was disbelieving. 'They'd lynch him there. He's a bloody Boston Brahmin.'

The Russians all smiled as if they appreciated the choice of name. If McAllister had been female he might have picked the state of Virginia.

'Just got in,' McAllister was saying, 'half an hour ago. Hour maybe. Doesn't time fly when you're having fun, dodging the pursuit car. Plane was a little late taking off from Frankfurt. I guess Pan Am was hoping to round up more passengers.'

'Frankfurt, Mr Tex?' Yuri said, or it might have been Alex. 'I thought you'd come from Washington.'

'Oh I did. Yes sir, don't worry on that account. I was there yesterday. Got the full lunch treatment. Club sandwich. Couple of glasses of white. Milk, you understand. Your Mr Gorbachev would've approved. Surely would.'

There was more bobbing of the head as McAllister eased himself into operational mode. Jaeger turned quickly to Cox. 'The date again. December '89?'

'Right.'

'The Sovs were still the evil empire?'

'Crumbling at the edges.'

'And we're having a spies' get-together? They're still the enemy but we're having a joint planning session?'

Cox gestured at the screen.

McAllister was speaking. '. . . and in the morning I was

in Foggy Bottom – that's State to you – before going back to the Factory.'

'That's Langley to us,' a Russian said, and smirked.

'Now it's a long story,' McAllister said, 'which may find its way into the history books some day. We had meetings nine-to-five and then some. These are bureaucrats and a meeting is their natural habitat. Even their secretaries have meetings to fix when their bosses can meet up. OK, a lot of people wanted to get their objections on record. But we told them' – it seemed the Royal use of *We* – 'there is no record. There is only the decision. There is only here and only now. If you guys are worried about your pensions, you better walk. Of course, if you walk out this door, you might as well keep on walking, clearing your desk as you go. 'Cause if you don't play in the big games, why the hell are you on the team?'

The Russians weren't smiling now, just staring. Jaeger said in a low voice, 'McAllister played hard ball, always did.'

McAllister had the floor, metaphorically. He leaned an elbow on the table, the better to stab a finger at the Russians facing him, or to slip an aside to his own stooges. He was delivering what sounded like a well-honed lecture on the moral degeneracy of politicians. 'Let me enlighten you on the dangers of democracy, gentlemen, which I shall outlaw when I am dictator.' The Russians had sideways glances for themselves, not knowing if this was a wisecrack they should laugh at, the ranting of a megalomaniac, or the truth from a crafty old bird. 'OK, I was in Foggy Bottom, so named because it is so murky they can't see beyond the end of their pricks. I was with, oh let's call him the Chief Deputy to the Deputy Chief. They die for titles there. He was setting out parameters. You know what a parameter is? Heard about parameters?'

'A parameter is a limiting—' Fred the ex-embassy man began.

'A parameter,' McAllister cut right across him, 'is how far you can go before a politician begins to shit his pants. OK, the parameters here: No US lives at risk. No body-bags on CNN. No US property destroyed – we're not backing bloody red revolution, y'all hear?' His accent made a brief switch to the Texan he claimed. 'No overt US involvement. It's your backyard. It's your show. A nice clean operation while Uncle Sam is out doing the Christmas shopping.'

A Russian broke the silence. 'I want to be clear: the Soviet Union has the backing of the United States?'

'You got it. We are backing you. We are not fronting you. Nor are we fighting side by side with you. No sir, the Chief Deputy to the Deputy Chief said we stay in the background and our support will be characterized by meaningful silence. Silence is eloquent, silence is golden, he said.' McAllister sighed. 'Politicians never practise what they preach. Is that water in the carafe?'

'Yes.'

'I was afraid so. Water isn't good for my medical condition which is known as politicianitis. I'll let you guys in on what is loosely termed thinking in DC. Gorbachev is popular there. People can pronounce his name, the strawberry mark is a fashion concept, and Raisa is a whole lot sexier than Barbara. If Gorbachev was American he'd be a shoo-in for President in '92. So the cry echoes round the gigantic offices where great minds hone policy: Hey, we got to give Gorbie a hand, he's about to fall into this deep hole. He's been letting all these countries go free, your Czechs, your Germans, your you-name-it, and it's causing a stink round the samovars. He's giving our empire away, is the mutter among the grey men. Certain Generals have got together and are thinking a coup is in order. So we got to help him. Suppose we let Gorbie keep Romania, then maybe his Generals will stop breathing down his neck, they'll put Stalin back in his casket and the Soviet Union won't fall apart. Better we have one Gorbie to deal with than a dozen little fellows whose names we can't say. Great. That is the concept. Even the Great Communicator gets wheeled in on the act. He telephones A Certain Person. George, how are you keeping? Listen, George, you got to swing it for that nice Mr Gorbachev and it'll be good for you too. How come? Well, Romania is where the Pope lives, right, and the Pope is Polish and there are a whole lot of Polish voters in Chicago. So just make it right with Mr Gorbachev and you'll collect the Poles at the polls. George, that is a joke, you always used to laugh at my jokes. Oh shit.'

Now McAllister had the floor, literally. He went to the wall, raised his arms and placed his palms flat against the wood panelling. It was the position of a suspect being patted down by the cops. He stretched and strained and rotated his head then returned to the table. Everybody's eyes were on him the whole time. One of the Russians had half got up but was held back by a colleague's restraining touch.

'It's the overnight flight does it,' McAllister said. 'Always gets me in the fifth vertebra. That's the one to go for if you want to break someone's neck. Or so I've been told. Is it true?'

No one said anything.

'Only kidding. I wasn't going to try anything.'

But you could see how the wariness had gathered in the Russians' eyes.

'OK, so that's Mr President taken care of. All the Mr Presidents for all I know. Maybe they lined up Nixon, Carter, even Gerry Ford. Get that chewing gum out of your mouth and think straight. Then there were the neanderthals in the Senate to keep sweet. And all the tsars of Intelligence. Well, you know how it goes. You've got your own tsars in Moscow. Right? Right?'

Three heads nodded.

'So I would say everything has gone well. We've got the principle agreed. The practice, well the practice can always screw up. Real life gets in the way and kicks you—' He stopped, his mouth a thin line, his eyes suddenly narrow.

A bell had sounded a warning and every head turned to the right of the screen. To the table advanced a woman bearing a tray with cups, a sugar bowl and a glass jug of coffee. She put down the tray, her hip carelessly brushing the shoulder of one of the young Americans. She wore a blouse with large red poppies printed on it and the kind of jeans that hugged her figure in a way only capitalist jeans do. After due inspection of her, McAllister's eyes dropped to a notebook he had taken from his inner breast pocket.

Jaeger stared at the screen while he spoke to Cox. 'If it wasn't for McAllister, I'd say this was some kind of fake, disinformation. A TV movie without the car chase.'

'McAllister is the genuine article, not an impersonation?'

'No actor could do McAllister. McAllister *is* an actor. He's on stage. He's playing with those guys. And you never ran into him?'

'Never.'

'He did Asia, El Salvador, Beirut. Frankfurt was his last posting.'

'So we never met.'

The woman had walked out of screen. The American whose shoulder she had touched was gently rubbing the spot. 'She packs a good hip,' he said.

'Got the kind of legs I like,' a Russian said. 'One each side.'

McAllister raised his head from his notebook. 'When

you're ready.' The lads-in-the-locker-room atmosphere vanished. 'So you can report back to your tsars that you have the tacit backing of the United States government in any action taken to replace the Ceausescu regime by one more acceptable to the Kremlin. However . . .' The actor paused for emphasis. 'We do need to know we are in agreement on certain fundamentals. First, we do not ask to be told at this stage what precise action you propose. Meet again in a couple of days' time when Moscow has got its act together. Second, you may inform your tsars that the action should be appropriate, show just cause – protecting the lives of your citizens always sounds good – and that any action short of full-scale military invasion will be acceptable. Third, the timing. When?'

'About a week. A week, ten days.'

'Good. East Germany, Poland, all those places, Romania, we want to get it wrapped up. You know what I'm getting at? Make '89 a kind of marker, the year of change. Four, we believe a public trial of Ceausescu and his lovely wife would be counter-productive. Could be riots, attempts by Securitate elements to release him, so on. Executive action.'

Silence.

'I take that as your agreement. Five, who do you propose as a replacement for Ceausescu? Fred, care to speak?' McAllister produced a ballpen which he clicked. 'A name, Fred, who gets your vote? Spell it if it needs spelling.'

'There are many different ideas in Moscow,' Fred began.

'Differences which you will resolve to get what you have decided. Who is it, Fred?'

'The KGB favours the collegium approach, decisions shared, the spread of power, no one too strong.'

'Load of garbage, but it's your show. I need to tell Langley and thus Washington who the top dog will be. Or in your version the pack of hounds.'

The three Russians conferred while McAllister drummed a tattoo on the table with his fingers.

'At this stage we prefer not to give the names—'

A fist banged the table so hard a glass overturned. 'Goddam it, do you think the United States of America is going to do this big favour of saving Gorbachev's hide and not even know who we'll end up with? You're out of your minds. We back you but only if we have full access to your plans. Is that understood? Or do I have to tell the US government to prepare to denounce the blatant interference by the Soviet Union in Romania's affairs?'

Silence again.

'Names.'

'Stefanescu, Mihai. Iliescu, Ion . . .'

'One minute.' McAllister looked up from his writing. 'These are the Christian names you're giving me after the surnames? The first names come second?'

'Yes.'

'Crazy. Go on.'

'Mincu, Octav. Baritlu, Grigore. Those are the names that are agreed so far.'

'Men? All men?'

'Yes.'

'Get modern. You need a woman. Then you win the feminist vote.'

'Panovf, Iuliana, has been mentioned.'

McAllister was still writing when the screen went blank.

'Why?' Jaeger asked.

'Tape ran out,' Cox said, 'or Vasile cut it to remove some reference, or the other thing – the useful info was already given.'

'I meant why did they hatch this lunatic plan to go along with a Soviet-backed regime here?'

'Lucas, it's the way Langley was, it's what Langley's

always done, and from all accounts it's what Langley is like now. Come on, you know. The Agency likes to think it's running the world, backing an invasion here, a coup there, a dictator nearly anywhere. Somebody "clever"' – and Cox made inverted commas in the air with his fingers – 'says, Why don't we have a reformed communist regime in a not very important country and help Gorbachev.'

'And another why, two whys: why was the tape made, why wasn't it passed on up the line for action? For God's sake, it's a warning about a coup.'

Cox shrugged. 'Maybe it was in a Securitate house. Securitate wanted to get rid of Ceausescu. Maybe it was in a Soviet embassy house. Lucas, I don't know, I simply can't answer. It's one for the conspiracy theorists.'

Jaeger sighed and shook his head. 'Mr Tex. Got to remember that.'

They lapsed into their own musings. Cox thought he heard a thump from somewhere in the house: Tudor closing a door, Tudor dropping a shoe, Tudor with the heavily pregnant Magda astride him. He sighed in his turn.

'That bottle – have you emptied it?'

'Not yet.'

'My father always said not to drink before breakfast. Is going on four in the morning before breakfast?'

'Simple solution,' Jaeger said. 'Cut out breakfast, then it's drinking before lunch.' He divided the last of the brandy between their glasses. 'Here's to Roy's farewell tour. How about the second tape?'

'They didn't have the courtesy to speak in English. Your McAllister was not on stage. Other players as before. Friend Tudor here gave me a running commentary. The Soviets were proposing a small-scale infiltration. No tanks, not the old-style Soviet invasion. These would be KGB in civilian clothes posing as tourists and crossing the border in humdrum Ladas. There would be several hundred of them, Fred or Yuri said. Your two men were looking serious but nodding agreement. Then what? one asked. From information received Ceausescu plans to speak from his balcony. Usual crowd directed to cheer. Only this time the crowd would have the KGB implants – Romanian speakers from Moldova – who would shout and boo. Timisoara, the other riots, now the capital. The KGB were to give the ball a push and it would start rolling.'

'And so it came to pass,' Jaeger said. 'Ceausescu and Elena executed, according to plan. Different faces at the top but the same different faces, if you follow me. Hey ho.' Jaeger peered into his snifter and finding a few drops in the bottom tipped them into his mouth. 'So now what?'

Cox didn't reply. Jaeger's head turned sharply and he saw Cox running a thumbnail over his moustache, eyebrows drawn together, a man agonizing over a difficult choice.

'Now hold it,' Jaeger said. 'Whoa, pull up there. An ugly thought has entered my head that you think those tapes ought to be made public. Or maybe shown to selected persons and their policy advisers and their assistants and their mistresses. That would not be a good idea. Roy, listen. There are these neanderthals in Washington who said we were too soft on the Russians during the Cold War and are too soft on them now. Those tapes are just more bullets for their guns. They see the KGB planning a coup to put their own men in – and the CIA are cheering them on. Never mind that it happened in the bad old communist days. The KGB may be yesterday's news and now we have the Foreign Intelligence Service. But the neanderthals say that the KGB will always be the KGB, never mind the initials, and they're even more dangerous, just lulling us lazy . . .' He seemed to lose the direction of his sentence and started again. 'I can see Congressional enquiries, I can see people hauled out of retirement and put under the bright lights, I can see Langley turned upside down again to shake out the softies. I can even see myself being flown back in chains, my good name abused, my pension rights cut off because I personally haven't throttled the bad men with my own hands. There is a vicious mood in Washington these days. They want blood. If they can't get Clinton, someone else will have to be sacrificed.'

Jaeger was on his feet and he opened a cupboard door, revealing files not bottles. He swung back on Cox. 'So why did you get me out in the middle of the night to look at that tape? I know you Brits. Full of honour and duty to the Queen. But you go for the Nixon doctrine: when you've got a man by the balls, all you've got to do is give a little squeeze. You want something. Out with it.'

Cox had said nothing. He'd let Jaeger have the doubts and make the running. 'Lucas, you make it sound like blackmail, and that's a dirty word. So – you keep the tapes.'

Cox stopped there. He didn't want a resentful Jaeger, he wanted a helpful Jaeger. Let him take that on board: we've seen the evidence of CIA collusion with the KGB. Now the evidence will be yours. Do what you like with it. Jaeger had gone very still. His eyes were testing each facet of Cox's face. His ears seemed to be replaying Cox's words.

'We're on the same side, Lucas. We're standing back to back. You're fighting your neanderthals in Washington. I'm fighting my politicians in London. Now, I told you there was another tape.'

'Your blue movie. I'm not in the mood.'

Cox didn't listen. He inserted the Liliana tape in the video player. Despite saying he wasn't in the mood, at first Jaeger sat forward as if he couldn't get enough of it. Then he sat back to distance himself from it. He frowned when the urinating began. He bit his lip when Liliana was wrapped in the tablecloth. When it was over he looked at Cox and said, 'Well, I'll be damned.' No particular shock, no outrage, a voice as flat as the speaking clock. A post-coital calm settled over them which Cox was in no hurry to break. Let Jaeger take his time.

'All right,' Jaeger said. 'I've seen the tapes. Tell me how things are. I'm all grown up and I reckon I can handle it.'

'It's bad,' Cox began.

Jaeger gave a tired little smile. Bad was their world, bad was their reason for existing, bad was the battle that was never quite won. Bad was the other half of them and without it they would be incomplete.

'It was bad to begin with and it's got worse.'

'The word is *gotten*. Speak proper, can't you.'

Cox smiled his tired old smile in return. Jaeger had pushed his anger on to the back burner.

'In Whitehall,' Cox said, 'they say that any important proposal you're putting before a Minister should be short enough to fit on a postcard. So, I'm sending you this postcard. It goes like this. On the first tape the Russians mentioned Octav Mincu as one of their potential leaders. He was acceptable to them. Mincu in fact is not in the government but he is a powerful man, connections everywhere. He's an arms dealer, offering chemical weapons to the warring tribes in Bosnia. He is the reason I came to Bucharest. Mincu is the one on the tape we've just seen who carried off the naked girl, by name Liliana Branoza. He is trying to carry her off again, this time to assist him in his chemical weapons deal – she is an interpreter. All that is bad enough, but now it gets nastier. On that same tape, following Mincu out of the room, is a man I recognized. He's called Wix.'

'Wix and Cox – great names you guys have. What does he do when he's not partying?'

'Wix is Deputy Chairman of the Tory Party in England.

You can say that is the respectable side of him. Sir Terence, knighted for public services, and so on. Knows all the big names, raises cash for the Party, does the round of the constituencies, activists love him. Then the other side of him is his business interests, a directorship here, a consultancy there. We've had occasion to take an interest in him before but, well, we were advised he'd done nothing illegal. One company he advises is ESI. ESI stands for Executive Systems International. Death merchants really. Arms for Allah and any crazy who will pay. A man was killed tonight to try to get that Liliana tape. The KGB-CIA tapes weren't of interest. Just the Liliana tape because it shows Mincu and Wix together.'

'Together six years ago.'

'If they'll kill to get the tape, it's because they're together now. Wix can buy people: politicians, civil servants, our man here.'

'Randy Andy?'

'The same. Wix is helping fix things again. I know it. I don't have to see his signature on a piece of paper. I can feel it in my bones. I can sense it in the air. Do you understand?'

Jaeger nodded. It's what the person in the field understood and what the person behind the desk said was just the jitters.

'There's more, of course, there's always more,' Cox said. 'But that is the postcard version.'

'Longest damn postcard I ever received.' Jaeger was massaging the back of his head as if there was an ache there. 'What was that medical condition McAllister said he had?'

'Politicianitis.'

'Politicianitis, right. Roy, I guess you and I are suffering from the same disease. Fatal, is it?'

'Sometimes.'

Chapter 17

They talked for three-quarters of an hour or more, sometimes of practical things, sometimes of the state of the world and mankind's ability to foul it up. It reminded Cox of those long ago all-night sessions at university. *Do I believe in God? Don't be an eejit. That's not the point at all. You should be asking – does God believe in me? Martin, old chap, that bottle isn't empty, is it?*

'We owe,' Cox said.

'Owe what? Owe who?' Jaeger was confused.

'We owe the Romanians for their half-cocked revolution. We owe the Bosnians and the Serbs that we don't close our eyes while Chummy slips in his stuff.'

'Chummy?'

'Mincu the smiler, the rapist, the pal of the KGB, the arms merchant.'

'McAllister retired,' Jaeger said. 'Couple of years back. I hear he got himself a place in Maine, up near Bar Harbour. God, that bastard, I could kick his butt for agreeing to back a bunch of KGB friendlies. Look at the mess this place is. Half-million buck apartments one end, barefoot kids the other, casinos in the middle.'

'The Middle East starts here.'

Jaeger frowned at that. Then, in one of those late night

swings of mood, he patted his pocket and said, 'The tape goes into the deep nuclear bunker. If it ever got out, it would crucify McAllister. The guy is still a legend but the neanderthals would be baying about him being a traitor.'

Perhaps Jaeger saw Cox as a legend too. Cox remembered their lunch and talk of fleeing to the Bulgarian border. Perhaps Jaeger thought there was a reflected glow in helping a legend. He hoped so.

On the way out, as he was about to unlock the front door, instinct made Cox swing round. Tudor Harasteanu, in a blue silk dressing gown, was standing halfway down the stairs. He took slow careful steps towards them as if afraid a creaking board would disturb Magda. Jaeger had turned back, so Cox said, 'This is Tudor. It's his house.'

'You're the friendly friend.'

Tudor gave a little puzzled shake of his head.

'We're on our way,' Cox said. 'Time is getting short.'

'Can I be of any help to you?'

'There was dust on Lenin's head,' Jaeger said. 'That's not right. The guy was a wholesale disaster for the twentieth century but there was never any dust on him. Just thought you ought to know.'

Jaeger turned the car and headed back into the centre of the city.

'Where can I take you?'

'Oh, just sort of in the centre.'

'Just sort of in the centre,' Jaeger mimicked. There was a tense silence while he digested this, uncertain whether to be angry at the evasion. 'We're on the same side, you know. Meant to be buddies.'

'Lucas, we are buddies, very tired buddies and maybe our patience is stretched to its limit. I'm not playing some tricksy game. I want to use a public telephone to see if I can raise Liliana. I want to visit a place I know she goes when she's disturbed. Also I want to walk a bit. I find things settle themselves in my mind when I'm walking by myself.'

'I just thought it will be dawn soon and you might like to get your head down for a bit.'

'I keep promising myself that,' Cox said. 'But now I understand why there is that sign at the back entrance to the Glasshouse in London: No rest for the wicked.'

Jaeger drove on in silence. He took small backstreets like a man familiar with the city. Cox turned once, thinking he recognized the British Council building he had visited. But that was a whole lifetime ago. Jaeger entered the Piatsa Romana and drew into the kerb.

'This do you? Central enough?'

'This is fine.'

'Listen. About your boy Andy. Do you want me to send a couple of my finest round to see him? A little talk? You know what I mean. Get a voluntary statement from him.'

'I don't think that would be wise.'

'What's wisdom got to do with it? That Andy knows stuff we could shake out of him. Roy, they're about to raise the curtain on the final act and the script isn't even written. You need all the help you can get.'

Cox had got out. Now he leaned down, put an elbow on the window frame and spoke to Jaeger.

'Call it a hunch. Another way of saying that is thirty-nine years' experience. Or maybe it's senile dementia. But I don't think Andy Crake is working to Mincu. He's working to Wix.' He patted his pocket. 'It was the tape I've got showing Wix that they were interested in, not the tape you've got that mentions Mincu and the KGB and CIA getting together. Let things run their course. Don't alarm them.'

Crake was standing in the shadow of the church of St Peter and St Paul. He remembered being at school, prep school, the boarding school before his father lost all his money to a swindler in Switzerland. *Do you sincerely want to be poor?* his father had muttered, aghast at the newspaper headlines at breakfast. *Well then, you're a roaring success.* It turned out it wasn't just his father's money that was gone but an unofficial loan from the printing works where he was a director. His father had disappeared and later rumours said he had started a new life in Santa Cruz in the lowlands of Bolivia, financial wizard to certain cocaine barons. Young Crake had returned to school after the half-term break because after all the fees were paid. Thereafter he was tossed into the state school pond to sink or swim or just tread water.

Crake stared at the tiny stained-glass windows planted in the grimy brickwork and wondered if there were lights and people inside. He looked at the entrance porch, so dark and beckoning. He remembered being outside his school chapel when Rowe, an older boy in his last year, had said, Come on into the vestry, I want to show you something, you're not a scaredy cat, afraid the Holy Ghost will get you? The chapel had been too dark even to see ghosts. A nightlight shone in front of the Calvary and Rowe had tugged the young Crake's arm and drew him into the vestry. Rowe had been fumbling with his own clothes and said sharply, Here, cop hold of this. Crake had found Rowe's member thrust into his hand, bigger and stiffer than anything he had seen before. Move your fingers, Rowe had ordered. Twat, I'll show you how. Crake had felt Rowe's hand delving inside his shorts and Rowe muttering, Cor, you've got a tiddler, needs some exercise to make it grow. Crake had broken away, stumbled over a pew, scrambled up and made for the chapel door with Rowe's hot voice behind him, the Calvary threatening him, the Holy Ghost pursuing him.

So money, sex and religion. From the age of eleven

Crake had known those were the dark forces at work in everyone's life.

He pushed open the door and slipped into the church, standing against the wall while his eyes adjusted to the dimness. There was a nightlight by the Calvary – yes, he remembered. Two candles burned in a sandtray in front of a statue in a niche. There was no other light source. He kept absolutely still, just his eyes slipping from shadow to shadow. But neither his eyes nor his ears told of another person. He was alone.

Liliana retreats to this church when she is troubled. That's what Gabriela had told him. Why? Does she come to meet some priest? Confess some secret sin that troubles her? She goes there to talk to God, Gabriela told him severely. Apparently God does not listen to her anywhere else. God is too busy or asleep or playing three-handed bridge with Peter and Paul. How does she talk to God? She writes letters, reminding Him to do certain things. Also, Gabriela had said, she sometimes writes letters to other people. No, Panda, I don't know why. It is a comfort, I think. Like it is a comfort to you when I touch you . . . like so . . .

There was the table covered with oilcloth that Gabriela had told him of. Supplicants post their letters under the offertory box, just stuff them under it. Later the letters are burned so that the smoke will rise to heaven and be delivered to God's address. The previous day's letters must have been burned because he found only one sheet. He carried it across the nave to the statue in a niche and tilted the letter to catch the candle light.

Dear Mr Cox, he read.

Crake closed his eyes and drew a breath and thanked whatever stars controlled his destiny that he had found the letter before it fell into Cox's hands or was delivered up to God.

Dear Mr Cox,

I am worried about you. First I tried telephoning you at the flat where I saw you and you held my hand and transmitted courage to me.

Crake tried to picture the two of them on a settee, with Liliana holding Cox's hand. Not holding anything else? Not one of Rowe's disciples? His eyes skipped down the page, caught by a name.

Tonight the ogre Mincu has telephoned me and I used up all my store of courage simply listening to him and making sense of the words he spoke. He definitely needs me later today (it is now the wee hours, as you say). He says a ship's captain is arriving, a Belgian who does not speak Romanian so I must interpret his French. There will also be an Englishman present so I can interpret for him too. Mincu says the captain's English is basic, mostly for swearing at the crew who come from Asia. But there must be some culture in him somewhere because his ship is called Cleopatra. You are surprised? Mincu asked me. But I have seen Elizabeth Taylor in the film. I like Cleopatra. She is a woman of very great experience.

It was terrible. His voice reached out on the telephone to touch me.

Mr Cox, I must see you again. For courage. To hear once more that what I have to do is important. I think God will guide you to this church and you will find this letter. If not, I pray God will guide your footsteps to the meeting place I suggest. Near the Capitol Hotel is a small passage that leads to Academy Street. I shall be in the café there at 9.

Liliana.

The letter had been written with a black ballpoint pen. Crake's pen was similar. By the light of the candle he made a discreet alteration to the end of the note. He held the paper with his thumb over her signature and touched it to the candle. He watched it burn until it was almost scorching his finger. Blowing out the flame he dropped what remained of the note into the sandtray. From the store of candles he selected the largest, one that would burn for hours. He stuck that into the sandtray by the charred letter.

Crake remembered an interview he had had in a building just off Whitehall before he was recruited into the Glasshouse. *Afraid the Foreign Office fought shy of taking you but thought we might be interested. It was something to do with your father,* the personnel officer had said. He gave something of a smirk. *Whereas we believe that a little criminality in the genes is not always a bad thing.*

Was that the first pink hint of dawn brightening across the rooftops or just the glow of another neon sign? Pepsi-Cola, Fiat, Levi's – the sun would definitely be rising in the west, Cox decided. Jaeger had done a full circuit of the Piatsa Romana and disappeared down the same street they had just travelled. As Cox's head followed Jaeger's progress he ticked off the people. A couple of dozen, maybe others he couldn't make out in the shadows. A car was parked and a pair of policemen watched and waited. For what? They weren't interested in the girls who stood by the kerb, each with the little hatbox of her trade. Cox had been spied out, Cox was being watched, and as he began to walk the nearest girl came towards him. Her face brightened with the light of her smile.

'Guten abend, chéri.'

Cox lifted a finger to his lips. Hush. Baffled, her smile switched off. Cox passed her. The second girl stepped out from the shelter of a doorway. She brought entertainment with her, the tinny sound of a cheap radio in her hatbox.

Radio Contact, he thought, remembering Gabriela. In a moment the music would stop and the announcer would read out his horoscope. You will meet a tall dark smiling stranger and he will take out a gun and shoot you. When Cox raised a finger to his lips to silence her offer of love, she had her own response. She lifted a finger to her lips and blew Cox a kiss. From the shadow of the doorway came a man's low laugh. Her pimp, Cox supposed. He cut away down a street where he saw a wall-mounted public telephone.

By a miracle the telephone wasn't occupied and when he lifted the receiver off its hook it gave a respectful hum: I am your servant and I await your command. It is going to be a day of miracles, he decided. Wix the Wicked will be revealed to be here arranging adoptions of Romanian orphans, Mincu will be sending blankets and medical supplies to the Bosnians, and Liliana's sleepy love-sated voice will answer the telephone.

A-one, a-two, I'm a bandleader counting for you, Liliana, like I've counted for you before. He listened to the rings. Pick up the telephone, be angry with me for waking you up, but just answer, let me know you are in the land of the living. It's Gabriela's good uncle calling. I'll be your good uncle too, your father, your grandfather. I could even be Gabriela's bad uncle Maximillian if that pleases you. But she wasn't going to answer the telephone, no matter how long he let it ring or what promises he made to her in his head. It was the night before battle. The General doesn't sleep, nor do the poor bloody infantry. A car's headlights swept over him, then another's, then he was alone again. He pressed the hook down to cut the connection and redialled, Crake's number. No answer either. Well then, miracles were being saved for later.

He started to walk. About two blocks, he told himself, a bit to the south, a bit to the west. It wasn't as if he had the Plough or the Bear to guide him because city lights or cloud cover had killed the stars. He had the gift of knowing which way to go as if he had a compass in his head. It wasn't a skill he had learned; it had always been there.

He saw the canopy over the door first, then the bulge of a great horseshoe tricked out in light bulbs and a sign that said: The Lucky Horseshoe. All the casinos had English names. He couldn't remember if Gabriela had said this was a casino she had been to with Crake, nor even if she had given him a name. But the next closest was behind the Capitol Hotel and he didn't want to go there; and the others he had noted were further away.

The doorman was kitted out as a US cavalry officer, Hollywood 1937. He leaned against the wall and was enjoying a yawn until he saw that Cox had stopped to inspect the photos in the display box. He spoke first in Italian, which Cox found a refreshing change, then in English.

'You want to go in? The gentleman very welcoming. Pretty girls. You like girl? Whisky?'

Was casino a euphemism? Like massage parlour or bagnio? But he saw a photo of men and women intent on a roulette wheel and another picture of a man holding dollar bills like a fan and grinning.

'Thought I might try my luck,' Cox said. 'Maybe I'll win the croupier's shirt.'

The doorman smiled with his mouth but his eyes had the glower of someone who did not understand. Cox noticed that where the cavalry officer would have a pistol, this man had a cosh. He unlocked the door and Cox knew no one left here until their debts were settled. He found himself ushered into what was no more than a passage with a desk to one side and a coat rail behind. He saw a couple of dozen empty coathangers and two dark raincoats. The passage made a right-angle turn. As he rounded the corner the manager appeared from his office. He wore a tuxedo with a fancy silver-threaded waistcoat and a string tie. He asked to see Cox's passport. Cox regretted he did not carry it with him at night 'in case the outlaws get me'. The manager frowned and asked for Cox's name and hotel. Cox gave a name and explained he was staying privately. He gave the address of the flat Gabriela had taken him to. The manager looked even more troubled but relented because, he said, he could see the mister was an English gentleman. Cox smiled his grave smile, his English gentleman's smile, and inclined his head. The manager regretted they would be closing in thirty minutes. That was what the authorities in their short-sighted way decreed, though it was always possible to arrange something private.

Cox passed through a pair of half-height swing doors. Welcome to the Last Chance Saloon. That is what it was like inside. Themed, Jaeger would call it. The bar was curved like half a horseshoe. The walls were wood panelled. Signs announced the times of the stagecoach to Laramie, warned against spitting and blaspheming, and promised whiskey at 10 cents. There was an upright piano and a tiny stage where a husky Marlene Dietrich would ask What the Boys in the Back Room would have. But the music that came from little speakers was subdued country, fiddle, guitar and accordeon. Since Marlene couldn't be present she had sent two of her girls decked out in fishnet stockings and costumes like swimsuits with flouncy skirts. The costumes were tight with uplift to make the bosom swell. Cox remembered a sort of spies' night out in a Munich club and his German host calling it a lot of wood in front of the hut. The girls' eyes lifted and Cox shook his head to dampen their interest. The room wasn't large but it had pillars so he assumed the rear of two buildings had been knocked together. There were five tables, only one busy at the tail end of the night. A croupier in black trousers, white shirt with metal concertina bands round the sleeves and a string tie. Two men in suits, a girl apiece. At a table next to a pillar sat a solitary man with a sheriff's star on his chest.

Cox ambled to the bar. The changing perspective confirmed there was no one else in the room. The barman put a cigarette into an ashtray under the counter and moved to serve Cox. No more brandy. This was definitely before breakfast and Cox felt that tightening of concentration that announced the dawn of D-Day. He ordered tomato juice. The barman wore a striped waistcoat and string tie and goldish cufflinks with a horseshoe motif. He had the broad face and slightly oriental features that Cox associated with Hungarians, the eyes pressed into slits from gazing across snow-covered steppes, the mouth half smiling as he took the money.

'It's not busy,' Cox said as an opener.

The smile broadened.

'Not many people,' Cox went on.

The eyes pressed tighter until they were like arrowslits.

'Couple of punters. And the girls. It's late, of course. That would explain it.' Cox felt he had beaten that subject to death.

'Yes?' the barman responded. 'Whisky? Nice time?'

'Thank you, no, I'm having a nice time already.' The myth was that taxi drivers and barmen were the source of all information but Cox abandoned the idea. *Akarhattalak,* he remembered. Possibly. *De nem szerethettelek.* Definitely not.

Cox ambled back through the saloon doors to the corridor where the manager's door stood open. The manager was murmuring into a telephone but as Cox stood in the doorway he put the receiver down.

'Please?'

'I wonder if you can help me.'

'You don't see what you like? You have special request?'

'Your establishment is above reproach,' Cox assured him. 'But I have a problem.'

'A problem? No problem. I know many girls, boys, what you like.'

'Decent of you but my problem is that I am looking for someone. We agreed to meet in a casino but I cannot remember which one.'

'This is the best,' the manager said. 'Very good place. No trouble. Good prices. Good girls, very clean.'

'True, but you see I am looking for this one particular person. His name is Crake, Andrew Crake. People sometimes call him Andy or even Panda.'

It was on the drive into the city centre that Cox had decided he must get after Crake. He didn't want the voluntary confession that Jaeger offered to get, signed in blood. If he tracked Crake down he might make use of him, tell him that he hadn't got the tape with Wix on it, that Vasile was murdered, and that he Cox was hightailing it out. Crake would tell Wix, Wix would tell Mincu, and the heat would subside. But at the mention of Crake's name a stiffness came into the manager's face.

'Shut the door kindly. You are Mr Peace, you say?'

'Preece.'

'Mr Preece, sit down kindly.'

'I prefer to stand.' To be on your feet, he knew, was to be one step closer to the door.

'No problem. Mr Preece, why you wish to find Mr Crake? He is friend of yours?'

'It is a matter of some delicacy.'

'I don't understand.'

'It is private business.'

'What kind of private business?'

'If I say it is private business, that is what it is. Private. I don't discuss it.'

At first the manager looked ready to argue with that, then his face lightened. 'You are English gentleman, I think, so I accept that.' The manager made a gracious gesture with both hands. 'You say you are not a friend, though you have private business with him. How can this be?'

'You and I have only just met so we are not friends.' Cox was patient with the manager. 'But if I were to tell you where you could get Cutty Sark Scotch at half price, that would be private business.'

'I understand,' the manager said. 'But also I think that if you told me that you would be my very good friend.'

They both smiled. The manager grew serious.

'Mr Crake used to come here. Sometimes he play a little. Sometimes he is friendly with the girls. Sometimes he have a drink, two drinks, nothing too much. I am talking about two years ago. No, not so much. I forget time. I live at night and the days are not real. One and a half years, maybe less. Then he comes one night and the security guard warns me he is drunk, little drunk, not loud drunk. He begin to play like he hasn't before. He has lei and he changes them into dollars and he loses. He changes English pounds into dollars and he wins a little and he smiles and then he loses. Then he shows credit card, no problem. And he loses. He is very unlucky man to lose so much.'

Cox slipped in a question in a low voice. 'A lot? How much did he lose?'

'The lei? Nothing. The pounds? I forget. But MasterCard I remember. We play in dollars here. It was twenty-two thousand eight hundred dollars. The whisky extra.'

Close on fifteen thousand pounds, Cox was thinking.

'But when we try with MasterCard they say no, his credit is all used up.'

'Twenty-two thousand eight hundred dollars is a lot of washing up.'

The manager looked puzzled by this remark, seemed disposed to take it as criticism of standards in his casino. But at that moment there were voices in the corridor and his attention shifted there. Cox listened too. Americans, maybe visitors to Liliana's Trade Fair. It was the men who had been playing roulette and the girls with them. There was discussion about whether the hotel would expect payment if the girls went to their rooms.

The manager recapped, 'Twenty-two thousand eight hundred dollars. Anyway, there is another Englishman playing and he says: Leave him alone, take your hands off him, I will pay. And I say: Do you know this man? Is he friend of yours? He says: No, but he is Englishman like me. I shall pay and tomorrow I take him to embassy to arrange things and see he flies home.'

'What a kind Englishman. But Mr Crake didn't fly home. He is here in Bucharest now.'

'Is true. He came here two weeks later. I hear him arguing with the doorman who will not let him in. So I go to speak to him. I say: All right, Mr Crake, you can come in, you can talk to the girls, you can have whisky. But play at roulette? Listen to what I tell you. Only one bet. Cash-cash, on the table. Otherwise maybe you go crazy again. And that is how it stays. One bet and no credit.'

'You are a wise man,' Cox said. 'But Mr Crake hasn't been here tonight? Had his one bet?'

'No, because the doorman always says to me when he comes.'

'You know, I think I have heard some of that story back in London. You know, at my club. That kind Englishman, it wasn't Wickstead by any chance?'

But Cox's probing seemed to rouse the suspicion in the manager. His lips were pressed together as if to keep the words in.

'Actually,' Cox lowered his voice, 'it's *Lord* Wickstead.'

'Something like that,' the manager allowed. 'Name is maybe shorter.'

'Like the man himself,' Cox said, raising his hand shoulder high.

Always try to leave on a bit of a joke, they said in the Glasshouse. A smile is your best exit.

Cox was walking again, west and then tacking to the north. Checking back over his shoulder he saw there was definite lightening in the sky. And no clouds. It was going to be a fine day.

So there we have it, Cox thought, the connection between Crake and Wix. Cox was crossing Piatsa Revolutiei. There was a name with lasting power. This revolution, the one before, the one to come. It could be used again and again, not like calling streets after politicians. Away to his right an imposing house had been gutted by an explosion, its roof blown off, bullet holes pocking its walls, soot streaks blackening the stonework. This square had seen some of the worst fighting in 1989. Mincu had come unscathed out of the botched revolution, his pal Wix still pulled levers back in London, and Crake ran errands and pimped for them. Why had Wix bailed Crake out? It was the bond of being English, Cox decided. Wix was of the Eurosceptic persuasion in the Tory Party, a polite way of saying he despised foreigners. Foreigners could do what they liked to one another and usually did, beat, torture, massacre and rape. It was expected of those who did not have God's blessing of being born English. But no foreigner could touch a hair of an Englishman.

Cox angled across the square past the National Art Gallery. It was still supported on crutches of scaffolding. Behind him now was the building that had once been the headquarters of the Communist Party. He remembered his earlier visit, when he had had to leave the country in a hurry, how he had got too close to the Communist Party headquarters and police had shouted and waved their arms to drive him away. The building was untouched. The security forces had been inside shooting out and the National Art Gallery had been in the line of fire.

Foreigners could even drop poison gas on each other. That, too, was all right by Wix. If there was ever a revolution in Britain and the people stormed the Party headquarters, Cox hoped the men who had the guns would all be on the outside and Terence Wix would be on the inside.

Chapter 18

A gypsy cart came down the street, a whole family squatting in the back. The horse's hooves were as loud as pistol shots on the cobbles. The wheels were clad in car tyres, making no sound. A battered lorry swerved round the cart to overtake on the wrong side of the road, a cloud of diesel smoke washing over the cart. Finally there was a tram, clanging its bell. From habit Cox noted its number. It was going to the Gara de Nord, round the next bend.

With the burst of traffic finished, Cox crossed to the side of the street with the Church of St Peter and St Paul. It was a silhouette against the dawn sky. He made out the little stained-glass windows, black against the black wall. Different shades of black? Was that possible? Maybe there was some light inside the church. Liliana had lit a candle or two. There was a movement behind him and when Cox turned he saw a boy standing quite close. He looked eight or nine. Could be eleven before he'd put on his spurt of growth. The boy was barefoot and was staring up at him.

'What do you want?' Cox asked.

The boy stared.

'Did Fagin send you?'

After a moment or two Cox took a wad of currency from his pocket and peeled off two 500-lei notes. The boy cupped his hands together to accept the money. He ran across the road, turned to look at Cox before disappearing into a gap between two houses. Was I sorry for him? A guilty conscience? I did it for luck, Cox decided. He pushed open the gate and went up the path.

He shut the door of the church and stood with his back against it. He had the feeling he was not alone. A night light burned beneath the Calvary. A large candle was planted in the sandtray and its flame swayed in the air current made by the door. The little windows high up showed pale with the dawn sky. He could see no one. When someone walked out of a church, did he leave an echo of himself behind? How about all the prayers that had been murmured here, were they trapped, floating about, unable to find a way out? He looked at the iron stove where the written prayers were burned. His eyes followed the long metal chimney that carried their hopes and fears up to the sky. He shook his head. No sleep, the brain began sparking with fancy ideas.

In strictly operational terms Cox was now going to clear a dead letter drop. First he walked up the nave, checked the side chapels, tried the door to what was presumably the vestry and found it locked. There really was no one. He went to the table covered in oilcloth and slipped his hand under the offertory box. Nothing. He tried to lift the box but a short length of chain secured it. He felt again. It puzzled him. Liliana had been out all night. Here was where she came when she felt troubled. Under the offertory box was where she posted her pleas to God. He bent to peer underneath. Nothing.

When he straightened he was facing the statue of whichever saint it was in its niche. Or was it the BVM? He couldn't make out from where he stood. The sandtray with its candle held him. A big candle, a big prayer. It was a candle that demanded to be noticed and when he stood over it he saw the blackened ashes and charred remains of a letter. It was mostly burned and scattered but he could make out two or three words. He picked the candle out of the sand and brought the flame low. *For coura,* he could make out. Also *God* on a flake of paper that had burned black with the writing showing up grey. The rest was too fragmentary to make sense of: *ain, pret f, Itu.*

But there was also a scrap of paper, the bottom of the sheet, that hadn't burned. When the flame reached the fingers, the paper had been dropped on the sand. The flame had sputtered and died. The candle was dripping wax so he jammed it back in the sand and lifted the paper and held it towards the wavering light. *itol Hotel is a small passage that leads to Academy Street. I shall be in the café there at 8.* It was signed *Liliana.*

Three chairs were jammed against the wall near the statue. Or it could be for queuing for the confessional. He'd overlooked the confessional so he checked it now – empty – then sat on one of the chairs.

She comes in here some time during the night, writes a letter most probably to me and then . . . and then burns it. Did that make sense? Or somebody else burned it, all except the piece at the end which gave a rendezvous. Did that make sense either?

The door of the church opened, letting in daylight. It was a woman dressed in black, bent over, using a cane to help her walk. The door swung shut so that the dark returned but only for a moment. She knew where the light switch was and four small lamps on the walls lightened the gloom. She crossed herself, forehead to chest, right to left, three times. She came further into the church, lowered herself to her knees and prayed. Cox watched her. She hauled herself upright and started on a tour of the church and at every statue and every painting she crossed herself three times. She arrived at the statue in the niche and crossed herself. Cox sat expectantly. He was next. She stopped in front of him but didn't cross herself. She spoke to him.

Cox smiled and shook his head. 'Well now, madam, I am not at all sure about that.'

She shifted the cane to her other hand so she could reach out to touch his shoulder. Her head was tilted to one side so she could see him better. She was asking some question.

'I expect you're wondering why I'm sitting here. Am I an early penitent? Got some urgent sin to get off my conscience? Well, maybe I have. Maybe I have at that.'

Liliana had called it a *passage*. An alley, he would settle for that. The Capitol Hotel was less than two hundred metres away but he'd never come down this alley before. No, alley was maybe the wrong word. Alley was dark and smelly. This was a corridor joining Victoriei and Academiei Streets. It had a couple of shops, a shuttered casino, a place with a sign saying 'American Pool'. On one side was a restaurant with a narrow terrace fronted by tubs of greenery. Two crates of empty mineral water bottles stood by its entrance. On the other side was what Cox assumed was Liliana's café. An awning sheltered outdoor tables. He could hear voices inside. No one sat outside. It was still early. A pretty young waitress came out and handed him a menu. He ordered coffee and a ham sandwich, my dear. Her hair was gathered by an elastic band and really did swish like a pony's tail as she went away.

Which way down the passage would Liliana come? Which way should he face? She'd see him either way. But he liked to see a person first, to see their private face before they put on their public face. Everybody had a public self and a private self. There was one more: there was a secret self. It was the one you tried to keep in its box. Cox's public self wanted to stop Mincu and would make use of Liliana. His private self wanted to protect Liliana, wanted her to pull out, it was too dangerous, it wasn't her battle. And his secret self? The one he queued at the confessional for? Did he have a secret fantasy? Perhaps it was to rescue Liliana. Ilona, he thought, I never rescued you.

'Mr Cox!'

He looked up from the plate where the ham sandwich lay half eaten. Andrew Crake was leaning over the wooden rail that marked the edge of the café's terrace.

'Are you all right? I've been worried about you.'

'Why, Andrew. Well met.' Cox stared at him, thinking, You've never been worried about anyone except yourself the whole of your life. 'Good of you to worry. Something new? I mean, to make you worry?'

It sounded like the news on the radio from inside the café. Crake had turned back to come through the entrance in the railing. Cox thought he heard the word 'Dayton' on the news. There was nothing Cox recognized about a murder at the Museum of National History. Also Archaeology. Then Crake was pulling out a chair to sit down.

'This is a stroke of luck. I was going to the Capitol to check, cutting through this passage, and here you are.'

He gave an order to the waitress. He spoke English. He should be speaking Romanian by now. Gabriela ought to give him lessons. This was – what – the fourth time he'd seen Crake. He'd made the courtesy call at the embassy. They'd met at the Enescu Museum where he'd assured Crake the Americans knew nothing. Well, they did now. In the park he thought Crake lacked commitment. And Crake had moaned that Bucharest was a backwater. Was plain old boredom the explanation? Could Cox go back and tell Personnel that Crake hadn't had enough to do? Some became drunks, some doubled with the other side, some gambled. Crake had done all of that.

Cox was watching Crake, not his face, watching his hands as he spoke, how they couldn't keep still. Sometimes his hands clenched into fists, then they moved a cup or a plate as if searching for something, now they rested on the table, palms up. Cox was reminded of the boy near the church, how he'd cupped his hands. The boy had been shaping up to dip into Cox's pocket, then he was begging.

All the time Crake was talking, about telephoning the Capitol, how the receptionist said he wasn't answering the phone in his room. Then Crake was told Cox had gone out. Finally, this morning, he was told Cox hadn't been in all night.

'Then I began to worry. This can be a dangerous city.'

'I thought you complained it was a backwater, nothing happened.'

Crake seemed to have his speech all prepared and the interruption made his hands clench again.

'There are dangerous areas. Drunks. If you're walking in the dark on your own—'

'The Middle East starts here.'

'People get mugged. Or murdered. Only this morning there was something on the news about a body found at the Museum of National History.'

'Also Archaeology.' Cox looked up at Crake's face. 'That's the way Gabriela said it to me.'

There! Crake was back into his stride again. 'Mr Cox, that's another reason I was coming to see you. I wanted to warn you about Gabriela. I think she knows Mincu. She may even be working for him.'

'What?'

It shocked Cox. For a moment his brain seized up, his heart seemed to stop. Gabriela working for Mincu? That was insane. That wasn't possible. Was it? No, it couldn't be. But he had certain images in his head: of Gabriela waiting outside his hotel last night and the security guard backing away after he'd seen they had met; of going into the room at the top of the museum, how Gabriela had not screamed but had actually pushed past him to inspect Vasile's body and had spoken so calmly, saying he was dead.

Gabriela in Mincu's pay? There was too much to rearrange in his mind and Crake was giving him no time. Now he had important information to give about Wix. He had telephoned London, first to Wix's penthouse flat, then to the Conservative Party headquarters, finally to his office in Northumberland Avenue. Wix, he learned, had come to Romania. Among his business interests he was also the wine adviser to a cruise line – a Norwegian one, Crake thought – and had come to taste the '94s that were being bottled.

'Staying in Bucharest?' Cox asked, looking up at Crake's face.

'He was. He left yesterday. It was just an amazing coincidence he was here. He flew on to Sofia. Also wine business.'

Cox's eyes dropped back down to his plate. He hadn't finished the sandwich. Perhaps the salami would have been better. He wished he'd had some sleep. Nothing made sense in his head, amazing revelations about Gabriela, amazing coincidences with Wix.

'Why do you think Gabriela is working for Mincu?'

'I have no proof. But last night I found a piece of paper she had dropped – she writes notes to herself because of her bad memory, Buy coffee, Make dentist appointment – and she'd written: Telephone O.M.'

'In English? So you would understand?'

'It is much the same in Romanian.'

Nothing was clear to Cox. Why had Gabriela taken him to see the tape in the first place? She'd said it was to help Cox understand Liliana. But Cox had been more interested in Mincu and Wix. Then they'd gone a second time to see the tape and found Vasile murdered. If she was working for Mincu, why do that? Well . . .

Cox said, 'We believe – more than believe, *know* – Mincu is up to something but we have no hard evidence. On the other hand, the evidence of my being in the room with the murdered Vasile is abundant. My fingerprints are everywhere. It seems that for the second time in my career I have to tiptoe out of the country.'

'I can get you a ticket,' Crake said. 'BA has a flight this afternoon. I know someone at BA. If the flight is full, I'll get them to bump one of the other passengers.'

Cox considered Crake, contrasting his dullness in Cismigiu Park with his eager-to-help air now.

'A British Airways ticket in the name of Cox is not my idea of tiptoeing out,' Cox said. 'Besides, I'm not passing through any X-ray security check with this.'

He patted both jacket pockets, one with Vasile's pistol, the other with the tape of Liliana, Mincu and Wix. For a moment they seemed to sit in a pool of pure silence, the noise of the traffic faded, the voices of passers-by stilled. Cox saw how Crake's eyes dropped and fixed on the pocket nearest him.

'There *is* something you can do for me,' Cox said. Crake's eyes held on his pocket for another beat before snapping up to his face. 'Tomorrow you can go to my hotel, settle my account and collect my things. Get your friend at BA to air-freight my bag to Heathrow.'

'What do I tell them at the hotel?'

'You'll think of something. No problem.' Cox thought it was the first time in his life he'd said *No problem.*

At the end of the passage they separated, Crake going north in the direction of the embassy, Cox heading the other way. Cox turned to watch Crake, how he darted between the traffic as he crossed the road, and once on the pavement never slowed.

Twenty-two thousand eight hundred dollars had bought Crake. And whatever he was being paid now.

It was half past eight when they left the café. Liliana had never turned up. By ten o'clock Cox had spoken to his Chief first at home, then again at the Glasshouse.

'All right,' his Chief said, 'for your information our naughty boy is not on a tour of Eastern Europe buying up Château Bateau for a cruise line. He has no connection with any shipping company. Tory Party apparatchiks say he went to Vienna for a wedding and then was taking a short holiday.'

'What a stupid lie for Crake to tell.'

'Or desperate. Your voice sounds tired,' his Chief commented.

'I can't imagine why,' Cox said. 'Unless it's like a sympathy strike, coming out in support of the rest of my body.'

'Thatcher outlawed sympathy strikes,' his Chief said. 'What's new?'

'No, tell me first about Dayton.'

'It's moving along. Uncle Sam is banging heads together, breathing down necks, flexing muscles. Write your own clichés.'

'Is Uncle Sam going to send in his young nephews in uniform?'

'It looks like it.'

'On the ground?'

'Yes.'

'So they'll want to breathe pure air.'

'Yes. Now your turn.'

'I've seen more videotapes.'

'Yes? More bad news for the Prime Minister?'

'For old Uncle Sam.'

'Embarrassing?'

'A mite.'

'A mite? That's not much.'

'All right, there's mite and might. Let's say mighty embarrassing.'

'Sometimes I have difficulty following you.'

'That's the idea. This is an open line,' Cox said. 'I don't want to be followed by just anyone.'

So it goes, Cox thought. Yes indeed. Voice tired, for heaven's sake. All right, he'd used it a lot yesterday, last night, this morning. But Jenny's mother had used her voice all the time. It had never got tired, only other people had.

He tried Liliana's number. He counted ten rings, was about to give up, decided to give it two more rings, then gave up. He rang Jaeger.

'Do you want the bad news first,' Cox asked, 'or the bad news?'

'Whichever.'

'The bad news is that I still cannot get hold of our young lady.'

'That's tough because I've got what you asked for.'

'I'll keep trying. The other bad news is that our man here is definitely on the wrong side. He's been bought.'

'Changed your mind? Want us to bring him in?'

'No. He's gone running off to report I'm carrying something very valuable. That should stir some interest. You know what Confucius said about fishing?'

'About fishing, no. But you're going to tell me.'

'When all other bait fails, put yourself on the hook.'

Keep busy, Cox told himself. Do enough things and you create the illusion you are achieving something. He walked to the Nord Hotel, taking good long strides like a man with a purpose. He was going to leave a message at Reception. He didn't know the names of the two men the Chief was sending but that was a detail. Call the receptionist My dear and give her his smile, his tired smile, and work something out.

He was walking to the desk when a voice at his shoulder said, 'Mr Cox?'

Cox saw a man in his late thirties, sandy hair going thin at the parting, a small scar on one cheek.

'And you are . . . ?'

'Monckton. Forbes will be with us in a tick. He's just gone to the heads.'

He looked fit. Ex-marine, Cox thought, the Glasshouse favoured them as being more stable than ex-SAS. 'You have some identification?'

Monckton opened his hand where he already held a card in his palm. Cox recognized the red stripe and nodded. The card vanished. Another man joined them and Monckton said, 'This is Forbes.'

They sat on padded chairs with plastic leather that squeaked. A low green plastic table was in front of them. Behind them was a rubber plant that might also be plastic.

'I didn't think there was a flight from Munich so early.'

'Munich–Athens yesterday evening. Athens–Bucharest night flight,' Monckton said.

'And you're in Munich permanently? I don't mean to pry, I just don't know you.'

'We've been in Hong Kong,' Monckton said. 'They're running that facility down before the handover. The Yanks can have it.'

'Munich's a doddle,' Forbes said. 'I mean, compared with dealing with your slant-eyes.'

They were sitting in the entrance lobby with people passing in and out. Mostly men, Cox noticed. The receptionist was also a man. His smile wouldn't have worked. No My dear.

'What are your orders?' Cox asked.

'Do whatever you ask,' Forbes said.

'At the moment,' Cox said, 'I haven't much to ask. Be ready is all I can say.'

'But will we be getting some exercise, do you think?'

The one called Forbes, darker and shorter than his companion, was leaning forward in his chair, the stance of an alert and eager man. It was the paleness of his eyes and their lack of any expression that made Cox's blood run cold.

Put it down to tiredness that Cox hadn't thought of getting in touch with Gabriela. Or approaching senility, he conceded. He rang the embassy and a cross female voice informed him that Miss Cotarla had telephoned to say she was indisposed and wouldn't be coming in. Indisposed? When had Gabriela learned a word like that? It must be diplomat-speak for saying she was confined to bed. With someone. He didn't know where she had spent last night but he tried her flat.

'*Alo,*' a voice said after the first ring, as if she'd been sitting right next to the telephone hoping for someone to brighten her indisposition.

'Gabriela, it's Mr Cox.'

There was a slight hesitation before Gabriela said, 'Oh Royston, I am so glad you have telephoned.'

It was Cox's turn to hesitate. 'I heard from the embassy you were not well.'

'It is nothing, Royston. I am tired, you know?'

'Yes, I know. Listen, I can't get hold of Liliana. She doesn't answer her phone. She didn't come to a café she said she'd be at. I'll have another look in the church—'

'But she is here.'

Cox took in a deep breath. 'Wonderful. I want to speak to her.'

'Hmm, she is in the bathroom right now and she must go out soon. Royston, she wants to see you. It is better y come here. Otherwise you miss her. Do you know I live, Royston?'

While Gabriela gave him the address, Cox thought: She has never called me that before. Even last night when she tried to stay with me, thoughts of seduction in her eyes, it was Mr Cox.

He stood outside the door, listening. He was an explorer about to go into an unknown land. The natives were female and surely friendly. One, in fact, was showing signs of growing familiarity. The door was made of thin wood and other doors he had passed had relayed sounds of a radio or a warring family. This door was silent. It was listening to him. He pressed a button and heard a buzzer. Now he heard movement, a shuffle on a rug. Or – the thought came unbidden – the sound of Gabriela's body restless inside her clothes.

'Who is it?' Gabriela was welcoming him in English, though guardedly.

'Royston Cox.'

The door was unlocked. Her eyes appeared first in the gap, then her face with her mouth puckered, then a shoulder. Peering beyond her, Cox saw no Liliana.

'Come in,' she said.

She locked the door behind him and pointed Cox towards the room ahead past a kitchen no bigger than a packing case. Cox entered what he supposed was the sitting room though he never had a chance to check because his eyes fixed on two men he had never seen before. One of them pointed a pistol at him.

Chapter 19

There is no silence like the silence a gun imposes. The room was empty of noise. Voices from the flats to either side were turned back. Outside traffic was stilled. Radios, televisions were switched off. Only heartbeats sounded. Guns unleashed noise too. But if that gun broke the silence, Cox knew, he wouldn't hear it. The pistol was pointed at his face. Did you see the bullet swelling as it came at you? He thought of the room at the top of the museum, how Vasile had pulled a gun and fired and missed, how Vasile had been shot in the chest and had an artery severed. A rash move kills.

A movement at the corner of his eye caught Cox's attention. Gabriela had crept to the side wall, distancing herself from Cox, out of harm's way if there was shooting. Cox thought of Crake's warning. Crake had been lying about Wix. Suppose he had been telling the truth about Gabriela? He turned his head to see what expression her face bore. Was she smiling, bored, excited, eager, worried? Her eyes had widened as if to take in every detail. Was she a voyeur? Or she could be terrified. Her mouth opened but at a word from one of the men it closed.

The absolute silence couldn't have lasted more than a few seconds. Cox understood it was the silence of death he was experiencing, his own death. Most of the people who had been active during the Cold War – in the field, that is, not the ones sitting in warm offices with a cup of coffee on the desk and the sound of telephones and typing – agents had nearly all experienced something like this. Cox had too, in East Berlin, when Source Heinz had popped up in the taxi with a pistol. The '50s had been vicious. By the '60s and '70s certain ground rules were developed: that you did not gratuitously shoot their men because they could do the same to your men. It wasn't chivalry. It was an acceptance of reality. The alternative was tit-tat-tit-tat, a machine gun rattle as agents and sub-agents and sources and suspects and people who simply got in the way were killed.

This was different. The men who faced Cox belonged to no formal organization. It was likely they had been Securitate. Now that they had gone private, no unwritten rules applied.

The man with the gun spoke. Gabriela said, 'He wants the videotape.'

As Cox had known. But for reasons of self-regard and professional pride – even if there was no other reason – it was necessary not to collapse at the first demand of the adversary.

Cox asked, 'Which videotape is this?'

She said, 'You know, the one from—'

'I'm not asking you. I'm asking him. He seems to be the one in charge. At least he's the one with the artillery. Go on. Ask him.'

She did ask him, which only raised the man's anger.

Gabriela said, 'What he said was, the tape you took last night from Vasile's office.'

'Why does he think I still have it?'

'Please, Mr Cox, you will make him very cross. Then it will be bad.'

It had gone back to formality. Calling him Royston had

been her way to alert him of something strange, always providing he was sharp enough.

'Does he think I'd carry it round with me? There are pickpockets in Bucharest. Only this morning—'

But the man was gesturing to the side pocket of his jacket.

'He says it makes your pocket grow.'

'You mean bulge.'

'Please,' she whispered.

'He can't shoot me in here,' Cox said. 'The neighbours will hear. Tell him his gun is useless, it will make too much noise, it has no suppressor, no silencer.'

Gabriela interpreted one way, then the other. 'He says the neighbours will think it is a television show.'

There was a limit to the man's patience. Cox had passed over the line and the man came forward, the pistol pointing at Cox's chest, a target impossible to miss. But he was cautious. He detoured round Cox to stand behind him. Cox felt the muzzle of the pistol cold against the nape of his neck. At the training gym outside Croydon Cox had been taken again and again through the moves that could disarm a man who stood behind you with his pistol in your back. But against a pistol pressed tight against your neck – the fifth vertebra as McAllister said – any move could be suicidal. Thirty years ago when he was younger, fitter, faster, he might just have risked some distracting move or shout, an elbow, a heel against the man's instep. The risk was not worth it. There was just the one possibility: the man was right-handed because that was how he carried the pistol, and the tape was in Cox's right pocket; would he contort himself reaching with his left hand or would there be a hint of an opportunity as the pistol changed hands? But the chance never came. He called to his colleague.

The second man came forward with caution, eyes holding Cox's eyes. Cox smiled at him. The man stopped. A smile under duress – what does it signify? Such a smile is troubling, denting the opponent's confidence. Was there some superhuman act that Cox was about to perform? Cox's smile broadened. Come on, come closer, I know all the tricks, I'm a magician. For a few moments it was Cox who had the initiative. It's a few more moments of life, Cox knew. Once they'd checked it was the right videotape, what reason was there for keeping him alive? At a growl from the gunman, his colleague took the final step forward, dipping his hand into Cox's pocket, withdrawing the tape, holding it up. And the door buzzer sounded.

The man at Cox's back was startled. Cox felt the tremor that ran through his arm, his hand, his pistol and into Cox's neck. His finger would be resting on the trigger, even squeezing the trigger. He could be one of the boys – Securitate, gang, no difference – who liked to take up the slack on the trigger. They were eager, ones who liked to shoot. One more buzz, one more tremble in his arm, one reflex tightening of the finger . . . The room was so still that Cox was aware of a small movement by Gabriela pressed against the wall. He didn't move his head, just his eyes. Gabriela was yawning. Boredom? More likely it was how tension took her. On one side of her was a poster of Big Ben and the Palace of Westminster. Well, she did work for the embassy. On the other side was a potted plant, a jungle plant with big leaves, climbing towards the window for light. Or to escape. Ah yes, escape.

If Liliana had been here and counting, Cox thought, she would just have reached two hundred and ninety-eight, two hundred and ninety-nine, three hundred.

The man with the gun spoke and his mate moved towards the front door of the flat. The man spoke again and Gabriela interpreted, 'He says if you move he will shoot. He says if you shout a warning he will shoot.' The man spoke again and she said, 'He asks if you came with anybody.'

'You let me in. You saw there was no one in the corridor.'

Gabriela translated. The gunman said nothing but twisted his gun hand so that it seemed he was screwing the muzzle deeper into Cox's neck. Cox could see Gabriela but not the front door. He kept his eyes on her face, saw her mouth open in a hint of a smile, the tip of her tongue between her teeth, a shine to her eyes. She wasn't frightened, she was excited.

The buzzer sounded again. Oh dear, oh pray. For a moment Cox closed his eyes, his neck muscles bunched, feeling the bullet he wouldn't feel. That second buzz was louder, he would say, impatient, angry, yes. The man at the door spoke, a short sharp sentence, a question maybe. No answer. Cox found he had been holding his breath and let it out. Three hundred and twenty, thirty, forty, however many seconds Liliana would have counted. He took another breath and held it. Still staring at Gabriela he thought she had done the same. He heard the key turn in the lock. He heard the handle turn, or begin to turn, but the handle seemed to open not the door to the dingy corridor but a door into a different world altogether. Chaos, noise and violence erupted. There was a cry and thump of a body being slammed against the wall.

'Freeze, freeze, freeze.'

It was Forbes. He didn't shout but his voice had a low harsh vibrancy.

'You! Don't move or you're dead.'

The pressure of the muzzle against Cox's neck had gone. He sensed the man behind him moving, turning to confront the sudden new danger.

'Drop it. Drop the gun.'

Cox was turning now. He saw Gabriela pressed against

the wall, hand raised to her face, thrill, shock, fear showing through her fingers. He saw through into an entrance hall little bigger than a wardrobe. He saw the man thrown onto the floor against the wall, shaking his head, dazed by the front door bursting open. He saw Forbes crouching with his knees bent, a dark bunched animal. He was holding the pistol two-handed, the pistol Cox had given him, Vasile's pistol. He saw beyond Forbes the pale figure of Monckton with a knife in his hand, blade flat, moving to kneel beside the man on the floor, resting the tip of the knife under his ear. At once the man stopped shaking his head.

Cox glimpsed another movement, by the gunman who'd been so close behind him. He was moving now. He didn't understand English but he surely understood a tone of voice. Everybody understood a pistol aimed at their head. So why did he make his move? Did he think he was faster? Invincible? Was it the arrogance of an ex-Securitate man who'd always had his own way? His arm with the pistol was swinging round when Forbes shot him. The bullet entered somewhere high up in his face, penetrated the skull and entered his brain. The gunman stumbled back and Cox caught him in his arms. The man must have been killed instantly. He sagged, a dead weight, and his pistol clattered away under a chair.

Cox stooped to let the body slide to the floor. When he straightened he found that Forbes had come forward and stood with his gun pointing down in case there was any twitch of life.

'Give me the gun,' Cox said. 'Forbes, give me that gun.'

Forbes frowned at Cox, puzzled, perhaps forgetting who he was. His eyes blinked three or four times before he handed the pistol over, butt first.

Listening, Cox heard the sound of a family arguing in the next flat. No one paid heed to a single gunshot. It could have been a car backfiring or, as the gunman himself had said, part of a Saturday morning cops-and-robbers show.

'You said five minutes,' Forbes said. 'Know your villains, don't you? Six minutes and I reckon it would be you listening to the floorboards.'

Forbes turned his head to wink at Gabriela.

'Morning, angel. How's tricks?'

Monckton had wanted to cover the dead man's face and torso with a sheet. Gabriela was outraged that she should lose something so useful. In the end an old newspaper was found. Cox's eye was caught by a photo of a farmer beside a cow with a prize-winner's rosette draped round its brow. A small wet patch appeared in the newspaper, staining the cow's udder a mottled red.

Gabriela was trying to apologise to Cox, explaining how the men had pushed their way in when she answered the buzz, how they had forced her to telephone, how it was *dreadful*, Mr Cox. Cox appeared to be more taken with the stain on the cow's udder until suddenly he swung on Gabriela, catching her jaw in his hand as he had last night and bringing her face close to his, his eyes staring into hers. She made a little noise and went still.

'Where did you spend the night?'

She swallowed. 'With a friend.'

'I want the truth. I can tell if you lie. I'll see it in your face.'

'I did. I was with a friend. You told me to.'

'Name?'

'Stephan.'

'Stephan what?'

She swallowed again. Cox could feel the contraction. 'I'm not sure. No, I remember. Viteazul.'

'You *remember*?'

She said nothing. Her eyes flicked away to Forbes who was watching closely and back to Cox.

'His telephone number. Do you know that?'

'I must look it up.'

'Gabriela, don't look away. Look into my eyes. You didn't spend the night with anyone called Stephan. Who was it? Crake? One of these?' Cox jerked his head at the newspaper-covered corpse.

'Jesus, you're wasting your time,' Forbes said. 'I'll get the truth out of her. No sweat. Girls like her lie as easily as they drop their knickers.'

'Go and look out of the window,' Cox ordered. 'Check the street. Make sure there aren't any baddies loitering. Go on, do it.'

'I swear it, Mr Cox.'

'Who is he? Who is this Stephan?'

She didn't answer.

'Where does he live? How old is he? How long have you known him? What is his work? Come on.'

'He works in the metro.'

'He works in the metro. What does he do?'

'He drives the train.'

Cox waited. She needed time. Not to invent, he was beginning to believe, but to come out with it.

Gabriela said, 'It was nearly midnight. What was I to do? You wouldn't let me come with you. You wouldn't let me go to Panda or sleep here. You wouldn't let me go to Liliana or that flat I took you to. Who do I telephone who isn't already in bed with someone? The ambassador maybe, tell him to get his wife to move over? I took the metro and at the end of the line . . .' She lowered her eyes. 'I went to the front of the train and spoke to the driver. I told him I'd had a row with my man and had nowhere to sleep.'

She stopped. Cox still waited but she'd confessed all she was going to. She straightened her shoulders and lifted her gaze to stare into Cox's eyes again. She raised a hand to move his fingers from her jaw.

'Nice, yes?'

'Do you have any rope, miss?' It was Monckton, the reserved one in comparison with Forbes.

'Rope?' Gabriela was puzzled. 'Why do you want rope?'

'To tie up the prisoner. He's in the other room and he's all right for now. I used one of your belts to tie his wrists behind his back, like, then lifted the bed over him so the leg of the bed is between his arms and his body. It'll hold him. But he could always thump on the floor with his heels and bring someone up from downstairs to complain. Now if I had rope I could tie him proper so he couldn't do a thing. See what I mean?'

Gabriela stared at him. 'I haven't rope. I don't tie people up.'

'Thank you, miss.'

Monckton had a Midlands accent. Cox had always considered the Brummie accent the homeliest in England. Trussing a man and lifting a bed on top of him didn't fit his idea of homely.

Cox moved to the window to stand beside Forbes. Forbes pointed down the street to the left. 'Kids are the same everywhere. They don't need computer games to keep them happy. Give them a tin can to kick around. You want me to check out this Stephan bloke? See if her story holds up?'

'I didn't know you spoke Romanian.'

'With respect, Mr Cox, you're something of an intellectual. You think you need words to find things out. But if I go man-to-man, say "Gabriela?" and give him a nudge, then I see what he does. If he grins back, then it's OK, they were pals between the sheets. See what I mean?'

'She was telling the truth.'

'Girl like that, bit of a tramp, you shouldn't be too trusting.'

'A girl like what?' Cox asked sharply.

He stared down into the street. The concrete blocks of flats stretched down both side of the road. Cars were parked at the kerb because no garages had been built for the flats. No worker in socialist Romania had been meant to own a car. The concrete was an unrelenting grey. Even the tops of the buildings that caught the morning sun didn't sparkle. The architect who'd drawn up the plans had done well: the little estate of dwelling units caught the essence of Ceausescu's Romania. It put Cox firmly in mind of a prison.

He became aware that Forbes had asked him a question and was waiting for an answer. He leaned closer to speak with quiet intensity. 'Didn't you see what it cost her to tell me what she'd done? She sleeps around, she's something of a trollop. But to have to pick up some strange man at the end of the metro line just to get a bed, that's terrible.'

Forbes was looking at him, an eyebrow raised.

'Well, look at her flat,' Cox went on. 'Look at this block of flats. Look at all the blocks. Can you blame her for wanting to be in someone else's cosy apartment? In Ceausescu's day, you know how you could judge someone's importance? You looked up. The higher the ceiling, the more important the person. People of no importance had low ceilings because that meant there was less air to heat. True. So look around you. It's like a cave here. She meets someone from the embassy and enjoys a bit of comfort. To her, luxury. But a train driver . . . He'd have somewhere like this.'

Forbes didn't comment. I'm talking too much, Cox told himself. Because I feel the weight of guilt on me. I was the cause of her picking up that man. She didn't betray me, only herself.

All the time he spoke he was watching the street below, how an approaching figure crossed the road at an angle to skirt the boys kicking the can, then turned in towards the entrance to their block. He turned to face the room. Gabriela sat in a chair, turning the pages of a magazine without pausing to read.

'She's coming,' Cox said. 'I just saw her crossing the street.'

Gabriela led Liliana to the living room, holding her hand as if she was a child or a lover. Bring her straight in, Cox had ordered, don't stand gossiping because anyone passing in the corridor can hear you through that door. Liliana had no warning about what she would face and she stopped in the doorway. There was a corpse on the floor covered in newspaper, two men she'd never seen before, Cox. She glanced to her left into the bedroom where a man lay trussed with the bed on top of him. She looked back at Cox. She had bright eyes and colour in her cheeks as if she'd been on a long hike. She was standing very erect. Like a Guardsman, he thought, very different from their first meeting when she had run from him. And what does she see when she looks at me, he wondered. An old fellow with a greying moustache, face pallid, dark pouches under the eyes. The flesh felt as if it was crawling over his cheekbones, which was how exhaustion took him these days.

'Mr Cox,' she said. Nothing more.

'You're safe.' Cox smiled his relief. 'I didn't know where you were. You didn't answer the telephone.'

'It was you,' she said. Her voice was quiet.

'Why didn't you answer? I was worried.'

'Because he'd telephoned earlier. I didn't want to hear his voice so close to my ear again. Every time the telephone rang in I looked at it. The room was dark, of course, but I could see his face where the telephone is. His smile.'

There was no need to ask who *he* was. Cox said, 'Why did he ring you?'

'Instructions for today. Also personal things. I don't want to talk about it.'

'About today . . .' Cox broke off because she'd turned her head. Forbes had locked his gaze on her. Liliana raised her chin a fraction and stared back at him until he frowned and looked away. 'We should speak alone,' Cox said.

There was nowhere but the bathroom. Liliana took the stool next to the shower. Cox lowered the lid on the lavatory seat and the thin plastic sagged under his weight.

'I went to the café,' he began.

'So did I,' she said.

'I was there for half an hour.'

'So was I.'

Like a married couple trading accusations, he thought. He could hear Forbes's voice, though not the words, and Gabriela's reply. He could hear the drip of the shower. He could hear an electric razor in the bathroom above and he lowered his voice.

'The café near the casino in the passage?'

'Yes. I thought you hadn't got the letter I wrote.'

'Did you burn it after you wrote it?'

'Of course not. Why would I do that?'

Cox shrugged. 'Someone did. There was a corner left, a scrap, giving the rendezvous.'

'For nine?'

'For eight.'

'Show me.'

Cox shook his head. 'Someone burned it and left the scrap for me to find. Standard procedure is not to remove something like that. Then if the opposition checks – have

I come, have I read the message – they're left wondering whether I'll fall into the trap. Well, he came to the café anyway.'

'Who?'

'Andrew Crake.'

She turned her face towards the door as if she could see through it to Gabriela.

He said, 'Crake tried to persuade me she was working for Mincu.'

Liliana looked back at Cox. He could see she was puzzled, remembering how Gabriela had insisted she meet Mincu and have dinner with him.

'She's not, of course.'

She nodded. 'In my letter I told you what Mincu said to me on the telephone. Not the personal things.' She made a gesture with her hand, pushing the memories aside. 'They weren't bad, the things he said, it was the way he said them. He wants to pick me up this afternoon to drive out to his house in the country. He said—'

'Just a minute. Did he tell you where his house was?'

'No. He said there was a man he needed me to interpret for. What kind of man, I asked. A Belgian, the captain of a ship. The ship is called the *Cleopatra*.'

'He *gave* you the name of the ship?'

'No. But I have a friend who works for the Port Authority in Constantsa. I telephoned him. He is someone I know from five years ago. We talk about this and about that. Then I ask him about any Belgian ship, or maybe a ship with Belgian captain. He says he will telephone me back but I say no, I will wait while he checks. So there is silence and then he comes back to say there is no Belgian ship but there is a ship registered in the Philippines which has a Belgian captain. He is called Van den Doel and the ship is the *Cleopatra*.'

And she lifted her head a fraction so she could look Cox

in the eyes. She was expectant, wanting congratulations, you've done marvels, well done, Ilona couldn't have done better. But a gift like this made Cox suspicious. Would Mincu give away any information to Liliana, even that the captain was Belgian? But then he thought: Last night Mincu didn't know of Cox because Crake was working for Wix; it was like having a cut-out. Today, well today was different. Wix had told Mincu and here was the proof: one corpse, one man trussed with a bed on top of him.

Cox took one of her hands in both his, squeezed it and smiled. 'My dear, you've done wonders. This one piece of information about the ship is priceless.' For a moment his brain skipped ahead. Assuming the *Cleopatra* was carrying Mincu's cargo of chemical weapons, who could he alert? Police? Army? Who could impound it? Who wasn't corrupted? How far did Mincu's reach extend? Jaeger, he thought, he'd need his help. He took a breath and came back to Liliana. 'My dear, listen.' He squeezed her hand again. 'By this morning Mincu knows about me and your connection with me. So your part in this business is finished. Later I shall—'

'No. I'm going on. I'm keeping the rendezvous. There will be other things I can find out for you.'

'The danger is too great. Really you cannot.'

'Oh, but I can. And I will.'

And that was it. She got up from the stool to finish the discussion. Her face had set with the decision she had made. Cox could think of nothing more to say.

She'd gone out of the bathroom, leaving him sitting on the lid of the toilet seat. When he shifted his weight, the plastic squeaked. He could hear her voice, then Gabriela's. They spoke Romanian and Cox knew Monckton and Forbes would be staring at them. Perhaps Gabriela had kissed

Liliana on the lips, which certainly would have set Forbes's mind speculating.

The thing is, Cox told himself, she must understand, *must*, that if she goes on now she won't come back. Yet she insists on going on. He couldn't stop her. It was with her that Mincu had made the arrangement. If she didn't meet him, Mincu would realize that something was badly wrong and change his plans at once, get the *Cleopatra* out of Constantsa harbour and away to sea. Yes, she was right: she had to go on.

In all his years in the Glasshouse he had never sent anyone on a suicide mission. He should never have made use of an ordinary member of the public. It was a terrible, terrible thing he had involved her in. A girl, too. He closed his eyes. You're a miserable sod, he told himself, now you're feeling sorry for yourself instead of her.

He got slowly to his feet. Was that the lavatory seat creaking or his knees? Come on, there was a lot to do, a lot.

Chapter 20

There were other telephone kiosks but he rejected them, as he had rejected the telephone in Gabriela's flat. This was no longer a communist country where telephones were routinely tapped. But the old system had never been properly dismantled, the furniture had just been shifted around. Cox assumed the two men Mincu had sent were former Securitate thugs. Mincu could easily have someone listening on Gabriela's telephone as well.

Pay telephones had appeared on the walls of buildings in the most unlikely places. Each had little protective screens of Perspex to give the illusion of privacy. But to be using one of those telephones in the street made Cox conspicuous. He felt like a butterfly impaled in a display case, open to everyone's gaze.

Gabriela's flat was not far from Nord station. He went through the booking hall into the concourse. A train had just come in so he wandered on to the platform. Berlin–Praha–Budapest–Bucuresti read the board on the side of the first carriage. In the old days a journey through badlands with frontier controls every few hours, eyes lifting from the passport photo to study your face and the sudden stab of panic in the guts: What name was it they'd given me this time?

Cox shook his head. Paranoia, he knew.

He stayed a minute longer looking at the disembarking passengers, single men walking fast, whole families gathered round cheap suitcases tied with rope, conscript soldiers, a young couple. They're honeymooners, he decided, see how she clings to his arm. What am I doing here, he asked himself. He wasn't looking for someone. He was looking for his past, for old patterns of behaviour, for the caution and suspicion that had rusted away working in London. This was how you used to live, he told himself. He remembered the journey Prague–Brno–Breclav. They'd had passport control and customs check and the train had trundled out of the station. Then it had stopped, still on the Czech side of the Iron Curtain. Why didn't it go forward into Austria? What were they searching for? Ten minutes, fifteen minutes, the talk in the carriage dwindled to silence. There was the crash of boots marching along the track, a whistle, a shout. The train started again. Cox never knew what caused the hold-up but he remembered how the sweat had crawled down his chest. He even remembered the metallic taste in his mouth and supposed it was fear.

'Who the hell is that?'

The telephone had been answered on the third ring and the voice spoke English. Or rather, American.

'We don't give names,' Cox said. He'd seen the pay phone become free in the concourse and moved swiftly to take it.

'You,' Jaeger said. 'Sounds like you're at Grand Central.'

'That's right.'

They paused, both taking stock. Their silence brought back the days of the Cold War when you trusted nothing – telephone, taxi, private car, hotel room, a woman who caught your eye, a man reading a newspaper at a café table. Or a man in a leather jacket. Cox had seen him enter the concourse and pause. Now the man began walking across the concourse.

'Is it good or bad?' Jaeger asked. 'Your news, I mean.'

'It's both.'

The man in the leather jacket changed his angle a fraction so he was headed directly at Cox. Under the jacket was a sweatshirt advertising Camel cigarettes. Below were blue jeans.

'I've got what you asked for.'

'And I've got information for you,' Cox said. 'Urgent. We'll meet.'

'Name the place.'

'In the park. Where they play chess. Know it?'

'Sure.'

'One o'clock.'

'Shit. That's my lunch hour.'

But the man had stopped quite close to Cox so he hung up without saying goodbye to Jaeger. Just as his Chief would have done. The man in the leather jacket took a step forward. 'My friend, you want to change dollars? Deutschmarks?'

Just like they used to in the days of the Cold War when you were never certain if it was a black market tout or a secret police trap.

On Sunday mornings his Chief liked to play golf. Communication was no problem because he kept a mobile phone in a pouch among his clubs and he'd excuse himself and walk off a little down the fairway and turn his back. It was common knowledge that his Chief worked in the Treasury – or was it the Bank of England – and had something to do with Britain's balance of payments. *How's the pound doing today, old chap.* one of the foursome would ask. *Must be pretty dicey if they disturb your weekend.* His Chief would reply, *Down to fifteen ounces,* and they'd laugh. It was a ritual, as comforting as a g & t in Spikes bar afterwards.

'So what's new?' his Chief asked.

'I would say,' Cox swung round, his back to the wall, so he could watch the concourse, 'that we're in sight of the eighteenth green.' In the pause before his Chief spoke Cox could hear faint voices, a burst of laughter. It seemed a good day to be on the golf course in England.

'Wrap it up today, will you? Be on the plane home tomorrow?'

'Providing I'm not helping the police with their enquiries.'

The man in the leather jacket hadn't gone away. Passengers were still coming off the Berlin train and he spoke to two and was given a brush-off.

'You have a problem?'

'The population of Bucharest has decreased by one this morning.'

'Ah well.'

'As you say. Chummy is throwing a party this afternoon. He didn't send me an invitation so I may have to gatecrash.'

'Interesting guest list?'

'Yes.'

'More.'

'It's not your actual jet set. More your international boat set. Boat set. Got it?'

'Sailing on?'

Cox sighed. Damned open line. 'It's brush up your Shakespeare time. Ready? Age cannot wither nor custom stale her infinite variety.'

Cox stopped. His Chief was considering this. Cox could hear a bird singing, a blackbird in England, but no more laughter or voices. His Chief would be playing a foursome and the other three must have wandered off down the fairway leaving his Chief with his balance of payments and the blackbird. Cox closed his eyes for a moment to hear the birdsong better. He felt tired and alone and far from home.

'More?' his Chief asked.

Cox opened his eyes. The man in the leather jacket was doing some business. A passenger from the Berlin train had Deutschmarks to change. In Old Nick's days you could get seven or eight times the official rate changing money on the street, and the men in leather jackets had loitered outside all the hotels. Now you might get five per cent more and nobody bothered.

'Nothing more,' Cox said.

The blackbird was cut off in mid-song.

A woman wanted to use the telephone.

'My dear, just one more. Very brief. I promise.'

Cox gave her his best smile, his sincerest, his oldest, his tiredest smile. She was so taken aback she smiled in return and stepped back.

He dialled and counted the rings. One, two, three, four. Just like Liliana would. He rang off and redialled. This time the telephone was answered at once. No one spoke. Cox waited. Finally a woman began to sing.

'*Frère Jacques, Frère Jacques.*'

She stopped. It had been Gabriela's voice, a little uncertain. All was well. If she'd been under duress of any kind she would have continued: *Dormez-vous? Dormez-vous?* When he'd instructed her she had first of all wrinkled her brow then giggled. Yes, she would do this for Mr Cox. No, she wouldn't answer the phone if it rang normally. No, she would say nothing else. Even with a dead body on the floor of her flat it seemed a bit of make-believe.

Cox said, 'One o'clock.'

He rang off.

* * *

Cox walked along the central path in Cismigiu Park, past the bench where he'd sat with Crake, giving him a little lecture, trying to pump up his enthusiasm. He remembered Crake's startled reaction when he traced Wix's name in the dirt. Well yes, Wix had turned out to be his master.

Narrow flower beds bordered with low box hedges ran beside the path. Marigolds had finished their summer blaze and now stood withered and forlorn. Two women with their hair tied up in scarves were pulling up the dead plants and dumping them in a cart. A five-year-old boy played beside them with a beer bottle cap, kicking it into the path in front of Cox. Cox made a big fuss out of picking it up, cranking his arm round several times before lobbing it gently back. After a few steps he turned back to wink at the boy. There was nobody following him.

He passed between straggly bushes that looked like a hedge gone wild, into the area where the chess players met. At a glance he estimated thirty men and one woman. Cox toured the tables then stopped to watch her play. She was young, buxom and very pretty except when she smiled. A front tooth was missing. She was playing blitz chess, impetuous, regardless of consequences. Perhaps she treated life the same way and that was how she'd lost the tooth. He watched her lift a knight high and bang it down on an opponent's bishop. He pushed forward a pawn to remove the knight. Swiftly she slid forward a bishop to take the pawn. She lost the bishop but now her hand was resting on her queen. She felt Cox's gaze on her and lifted her head to stare him straight in the eye, like a challenge. Cox had never had a woman so reckless and, drawing a deep breath, never would.

'They play all year.' Unnoticed by Cox, Jaeger had come to stand beside him.

'Right through the winter?'

'It's their special pleasure. I came in February last year. There'd been a fresh fall of snow and everybody seemed to have gone skiing at Brasov. Me, I'm not built for skis. I came here on Sunday afternoon. They just brushed the snow from the tables and got down to it. I had never understood chess before. It is an addiction, a religion, a drug, a life. What is it instead of? Then I got it. It is intellectual murder with none of the risks of the real thing.'

'Speaking of which . . .' Cox paused. Jaeger's eyebrows asked a question. 'Yes, this morning. Nobody you know. There were two of them ambushing me and now there is one.'

'Need help in clearing it up?' Jaeger said it casually as if it was perfectly normal for him to tidy up after a murder.

'Maybe later.'

Cox had sent Monckton out to buy rope. The live thug should be gagged and properly bound by now. He wasn't a threat.

'This is the box of tricks,' Jaeger said, lifting the attaché case from his side. It was of black leather with brass hinges and clasps and a combination lock. It looked perfectly normal to Cox's eye and he hoped to everyone else's eye: smart as befitted someone from the Foreign Ministry who interpreted for important foreign businessmen but not sparkling new. Cox admired a scuff where a shoe had kicked it, a dent in one corner where it had been dropped.

The woman playing chess had just exchanged queens and seemed delighted. She laughed and sought out Cox to see if he appreciated her daring. She brushed back a lock of hair that had fallen over her eyes so she could see better, or so Cox could see her face better. He saw her glance shift away over his shoulder and hold. Her opponent made his move but for a moment she continued staring at whatever had caught her interest. She looked back at Cox. She lifted a cigarette from a packet without looking at it, took the cigarette from the hand of the man beside her and touched its glowing end to her own. All the time staring. She's proposing marriage to me, Cox thought, or something looser. I'm foreign and therefore I'm rich. Then a change came to her face, a dullness, and she looked down at the chessboard once more. At that moment Jaeger spoke.

'Got company, Roy. Couple of good lookers, one apiece. Do you like 'em blonde or brunette?'

Turning, Cox was face to face with Gabriela and Liliana, arms linked. It's so she won't run away, though he could no longer be certain which *she* that was. He made the introductions, first names only, and they left the chess arena with its frowning players and noisy kibitzers and silent watchers.

In the centre of the park was a small ornamental lake. Rowing boats were tethered to a landing stage but no one was using one today. A café had tables spread out beside the water. Liliana and Cox had coffee, Jaeger had Coca-Cola. Jaeger needed food and sent Gabriela to a pizza place he'd noted up the hill.

'Double everything,' he ordered.

'Please?' Gabriela was puzzled.

'The gunk they pile on top – pepperoni, tomatoes, cheese, olives. Tell 'em to double up. If a thing's worth doing, it's worth doing twice. Right?'

She smiled and went off. Jaeger's eyes lingered on her as she walked, marvelling how her hips swung as she moved. As if she knew she was being watched, a hand reached behind to smooth her rump.

'Gabriela, you said?' Jaeger asked.

'Yes,' Cox said.

'Works at your embassy?'

'Yes.'

'Her Majesty's handmaiden and all that?' Jaeger sighed. 'All right, folks. Business.'

'I want you to meet Rover.'

The cups and glass had been pushed aside and the attaché case laid flat on the table. One of Jaeger's big hands patted it as if it was a friendly dog.

'Rover is a good fellow, house-trained, loyal, doesn't bite.'

Jaeger smiled at Liliana but got nothing back. His eyes lingered on her and his smile faded. What in God's name was in Cox's mind, using someone so young, so frail? She looked in need of protection, daddy's arm round her shoulder.

'Rover's got one trick,' Jaeger went on. 'He doesn't come when we call. On the contrary, when Rover calls we come running. Rover was designed bearing in mind the dangers of frontier crossing into enemy territory. As I understand it, this is your intention today.'

She gave the slightest nod. Her eyes moved up from the briefcase to his face. Her eyes were so round, with no guile in them. Jesus, she was Bambi and the wolves were circling. He took a deep breath.

'To look at it's an ordinary briefcase, the kind any executive or lawyer or interpreter might carry. Got metal panels all round under the leather but that's nothing special. Provides strength. The metal panels serve two functions. First, they defeat any detection equipment at airports. Second, there is an antenna circuit printed into the metal. Activate Rover and it will transmit on a given frequency within a restricted radius to a friendly receiver. That's us. You've got no knobs to mess with, no tuning to do. So how does it work, you're asking? Simple.'

Jaeger fiddled with the combination lock and clicked open the case.

'The combination is easy to remember. 1776. It's a very patriotic lock.'

'So it's an American case, Mr Lucas?' Liliana asked.

'You bet.'

'Then I must remember that for today I am a patriotic American.'

Jaeger frowned at her and went on. 'What you do is place the case on a table or desk and open it up as if you wanted to get something out. We've put in a copy of today's *Libera*, a pad of paper, French-Romanian and English-Romanian dictionaries, nicely used. You should sign them, I think. Also add something of your own. Your engagement diary would be good. See, opening it up sets it transmitting, so leave the lid open. Microphone's been incorporated into the manufacturer's logo. Neat, right? Nothing shows. Latest flat batteries courtesy of NASA down the side panels. Other stuff built into the carrying handle. Antenna, as I said, in this panel. Just remember to keep the lid open and we'll hear whatever's being said in the room.'

Jaeger sat back and pulled a grin at Cox: I got the hardware you asked for, it's the software I'm worried about; she's so tender and vulnerable. He kept the grin going but since there was nothing humorous in the situation the grin was troubling and at odds with the coldness in his eyes. I believed you were an old-fashioned English gentleman, Jaeger thought, but you're a hard bastard. This is no fifty-dollar hooker, this is like the daughter I never had.

Cox, studying Liliana, felt neither a hard bastard nor an English gentleman. He felt numb. Liliana seemed unnaturally quiet. She was like someone resigned to death, a Jihad suicide bomber already looking forward to martyrdom and a reward in paradise. She'd asked only one question whose irony had passed Jaeger by. We're too much for her, he thought, he'd need to get her alone.

'We'll be close,' Cox said, 'very close. We'll be following you from your pick-up point to his country house, wherever that is, and be within transmission distance. We'll hear whatever is going on in the room where you are, once you've lifted the lid. Any hint of trouble, we'll come in.'

Liliana's eyes went from one to the other, measuring them, one old, one fat.

'Not just us, we have others,' Cox said, divining her concern. Others who were younger, fitter, faster, more murderous, but he didn't say that. 'Do you know who's going to be at this meeting?'

'Not everybody.'

'Some, then?'

'Him, of course.' They both understood Mincu. 'I am told two men from the Balkans.'

'Men from the Balkans?' Cox said. 'Is that how he describes them?'

'It's what he said. Then there is the captain of the ship.'

Jaeger raised his eyebrows at Cox.

'It's the good news,' Cox said. 'Tell him.'

She told him. There is this ship. By name the *Cleopatra*. Docked in Constantsa. The crew is from the Far East, the captain is Belgian. Liliana was to do the interpreting. Her voice was quiet and matter of fact. She could have been describing a visit to her aunt.

Jaeger turned on Cox. 'Well, that's it, for God's sake. It's gift wrapped for us. I've got friends in the police here, guys who're *hungry* for promotion. Give them the word, they'll be down to the port, have the cargo impounded, strip the boat naked, slap the crew in leg irons, put the thumb screws on the captain. It's—'

'The Captain is no longer on board. Right, Liliana?'

She nodded.

'At present nothing links Mincu to that boat. If he loses that cargo, he won't be out of business. He'll just start again. And you may have ambitious cops you can call on. Mincu probably has the Chief of Police, not to mention a couple of government ministers in his back pocket. But when Liliana takes this in,' he patted the briefcase, 'and we record that meeting, then we have evidence that nails the captain, Mincu, Wix and the men from the Balkans. Right, Liliana?'

'We get *him*,' she said. She stared away across the little lake as if she spied the promised land.

Cox made Liliana carry the briefcase, to get accustomed to having it at her side. There could be nothing worse than leaving it on a side-table somewhere because she was unused to it. Knotted round her neck she wore a navy blue scarf with white polka dots and he made her tie it to the handle. 'That makes it yours,' he reasoned to her. 'No one else will walk away with it.'

They took the path beside the little lake, their shoes crunching the first dried leaves of autumn. At a café table across the water he could see Jaeger biting into a slice of pizza, Gabriela on a chair beside him. She was talking and had laid a hand on his elbow. Jaeger said something through a mouthful of food and Gabriela laughed, ducking her head towards him so that her hair flowed over his arm. So, goodbye Panda, hello Lucas. Or Lukie. Or Fluke. As one door closes, another opens, especially if you push as hard as Gabriela was.

The sun suddenly flashed off the water and Cox found himself whisked back in time to Norfolk. He was walking along a cliff edge early one Sunday morning with the sun dancing off the sea, Jenny at his side. Only she wasn't.

She was distant until abruptly she turned on him. *Who is it then? Who're you seeing?* They'd been married three years and Cox was seeing nobody. *Well, you came home after midnight three nights last week.* Somehow Cox had never got round to telling her precisely what he did. 'A department of the Foreign Office' was the accepted weasel phrase. It's a research job, he'd say. Political research, if he was pushed harder. Different currents within the Party in various Iron Curtain countries, any glimpses of opposition, that kind of thing, if he was really pressed. Now he told her it was not some red-haired beauty he'd been courting but a bullet-headed driver from the Hungarian embassy who was having a crisis of conscience. He wanted asylum but Cox's superiors preferred him where he was and passing them information. Jenny had shaken her head so the sun sparkled in her hair. *Have I got it right? I'm married to a spy. Is that what you're trying to tell me?* She wasn't angry, or disapproving, or shocked. She was quite calm now. She just found this newly revealed secret life of her husband difficult to absorb. *Getting secrets from a Hungarian? Probably some fascist. Why you?* It's what I do. *Yes, but why do you do it? Is it hatred of their system? Helping oppressed nations? Revenge?* Revenge was possible, he agreed. That seemed interesting as a motive, and Jenny knew he'd been in Budapest in 1956. *Maybe your driver was driving one of the tanks that crushed the revolt.* More likely Tibor was throwing bombs at the tanks. Yes, that's why I spend so much time with Tibor, because of what he did during the uprising. I'm trying to persuade him that reporting to us on the military attaché he drives is almost as good as tossing a petrol bomb at a Russian tank. Definitely. He remembered gulls wheeling and crying out to sea and had some idea of the cock crowing as Peter denied Jesus. Fanciful twaddle. But he never mentioned Ilona.

Now he said to Liliana as they walked side by side,

'You're absolutely positive you want to go through with this?'

'Yes,' she said.

'You'll be in dreadful danger.'

'Do you think I don't know that?' They walked some steps in silence, the briefcase bumping against her knee. 'He's killed me once already. Mincu has. Years ago. The person I was died and it was Mincu who did it. You understand? No, how could you. You don't feel it in here.' She laid a fist against her stomach.

Revenge, he thought. Who has the right to deprive her of that? And her cause serves my cause. But her vulnerability was frightening. Crake knew about her. Crake must have told Wix. And Wix would tell Mincu. To send her unprotected into Mincu's house ... He and Jaeger would be close but close wasn't the same as being with her.

On one side of the path was the little lake. On the other side was a tangle of bushes. They came abreast of an opening and Cox glimpsed a small cleared area, a circle with the stumps of fallen pillars. Had it been a temple? Roman ruins? He could see broken columns like fallen soldiers. The place was deserted. No one would see them.

'Come in here a moment,' Cox said.

Chapter 21

They waited at the kerb until the lights turned green.

'I'm too old to take my chances with Bucharest drivers,' Cox said.

'I'm too fat,' Jaeger said. 'They can't miss me.'

They had Monckton and Forbes with them now, one twenty metres behind, the other across the road. Gabriela was out in front. It was like some battle group steaming in the Atlantic, destroyers on patrol protecting the aircraft carrier. Gabriela twisted to check they were there, the angle she had turned just happening to thrust out a breast towards them. Correction, towards Jaeger. Her eyes, too, seemed not to be focused on Cox. For the moment Jaeger was too preoccupied to respond.

'You're a bastard. You know that?'

'I know that,' Cox said, 'but what branch of bastardy are you putting me in?'

'Don't get smart with me, Royston Cox. You know damn well. Letting her go on when we could simply have the cargo seized. Letting her get picked up and driven out somewhere in the wilds and walk right into a trap. She'll do the translating for Mincu and the captain and the other heathens and then, while we're still ringing the front doorbell . . .' He drew his finger across his throat. 'She's laying her life on the line for you. You're using her.'

'Has it never occurred to you,' Cox said, 'that she's using us? Revenge isn't sweet. Revenge is a hunger and we're giving her the chance to feast.'

Jaeger grunted. A grunt as agreement, a grunt as disapproval, a grunt as a sign of deep thought. All those, Cox decided. He looked at his watch.

'How much further?'

'Not far. Half a mile. Less.' Jaeger gestured to the right, at a building like a Christmas cake. 'That's the opera. When I arrived in this God-forsaken hole I wanted to learn the language. I got a woman as a teacher. She was some sort of goddess at the opera, people talked about her as the new Callas, only she needed money to pay the bills. You know the movie, *One Flew over the Cuckoo's Nest*, Jack Nicholson?'

'I know the book, Ken Kesey.'

'The same. Well, she told me they made an opera out of it. This was back in the time of Ceausescu. The censors thought it was fine, a biting criticism of decadence and cruelty in the United States. OK, the rehearsals go well, they all know their parts. The scenery, well, the scenery is kind of extravagant, she says. Stuff left over from doing the Ring Cycle. Who cares? Who goes to the opera for the scenery? Then disaster. The very week *Cuckoo's Nest* opens, the orchestra is sent away. There's been some cock-up in the Ministry and the band is packed off for a tour in the sticks, bring culture to the cows. Opening night, no orchestra. You following?'

'I'm right with you.'

Jaeger gave him a look and went on. 'They open. Still no band. My Romanian teacher is a soprano. Her lungs – you know, I never heard her sing but those lungs looked powerful. Her part is Miss Ratched, Big Nurse. The curtain goes up. The scenery's all wrong so they cut half the lights. The audience is freezing because it's February and there's no heating. There's no orchestra, no music. So they don't sing the songs. No arias for Big Nurse. Instead they *speak* the lyrics.'

Jaeger stopped. He turned towards the opera house as if he could hear that first night.

'And you know what? The audience went wild. They were clapping, they were out of their seats, they were cheering, stamping their feet, shouting for encores. Because they didn't see it as condemning Yankee imperialist capitalist society. They saw it as a story of power and manipulation. They saw Big Nurse as Elena. They saw Macmurphy as the poor bloody ordinary man. To them it was a struggle against Ceausescu's authority in the madhouse of Romania and they loved it. What a night!'

'A triumph?' Cox suggested.

Jaeger screwed up his eyes as if shampoo had got in them. 'With a triumph like that, in Big C's time there were no second nights.' He started walking again.

They'd left the opera house behind and entered an industrial wasteland. To the left the river had been tamed and ran between straight concrete banks. To the right abandoned railway tracks disappeared into clumps of weeds. Factories of bricks and breezeblocks and corrugated iron seemed deserted until you saw plumes of grey smoke from tall thin chimneys.

'What do they make there?' Cox asked.

Gabriela was walking with them now. She shrugged. 'I don't know.'

'Pollution,' Jaeger said.

A high fence ran the length of the industrial estate to discourage looters. Between the fence and the road was a long line of wooden huts. In London you would say it was where cabbies had tea and bacon butties. Some indeed had taxis parked in front. One was a café. Another offered cheap flights to New York and Bangkok. Others sold jeans or did photocopying. The Rebecca Money Exchange had an Alsatian beside its door. As to the rest, they had no signs. Men with sideways eyes stood in twos and threes. If you didn't know what went on inside these huts, you had no business asking.

Jaeger was counting off the huts. He slowed at the eighth but his eyes were on the one ahead. On its door was a poster for Hollywood cigarettes with the slogan 'Go for it!'

'You want to stay back a little?' Jaeger suggested. 'You're the star, been strutting your stuff all over town.'

Jaeger advanced on the hut with Gabriela at his side, Jaeger to provide the authority, Gabriela to do the speaking. Despite the opera goddess as teacher, Jaeger seemed to have little Romanian. The French said that a foreign language was best learned on a pillow, so perhaps he'd never taken her to bed. Or if he had, she'd been improving her English.

Monckton and Forbes eased into position at Cox's side, one to each elbow, as if he was the Paraguayan President mingling with his grateful subjects. Forbes, who kept flexing the fingers of his right hand, was outstaring a pair of boys in leather jackets. 'This isn't the kind of area you want to walk in on your own after dark, Mr Cox.'

'I'll bear that in mind.'

'If those poofters don't watch it . . .' Forbes raised himself several times on his toes like a sprinter preparing for a race.

'I don't see any Merc,' Monckton said. 'I thought Jaeger was promising us a Merc.'

'Indeed he did,' Cox said. 'But they're security conscious the same as we are. You don't park it by your own front door. You leave it by someone else's front door. Just in case the police stir themselves.'

Jaeger's own car was no good. Cox and Jaeger agreed on that. Effectively they were in operational mode in a hostile country where nothing could be taken as safe. They had to assume Mincu knew the connection between Cox and Jaeger. They couldn't rent a car from Hertz because Mincu might check that. The same for taxis. They had to assume he had contacts in the police, the security service, the government, the armed forces. And in the mafia or whatever the criminal half-world call themselves here, Cox said. In the mob, Jaeger agreed. Except – he wagged one thick finger for extra emphasis – *except* for a couple of fellows I know, the Lup brothers, Dimitru and Sever. They're safe, we can use them. How can you be sure? Cox asked. Because the suckers believe I can swing them green cards for the States. Their brother is already there and they want to help out in his business. Isn't there a join-the-family policy? Sure, said Jaeger, but it doesn't hardly apply when the brother is in jail for shooting someone and his business is burglary.

'Let's go walk-about for a few minutes,' Cox said, 'so we don't stick out so much.'

They turned to retrace their route down the line of huts to the corner and back.

'How secure is the car?' Monckton asked.

'I'm told it has German licence plates,' Cox said.

'Bloody terrific.' Forbes sniffed. 'Nicked Merc for hire, top condition, one careful tank driver.'

Monckton was concerned. 'German plates? And it's hot?'

'Mr Jaeger says German plates usually buy a little extra indulgence with the traffic police. It's new in town. Just arrived via Austria and Hungary. Next week, so Mr Jaeger says, it will change nationality, new papers, Bucharest licence plates. Jaeger says the German embassy makes a fuss about twice a year and the police stop a few Mercedes and inspect their papers. The wise keep some dollars handy in case that happens. Fifty is apparently the going rate. Mostly the cars go on further east. Istanbul is first stop. Syria is better. The German embassy never complains in Syria. They did a couple of times and found all their *own* cars were stopped four or five times a day. When they showed their—'

'Mr Cox,' Monckton said. He'd laid a hand on his elbow and was turning him towards a rack of denim clothing beside one of the huts. 'I think you should look at these jeans.'

'Me? Jeans?'

Then he saw the car cruising gently towards them, two uniformed police in front, a man in plain clothes behind. All three were licking ice cream cones, even the driver. Cox pulled a pair of blue jeans off its hanger and gave an intense inspection to the leather patch sewn onto its hip pocket. *Coyote,* he read, *the Jeans that Won the West.* In smaller letters: *Made in Taiwan.* The jeans entirely covered his face and the police car was lost to sight. He glanced behind him but Forbes and Monckton had vanished on the sound reasoning that a group of three men stood out more than a lone man wanting to buy an item of clothing.

The owner of the hut appeared and was addressing Cox. When Cox didn't respond, the man said, '*Hundert Deutschmarks.*' When Cox still didn't respond, he held out a hand, palm up, snapping his fingers. He thrust his hand into Cox's chest, then jerked it up so he tilted Cox's chin. Forbes and Monckton appeared at the man's back and moved to stand beside him, close, crowding him.

'Where's your manners, sunshine?' Forbes said. 'We're pals of Dumbo and Sevvy Lup, get it? Fucking ease off.'

The owner's hand dropped away. He looked at Forbes,

then at Monckton, and seemed to recognize them as kindred spirits. Friends of Dumbo and Sevvy Lup indeed. Nodding, he edged carefully away.

Lup, Cox thought, his brain hopping and skipping through his exhaustion. Of course. Old and respected family name. Ancient pedigree, a long and noble line of Lups. From the Latin. Wolf, ideal name for a crook.

The hut with the Hollywood cigarette poster was the third down from them in the row. Out of its door came first Jaeger, then Gabriela, finally one of the princes of the Lup blood who was paying close attention to how Gabriela moved. Jaeger raised an arm and the sun glinted off the key dangling in his hand.

Despite its air conditioning, the car's interior smelled ever so slightly of cigar smoke. Its formal owner was some kind of Euro-prosperous *Wirtschaftwunder.* The licence plates said it came from Munich, which seemed to disgust Forbes. 'Bloody home from home. Krauts taking over everything.' It had probably been spirited over the border into Austria while its owner was stitching together another deal over lunch.

'He had the whole area cleared, forty thousand people kicked out of their homes. That right, Gabsi?'

'Yes,' she said.

Jaeger continued with his guided tour patter as if he'd forgotten Cox had been in Bucharest before. Perhaps it was for the education of Forbes and Monckton.

'Whole damn district was razed, churches, fine old houses, a monastery, some famous hospital. So famous I can't remember its name.'

'Brancoveanu,' Gabriela supplied.

'Why, thank you, ma'am. Regular little mine of information.'

Gabriela gave Jaeger her brightest smile. She shifted

her seat belt into a more comfortable position which happened to lie between her breasts. Each time Jaeger turned his head to check the traffic he could admire their perfection.

Jaeger piloted the car through the maelstrom of Piatsa Unirii, manoeuvred past a tram and stopped at the kerb. 'We'll be OK for a spell,' he said. 'D on the ass end is next best to CD.' His little extra indulgence. 'You know what ass is?' he asked Gabriela.

'Is a donkey.' Wide innocent eyes held Jaeger's, daring him to laugh at her. She knew if you had *pitsigoi* in front, you had *ass* behind.

'There's a good girl.'

Now it was a case of waiting and watching. Mincu had wanted to pick Liliana up at her flat but she wasn't having any of that. Nor would she go to his millionaire's apartment. The compromise was the Piatsa Unirii, a few hundred metres from the apartment. Four o'clock. At ten minutes to the hour Liliana appeared up the metro steps and crossed to stand with her back to the fountain. She put a little overnight bag on the pavement at her feet but the briefcase with the polka-dotted scarf tied to its handle she didn't let out of her grip. Hanging by a long strap from her left shoulder was the bag where she kept her keys, lipstick, comb – 'my women's things', as she'd told Cox when she opened the bag to him in the ruined Roman temple.

Cox had the right-hand window in the back seat. He stared at Liliana, trying to read her mood from every little gesture. She took a handkerchief from her shoulder bag to dab her face. Did she have a speck of grit in her eye? Was she sweating with nerves? She blew her nose. She raised her left arm to look at her watch. Nerves again? Impatient to get on with it? No, she's counting. Not counting up, counting down, how many seconds to pick-up, three hundred and sixty, three hundred and fifty-nine, three hundred and fifty-eight, how much of her life remains to zero. She rubbed her nose with the back of her hand in a most unladylike manner which greatly pleased Cox. She can't wait, she's got more guts, more backbone, more spirit than any of us. She turned sharply, not to look at their car – *don't* do that, he'd pleaded – but at a young boy who was whooping by the large circular pond that surrounded the fountain. A McDonald's – Romania's very first – had opened inside the department store by the bridge and the boy was sailing one of the dinky boxes the hamburgers were sold in. The boy had a handful of gravel and was bombarding the boat. But it wouldn't sink.

You want your country to take its place among the grown-ups, you have to have a flag, an airline and McDonald's. What on earth am I thinking about? Cox wondered. I'm not thinking. I'm too exhausted for that. Jaeger burst in on his non-thinking.

'Jesus, let's call this whole thing off.' Troubled eyes sought Cox's in the driving mirror. It was a reprise of what he'd said as they walked down the line of huts. 'One of your boys go over and haul her in. Roy, I'm not as old as you but I *am* old enough that I don't give a shit about PC. I'm old enough to remember when we didn't send a girl out to do our fighting. We went out and did our own fighting and when we got back the girl was there to dress our wounds and give us comfort.' Jaeger's hand moved and Cox thought it ended up on Gabriela's knee. Her head tipped forward and her mouth lifted at the corners. 'It's not *her* war, it's *our* war.'

Jaeger's eyes found Cox's in the mirror again and Cox held them.

'If we call Liliana off now, we ruin everything. I believe Mincu would abort. If you call up your police pals and they raid the ship and confiscate the nasties, well and good. But Mincu will go free.' He'd already said this to Jaeger but he said it again. 'If Liliana goes ahead, we have the evidence, the recorded evidence.' He nodded at the briefcase on Monckton's knees, the twin to the one Liliana carried. 'We get Mincu and the captain and the Bosnian Serbs or whoever and we probably get Wix as well. I hope so. I truly hope so. All the greed and decadence and disgusting—' He broke off, collected himself and went on more calmly. 'We not only bag a lot of awful people, we stop a bad war turning disgusting and save our boys and probably your boys from chemical threats. It's the kind of success that'll grow into a legend. And we will have done it.'

Have I convinced Jaeger? Cox wondered. Have I convinced myself?

Liliana was peering up the boulevard to the marble palace at the end that Ceausescu had built. Old Nick had never been able to decide what to put at its four corners, rejecting each plan that the architects produced. The palace was a monstrous wart on the skyline, both grandiose and uncertain. It was like an inflated provincial post office put up by Mussolini in his New Roman Empire delusion. But Liliana wasn't the amazed gawping tourist, Cox realized, she had spotted the policeman crossing the square at an angle. He was making for the Mercedes and Liliana knew it though she hadn't so much as glanced in their direction. As if a sudden decision had been made she picked up her overnight bag and hurried to cut the policeman off. He recognizes the car, Cox thought, Interpol has flashed the licence number to the local flatfoots, he sees his moment of glory. Now he'd stopped, his eyes still on the Mercedes parked so illegally, but his head lowered to catch whatever it was Liliana was saying. Finally his gaze dropped to her face.

'Can you lip-read, Gabsi?' Jaeger asked.

Liliana opened the attaché case, the one with the polka-dotted scarf on its handle, and brought out a notebook.

'Monckton, switch on,' Cox said. 'Move it.'

Monckton moved but it wasn't fast enough for Cox who stared at his agent who'd placed herself so nimbly in the path of trouble. What's she saying? What's he saying? Why is he raising a hand? Is he signalling to someone? Send reinforcements? He glanced at Monckton who had the lid of the case open and was turning a knob. NASA, you can land a man on the moon, don't let your batteries fail now. Langley, I'll forgive you nearly everything, your bully boys, your global warriors, your McAllisters, your dictator lovers, your anti-terrorist terrorists, provided the toy you've— Suddenly Liliana was in the car with them. First her voice, then the policeman's, hers again and the policeman's almost at dictation speed.

'It's an address,' Gabriela said. 'Calea Floreasca. He's telling her how to get there. She must take the metro to Piatsa Victoriei, change and go to Stefan Cel Mare. See? Now he is writing down the name of the station in her notebook.'

Liliana had her head to one side and was smiling up at the policeman.

'Miss Cool, eh?' Forbes said.

'He is saying her cousin must be rich man to live there,' Gabriela said. 'She says, no, he is servant. Now he is saying . . .' She paused to listen. 'He says the man is very lucky to have her as his cousin. She says she is of no interest to her cousin, he is . . . you know . . .' She giggled and tilted a hand back and forth.

So wrapped up were they in this little piece of street theatre, they didn't notice the arrival of Mincu. But they heard the impatient blaring of a horn and there he was, not thirty metres from them, pulled up at the kerb in a Mercedes of his own. He had the window open and was leaning out, shouting some question, a hand raised palm upwards as if testing for rain.

'He'll want to know what the hell is going on,' Jaeger said. 'Is she in some kind of shit? Is she goodie two-shoes, a snitch reporting to the cops? Jesus wept.' His voice was tense with anger. He was gripping the steering wheel as if otherwise he might just jump out of the car and go and hit someone, anyone.

And she'll invent something, Cox thought, pick some story out of the air. She can do anything. She can do a soft shoe shuffle. She can dive from the high board. She can do a fan dance. She can fly.

Her voice was no longer in the car. She had shut the attaché case, smiled sweet thanks to a very puzzled policeman, and was making her way towards Mincu. Just once her face was turned in their direction, but that was checking the flow of the murderous Bucharest traffic. Jaeger turned the ignition key.

Despite himself, despite his bone weariness, Cox felt a little lift of exhilaration. Battle was being joined. Swiftly a sense of shame swept over him because, as Jaeger had pointed out, Liliana was the soldier at the front, advancing on the enemy. They were the Generals sitting comfortably in the field headquarters.

Chapter 22

'This is not going to work.' Jaeger was angry still. It was the first thing anyone had said except for the general crowd noise when some idiot chose to think a red light was optional and sailed serenely across their bows while their brakes threw them forward and their tyres screamed. Jaeger had said it was another thing to lay at Big C's door: because there'd been no private cars then, people still couldn't get their minds round the idea of other drivers on the road.

'You know that? Not going to work. Mincu'll rumble us. He'll look in his mirror and say: Hello, fellow Mercedes driver behind me, wonder if it's anyone I know? Five minutes later he'll see us again and say: So, are we going to the same party? Another ten minutes and he'll say: Get lost. He'll put his foot down and we'll still be there, like we're on a rubber band. Then he'll get on his cellphone – notice the aerial – and order up a helicopter gunship. Or a police road check. Or a bloody great sixteen-wheeler *plus* trailer to run us into a ditch. Or he'll wait until we reach his country house – wherever that is – and then his gorillas will fall on us out of the trees.'

Jaeger slowed to let a saucy Fiat Uno overtake. There were now three cars between him and Mincu.

'It's OK in town.' Jaeger picked up his lament. 'There's other stuff on the road so he'll get different cars in his mirror. Once we're clear of Bucharest traffic I'll have to fall right back and then we'll lose him. We'll be half a mile behind him and he'll go over a hill and take some turn-off we don't see and he'll have vanished. He knows where he's going but we don't. So . . . Hi there! You guys in the back gone to sleep? I don't hear any words of comfort.'

The car went on in silence.

At first Mincu had headed south-west through the suburbs as if he was making a dash for the Bulgarian border. When he reached the ring road he turned right so he was heading virtually north.

'We call this, where I come from, the beltline, Gabsi. And like my belt these days, it doesn't quite meet in the middle.'

A sign ahead pointed to the *Autostrada* but Mincu rejected that. They followed him at a respectful distance through the muddle of a junction where Jaeger hunched tensely over the wheel. Mincu's Mercedes was silver which made it stand out from the crowd. When they ran into a traffic hold-up they were stationary just two car lengths from it. Mincu's car was in a different lane, giving Cox a view of the back and left side of his head. I saw him at the beginning of the operation, Cox thought, and now at the end. All the rest of the time he has been a will-o'-the-wisp, a shadow, a second-hand voice. Real, nonetheless. Two men dead, a shipload of nasties, people good and bad doing his bidding. Now here he was, very real, head turned towards Liliana, talking to her. Suddenly he was talking in their car and Liliana was answering him.

Cox swung on Monckton. 'You left it on receive?'

'Yes.'

'Press the record button. Gabriela, what're they saying?'

She had turned in her seat so she could stare at the attaché case. 'He asked what the policeman wanted. She says he was asking her to come out with him. What was he writing in your notebook? His nearest metro station, Stefan Cel Mare? Here, you see? I told him that was area for rich people, diplomats. He said he had small flat over garage. Did he ask your name? No.'

Gabriela had no voices for them. It sounded like computer-speak. The traffic started moving again and Mincu, apparently satisfied, concentrated on driving. A sign pointed to Ploiesti and Brasov. Liliana spoke.

'Are we going to Ploiesti?' Gabriela translated. 'No. Brasov, then? What does it matter? Why do you want to know? I should have brought warmer clothes. My house is heated.' There was a pause. Mincu spoke. 'Sinaia. Do you know Sinaia? She says, I went skiing there once.'

The talk died again. And Jaeger took his foot off the accelerator. He caught Cox's eyes in the mirror.

'Isn't she wonderful? Isn't she a paragon? I'm going to offer her a job when this is over.'

Cox marvelled at the switch in Jaeger's views of sending a woman out to do battle.

Mincu's Mercedes was pulling away from them. The land was flat, the road was straight, and Jaeger was content to let the distance separating them grow. A fading voice, Mincu's, came over the radio. Gabriela said, 'How well do you remember Sinaia? Did you visit the monastery? My house is there. It is a nice place but a little small. I look for house somewhere else, in Spain.'

Listening to Mincu's voice as well as Gabriela's translation, what struck Cox was the distance in it, the chill. This was no seducer planning a weekend's pleasure.

The road was climbing beside a stream. It was in the best tradition of streams, splashing and chuckling between rocks, white foam on black water. Big beech trees were half bare, a golden brown carpet of leaves underneath. Old man's beard scrambled through alders. Looking up the mountainside, Cox saw the line where the trees changed to pines and, higher still, the line where the pines stopped. They passed a sawmill and saw the tops of hotel buildings beyond the next bend.

'We're entering badlands,' Jaeger said, 'and it occurred to me we shouldn't go in naked. One of the wolf cubs – Dimitru the bad as against Sever the seriously wicked – asked if I wanted the Mercedes with or without. Gabsi, honey, open that glove box, will you.'

Gabriela pressed the button. The lid fell open, a little light came on, winking off the corners of a pistol.

'It's a Walther .38,' Jaeger said, 'all dressed up and raring to go. Honey, will you take it out and pass it to friend Forbes in the back? It's OK, it won't bite.'

Forbes checked the safety was on, checked it was loaded and sighted out of the window at a sign that said: *Sinaia. Willkommen. Bienvenue.*

'Remember Kowloonside?' he said to Monckton, hefting the pistol in his hand as if it was a bag of cherries. 'One Shot Fu Wah?'

'Too true. Poor bloody sod.'

They grinned at some shared memory.

The main street had hotels on one side, a few shops, offices and a bit of neglected municipal park on the other. At first sight the main street was all there was, then beyond the hotels you noticed a network of smaller roads leading uphill lined with houses with steep roofs to defeat the snow. The hotels seemed marooned in seas of Tarmac where cars and coaches were moored. Jaeger drove slowly past a police car, murmuring, 'We're just friendly German tourists looking for a hostelry that will welcome four men sharing one woman. Yes *sir.*' A little further they drew level with a man in a brigand's sheepskin jacket and wild hair escaping from under a woolly cap. 'Ask him.'

Gabriela turned back from the window. 'Easy, he says. We must go to the end where the road turns round to the left. There are army houses and a cemetery. Then there is the monastery.'

'And then there is Mincu. We hope and pray.'

Jaeger resumed his gentle drive down the main street while Cox eyed the door mirror, just in case the police were intrigued after all. They passed a gate to a small army establishment, saw the crosses of a cemetery and the monastery beyond, but by then they'd also seen where Mincu lived.

'There,' Cox said, pointing ahead.

'Has to be, right?' Jaeger said.

Between the cemetery and the monastery was a villa set well back from the road in a garden that was all grass and fir trees. A waist-high wall topped with a wire fence marked the boundary. At the gate were a pair of soldiers.

'Perhaps the house belongs to army General,' Gabriela said.

'Honey, he's *bought* the General and the soldiers were included in the deal. See, there's his car.'

A drive of grey stone chippings led to the front door where the Mercedes was parked. Two other cars were in a bay beyond. Jaeger kept driving at the same sedate pace. Cox ordered everyone else to keep eyes front while he alone indulged a tourist's curiosity. The guards, he decided, were conscript boys. They had pudding-bowl haircuts and unlined faces. One slumped against the gate. His companion had a cigarette in his mouth and his head twisted to keep the smoke out of his eyes. Were they always there? A special show of force for today? What were their orders? Were they trusted with ammunition for the heavy old rifles that leaned against the gatepost?

He looked beyond them. The sun had sunk behind a mountain and the sky was darkening. The house was in debased alpine style, stone clad with wooden balconies for the first-floor windows, a bit of half timbering above, and above that dormer windows let into the steep-pitched roof where the maids shivered in their beds. The roof seemed made of grey slates which in the dusk light looked wet. At one corner of the house a circular tower had been tacked on. It was where the prisoners were kept. Or the mad first wife. The fanlight above the front door blazed but the windows to either side were curtained and so hidden to Cox's gaze. On the first floor one window showed light. A figure crossed in front of it and he thought it was Liliana but by then they had driven on and the chapel of the monastery hid the house.

They were standing in the cemetery, all five of them. The car was tucked into a niche by its gate. Monckton said they were parked in the space used by the hearse and Forbes told him to stop being so bleeding cheerful. It turned out to be a military cemetery with neat rows of crosses made of cement, rain-stained and lichened. By the fading light Cox made out Romanian names and other crosses that simply said *Deutsche Helden.* The graves dated from the First World War and there were a lot more Romanians killed than Germans. Gabriela was nervous and stood close to Jaeger, resting a hand flat on his chest. Twenty-four hours ago, less, I was being pressed by that hand, Cox thought. It was a beggar's hand, and was rebuffed.

'Ease off, honey.'

'I don't like graves at night.'

'So long as they're someone else's.'

Forbes produced an instrument from his pocket that looked like a flick-knife. 'Swiss Army knives are for playboys. Corkscrew, toothpick, all that gracious living. This is if you mean it.' Climbing up on the wall, he cut open an entrance through the wire fence big enough for Jaeger. Inside the grounds Forbes put a finger to his lips and left them in the gathering dusk for what he called 'a little look-see'. They stood without speaking. Cox imagined he could hear one of the soldiers cough. How could the soldiers not have heard them? Because they're alert to what's in front of them, not behind. Monckton was kneeling by the attaché case which lay open on the ground.

'Still receiving?'

'She's not transmitting.'

She was using her women's things, powdering her nose. She was being introduced to the ship's captain, charming Wix. She's had all her bags taken away from her. She's locked in the tower. Cox didn't know. He could only hope at the critical moment she would get the chance to open the attaché case – looking to check a word in the dictionary, say – and they'd hear her and Mincu loud and clear.

Oh dear, oh pray, Cox thought. Very much so.

He heard a voice from the house, very faint. Two voices, male. Even tones, measured, alternating. Now one man appeared to be reading a list.

'Still nothing?'

'Well, you'd hear, wouldn't you?' Monckton said, and gave an unnecessary tweak to a knob.

'Roy,' Jaeger murmured, 'that's not from the house. It's from beyond.'

Cox moved his head a fraction and isolated the source. Beyond the house was the monastery. What had sounded like a man reciting a list of nasties turned into a monk reading from the scriptures. A second male voice joined in chanting the office. Get off, Cox told them in his head, you're clogging the airwaves.

'I have to go to the toilet,' Gabriela announced abruptly.

'Jesus wept,' Jaeger muttered. 'Then go.'

'Where?'

'Go behind a tree. Don't go far. We'll need you when she starts talking to Mincu.'

'It's not polite, so close.'

'Dear God, do you think we're interested in you making susu?'

From a sense of delicacy or because the urge receded, Gabriela didn't move. Forbes appeared from the direction of the house.

'No dog, which is a bonus. Can't stand the buggers. The front room, this corner, I can hear two men's voices. Speaking English, I think.'

Wix and Mincu, Cox registered.

'At the back is like a pantry, no curtains. Three men sitting round a table, not speaking to each other. One man is sitting a bit separate. Ship's captain, I reckon. Sort of two-by-four build, bit of beard, black going grey. Other two are younger, pair of crooks. There's a bottle of hooch on the table. There's a side door. I tried the handle and the good news is it's not locked.'

'Good,' Cox said. 'I mean well done.'

'What do we do now?'

'Nothing.'

'We could take them.' Forbes had the pistol in his hand. 'Through the side door, softly, softly.'

One Shot Fu Wah, is that what happened to him? What Forbes was trained for was the military solution. Which was not what Cox was after. Information, Mincu condemning himself, implicating others, naming the guilty names, the sea and land routes, the pay-offs. I am a spy, Cox knew. Spying is a waiting game until the last piece of the jigsaw falls into place.

'We wait.'

It was fully dark. There was no peep from the attaché

case and Monckton had rechecked: yes, it's on receive, no doubt. Cox was not concerned. The first-floor window where he thought he'd seen Liliana – *almost* certain he had – was out of sight at the front of the house. But as darkness fell a patch of light had grown more obvious on the pine trees in the front garden. That's her, he reasoned. She hasn't been summoned. Or she's readying herself. With darkness had come a sudden chill as cold air rolled down the mountain. Gabriela moved closer to Jaeger who put an arm round her shoulders. Just for warmth.

Cox wished the communication channel was two-way. He very much wanted to speak to Liliana, partly to reassure himself, partly to tell her how close help was. He'd like to 'transmit some bravery' as she'd said in that flat Gabriela had found for him. She had said Mincu had invited her to a party to celebrate the end of the Trade Fair. Here she was in a guarded villa in the mountains a hundred and fifty kilometres from Bucharest with a man who intended to kill her. Some party.

He grew aware that Jaeger was staring at him. The moon hadn't risen but there was starlight so that he could see Jaeger's face though not the expression. But he could imagine. Jaeger applauded Liliana's spirit but thought Cox was wrong to be putting her in danger. Jaeger leaned closer. This was to be his last appeal, murmured, man to man, no one to overhear the moment Cox wavered and his resolve crumbled. So Cox was surprised by the confiding tone in Jaeger's voice.

'I was in Nicaragua one time. It was when the *Contra* thing was running and we were waiting in a clearing in the jungle for some guy who was supposed to be Ortega's driver. Or his bodyguard. I forget. Anyway, driver or bodyguard, he was our joe. On the other hand, being Nicaragua, he might be doubling. There was just me and Cardozo and a million mosquitoes and it was the hot season. Boy, I was sweating.

I just want you to know my palms are sweating the same now. Maybe more. Feel.'

But he didn't hold out his hand.

The patch of light on the pine trees went out and Cox's head lifted, then Jaeger's, finally everybody was staring at dark nothingness. Cox switched his attention to Forbes.

'You know the way in. The first hint of trouble, move fast. The gun is the last resort. If there's bloodshed we have a lot more trouble to deal with.' Forbes didn't reply. 'You hear me?'

'Yes, Mr Cox.'

'You'll record everything that's transmitted,' Cox confirmed with Monckton.

'Yes.'

'You still want to go through with this thing?' Jaeger said. 'Suppose we went in now—'

That was as far as he got. Mincu's voice was coming from the receiver, then Liliana's. Gabriela turned a fierce interpreter's gaze on the attaché case.

'He says, What are you looking for in there? She says, My glasses. He says, I've never seen you wearing glasses. She says, Only for reading. I think I have lost them. Maybe I forgot to bring them.'

Back and forth, like a tennis match, a short rally. Cox squeezed his eyes shut. This is not appropriate. This is not Wimbledon. In exhaustion his brain tended to slip its leash and wander off on a track of its own. Had the two-by-four captain been sent for, and the pair of crooks from the Balkans? Van den Doel was the captain's name. What were the buyers called? Which of the warring tribes of Bosnia were they from? Cox opened his eyes. The silence seemed to have run on rather long. He looked at Monckton crouching on the ground. Had Liliana shut her attaché case? Had it taken from her? Monckton looked up at him, shrugging.

'Sit down in that chair,' Mincu said.

'I prefer to stand,' Liliana said.

Wimbledon again, a very short sharp rally. Two things made Cox frown. The first was the increased frost in Mincu's voice; the second that he'd spoken and she'd answered in English. Mincu spoke perfectly serviceable English, he tended to forget that. Like a wily interrogator he pretended otherwise so he could hear the conversation twice and give himself extra thinking time. Now he spoke English as a courtesy.

'This is a colleague of mine, British. I thought I needed you to translate to the ship's captain but my British friend speaks French so I do not need you. Which is just as well. My friend told me you are a spy and I did not believe him. I said you were a pretty girl and you were shy, even nervous. But he insisted you were a spy because someone at the British embassy told him. This is correct?'

The question wasn't to Liliana but to Wix who said, 'Yes.' He said it *Mmyers* through lips that were pursed with disapproval. And Cox knew that *now* was the time to go in, *now* was when Liliana needed to be rescued. He looked towards Forbes who was checking the safety catch on his pistol.

'Two chaps went to your friend's flat and she got your *controller* – is that what you call him? – to come. Now one of those chaps is *dead.* He is shot in the face. *Mmyers.*'

Certain voices filled Cox with loathing. He remembered a news broadcast from some Party conference, Brighton or Harrogate, and Wix baying for blood, how they must *beat* the criminals, hit them for *six,* smash the terror gangs on our city's streets with an *iron fist.* How the faithful had cheered.

'Shot in the face, d'you hear?' Wix again.

'Get away from me,' Liliana said. Her voice had grown shrill, urgent. 'Keep away.'

They heard her cry out and a sound like a hand slapping a face hard and the crash of wooden furniture.

'What are you doing?' Still Wix. 'Good God, you little hellcat.'

Forbes was pelting for the side door, Monckton was up on his feet and starting to follow, Cox and Jaeger were moving, Gabriela had a hand raised to her face in sympathy when they heard the gunshot from the house. After the shot the world was frozen in a moment's respectful silence. Cox remembered Budapest and how Ilona had stood naked looking out over the city while the sound of gunfire reached up to them. And how later one of the bullets must have found her. He remembered tanks and Lovelace and *Akarhattalak*. Then the past was wiped out and the present was all confusion.

Forbes was flattened against the wall of the house, head cocked to listen. He flung open the side door and went inside in a crouching scramble. Monckton was behind him. Then Cox. Then Jaeger. Then Gabriela who now had both hands over her ears because if she heard no shots then all was well. There were shouts from the pantry at the back, voices calling from the gate. But from the front room, absolute hush.

Forbes pushed open the door and dashed in five or six steps and halted, his hand with the gun pointing at a target on the floor somewhere to his right. Monckton followed and froze in the same position. Cox and Jaeger followed. To their left a voice said, 'You! You there! Drop the pistol. Drop it *now*.' Forbes hesitated. '*Now*.' He opened his hand and let the gun fall. Wix stood across the room with a pistol aimed at Forbes, then fanning across the four of them. 'Anyone moves, I'll shoot. I mean it.' He sounded jittery enough to mean it.

Liliana was slumped in a chair, eyes closed, handbag clutched to her chest. On the floor lay Mincu.

'She shot him. The girl did. She had the gun hidden in her handbag and she killed him. Then she collapsed in that chair so I have the gun now. I'm in charge.'

Cox studied him. The smile that had so nauseated him in newspaper photos had vanished. His mouth had an irregular curve to it like a sneer but it was probably tension. There were patches of white skin under his eyes and two deep furrows between them. The gun didn't settle, now favouring Monckton who was taking deep breaths, now Jaeger who cleared his throat. To Cox's eye Wix was a man out of his element, with a voice used to commanding secretaries but which now carried no conviction.

Mincu had been shot in the chest. She could have aimed for his head. If she was flustered or hurried, his stomach was a target she couldn't miss. But she'd chosen his chest, a bit left of centre, as if she needed to hit him in the heart not just to make certain of killing him but because she thought that was where the evil in him lay. Hatred had guided the bullet. He lay with his arms flung out as if he'd been crucified not shot. His mouth was open. He'd been screaming something: *Don't do it.* Maybe just her name: *Liliana*, shouted out and transmitted to their attaché case while they were running towards the house. *Liliana*, put that gun down. Something.

'Right. Kick that gun over here. Careful how you move.'

Forbes edged the toe of his trainer beside the Walther and with a quick flick sent it slithering across the floor to a side wall.

'I said *here.*'

'My foot slipped. Sorry and all that.'

Wix eyed the distance to the pistol then eyed the distance to Forbes. He yelled, 'François! Ivan!'

'I don't think they were too happy about events,' Monckton said. 'They scarpered. I think actually you're on your own. There's you and there's us.'

'Don't move.'

But Forbes and Monckton had already moved, shuffling sideways, spreading the target a little more. There were shouts outside, from the soldiers and the Bosnians.

Wix's eyes centred on Cox. 'You're the boss, aren't you? You're English. Cox, isn't it? Answer me.'

'Yes.'

'Got that videotape? Come on, you know what I mean. It's in your pocket. I can see it is. Take it out and throw it in the fire. No, don't throw it. Go over slowly and put it on the fire. Go on, do it now.'

For the first time Cox registered the room they were in. A log fire burned cheerfully. On the hearth was a wolf skin. Above the fireplace half a wild boar charged out of the wall just as half an elephant had charged in the museum. In one corner a bear on its hind legs snarled defiance. A dark wooden table held the attaché case open on it. Four heavy armchairs made a semi-circle. A glass-fronted display cabinet had china plates with hunting scenes.

'The tape,' Wix said. 'Hurry up.'

'Why don't you come and get it.'

Wix frowned, puzzled what to do. Then the frown cleared and he acted. He raised the pistol up to his face, one eye closed, sighting down the barrel with the other. Cox found himself staring back at the pistol he'd given Liliana in Cismigiu Park, in the ruins of the Roman temple, hiding it under her women's things in her handbag, warning her: Only use it as a last resort.

He could see how Wix's finger tightened on the trigger. Forbes, seizing his chance, was tensing to charge, had taken the first step, as time ran out. Wix squeezed the trigger. There was a sharp click. He squeezed again and got another click.

Only use it as a last resort, Cox had said, because there's only one bullet left.

In frustration, in fury, Wix hurled the pistol and it hit the wall behind Cox. Monckton stooped.

'Don't touch it,' Cox ordered.

The two soldiers entered the room with Gabriela between them as if they'd captured a prisoner. Their eyes were wide, their rifles poked everywhere. Seeing the corpse on the floor, they aimed their rifles at it. Jaeger had moved to the centre of the room. From an inside pocket he took a passport.

'I am an accredited American diplomat from the embassy in Bucharest. See, it says here – United States of America. Diplomat. You understand English? Tell 'em, Gabsi. Look, one of you go and fetch your Colonel or your General, whoever your big boss is. This is my English colleague. Roy, you tell them how it is. I've got to find a telephone, get that ship impounded.'

Cox looked round. 'Where's Monckton?'

'Here.' He straightened from picking up the other pistol that Forbes had kicked away, slipping it in his pocket.

'You left the box of tricks on record?'

'Yes, like you said.'

'Now I say this. Go outside, take the tape out and destroy it. Got that? Destroy it. Cut it up. Burn it. Don't just chuck it in a bin for someone to find.'

Wix had taken a step forward and spoke loudly to an uncomprehending soldier. 'Never mind what he said, the American. I am in charge here. I am Sir Terence Wix. You understand what a Sir is? It's an honour from our Queen. Queen, you understand? Oh, for God's sake. You, girl, you tell him.'

'Liliana, are you all right? Did he hurt you?'

She touched her cheek, then looked up at Cox. 'I'm all right. I had to kill him, you know. The Englishman hit me and when I looked in Mincu's face I saw he was smiling and I remembered how he had smiled before and I knew what he wanted to do with me.'

'I understand. Just don't say anything.'

'I was going to poison him. Then you gave—'

'Liliana.' He rested both hands on her shoulders. He stared into her eyes and wasn't certain what they were seeing, him or Mincu at the birthday party in the Bucuresti Hotel. He gripped her shoulders tighter and spoke as if she was a child. 'You must keep quiet. Listen to me, pay attention. You've been extraordinarily brave. You've been in a lot of danger. You've been witness to a horrible murder and you're naturally shaken.'

'Witness? Her?' Wix swung round from the soldier. 'She *did* it, Liliana. She pulled out the gun, she aimed it, she squeezed the trigger, she killed him. I saw her do it. *I* was the witness. Where's the other girl got to? Here, you tell the soldier, go on, tell him. That's an order.'

Cox stared at Wix, feeling a great calmness descending on him. How many times were you blessed with the chance to do something wholly good? Cox was smiling. It hadn't reached his face but he was smiling inside because of the lightness he felt. All the bad things in his life, the rows with Jenny, the squalid manoeuvres in the Glasshouse, the compromises, the wriggles, the half-truths, the times when he had blanked out his mind as someone in Lübeck or Gdansk or Plzen no longer answered, everything that had shamed him was in one pan of the scales, and this moment was in the other pan. With this single action, he felt, he was wiping the slate clean, redeeming himself. Ilona, if she was in some form present in the room, must be nodding agreement. Yes, Cox, your life has not been frivolous after all. Do it. Just do it.

'No, actually,' Cox said. 'You killed him.'

All movement in the room seemed to die.

'What? Now look here. That's a damned lie. I saw her do it. What the hell are you talking about?'

'You killed him. You, Sir Terence Wix.' Using a handkerchief, Cox held up the pistol by the tip of its barrel. 'It's your fingerprints on the gun.'

Wix shook his head. His eyes were seeing things, that pistol wasn't really being held up as evidence. His hearing had gone muzzy, Cox hadn't really accused him. It was all beyond him. He peered at Cox but seemed to have difficulty making him out.

'Rubbish,' he said. 'Bollocks. Absolute bollocks.'

'*Your* fingerprints. Also,' Cox felt the smile in him widening, 'also the same gun was used to shoot a man at – Liliana, what's the address of Gabriela's flat?'

Liliana seemed too astonished to reply.

'Also, a room at the top of the museum, bullets fired from this gun, *another* body. Three murders. You were desperate to get back the videotape. It does show you in an interesting light.'

'Now look here, Cox. I don't find this funny.'

'No,' Cox said, 'I don't suppose you do.'

'The Prime Minister,' he began but seemed unable to think how to continue.

Oh dear, oh pray, Cox thought, please spare me that.

THE MUR

Brian Lane is an expert in the field of true crime, and is the author of *The Encyclopedia of Forensic Science* (Headline, 1992), *The Encyclopedia of Women Killers* (Headline, 1994) and (with Wilfred Gregg) *The Encyclopedia of Serial Killers* (Headline, 1992) and *The Encyclopedia of Mass Murder* (Headline, 1994). He founded The Murder Club in 1987, and compiled the formidable six-volume series of *Murder Club Guides* to Great Britain.

Brian Lane came to writing via fine art, theatre and experimental music and also spent a number of years with the United Nations in Geneva and Vienna. Now living in London, he continues to research, write and lecture on true-crime subjects.

Also by Brian Lane

The Murder Club Guides (6 vols.)
The Murder Guide to Great Britain
The Murder Guide to London
The Butchers
Murder Update
The Encyclopedia of Serial Killers (with Wilfred Gregg)
The Encyclopedia of Forensic Science
The Encyclopedia of Cruel and Unusual Punishment
The Murder Yearbook
The Murder Yearbook: 1994 Edition
The Murder Yearbook: 1995 Edition
Chronicle of Twentieth Century Murder
The Encyclopedia of Women Killers
The Encyclopedia of Mass Murder (with Wilfred Gregg)
The Encyclopedia of Occult and Supernatural Murder
The Encyclopedia of Occult, Paranormal and Magick Practices

The Murder Book of Days

Brian Lane

HEADLINE

First published in 1995
by HEADLINE BOOK PUBLISHING

10 9 8 7 6 5 4 3 2 1

ISBN 0 7472 4737 4

Typeset by Keyboard Services, Luton, Beds

Printed and bound in Great Britain by
Cox & Wyman Ltd, Reading, Berks

HEADLINE BOOK PUBLISHING
A division of Hodder Headline PLC
338 Euston Road
London NW1 3BH

Contents

Acknowledgements

As always my sincere thanks to all the team without whose support, enthusiasm and effort Brian Lane could not survive as a moderately sane, moderately happy, moderately solvent author. For this, *The Murder Book of Days*, my special thanks to Bela Cunha for her patience, and to Sarah Hughes at Headline for hers – both far beyond the call of duty.

Introduction

Given that in the United States alone there is a murder every twenty-two minutes (Britain has a somewhat more modest two per day), the compiler of a *Murder Book of Days* might seem spoilt for choice. In reality, of course, although there have been countless murders over the past few centuries, very few of them are of even the most passing interest. They are simply 'killings' – tragic for those concerned, but forensically uninspiring. For this reason it was decided to collect together cases which, in themselves, were landmarks or superlatives in one way or another, and then plot them on to the calendar.

It became apparent early in the exercise that many of the most significant dates were in fact not the date of the murder; often the murder was the least interesting aspect of a case. It may have been that some other event in the crime's chronology was its outstanding feature – the discovery of the corpse, the arrest of the suspect, a forensic discovery, the trial, or execution.

By using this device it was possible to embroider a tapestry of crime using the calendar as a background. The result has been widely varying *types* of story, spanning the past three and a half centuries and much of the globe. One thing to emerge from the research into this compilation is that there is no identifiable pattern of homicide from one year to another, one decade to another, or one century to another. Clearly in an age when semi-automatic assault rifles can be bought over the counter there are going to be more mass shootings, in the same way that in an age where a huge range of domestic products, from cosmetics to sheep-dip, contain lethal doses of arsenic there are going to be a lot of arsenic poisonings. Throughout the period covered by this book the same basic weapons have been used – guns, blades, poisons, bludgeons and ligatures. As to motives, they have not changed since Cain slew Abel. Indeed, although there are variations on the themes, the number of motives for murder can be reduced to six. In her excellent study *Murder and its Motives* (1924), Miss F. Tennyson-Jesse presented these classifications – Gain, Jealousy, Revenge, Elimination, Lust and Conviction. There is no evidence to the contrary whether it be 1495 or 1995. The things that are *never* the same are the characters who act out these dramas; for this is a book about *people*, often quite extraordinary people; people whose only common link is that they became involved in that most wicked of crimes – murder.

Brian Lane
London, March 1995

January

1 January

1845 (England) The trial of John Tawell for the murder of Sarah Hart at Slough attracted much attention not only because of the cruelty shown by this apparently kindly and charitable Quaker in poisoning the victim of his seduction, but also for the novel way in which he was apprehended. Though Tawell lost no time in fleeing the scene of his crime on a train from Slough to London, the electric telegraph, which had only very recently been established on the Great Western Railway line, outstripped him, and a police officer was awaiting his arrival at Paddington. At his trial between 12 and 14 March 1845, the jury heard evidence from Mary Ashley, a next-door neighbour, that she had seen John Tawell enter Sarah Hart's cottage on the evening of 1 January. Shortly afterwards she had heard 'a sort of stifled scream', followed by Tawell's abrupt departure. Elaborate and detailed medical evidence resulting from the toxicological tests carried out at post-mortem identified the cause of Sarah's death as a bottle of porter laced with prussic acid. Following the briefest of retirements, the jury found John Tawell guilty of murder, and Mr Baron Parke, after speaking on the hypocrisy of the prisoner's assumption of the garb of a virtuous, peaceful and benevolent body of religious persons, passed on him 'the dread sentence of the law'; which he suffered on 28 March 1845.

2 January

1917 (England) Towards the end of 1916, twenty-two-year-old Leo George O'Donnell, a sergeant with the Royal

Army Medical Corps, found himself stationed at Aldershot barracks in Berkshire. On New Year's Day, 1917, he announced his engagement to the daughter of Lieutenant Quartermaster William Watterton, an officer attached to the nearby military hospital. Miss Watterton and her best friend lost no time in organising a celebration. The commandant, we know, gave his blessing to the prospective bride, her father and her chum (not to forget George O'D) taking a trip to sample the delights of London. With some glee, the girls returned to Lieutenant Watterton's home on the base. Of Will Watterton there was no sign, so the young nurses sat down to wait. And wait. And . . .

At around 11.30 p.m. George arrived; and as far as he knew, Lieutenant Watterton had rushed off to keep an appointment earlier that afternoon. But O'Donnell had something else on his mind; something that would eventually hang him. It was the disappearance of what George called his 'short stick' – a kind of 'swagger stick' which he affected, and laid claim had been carried during the Easter Rising in Dublin. [I am indebted to that doyen of crime historians Edward Spencer Shew for pointing out that this 'short stick' was, in fact, 'a lavatory brush from which the bristles had been trimmed'.]

On the following morning – 2 January – some children made the ghastly discovery of William Watterton's body lying in a practice trench on Smallshot Hill, near Aldershot; he had been savagely battered. In the next trench lay nothing less than Sergeant O'Donnell's 'short stick'. A convenient weapon, some might have thought.

Probably they were the same people who ensured that Leo George O'Donnell was arrested and charged with murder. And then tried before Mr Justice Darling at the Winchester Assizes in February.

Mad George put up one of the most spirited defences of his time. Having failed – despite the lure of '£250 down' – to persuade his friends to concoct an alibi, Sergeant O'Donnell went for the next best thing. He suggested – with a straight face, so it is said – that Lieutenant Watterton had, in his time, 'done a great wrong to a wealthy Spanish girl', and was being blackmailed by a (murderous) illegitimate son! Yes, it was too much for the jury as well, and Leo George O'Donnell was convicted of murder and sentenced to death.

But if the authorities thought they had heard the last of O'Donnell, they were wrong. For George took an uncommonly serious interest in his forthcoming meeting with the hangman, and was forever worrying the prison staff over such details as the length and thickness of the rope, and of the estimated 'drop'. And there was one other vitally important detail on which George O'Donnell needed to be constantly reassured by Winchester's prison governor – that nobody with cross-eyes would be permitted to attend the execution. Such men, he claimed, had always been a source of bad luck to him. It is to be assumed that George was granted this final eccentric wish, because apart from showing a lively interest in the whole procedure he went, apparently untroubled, to the scaffold on 29 March.

3 January

1955 (India) It was on this date that, whatever comfort it may have brought her, Rattan Bai Jain achieved a kind of national celebrity. For a start, she was the first woman to be executed on the Indian sub-continent since its independence from Britain in 1947; she was also the first woman *ever* to be hanged in the capital, New Delhi. The circumstances which led to Rattan Jain's untimely death took place some eight months previously.

On 1 May 1954, three teenage girls were rushed to a New Delhi hospital after collapsing with convulsions at their homes. Despite the best efforts of hospital staff, eighteen-year-old Kanta died the following morning. In trying to find a link between the three young victims, the toxicologist learnt that they all worked at the Nari Kiwan Karyalaya fertility clinic run by a couple called Milkhi Ram Jain and his wife Rattan Bai Jain. Mrs Jain was evidently the dominant partner, and she had made such a success of the business that they now employed a manager to run it. An examining magistrate was appointed to investigate the death of Kanta and the illness of the other two girls, who remained on the critical list. He visited Mrs Jain who thought it likely that they had eaten something disagreeable at a picnic she had heard them planning. The police and magistrate left the clinic and returned to the hospital to be informed that young Raj Rani's condition was worsening; she died the following afternoon. The next person interviewed was the fertility clinic's manager, Jagannath, who was adamant there were no poisons kept at the clinic; what was more, he knew of no picnic. Asked if the girls had eaten anything out of the usual, Jagannath suggested: 'It might have been the peras' (peras are a sugary confection popular with young girls). Indeed, the nurse attending Raj Rani reported that the girl had been mumbling something about peras before she died. The last of the three victims, Satyabala, died the same evening after telling nurses that Mrs Jain had given her peras. Analysis of the stomach contents of the three girls established that each had received a lethal dose of white arsenic.

The police applied for a warrant to arrest Mrs Jain and her husband but when they arrived at the house the couple had fled. They were eventually detained at Jakhai and returned to New Delhi for questioning. Milkhi Ram Jain denied any involvement but confided that his wife was insanely jealous of the pretty young girls they employed. Mrs Jain admitted giving sweets to the dead girls, but accused the manager, Jagannath, of coating them with arsenic. Jagannath naturally denied this, and all three suspects were kept in custody while inquiries continued. The police had a lucky break when they talked to a pedlar of herbs who remembered selling Mrs Jain arsenic, which she claimed she needed to kill vermin. In view of this evidence Mrs Jain was charged with murder.

The trial opened on 6 July 1954, before Mr Y. L. Taneja, the Additional Sessions Judge, and four assessors. After more than twenty witnesses testified, Rattan Bai Jain was found guilty of murder and sentenced to death. Her appeal was dismissed by the High Court of the Punjab on 3 September and her application for leave to appeal to the Supreme Court of India was rejected. A petition for mercy to the President of India also failed. Of Rattan Jain's ignominious end, we already know.

4 January

1777 (England) Jacques Mondroyte was a jeweller and watchmaker from Paris, who had journeyed to London in order to find a market for various articles of his manufacture. His stock consisted of curious and costly articles worth, as was computed, a few thousand pounds. He took lodgings in Prince's Street and employed one Francis Mercier (alias Louis de Butte), who had resided some time in London, as his interpreter. Mercier was paid well and treated more as a friend than as a servant.

It seems that this ungrateful villain had for some time determined on killing his employer in order to take possession of his entire valuable property. To this diabolical end he gave orders for an instrument to be made of a most singular construction. It was shaped somewhat like an Indian tomahawk, and this instrument of death he concealed until an opportunity offered itself to complete his detestable purpose.

One day Monsieur Mondroyte invited Mercier to spend the evening in his company; they played at cards, sang some French songs, and took a cheerful glass, but with that moderation from which Frenchmen seldom depart. Thus it grew late when the interpreter offered to stay the night. As soon as all the inhabitants were wrapped in sleep, Mercier took from the lining of his coat the fatal weapon, with which he struck the sleeping victim repeatedly until he was dead. He then plundered the apartment and made his escape.

The next day, and for some days following, the wicked Mercier had the effrontery to return to the house and ask after Monsieur Mondroyte, until the family below, entertaining suspicions of some foul play, procured a ladder and entered Mercier's chamber window. There they discovered the body, which had begun to putrefy.

Mercier was arrested on alighting from a post-chaise after jaunting with a woman of the town, and held in custody. In his lodgings were found sixteen gold watches of great value, and a number of diamond and other rings, a variety of trinkets and seventy-five guineas. He confessed the property was that of Jacques Mondroyte, was convicted at trial and sentenced to be hanged opposite the place where he committed the murder.

(Derived from *The Newgate Calendar*)

5 January

1937 (England) Frederick Nodder murdered ten-year-old Mona Tinsley at Hayton, Nottinghamshire, but as no body was found and there was no proof that a death had occurred, Nodder was convicted only of abduction. On 6 June, while he was serving his sentence, Mona's body was recovered from the River Idle and Nodder was charged with murder, found guilty and hanged at Lincoln Gaol on 30 December. Mr Justice McNaghten told him: 'Justice has slowly but surely overcome you.'

6 January

1985 (Canada) One of the most extraordinary cases of mass murder in Canadian legal history came to trial at the Quebec Superior Court on 6 January 1985. Denis Lortie stood charged with three counts of first-degree murder and nine of attempted murder, arising out of his attempt to assassinate members of the Quebec National Assembly on 8 May the previous year. The first anybody knew of the attack was when a heavily armed man dressed in army fatigues arrived at the legislature building and first sprayed the outside with bullets before entering and opening fire indiscriminately in the Chamber. Three officials, Georges Boyer, Camille Lepage and Roger Lefrançois, were shot dead and thirteen other people wounded. The man later identified as Denis Lortie, a Canadian soldier, was shouting, 'Where are the Assembly members? I want to kill them all.' He was eventually secured by police officers as a result of the courage shown by the Assembly's sergeant-at-arms, Rene Jalbert, who engaged Lortie in conversation and finally persuaded him to surrender. It was later learnt that Denis Lortie had left an audio cassette message at a local radio station in which he made clear his disapproval of the government and his intention to destroy it.

At his trial, witnesses testified that Lortie had screamed out: 'I'm going to rid the province of this government' while spraying the Chamber with machine-gun fire. Lortie's lawyers advanced a defence that at the time of the shootings he was suffering paranoid delusions about the government; in other words, it was an insanity plea. However, in his summing-up, Superior Court Judge Ivan Mignault warned the jury that although they could *consider* the psychiatric evidence, it should be treated as hearsay. On 13 February, Lortie was found guilty as charged and sentenced to life imprisonment with no possibility of parole for twenty-five years. Predictably, Denis Lortie appealed against conviction, and in September 1986 the Quebec Court of Appeal ordered a new trial on the grounds that the original trial judge had been in error when he ruled on the psychiatrists' evidence.

At his second trial, in January 1987, Lortie pleaded guilty to three reduced charges of second-degree murder and nine counts of attempted murder. After a lengthy hearing during which Lortie testified in his own defence, the judge, Mr Justice Jacques Ducros, refused to accept the guilty pleas because he felt Lortie had a possible defence against the charges; he consequently ordered a new trial before another judge. The third hearing opened on 24 March 1987 before Mr Justice Gaston Desjardins who, two days later, reversed the previous decision and *did* accept Lortie's earlier pleas of guilty. On 11 May Denis Lortie was sentenced to life imprisonment with eligibility for parole after ten years which was to include the three years already spent in custody prior to sentencing. An appeal against this sentence was dismissed by the Superior Court of Canada on 9 November 1990.

7 January

1973 (USA) Although he had shot four police officers, killing two of them, on the streets of New Orleans on 1 January, Mark Robert James Essex saved his main shooting spree until the 7th. Having commandeered a car, black militant Essex drove to a motel on Loyola Avenue where he shot a honeymoon couple dead. On the eleventh floor of the building he told a black maid: 'This is a revolution. I'm only shooting whites. No blacks.' He then began setting fires in the motel and shooting down into the street. Surrounded by an armed police assault team, Mark Essex held them off all day before deliberately breaking cover and being cut down in a hail of police bullets. Over a thirty-hour period the death toll was ten, with another seventeen wounded.

8 January

1886 (England) On 8 January 1886 one of England's best-known and most loved artists died and was buried in the tiny cemetery at Broadmoor – then officially called the 'Asylum for the Criminally Insane'. He was also one of Victorian England's best-known murderers.

Richard Dadd was born the fourth of seven brothers and sisters on 1 August 1817. His father, Robert, was a native of Chatham, and in business as an apothecary in that town. The Dadds were a cultured, moderately prosperous middle-class family and their fourth son received his education at Rochester Cathedral Grammar School, supplementing his classes with drawing lessons at William Dadson's Academy. In January 1837 Richard entered into full-time study at the Royal Academy School of Art, in London, where he established himself a modest reputation. He also began to receive the private patronage of Sir Thomas Phillips, a solicitor and former mayor of Newport.

It was as companion and draughtsman to Sir Thomas that Dadd departed England on 16 July 1842, following that Victorian middle-class pursuit – The Grand Tour. On this cultural trip Richard managed to complete many estimable watercolours and drawings. Unfortunately, by the time the two travellers began their return journey, Richard Dadd had become convinced that he was pursued by devils. When Richard arrived home in May 1843, clearly very seriously disturbed, nobody felt that the situation demanded any urgent remedial action. However, by August Richard's behaviour could be ignored no longer as his manic flights from imagined persecution became a public embarrassment.

Still unconvinced of the urgency, Robert Dadd was persuaded to take a trip to Cobham with his son on 27 August. That evening the pair took a stroll through the darkening acres of Cobham Park. Here Richard made a frenzied and murderous attack on his father and left him dead, his body a bloody mass of stab wounds and razor cuts.

Richard immediately fled to France, where he might well have remained undetected had he not tried to cut the throat of a fellow passenger on a stage-coach they shared at Fontainebleau. The result was that Richard Dadd was confined, without trial, to a French asylum. There he remained until 1844, when he was extradited to England and quietly relegated to the Bethlem (or Bedlam) Hospital at Southwark. It was here that Richard was encouraged to take up painting again and embarked on the most brilliantly productive four decades of his artistic life. At the Bethlem, and later at Broadmoor, Dadd created a series of obsessive allegories crowded with the unreal denizens of his fantasies – the fairies, goblins and spirits that characterise his most popular works.

9 January

1993 (USA) In the early hours of this Saturday morning, the parents of one of the kitchen workers at Brown's Chicken Restaurant grew anxious that their son had not returned home from the night shift and telephoned the police. Brown's is one of those single-storey fast-food places popular with travellers, and sat at the side of the busy four-lane highway that runs through Palatine, a suburb north-west of Chicago. When they arrived, the police found the back door to the restaurant open. After stepping cautiously inside, officers found a trail of blood leading to the large walk-in refrigerator where four bodies lay; nearby were three more. The victims were later identified as the manager, Dick Ehlenfeldt and his wife Lynn, the cook, Guadalupe Maldonado, and four students employed part-time. They had all been shot.

It was an educated guess that the gunman entered through

the rear door of the building while staff were counting the takings and clearing up after Friday night's business. The question nobody has yet been able to answer is: who was it? The so-called Chicago Restaurant Killings were but one example of a massacre taking place in an American fast-food outlet; the grim twist in this case was that the victims were not customers, but staff.

10 January

1923 (England) As the result of a public health order to investigate 'unsanitary conditions', police broke in to forty-seven-year-old Cecil Maltby's London flat and found the putrefied body of his mistress in the bath. Maltby had shot Alice Middleton on about 24 August of the previous year, and had been living with the corpse ever since. When police entered the apartment, Cecil Maltby put a bullet through his own head.

11 January

1920 (England) We do not know when, or in what circumstances, Albert Burrows took a wife; nor do we know much about her save that she was a hard and rather grasping woman. Of Burrows' mistress we know a little more. She was christened Hannah Calladine, though Albert called her 'Nance'. She was nearly thirty years younger than Burrows, and in October 1918, when she was twenty-eight, Hannah did him the disservice of producing a son. Typically, Albert panicked and 'married' the woman, which earned him six months in Derby Gaol for bigamy. When he came out, he was presented with a bastardy order requiring him to pay Miss Calladine seven shillings a week. Of course Albert did not pay her a single farthing, and November 1919 found him once again behind bars. Hannah, meanwhile, in a fit of pique, presented herself on the doorstep of Mrs Burrows, who was not unnaturally very put out. In fact she had a maintenance order sworn against her husband. The case was to be heard on 12 January 1920.

Albert was clearly in a bit of a mess. He didn't have any money, and with more desperation than common sense, he devised a further, less costly option than paying either the maintenance or the bastardy order. On a pretext Albert Burrows persuaded young Nance and fourteen-month-old Albert Edward out on to the lonely Simmondley Moor. Beneath the moor lies part of the once thriving Derbyshire coalfield, and it was at the bottom of one of the disused airshafts which ventilated the mines that Hannah Calladine and her son began their eternal rest. On the following morning, 12 January 1920 (the day on which Mrs Burrows' maintenance order was to be heard), Albert was once again at the opening of an airshaft on the moor; it was time for three-year-old Elsie Calladine to join her mother and stepbrother.

Speeding back to town, Albert was just in time to catch his wife before she went into court. Although he was unable to persuade her to drop the maintenance claim, they were subsequently reunited. As for the sudden disappearance of the Calladine family, Albert explained that Hannah was living and thriving in Stretford where she worked for one of his relatives, and the children had been found excellent foster homes. And it is likely that Hannah and her babes would have remained 'lost' for ever, and their murderer unvisited by Nemesis; but Albert Burrows had a habit even more repellent than killing children. He liked to rape little boys – and then kill them.

In March 1923 the abused and broken body of four-year-old Thomas Wood was found at the bottom of an airshaft on Simmondley Moor. And having associated Albert Burrows with this vile crime, the police were minded to recall the Calladine disappearances; before long, their bodies too had been recovered from under the moor. At the Derby Assizes in July 1923 Burrows was tried and, after a jury retirement of only eleven minutes, convicted of murder. It is characteristic of this blustering bully that Albert Burrows' only reaction was: 'I shan't be like Charlie Peace; I shan't tremble when I go to the scaffold.' He got his chance to prove it at Nottingham Gaol on 8 August 1923.

12 January

1992 (USA) The trial of highway hooker and serial killer Aileen Wuornos, by this time known as the 'Damsel of Death', opened at Deland, Florida. Although she had made a videotaped confession to seven killings, there was only one charge on the present indictment – the first-degree murder of fifty-one-year-old Richard Mallory, her first victim. According to the state prosecutor, 'Lee' Wuornos had been plying her trade when she was picked up by Mallory who drove her to a secluded woodland area close to Daytona Beach where they engaged in sex; Wuornos then shot Mallory and robbed him. Although she was found guilty of this and subsequently of other murders, Wuornos has consistently maintained that she killed only in self-defence when her clients became threatening. At present, Aileen Wuornos awaits the implementation of her sentence on Florida's Death Row.

13 January

1925 (South Africa) Petrus Hauptfleisch was what might be called a heavy drinker. It had put paid to his job and it had put paid to his marriage. Now, unable to bear the thought of looking after himself, he was living with his mother despite his intense dislike of her. On the morning of 13 January 1925, Hauptfleisch was seen running out of the front door yelling for help – his mother was on fire! And it was just as he had said – the unfortunate Mrs Hauptfleisch was lying dead beside the kitchen stove, her face and body severely burnt.

The forensic evidence in the trial of Petrus Stephanus François Hauptfleisch succeeded in demolishing the entirely false account that he had given of his mother trying to clean the stove's chimney by burning it out with petrol, and he was found guilty of her murder and hanged shortly before Christmas 1926.

14 January

1975 (England) 'Beech Croft' was the home of the Whittle family in the village of Highley in the county of Shropshire. On the morning of Tuesday 14 January 1975, Dorothy Whittle was surprised, and not a little alarmed, to find that her seventeen-year-old daughter Lesley was missing from the house. In her place were a number of messages pressed out of red Dymo-tape which left the family in no doubt that Lesley had been kidnapped. The ransom demand was £50,000. Despite warnings against it, Lesley's brother Ronald sensibly made contact with the local police, who in turn called on assistance from Scotland Yard.

The first major clue was provided by a police report of an incident that occurred in Dudley not long after the abduction. Gerald Smith, a security officer at the Freightliner container depot was on a routine patrol when he saw a man loitering at the perimeter fence; as Smith turned to report the matter to the police he heard the loud report of a gun and felt a searing pain in his buttocks. The attacker then emptied the remaining five bullets into the unfortunate watchman and made off. Remarkably, Gerald Smith was able to crawl to a telephone and alert the authorities. Subsequent ballistics tests on the spent cartridges recovered from the scene revealed that they had been fired by the same gun that had been used in two previous crimes. The first had been the killing of Donald Skepper during a nocturnal raid on his sub-post office on 15 February 1974. The second was a similar robbery on 6 September when sub-postmaster Derek Astin was shot dead. Both these and a later violent robbery and murder in mid-November had been carried out by a man whose disguise of a black hood had led to his being nicknamed the 'Black Panther'.

When officers investigating the Dudley Freightliner shooting traced the green Morris 1300 saloon car that had been seen parked at the depot they were rewarded with further vital pointers to the identity of the man who had so recently added kidnapping to his record of robbery and murder. Among the items removed from the vehicle was a number of Dymo-tape messages, quite clearly pieces of a ransom trail.

Just before midnight on 16 January, Ronald Whittle received a telephone call from a man claiming to be Lesley's captor. Following a trail marked by Dymo-tape messages, Ronald arrived at Bathpool Park in Staffordshire. No contact was made, and it was not until two weeks later, when police teams with tracker dogs made a thorough search of the underground culverts running beneath Bathpool Park that the mystery was solved. At the bottom of one of the ventilation shafts, officers found the naked body of Lesley Whittle. Around her neck was a wire noose attached to the iron ladder. The Black Panther was now Britain's most wanted man.

Almost a year later, on the night of 11 December 1975, PCs Stuart Mackenzie and Tony White were on routine Panda car patrol in the Nottinghamshire village of Mansfield Woodhouse. Seeing a suspicious-looking man carrying a black holdall, the officers decided to investigate and found themselves facing the barrels of a sawn-off shotgun. Forcing the policemen back into their car, the stranger climbed into the passenger seat and ordered PC Mackenzie to drive. Despite what must have been a terrifying ordeal, Mackenzie had the presence of mind to jam his foot on the brake at a T-junction which unsettled the gunman sufficiently for PC

White to make a grab for his weapon. In the struggle which followed the shotgun exploded into action and, despite injuries to White's hand and Mackenzie's eardrums, they managed to subdue the gunman. The two constables had just ended the criminal career of Donald Neilson, alias the Black Panther.

When police searched Neilson's home in Bradford they found all the evidence they needed to bring four charges of murder against him. For these wicked crimes he would receive life sentences; for kidnapping Lesley Whittle he was condemned to sixty-one years' imprisonment.

Gerald Smith died of his injuries in March 1976; however, the laws of England require that a person dies within one year and a day if a charge of murder is to be brought.

15 January

1947 (USA) It was in the early morning that the body of a young woman was found on a waste lot outside Los Angeles. She had been inexpertly hacked in half at the waist, and the remains had been grotesquely mutilated; on one of her thighs the letters BD had been carved with a knife. A fingerprint check proved the woman to be Elizabeth Ann Short, also known as the 'Black Dahlia'.

Elizabeth was born in Medford, Massachusetts, and in 1942 she left home and worked as a waitress in Miami. With America's involvement in the Second World War, the country was filling up with handsome young men in uniform, and 1943 found Beth in California where she continued waitressing, 'modelling' and entertaining the troops. When this piece of self-sacrifice came to the notice of the authorities, via a police raid on a bar full of sailors, nineteen-year-old Beth was dispatched home to her mother. Within days she was off again, and this time landed a job in the stores at Camp Cooke, where her friendly nature soon earned her the accolade of 'Camp Cutie of the Week'. Then Beth decided to swap 'Camp Cutie' for 'Screen Cutie' and took a ticket to tinsel town.

Once settled in Hollywood, she set about reinventing herself as the enigmatic 'Black Dahlia', emphasising her naturally black hair by never wearing clothes of any other colour – from her underwear outwards. She was, by all accounts, much more successful at getting into producers' beds than into their films. It was while she was living this rather uncertain life that Beth Short disappeared. On 8 January she was known to have asked a man friend named 'Red' to drive her from the house at Pacific Beach where she was staying to the Biltmore Hotel in Los Angeles. She was sighted a couple of times over the next few days, and was then missing until her remains were found on the 15th. Ten days after the discovery the police had taken a number of confessions from the usual bunch of local wackos, but nothing more positive.

Then the first real clue turned up. The *Los Angeles Examiner* received an envelope on which was pasted in cut-out letters the message: 'Here is Dahlia's belongings. Letter to follow.' The belongings consisted of Elizabeth Short's birth certificate, social security card and other oddments such as snapshots and newspaper clippings; there was also an address book with one page torn out – presumably the page on which the name of the sender was written. The promised letter proved to be something of an anti-climax; it read: 'Have changed my mind. You would not give me a square deal. Dahlia killing was justified.' Elizabeth Short was buried in the Mountain View Cemetery on 25 January 1947. To date her murder remains unsolved.

16 January

1988 (USA) On 16 January 1988, Rena Chapouris was found dead in her south Richmond, Virginia, home. She had been stripped naked, bound, strangled and bludgeoned; a bloody claw-hammer was found by the body. A few blocks away on the same day, twenty-nine-year-old Michael St Hilaire was found hanging from a wire attached to an overhead pipe.

At the time the police were desperate to catch a serial rapist/killer who had been given the *nom-de-guerre* 'Southside Slayer' from the location of his crimes. The first murder was committed in 1987, when Debbie Dudley Davis was found raped and strangled in her Richmond southside apartment. Two weeks later Dr Susan Hellams, a neurosurgeon, met a similar tragic fate, followed by Diane Cho and Susan Tucker. Just the following month Rena Chapouris was found dead. The fact that she had not been raped seemed to indicate that this was a copy-cat killing, and the apparent suicide of Michael St Hilaire made him the likely candidate for the copy-cat.

As for the Southside Slayer, he turned out to be Timothy W. Spencer, who was arrested later in the month of January 1988, and his culpability for the four original rape/murders was confirmed by genetic profiling – so-called 'DNA fingerprinting'. This same method of testing also linked Timothy Spencer with a much earlier killing, that of Carol Hamm at her home in Arlington in early 1984. Unfortunately, a man named David Vasquez had already served five years of a thirty-five-year sentence for that crime.

Spencer became the first person in the state of Virginia to be convicted on DNA profiling, and he was sentenced to life imprisonment for the murder of Susan Tucker. He was tried a second time for the rapes and murders of Debbie Davis and Susan Hellams, and on this occasion the jury demanded the death penalty. However, given America's seemingly interminable appeals procedure, this sentence is likely to be delayed for some years.

17 January

1977 (USA) The headline in the *New York Times* screamed 'Gilmore Faces Execution at Dawn'; the media circus was in full swing as the United States prepared to implement the death penalty for the first time since the ten-year moratorium began in 1967. The hapless centre of all this attention was a born loser named Mark Gary Gilmore. By the time he was paroled in 1976, Gilmore had spent the greater part of his adult life in prison. In July of the same year he shot and killed a twenty-four-year-old gas-station attendant in Oren, Utah; the pickings from the robbery were slim, the murder senseless. Equally pointless was Gilmore's killing of the young manager of the City Center Motel the following day, his only reward the contents of the petty-cash box. Gilmore made no attempt to evade arrest and was taken into custody that same night. He was subsequently tried, convicted and sentenced to death.

Despite the considerable national outcry at the prospect of a return to the barbarity of state executions, Gilmore himself remained determined to die – by his method of choice, a firing squad. It is not certain how far he was aware that his execution would herald a renewed wave of judicial killing, but if he was it is unlikely to have made much difference.

About fifteen minutes before eight o'clock on that January morning Gary Gilmore was transferred from Death Row to the execution shed, where a leather-backed armchair had been raised about a foot off the ground on a small stage. Behind the chair was a wooden barrier, and between it and the concrete-block wall sandbags and an old mattress were piled to soak up the bullets. Thirty feet away, and directly in front of the chair was a long black cubicle made of black muslin stretched over a timber frame; along the front five small openings had been cut. Inside was the firing squad. After the usual preliminaries, Gilmore was loosely bound to the chair and cotton wool earplugs were handed out to the official observers. Asked by the governor if he had any last messages, Gilmore looked first up at the roof, then straight ahead, saying 'Let's do it!' At that sign a black hood was eased over his head and a black target with a white circle was pinned over his heart. At a motion from the governor a volley of gunshot ripped into Gary Gilmore's body and filled the void of the execution shed with a deafening crash. Two minutes later the doctor pronounced life extinct.

The executioner was back in business.

18 January

1803 (England) George Foster was executed at Newgate for the murder of his wife and child by drowning them in Paddington Canal. When his body had been cut down, it was taken to the house of Professor Aldini who experimented on the corpse with the new 'Galvanic' process. By passing electricity through the body it appeared to come to life, the jaws quivering, muscles contorting, and one eye opened; subsequently the right hand was raised and the legs and thighs set in motion. Needless to say, the unfortunate Foster's spirit remained dead!

19 January

1939 (England) Shortly after lunch on 18 January 1939, eleven-year-old Pamela Coventry set off from her home in Hornchurch to meet some friends on their way to a dancing class. Pamela did not arrive and her chums went on without her. When she failed to return home that night, Mrs Coventry reported her missing. On the following day, the 19th, a passer-by found Pamela's body on an airfield close to her home; she had been strangled and sexually assaulted, and her legs had been trussed up with green twine and electrical flex.

It was Sir Bernard Spilsbury who conducted the post-mortem examination on Pamela Coventry's body, and in untying her legs the pathologist found a hand-rolled cigarette-end caught between her thigh and abdomen. Several days after the discovery of Pamela's body a parcel was found containing a school badge, some buttons and a length of electrical flex similar to that used to tie the victim's legs. These objects had been wrapped in a copy of the *News Chronicle* dated 11 January.

Convinced that it was a 'local' murder, the police eventually targeted twenty-eight-year-old Leonard Richardson. Richardson had been at home on the day Pamela had disappeared, and he lived close to the airfield on which she was found. Furthermore, his garden shed revealed green twine of the type used to bind her legs. For officers interviewing Richardson, final 'proof' seemed to be offered when he took out a pouch of tobacco and proceeded to roll a cigarette. A more detailed search of the Richardson home led to the discovery of a raincoat spotted with human blood and a pile of old copies of the *News Chronicle* – significantly missing the issue of 11 January. And so Leonard Richardson found himself facing an Old Bailey jury charged with murder. He was fortunate in having no less a champion than the redoubtable pathologist Professor Francis Camps to analyse the evidence in his defence. As for the twine used for tying the victim, this was of a type so common that most gardeners in the area – and beyond – would also have a ball in their shed; the bloodstained raincoat proved to be a bit of a red herring when it was realised that Sir Bernard had omitted to take a sample of Pamela Coventry's blood for comparison – and so Richardson's claim that it was his own, the result of a minor injury, could not be discredited. Camps had engaged the assistance of experts from the tobacco industry in the matter of the cigarette-end found in association with the victim's body. They were able to state categorically that there were no characteristics to distinguish that clue from any one of dozens of similar cigarette-ends collected randomly for comparison. Indeed, so weak was the prosecution case, that Richardson's counsel submitted that there was no case to answer; a submission with which the jury concurred. The murder of Pamela Coventry remains unsolved.

20 January

1843 (England) In London's Downing Street, Daniel M'Naghten drew a pistol from beneath his greatcoat and shot dead Edward Drummond, secretary to Prime Minister Sir Robert Peel. The ball had been intended for Sir Robert himself, but Glasgow-born M'Naghten, unfamiliar with the Prime Minister's appearance, had simply taken a guess.

At his Old Bailey trial, it transpired that M'Naghten had developed a suspicion that 'Tories' were persecuting him. The matter was a grave one – not only had murder been committed on the open street, but Her Majesty's first Minister could so easily have been the victim. Thus it was not without a strong element of self-interest that Parliament voiced its dissatisfaction with the jury's verdict that M'Naghten was insane and should therefore, out of humanity, be committed to hospital (instead of the gallows). The matter was finally referred to the House of Lords.

Their Lordships in turn requested Her Majesty's senior judges to advise them on what, by now, had become a confusing and confused debate. The collective answer given by the fourteen judges established what became known as the M'Naghten Rules, in essence:

> Jurors ought to be told in all cases that a man is presumed to be sane, and to possess a sufficient degree of reason to be responsible for his crimes, until the contrary be proved to their satisfaction; and that to

establish a defence on the ground of insanity, it must be clearly proved that –

> At the time of committing the act, the party accused was labouring under such defect of reason, from disease of the mind as not to know:
>
> a) The nature and quality of the act he was doing; or if he did know it
>
> b) That he did not know he was doing what was wrong.

This compact, simple guideline was adequate only until the science of medicine began its rapid advance. Revolutions were occurring in the understanding of the mind and its disorders and, inevitably, the M'Naghten Rules were left hopelessly outdated, thoroughly defective and in desperate need of amendment – indeed, were it not for the fact that the Rules were loose enough to allow for imaginative interpretation by the learned judges, and a willingness to co-operate on the part of expert psychiatric witnesses, it is certain that there would have been many miscarriages of justice.

21 January

1975 (Canada) Soon after midnight on 21 January 1975, a fire was reported at the Gargantua club, a sleazy haunt of Montreal's underworld. The fire service was called out but before the blaze was brought under control, the building was gutted. When firefighters were checking the scene they discovered a padlocked refrigerated storeroom which had a jukebox pushed hard up against the door. Removing this obstacle and breaking down the door, investigators found the bodies of thirteen people, four later identified as employees, the others presumed to be customers. One man, Rejean Fortin, the manager of the club, had been shot, while the other twelve had died of asphyxiation. Fire experts were able to confirm that gasoline or some other type of accelerant had been sprayed around the club before it was set alight.

The Gargantua had earlier been the scene of a double murder, when, on 30 October 1974, Roger Levesque and Raymond Laurin were shot down by armed gunmen. Following police investigations, a coroner's warrant for the arrest of Richard Blass was issued. Blass, who had escaped from prison a week before the shootings while serving a sentence for armed robbery, was popularly known as 'The Cat' and was considered to be one of Canada's most dangerous criminals. It was no surprise, then, when police named Richard Blass as their prime suspect in the arson attack and a major manhunt was launched. It was reported that detectives believed Blass had wanted to silence two people at the club who knew of his involvement in major crimes, and that the others were killed simply to eliminate all witnesses.

Richard Blass was traced to a mountain-top cottage near Val David and during a twenty-man police raid on 24 January, he was shot twenty-five times by two police sergeants with 9mm sub-machine guns. The police later claimed that when they broke into the cottage Blass had a revolver in his hand and therefore they had to shoot to kill.

At a subsequent inquest on the Gargantua victims, witnesses named Blass and one of his associates as being responsible for the killings though there was never enough evidence to bring the second man to trial.

22 January

1992 (USA) By 1992 the number of judicial killings in the United States had escalated to thirty-one, among them Mark Hopkinson and Joe Cordova, both of whom lost their lives on 22 January.

Hopkinson had been convicted of ordering the triple murder in 1979 of a lawyer named Vincent Vehar, with whom he was feuding, and Vehar's wife and son. The contract was carried out by Mike Hickey who planted a bomb in the Vehars' home. Hickey was granted immunity from prosecution in return for testifying against Hopkinson. Another of the witnesses at the trial was to have been Jeffrey Lynn Green, but Hopkinson contracted his killing before Green could give evidence. It was the first time since the reintroduction of the death penalty in 1976 that a prisoner was executed who had arranged but not been present at the murder. On 22 January, Mark Hopkinson was given a lethal injection at Rawlins; it was the first execution carried out by the state of Wyoming since 1965.

Meanwhile, in Texas – the state with the greatest number of executions since reintroduction – Joe Angel Cordova was also receiving a lethal injection. Cordova was convicted of abducting thirty-two-year-old Masel Williams from a telephone booth in Houston on 27 February 1982. The captive was taken into some nearby woods and robbed, stripped, and, as he pleaded for his life, shot at close range in the chest with a shotgun. It was said in Cordova's defence that he had spent the hours before the killing drinking and sniffing paint thinners, and 'when Joe Cordova's drunk, he's crazy'. The US Supreme Court turned down his eleventh-hour appeal, and at midnight on 22 January, thirty-nine-year-old Joe Angel was judicially put to death; the forty-third person to have been executed in the state since 1976.

23 January

1934 (USA) Six heavily armed officers were waiting in ambush along the highway outside Gibsland, Louisiana, as, just after nine in the morning, a tan-coloured Ford V-8 came into sight. The car was driven by a gangster named Clyde Barrow; beside him a woman sat eating a sandwich – her name was Bonnie Parker. As the V-8 approached the waiting officers, their guns burst into action and upwards of 150 shots were fired into the car, fifty of them ripping into the bodies of its occupants. One officer said later: 'We just shot the hell out of them . . . they were just a smear of wet rags.'

Although Hollywood has done its usual whitewashing job on Bonnie Parker and Clyde Barrow, the reality was far different. This is one contemporary description of them: 'They were kill-crazy punks and clodhoppers; they were bad news to decent bank robbers – gave us a bad name.' That was said by John Dillinger, whose far from angelic record had already earned him the distinction of Public Enemy Number One.

Clyde Barrow, a latent homosexual with a passion for guns and cars, became acquainted with Bonnie Parker in January 1930; he was just short of twenty-one and Bonnie was eighteen months his junior. Sadly for them both, Barrow was arrested on the day after they met. The couple started their liaison in 1932, when Clyde was released from prison, and from then on they were inseparable. As the 'Barrow Gang' (including, at various times, brother Buck Barrow, Buck's wife Blanche, Ray Hamilton, W. D. Jones and a few others) Bonnie and Clyde embarked on a series of armed robberies and murders that would spread terror through the south-western states of America over the following two years. It is impossible to calculate the total number of crimes committed during this period, but still the notorious gang narrowly escaped capture.

In January 1934 Bonnie and Clyde broke their old friend Ray Hamilton out of a Texas prison along with fellow-convict Henry Methven. Methven joined them in their killing and robbing spree, but this was to be their downfall. It has been suggested that Methven's father alerted the police to the gang's movements in an attempt to secure immunity for Henry. The end came on a dusty road in the middle of nowhere. Ironically, it was not long before that Bonnie

Parker, incredulous herself that they were still at large, was moved to comment: 'It can't be long now before they get us.'

24 January

1907 (England) Seventy-five-year-old William Whiteley was striding with satisfaction around the office of his famous Westbourne Grove emporium. He had some reason for complacency – the self-styled 'Universal Provider' had founded the first British department store in the 1880s, and was now indisputably the foremost shopkeeper in London. True, his rise to success had earned Whiteley his share of unpopularity and the jealousy of his business rivals but now, a quarter of a century later, he was a man at peace with the world, or at least with his modest part of it.

Suddenly the calm efficiency of Whiteleys store was disturbed by a young man striding purposefully into the master's office, and after a brief but violent quarrel, drawing a revolver from his pocket, and in full view of witnesses, firing three shots. Either of the first two bullets would have proved fatal to old Whiteley as he slumped to the carpet, but the third shot, from a gun now turned on himself, failed to dispatch the assassin, entering his right eye-socket and exiting at the root of his nose.

While the man now identified as Horace George Rayner was rushed to St Mary's Hospital for emergency surgery, a message was found scribbled in a notebook among his possessions; it read: 'To all whom it may concern; William Whiteley is my father.'

According to the story, George Rayner – Horace's foster-father – once had a mistress named Emily Turner, who had a sister Louisa. It transpired that George and Emily and Louisa and William Whiteley made up a fairly frequent foursome – the result of which fun and games was the birth of two illegitimate children to Emily and one to Louisa.

The brief trial of Horace George Rayner took place in March 1907, the first murder case to be tried in the newly rebuilt Old Bailey. Rayner pleaded not guilty by reason of temporary insanity, and the sordid story surrounding his disputed paternity went a long way to arousing the sympathy of the general public. Which, while it did not excuse an act of cold-blooded murder, did ensure the mercy of Horace's reprieve from the statutory death sentence. Twice Horace Rayner tried to commit suicide before he was released from prison in 1919 after serving twelve years of his life sentence.

25 January

1919 (England) Mrs Elizabeth Ridgeley was found battered to death in the small kitchen at the rear of her shop in the town of Hitchin, in Hertfordshire; beside her lay the body of her constant companion, a small Irish terrier. Both had been killed by blows from a four-pound sash-weight which had been left bloodstained at the scene of the crime. Despite the savagery with which Mrs Ridgeley had been beaten – her head and face suffered laceration wounds and there were abrasions on her back and arms – police officers investigating the murder decided that the unlucky woman had died as the consequence of an accidental fall. (It is not recorded whether they also thought the dog had taken a tumble!) The result of this ill-considered assumption was an investigation by the local police which was as farcical as it was inept. It is only fair to add that Scotland Yard was eventually summoned, but by then it was too late. Asked later in court whether the premises and its contents had been properly searched for fingerprints 'everywhere a man might put his hands', a senior local officer said in evidence: 'No; Superintendent Read had a magnifying glass and a candle, and he found nothing.'

In the end it was John Healy, a thirty-three-year-old

labourer, late of the Munster Fusiliers, who was put on trial charged with Mrs Ridgeley's murder. The fact is that Healy was only suspected because he had been seen near the shop around the time of the crime; there was no scrap of forensic evidence on which to build the case. Indeed, it is difficult enough to understand how the charge could ever have been brought, but quite inexplicable that Sir Edward Marshall Hall KC, one of the most celebrated counsel of his day, should have agreed to present the prosecution (a rare divergence from his customary role as defender). Marshall Hall's reconstruction of the case was that Healy had secreted himself in the shop until Mrs Ridgeley locked up and went into the back kitchen to count the takings. Then he jumped out of hiding, startling the wee dog which leapt up and bit his hand. The only evidence for this last assumption was that John Healy had a minor injury on his hand which he swore was sustained in an accident at work. Having disposed of his canine attacker with a swift blow to the head with the weight, Healy then dispatched poor Mrs Ridgeley.

Despite his customary eloquence, even Marshall Hall was unable to make an impression on the jury. Even less surprising in view of Mr Justice Darling's frequent scurrilous comments on the police investigation. At one point he commented: 'Every precaution seems to have been taken in the early days to ensure that nobody should be detected.' Later the judge referred to the initial accident theory as 'absurd', adding: 'I cannot imagine how *anyone* could think so.' The result was that the twelve jurymen took just a few minutes to find John Healy not guilty. The killing of Elizabeth Ridgeley and her dog was never solved.

26 January

1932 (England) Young Annette Friedson had made the decidedly ill-considered move to become friendly with a thirty-six-year-old married man named Maurice Freedman, who lived mostly by borrowing money and gambling. It will come as no surprise that Miss Friedson's parents were less than enthusiastic about the match, and as a result of their gentle persuasion she told Freedman that their times together must come to an end. Freedman was furious at this rejection, and so thoroughly nasty a bit of work was he that Annette's brother began to accompany her to her typist's job in the City of London each day, for fear that Freedman would get up to some mischief with her.

However, on the morning of 26 January 1932, Maurice Freedman was waiting *inside* the office building, and as Annette walked through the door he drew out a razor and cut her throat. He then made off with understandable haste, later ditching the murder weapon on a London bus, where it was found and handed in to the police.

It did not take detectives long to bring Maurice Freedman into custody; indeed there was a certain irony in the situation which cannot have escaped the investigating officers – Freedman was himself a former policeman. During questioning, Maurice Freedman claimed that he had gone to Annette's place of employment in order to try to effect some kind of reconciliation; he had taken the razor – an open type, of the sort normally called, appropriately, 'cut-throat' – in order to kill himself if Miss Friedson rejected his plea. However, after a brief struggle, Annette had grabbed the blade and pulled it across her own neck. Freedman, so he said, had fled in panic.

Although he denied all knowledge of the razor found on the bus, it was obviously connected with the death of Annette Friedson. For a start, it was stained with blood of the same very rare group as the victim's; furthermore, hairs attached to the weapon were proved to match those on a fur collar worn by her during the attack. Medical reports indicated that Miss Friedson's wounds were consistent with having been inflicted with a razor of the type found on the bus – a 'safety' razor in a special patent holder – but not with a 'cut-throat' razor as claimed by Freedman, and which he said he threw into a canal. The final link connecting their suspect with the murder weapon was when police found the driver of the bus on which it had been found, and he identified Freedman as having travelled on it at the appropriate time.

Following an unremarkable trial at the Old Bailey, Maurice Freedman was convicted of Annette Friedson's murder, and on 4 May 1932 he was hanged at Pentonville Prison.

27 January

1921 (England) Thirteen-year-old Donald Litton murdered Miss Sarah Seabrook in the course of robbery. It transpired that Litton's motive was that he wanted money in order to go on a school trip to the zoo. Found guilty as charged, he was ordered to be detained during His Majesty's pleasure.

28 January

1829 (Scotland) We will never know the full extent of the murderous careers of body-snatchers William Burke and William Hare, but during the months between December 1827 and October 1828, no fewer than sixteen victims ended up on the dissecting table at Dr Robert Knox's Academy of Anatomy in Edinburgh's Surgeons Square.

On 29 November 1827 one of Burke and Hare's fellow-residents at Logue's Lodging House passed away owing Hare £4. Old Donald's body never got as far as the graveyard, but became – for the profitable sum of £7 10s – the first of many transactions between the terrible twosome and Dr Knox. Transactions in which the doctor could be very sure of the freshness of the merchandise, for Burke and Hare were far too impatient to wait for their stock to die naturally. A likely subject would be lured to the lodging house with promises of a good time by either Maggie Laird – Hare's 'wife' – or Helen M'Dougal – Burke's. Once inside, the victim would be rendered senseless with drink and then lifeless by suffocation. This latter method was preferred because it avoided 'spoiling the merchandise'.

It was on the last day of October 1828 that Nemesis finally caught up with Burke and Hare and their treacherous consorts. A beggar woman named Margaret Docherty had given up her life in the service of science and was awaiting delivery, when the body was discovered under a pile of straw. Hare and Maggie Laird turned King's evidence against their accomplices, and the wretched Burke and Helen M'Dougal faced the High Court of Justiciary on 24 and 25 December (Christmas was not celebrated in Scotland at that time). The case against M'Dougal was found 'not proven', while in passing sentence on William Burke, Lord Justice-Clerk Boyle told him that rather than adopt the option of exhibiting his body in chains, he would instead, with supreme irony, order that his body be publicly dissected.

Burke was hanged on the gallows at the head of Liberton's Wynd on 28 January 1829. Maggie Laird and Helen M'Dougal escaped lynching by a bloodthirsty mob only by the intervention of a large number of police officers. William Hare and Dr Knox fled Edinburgh for London, where the surgeon became a humble general practitioner, and the body-snatcher a beggar. In 1830 the Anatomy (or Warburton's) Act was passed which effectively put a stop to the private trade in dead bodies.

29 January

1979 (USA) Monday morning, and sixteen-year-old high-school student Brenda Spencer makes her way to the Cleveland Elementary School, taking up a strategic position outside the still shut gates. Shortly afterwards the principal unlocked the building, and as the children were bustling around making their way to the main entrance, Brenda Spencer opened fire with a .22 semi-automatic rifle. Miraculously, only two people were killed during the shooting spree – principal Burton Wragg and the school janitor. Nine children between the ages of six and twelve suffered bullet wounds.

Back home, Brenda locked herself in and waited. In no time at all, the outside of the house was swarming with heavily armed police officers and, more important, the media circus that always follows in the wake of tragedy. At last Brenda Spencer was the centre of attention. For two hours she spoke to news reporters down the telephone line, but in the end there was just one question that everybody wanted answered – why did she do such a thing? Now there are many motives for murder, almost as many motives as there are murderers; but there can be few more fatuous excuses for taking two lives than that now offered by Brenda Spencer. 'I just started shooting,' she told the newsmen, 'that's it. I just did it for the fun of it. I just don't like Mondays . . . I did it because it's a way to cheer the day up. Nobody likes Mondays . . .'

It needn't have been a Monday, with such a disturbed personality anything could act as a trigger. Brenda had been living with her father ever since his divorce from her mother, and this disruption can at least partly explain the reason why she had become a problem child. However, even before her mid-teens, Brenda Spencer had been involved with drug misuse and petty theft, and had developed an unhealthy addiction to violent films. For a number of years she had owned a BB gun with which she used to kill birds and break windows. Then at Christmas 1978, Brenda's father bought her a proper gun as a present – it was the weapon she used to shoot up the Cleveland Elementary.

Brenda Spencer stood her trial in Santa Ana, California, where she faced two charges of murder and one of assault with a deadly weapon; she was convicted on all three. For the former charges she received two sentences of twenty-five to life, for the latter a concurrent forty-eight-year term.

30 January

1959 (Switzerland) To have killed, got away with it and then publicly confessed is a rare thing indeed. To then go out and kill again is, in my experience, unique. It is the special kind of notoriety that, on 30 January 1959, was achieved by Brian Donald Hume. But this tale begins a decade earlier, on 21 October 1949 . . .

It was a surprise for wildfowler Stanley Tiffin to find a bulky, water-logged bundle in the middle of the Tillingham mudflats; it was the surprise of his life to discover that it contained the torso of a human male, albeit modestly dressed in a silk shirt and underpants.

Forensic investigation later identified the remains as those of Stanley Setty, a man with a record of fairly petty crime and frequent dishonesty. As it seemed that the most likely way for the bundle to have arrived where it was found was to have been dropped from an aeroplane, inquiries were made at local airfields. This line of investigation turned up the name Brian Donald Hume, a former RAF pilot, who had hired a light plane into which he had loaded two packages on the outward trip from Elstree to Southend, and a further, larger, parcel on the return trip.

Like Setty, Hume was a minor crook with a known police record, and under questioning readily admitted knowing Setty and doing business with him (mainly in the field of used cars). He also agreed that he had hired a light aircraft in order to drop three packages on to the Essex marshes. He had been paid to do it, so he said, by three men; the reward was £50. It seemed an altogether too suspicious story to the police; but not as suspicious as the copious bloodstains on Donald Hume's living-room carpet.

Hume was put on trial in January 1950, and was surprisingly convicted only of being an accessory to murder. The jury had obviously swallowed the 'three men' story. Donald Hume spent a mere eight years in prison and, on his release in 1958, promptly sold his confession to Stanley Setty's murder to the *Sunday Pictorial*. With the proceeds of this deal, Hume set off for a life of luxury in Zurich.

Easy come, easy go, they say. And this certainly proved the case with Donald Hume. Within a year his high-living had decimated the blood money he got from the *Pictorial*, and the coffers needed refilling. To this end Hume, on 30 January 1959, held up a bank at gunpoint. Unfortunately in the process of the getaway he shot and killed a taxi-driver; a crime of which the Swiss do not approve. The court sentenced Hume to life imprisonment, though when, in 1976, he was showing all the symptoms of insanity, the Swiss authorities cut their losses and returned him to Britain to be confined in Broadmoor.

31 January

1679 (England) Reverend Robert Foulkes was executed at Tyburn tree for the murder of his illegitimate son.

> This unhappy gentleman was a divine of the Church of England, and was very much esteemed for his learning. Few men were more capable of shining in a church, or had a greater share of that sacred eloquence so requisite in a preacher. He was a minister at Stanton-Lacy in the county of Shropshire, where he was exceedingly admired till his crimes came to be known, and where he might have been beloved till death in a natural way had taken him hence, and then universally lamented, if his heart had been as well furnished with grace as his head was with knowledge and his tongue with expressions.
>
> A young gentlewoman with a considerable fortune,

who had been left an infant by her parents, was committed to his care by her executors, as to a man whom, they trusted, would not only deal justly by her, but also instruct her betimes in the principles of religion, and her several duties as a Christian. But alas! how weak is human nature, and how soon we are tempted aside from the ways of piety! Mr Foulkes, instead of answering the purpose of the young woman's friends, was soon smitten with her charms, and took an opportunity of discovering a criminal passion for her, though he had at that time a very virtuous wife and two children living. The young lady too easily consented to gratify his lust, and they continued their conversation together till she became pregnant.

All the means he could think of to secure an abortion were now tried, and they all proved ineffectual; so that they must both be exposed to scandal, unless she could be removed to some convenient place, remote from the eyes of the world, and from the jealousies of Mr Foulkes, where she might be delivered of her burden, which was not yet perceived. A plausible excuse for his going up to London was soon formed, and for his taking Miss along with him, who at that time was under twenty years of age. When they arrived in town they took a lodging in York Buildings in the Strand, where she lay in, and where (shocking to think of!) the child was privately murdered to prevent the infamy that might follow.

But divine vengeance would not suffer this horrid deed to remain long concealed, for before Mr Foulkes went out of town the girl was examined upon the suspicion of some women, when she confessed the whole, and charged Mr Foulkes with the murder, who was thereupon apprehended and committed to Newgate; in a short time after which he was condemned to the sessions house in the Old Bailey, upon the evidence of the young woman. On 31 January 1679, he was hanged at Tyburn.

(*The Newgate Calendar*)

February

1 February

1935 (USA) Kenneth Neu had been writing his swan song for days; and today was the day he got to perform it; it was called 'I'm Fit as a Fiddle and Ready to Hang'. He did. Twenty-five-year-old Neu, who had a history of mental instability, was picked up in New York's Times Square by wealthy theatre-owner Lawrence Shead on 2 September 1933. Neu thought the older man was going to give him a job, but when they got back to Shead's hotel room it was obvious the man was looking for sex. Neu strangled him, stole his watch, money and one of his suits. Two weeks later, Kenneth Neu killed and robbed a store-keeper and was picked up driving his second victim's car and wearing his first victim's suit. Neu confessed and, despite conclusive evidence that he had suffered brain damage as a result of neuro-syphilis, he was convicted of murder and sentenced to death.

2 February

1931 (England) What was to become one of the most enigmatic crimes in British legal history began on the evening of 19 January 1931. That was when William Herbert Wallace, a respectable, mild-mannered agent for the Prudential Assurance company, arrived at the Liverpool Central Chess Club for his regular game. When Wallace arrived the club captain gave him a telephone message which had been left at about 7.30 by a man calling himself R. M. Qualtrough and asking that Wallace meet him the following evening at an address in Menlove Gardens East, Mossley Hill. Although he had never heard of anyone named Qualtrough, William Wallace assumed that it was a business call, and set out at 6.50 to keep the appointment as directed. It was not until two hours of frustrating searching and asking directions had gone by that Wallace came to the inevitable conclusion that there was no such street as Menlove Gardens East in Mossley Hill, though there was a Menlove Gardens.

William Wallace was not a happy man as he arrived back home at 29 Wolverton Street at about 8.45. According to Wallace's later statement, he had found the front door to the house 'stuck', and asked for help from his neighbour Mr Johnston; Johnston discovered that the back door opened quite easily. Wallace had only been in the house a moment before discovering the dead body of his wife Julia on the parlour floor; she had been savagely bludgeoned about the head. Mrs Wallace's body lay on a bloodstained and partly burned mackintosh belonging to her husband. The murder weapon was almost certainly the heavy iron poker which had been kept beside the fireplace and which was now missing, along with the sum of £4 from a cash box.

Although the mysterious call from 'Qualtrough' could be seen as a ruse to get Wallace out of the house and despite the fact that the Wallaces had always been a most conventional, devoted couple, the police were suspicious of William Wallace. One damning piece of evidence was the pathologist's estimate of the time of death being *before* Wallace left the house for his bogus meeting. Then it was discovered that the telephone box from which the call was made was located very close to Wolverton Street, so Wallace could easily have made it himself.

William Wallace was eventually arrested on 2 February and charged with the murder of his wife. His trial opened at the Liverpool Assizes in April and despite the lack of convincing evidence and the judge's recommendation that it was insufficient to warrant a conviction, the jury returned a verdict of guilty. Under sentence of death, Wallace appealed, and on 18 May the Lord Chief Justice overturned his conviction. In spite of the ultimate clearing of his name, William Wallace was nevertheless subjected to malicious gossip which ultimately damaged his health and led to an untimely death from kidney failure on 26 February 1933.

3 February

1929 (England) Joseph Clark was one of the most unlovable criminals ever to stand before a British jury, and when he was sentenced to death on 3 February 1929, there can have been few in court who shed a tear. Although he had been raised in America, Clark arrived back in England in 1927, aged nineteen. An amateur hypnotist of sorts, Joseph Clark used his gift to great effect in securing girlfriends who were readily forthcoming with whatever he asked of them – which was most often their money.

Clark also had a vicious streak which usually manifested itself in violence against women. In Birkenhead, for example, he attempted to pull the wool over the registrar's eyes and tried to marry a girl who was under twenty-one by offering him her older sister's birth certificate. When the ruse was seen through, Clark went berserk and tried to strangle his prospective bride, on the principle that if he could not have her he was going to make damned sure nobody else would.

In 1928, we find Clark – for no honest reason calling himself Kennedy – lodging with a Mrs Alice Fontaine in Northbrook Street, Liverpool; part of the interest was clearly the landlady's daughter, also called Alice, from whom Clark regularly scrounged money. He also failed to pay a single penny piece for his board and lodging, which did not amuse Mrs Fontaine who threw him out on his ear. Clark's response was to begin sending both Alices a series of the most foully obscene letters. This unpardonable behaviour culminated, in October, in Joseph Clark letting himself in the Fontaines' home and bursting into the younger Alice's bedroom while she prepared herself for church. He tried to strangle her with a pyjama cord, and she fell unconscious to the floor. Thankfully Alice recovered, despite Clark also trying to cut her throat. Mrs Fontaine was not nearly so lucky, and Clark succeeded in his attempt to strangle her. Cynical scoundrel to the last, when Clark was taken into custody he claimed that just before she passed out, Mrs Fontaine gave him a warm smile and begged him to take care of Alice.

Joseph Clark's trial at the Liverpool Assizes was one of the shortest in British criminal history. Quite against the advice of his defence counsel, Clark decided to plead guilty, and was immediately sentenced to death. The whole process took but four and a half minutes. He was subsequently hanged.

4 February

1961 (England) Sergeant Wills Eugene Boshears, a US serviceman based in England, stood trial at Chelmsford Assizes. On the first day of 1961, a drunken Boshears had strangled Jean Constable in his flat at Dunmow, Essex. He claimed he must have killed her in his sleep, and when he awoke to find himself lying beside a corpse, panicked and dumped the half-naked Miss Constable off the Cambridge–Colchester road. In a unique verdict, Boshears was found 'guilty but asleep' and acquitted.

5 February

1920 (England) On 5 February 1920 Arthur Beard was on trial for the third time, a wretched and insignificant figure surrounded by the awesome splendour of the highest court in the land, the House of Lords; a man barely aware that some of the finest legal minds in the country were debating the continuance of his miserable life.

Beard had been employed as watchman at the Carfield Mills, Hyde, and during his 6.00 a.m. till 6.00 p.m. shift he was the factory's only occupant. On the evening of 25 July 1919 young Ivy Wood had returned home from school only to be sent out again on an errand for her father. She was last seen by a youth named Ernest Gosling passing through the gates of Carfield Mills.

At 1.30 a.m. Samuel Bower, watchman at a neighbouring mill, was startled by a frantic Arthur Beard, somewhat the worse for drink, mumbling: 'I'm in a mess . . . I have found a girl pegged out. I was in the grounds near the dining room. I carried her on my back to the lodge.'

On the following day the police made a thorough search of the mill and in the cellar found signs of a fierce struggle; some of the tiles were chipped and revealed bloodstains to which were attached hairs of the same colour as the late Ivy Wood's. Dirt on the girl's clothing and on Arthur Beard's proved to be similar to that coating the cellar tiles. All of this, and more, helped to secure for Arthur Beard the ultimate sanction of the law – the death penalty.

But Arthur Beard was not going to the rope without a struggle, and that struggle was to stir the legal system right up to the House of Lords. The fact was emphasised that at the time he committed his dreadful crime Beard was drunk. If he was intoxicated, his lawyers argued, how was he capable of forming the *intention* to kill? Where was the 'malice aforethought' required to be proved before a person can be convicted of murder? Where indeed, concurred the Court of Criminal Appeal, and reduced the sentence to one of twenty years.

Perhaps echoing the unspoken feelings of an outraged nation the Crown, in the persons of Beard's prosecutors, took the matter still higher; to the House of Lords. And it was there that the historic decision was made. Lord Birkenhead, the Lord Chancellor, voiced the court's ruling: that Arthur

Beard may well have been too drunk to form the intention to kill, but he was clearly and provably not too drunk to intend rape, and as death was the direct result of an *intended* felony, then Beard must be guilty of murder.

In the event, even the unworthy Arthur Beard was the recipient of that other arm of the law – mercy. He was reprieved and sentenced to continue his term of imprisonment.

6 February

1989 (USA) It was the second time that Ronald Gene Simmons stood in the dock charged with murder; this time it was in Clarksville and he appeared charged with the killing of his family. But that was a couple of years earlier, in Russellville, Arkansas. Already, in 1981, the family had needed to flee New Mexico when Simmons, a former Air Force Master Sergeant, had made one of his daughters pregnant and charges of incest against him were pending. Now it was just before Christmas 1987, and Simmons had decided to give himself an early Christmas present by killing off his wife and children. On the morning of 22 December he first bludgeoned and shot his son Gene and long-suffering wife Rebecca; then he strangled three-year-old Barbara. After taking a break for a beer, Simmons dumped the bodies in a cesspit. Then he sat back and waited for the others: seventeen-year-old Loretta who was drowned in the rain-water barrel, then Eddy, Marianne and Becky. Around midday on 26 December, the rest of the Simmons family arrived on a visit. The first to die was Ronald's son Billy and his daughter-in-law Renata; both shot. Then grandson Trae was strangled and drowned, and daughter Sheila and her husband Dennis were shot. Simmons' child by his own daughter, christened Sylvia Gail, was strangled, and finally grandson Michael was dispatched. Ronald Simmons lined all the corpses up in the lounge, covered each of them with a coat and settled down to a couple of days watching television and drinking beer.

On the following Monday, Simmons calmly drove into Russellville and at a law office shot dead a former friend, Kathy Kendrick, after which he visited an oil company office where he shot dead a man named Chaffin. Next stop was a general store where he shot and wounded two people followed by another office where a woman was wounded. And then, as suddenly as it had started, the killing spree finished, and Ronald Simmons simply sat and waited for the police to pick him up.

First Simmons was tried for the shootings in Russellville for which he was sentenced to death for the two murders and given 147 years on the other counts. In neither of his trials did Simmons say a single word in his defence, nor would he entertain thoughts of an appeal against his collection of death sentences. On 31 May 1990, Arkansas governor (later President) Bill Clinton signed Simmons' execution warrant, and on 25 June he died by lethal injection.

7 February

1603 (Scotland) This trial, relating to the Clan Macgregor, affords characteristic evidence of the barbarous state of the highlands in those times, of the lawless manners of the people, and the despicable imbecility of the executive arm.

The charges the Laird of Macgregor faced told more about the outrage and desolation of the recent war than about the crimes of the felon. He was accused of having conspired the destruction of the name of Colquhoun, its friends and allies, and the plunder of the lands of Luss; of having, on 7 February 1603, invaded the lands of Sir Alexander Colquhoun of Luss, with a body of four hundred men, composed partly of his own clan of Cameron, and of lawless thieves and robbers, equipped in arms, and drawn up on the field of Lennox in battle array; of having fought with Sir

Alexander who, being authorised by a warrant from the Privy Council, had convocated his friends and followers to resist this lawless host; of having killed about one hundred and forty of Sir Alexander's men, most of them in cold blood after they were made their prisoners; of having carried off eighty horses, six hundred cows, and eight hundred sheep; and of burning houses, corn-yards, etc.

The jury unanimously convicted the prisoner who, in consequence of the verdict was condemned to be hanged and quartered at the Cross of Edinburgh, his limbs to be stuck up in the chief towns, and his whole estate, heritable and moveable, to be forfeited.

Four of the Laird of Macgregor's followers who stood trial along with him were convicted and condemned to the same punishment, eleven on 17 February and six on 1 March. A statute was passed in the year 1633 ordaining that the whole of the Clan Macgregor, which should be within the realm on 15 March thereafter, should appear before the Privy Council and give surety for their good behaviour; that each of the clan, on arriving at the sixteenth year of his age, should appear before the Privy Council on 24 July and find surety as required above; that the surname of Macgregor should be abolished, and the individuals adopt some other; that no minister should baptise a child, or clerk or notary subscribe a bond or other security, under the name of Macgregor, under pain of deprivation.

This Act was rescinded at the Restoration.

8 February

1983 (England) It was on 3 February 1983 that residents of the flats at 23 Cranley Gardens in the quiet north London suburb of Muswell Hill, found that their lavatories would not flush properly.

The problem had already defeated the local plumber when, on the following Tuesday, the 8th, help arrived in the person of Dyno-Rod's Mike Cattran. Cattran's first job was to inspect the manhole at the side of the house. This was never the most pleasant of tasks, but the stench which rose from the pit when the cover had been removed was appalling even by professional standards. Aiming the beam of his torch down twelve feet to the bottom of the hole, the plumber was alarmed to see a layer of whitish sludge, flecked with what looked horribly like blood; it was against all his better instincts that the Dyno-Rod man climbed down into the manhole, finding as he reached the bottom, chunks of rotting meat, some with hair still attached to the skin. When a full search of the drain was carried out next day by the police, further fragments of flesh and bone were fished out and quickly identified by the pathologist as being human. Detective Chief Inspector Peter Jay clearly had a murder on his hands.

Among the residents of No. 23, occupying the attic flat, was thirty-seven-year-old Dennis Nilsen – 'Des' as he preferred to be called. When Nilsen arrived home from his job at the Denmark Street Job Centre on that Tuesday evening, it was to be met by a trio of detectives. Nilsen expressed some surprise that the police should be interested in anything as mundane as blocked drains, and when told of the remains that had been found, he replied: 'Good grief, how awful.'

Acting on an inspired guess, Inspector Jay rounded on Nilsen with: 'Don't mess about, where's the rest of the body?' To the detective's great surprise, Nilsen turned and replied quite calmly: 'In two plastic bags in the wardrobe. I'll show you.'

On the way to the police station, Detective Inspector McCusker turned to Nilsen in the back seat of the car and asked casually: 'Are we talking about one body or two?' Dennis Nilsen looked up: 'Fifteen or sixteen since 1978: three at Cranley Gardens and about thirteen at my previous address at Melrose Avenue, Cricklewood.' And so began the extraordinary story of Britain's most prolific killer.

(On 4 November 1983, a jury found Dennis Nilsen guilty by a majority of ten to two on six counts of murder and two of attempted murder. He is currently serving a life sentence.)

9 February

1993 (USA) On 9 February 1993, a forty-year-old man named Damacio Torres rushed into the Southern California University Medical Center shouting that he needed help. As medical staff hurried to him they saw a .44 magnum in one of his hands and a sawn-off shotgun in the other. As he began to fire randomly around him, Torres was screaming above the blast of the guns: 'I want something for my pain!! Can't you understand, can't you see I need help?!!' As patients and staff fled to safety, Torres kept on shouting. The first victim was Dr Richard May, a bullet in his head; then two more of the staff were cut down before the gunman barricaded himself in X-ray with two hostages. While a police SWAT team surrounded the building, negotiators made contact with Torres. After five hours he surrendered his weapons and released the hostages. Under arrest, he insisted: 'I've got Aids; I just cracked; I've been mistreated here for years.'

10 February

1956 (South Africa) Elifasi Msomi, a tribal witch doctor, was executed at Pretoria Central Prison. He had been convicted of the murders of fifteen people – men, women and children, over twenty-three months from 1953 to 1955; it had been Msomi's belief that these 'sacrifices' would boost the success of his ailing business. In his defence the sorcerer claimed that it was not he but the *tokoloshe* (the native equivalent of the bogey-man) who had committed the crimes. In fact, so terrified were the local people that the *tokoloshe* would help his servant to escape, that the authorities were obliged to allow a deputation of chiefs and elders to view Msomi before and after his appointment with the hangman.

11 February

1939 (England) On the night of 12 February 1939 the body of a woman was discovered in her top-floor flat at Dover Street in the heart of London; she was almost naked and had died of two stab wounds. A police murder inquiry quickly revealed that she was twenty-six years old and her name was Georgina Hoffman, or sometimes she was Mary (or Iris) Heath. Or when she was singing with the band in a West End nightclub, she preferred the wholly more exotic 'Black Butterfly'. Inquiries at the club told detectives that on the previous evening, the 11th, the victim had been in the company of a young man whom she took back home with her – she did not confine her 'entertaining' merely to singing.

The trail eventually led to a twenty-three-year-old ship's steward by the name of Arthur James Mahoney, and when the police arrived on the doorstep of his mother's home in Brixton they found him in the middle of shaving. Without any word being said by the officers, Mahoney simply nodded over his shoulder and said: 'The knife's upstairs.' And that was not all, detectives also found a number of items of bloodstained clothing. This most obliging killer was immediately taken into custody and back at police headquarters he made a full confession.

According to his story, Mahoney had met Georgina Hoffman in the street on 9 February and she had taken him back with her and, after relieving him of a fiver, let him stay the night. Promising to return after buying cigarettes (which Mahoney also coughed up the money for), Mrs Hoffman met a girlfriend and spent the night away from the flat. Not surprisingly, Arthur Mahoney felt rather cheated and left the next morning in a less than good humour. However, that evening he was back again offering Georgina Hoffman his wrist-watch because he had no money; they appear to have stayed together at least for the evening. The night of the 11th, Mahoney met his new pal at the nightclub where she was singing and they returned late to Dover Street. Here, Mahoney confided that he still had no money and Georgina began to get angry. One thing led to another and, no doubt fuelled by drink, the couple fell to brawling, the result of which was that Mahoney stabbed the unfortunate Georgina to death.

Arthur James Mahoney's trial took place at the Old Bailey on 6 March before Mr Justice Humphreys. Mahoney, through his counsel, entered a plea of insanity and much of the evidence presented to the court was of a medical and psychiatric nature, with the defence calling on Dr Grierson, the Senior Medical Officer at Brixton Prison, to support the submission that on the basis of a record of sadistic impulses Mahoney could be considered insane in the legal sense. In a rather surprising verdict the jury found Mahoney guilty of murder, and he was sentenced to death. In fact the sentence was not carried out, and when the result of the statutory medical examination held in accordance with the requirements of the Criminal Lunatics Act of 1884, declared that he was insane, Arthur Mahoney was removed to Broadmoor, where just sixteen months later he died.

12 February

1865 (England) It was Sunday, and the prison sermon at Pentonville Prison was coming to a close. One of the convicts was surprised to find that the man who always sat next to him, George Townley, who never opened his lips in chapel, had suddenly joined in the last two verses of *Abide with Me* –

in a particularly loud voice. He closed his book sharply and, clasping it tightly in his hand, filed out of the chapel with the rest of the prisoners. Suddenly there was a shout of alarm, followed by a dull, sickening thud. Townley had thrown himself clean over the railings of the circular gallery on to the stone floor twenty-three feet below. Thus ended the life of one of the most controversial killers of his age.

George Victor Townley was the eldest son of a well-known insurance agent in Manchester, and in addition to well-developed musical gifts, he had refined literary tastes, considerable accomplishment as a linguist and perfect manners. In short, he was an excellent prospect for any young lady of good breeding requiring a companion. Such as Bessie Caroline Goodwin, the daughter of an officer in the Austrian cavalry. George and Bessie met at the house of relatives in the year 1859 and quickly fell in love and became engaged to be married. Sadly there was one stumbling block in the way of their future happiness – George was penniless and without prospects. Such a match would not do for the Goodwin family, and the young couple were forced to meet in secret. And things might have meandered along in this manner until George Townley achieved some earning power. But as it was, an incident occurred in the summer of 1863 which quite changed Bessie's outlook. A young clergyman came to stay at the house of Bessie's grandfather where she was living, and she fell in love with him. What's more he had excellent prospects and was considered by the Goodwins a most eligible suitor. Which rather put George Townley in the shade. Eventually the clergyman proposed marriage, Bessie accepted and wrote a farewell letter to George.

If only it were that easy. During the latter part of August 1863, a number of increasingly insistent and pathetic letters arrived for Bessie at Wigwell Grange; letters from a distraught George Townley begging her to see him one more time. Reluctantly, Bessie agreed and George arrived at the Grange on the afternoon of Friday 21 August. Fearful of angering her grandfather, Bessie Goodwin suggested they take a walk away from the house along Wigwell Lane. It was here that George Victor Townley plunged a knife into his former sweetheart's throat. Seeming to feel no remorse for this outrageous behaviour, Townley even helped a couple of passing farm-hands to carry the still living Bessie up to the house. Before they reached it, however, poor Bessie breathed her last.

As might have been expected, the main debate at George Townley's trial, which opened at Derby Winter Assizes on 12 December 1864, was the extent of his sanity. Regardless of the detailed evidence presented by Dr Forbes Winslow on Townley's behalf, the jury was inclined to consider him sane and guilty of wilful murder.

But that was not the end of it. After Mr Baron Martin had intoned the sentence of death from beneath the black cap, George Victor Townley became once again the property of the psychiatrists. First he was examined by the so-called Commissioners in Lunacy for their opinion of his mental state; they thought he was legally insane. Then Sir George Grey, the Home Secretary at that time called in a different quartet of specialists. Their unanimous decision was that 'George Victor Townley is of sound mind.' Upon which, in a moment of perversity, Sir George declared that he was commuting the death sentence anyway, and George Townley was incarcerated in Pentonville. Until 12 February 1865, that is, when he took his own life. So, by his act, perhaps, George Townley might be said to have solved the problem of his sanity or insanity.

13 February

1948 (England) Police Constable Nathaniel Edgar was found shot in the driveway of a house in north London.

Before he died, PC Edgar told colleagues that he had written the name and address of his attacker in the notebook in his pocket. Donald George Thomas was taken into custody at an address in Clapham where he tried to shoot the arresting officers, saying afterwards: 'You were lucky, I might as well be hanged for a sheep as a lamb.' Thomas was tried at the Old Bailey in April 1948; his death sentence was later commuted to life and he was released in April 1962.

14 February

1929 (USA) Among Big Al Capone's few effective rivals during those profitable days of Prohibition bootlegging in the 1920s was the audaciously successful George 'Bugs' Moran. Certainly the Moran gang's hijacking of the Big Man's liquor shipments, their blowing-up of his speakeasies, and the sniping at his lieutenants were costing Capone plenty of dollars; what was worse, his pride was hurting. Then 'Scarface' Al laid the plans for a brutal and most ingenious act of revenge. On 13 February 1929, Moran received a telephone call from one of his own bootleg suppliers – a haul of cheap whisky was waiting to be delivered to Bugs's warehouse. Arrangements were made for 10.30 on the following morning – 14 February, St Valentine's Day. While seven of Moran's gang were waiting in the warehouse, a police car screamed to a stop outside and out jumped two uniformed cops and three plain-clothes men. They relieved the gangsters of their weapons, lined them up against the wall, and straffed back and forth with their machine guns – stomach, chest, head. The seven dropped into a lake of their own blood.

So, with a squad of his men masquerading as policemen, Capone had the last laugh. Or did he? Miraculously, George Moran was late for that 10.30 a.m. appointment with death, arriving only after the real police had got to the scene of the butchery. In fact George outlived Al Capone by many years, succumbing in the end not to an assassin's bullet but to cancer of the lung.

15 February

1550 (England) The murder of Thomas Arden at his home in Faversham, Kent, on this date provided the material for one of the earliest English dramatisations of a true crime. We do not know who wrote the popular Elizabethan play *The Lamentable and True Tragedie of Master Arden of Feversham* (though some have claimed that William Shakespeare had a finger in its development), but we do have a number of facts about its main characters.

Arden was a Kentish gentleman and a former mayor of the town of Faversham ('Feversham' is an early spelling). He married Alice Misfin, stepdaughter of Sir Edward North, benefiting from a generous dowry, and, having acquired wife, security and family connections, promptly left Alice to her own diversions. These diversions were, in the main, connected with the pursuit of Thomas Mosbie, her stepfather's steward. Now, although it appears Arden was 'contented to wynke at her filthie disorder . . . and also invited Mosbye verie often to lodge in his house', Alice clearly felt that her husband was an unnecessary burden. So she persuaded a somewhat reluctant Mosbie to murder him . . .

In his turn, Mosbie employed two characters with the unlikely names of Black Will and Shagbag (or Shakebag), whose incompetence bordered on the burlesque.

After the conspirators had plotted over a cup of ale at the Fleur de Luce inn, there followed some of the most ludicrous assassination attempts in the history of crime. In one plan, Will and Shagbag lay in wait for Arden in the shadows of a shop. As Arden approached, the shopkeeper happened to swing open his shutters, which caught Black Will such a crack on the head that he fell unconscious to the ground and had to be helped back to the Fleur de Luce for a medicinal brandy.

Eventually it was decided that Thomas Arden should be dispatched in his own home, and to this end Black Will and Shagbag were hidden in the parlour while Alice persuaded her husband to play a game of Tables (a sort of backgammon) with Mosbie. While they were playing, the clumsy couple in hiding crept up on the unsuspecting Arden, and Black Will 'by means of a towel held in both hands, like a noose, pulls Arden off the stool'. Then each of the conspirators stabbed poor Arden and it was left to the buffoons Will and Shagbag to dispose of the body. Which they lifted up with a handful of straw from the floor, thus sowing a trail of debris after the corpse, and quite oblivious to the fact that they were leaving a perfect set of footprints in the newly fallen snow.

Such vile murder could not long be left undetected (especially given the clues left by Black Will and Co.). Vengeance was both swift and violent. Alice Arden was burnt alive at Canterbury on 14 March 1550; Mosbie was hanged in London; and Black Will was burnt on a scaffold at Flushing. Shagbag was said to have been murdered in an unconnected incident in London.

16 February

1954 (England/Germany) A career in crime which ended with suicide in a wood outside Cologne on 16 February 1954, began in Scotland back in the 1920s. On the morning of 17 March 1926, Mrs Bertha Merrett was sitting in her drawing room writing a letter; her son Donald was reading a book. Suddenly the maid heard the cry: 'Rita, Rita, my mother has shot herself.' When she reached the drawing room, the maid found Mrs Merrett lying on the floor, barely alive, with a bullet wound in her right ear. She was rushed to the Edinburgh Royal Infirmary where she later told a doctor: 'I was sitting down writing letters; my son Donald was standing beside me and I said "Go away, Donnie, don't annoy me," then I heard a kind of explosion . . .' On 27 March Mrs Merrett drifted into a coma and four days later she died.

Donald, meanwhile, was doing what he did best – indeed, what he had been doing for about a year. He was plundering his mother's bank account. This is why Mrs Merrett had to be disposed of; before she found out. John Donald Merrett was arrested and charged with matricide, though thanks in great part to Sir Bernard Spilsbury's testimony that the wound was entirely consistent with suicide, the trial ended in a 'not proven' verdict. Merrett was, however, convicted of forging his mother's signature, and spent eight months inside. Following this he changed his name to John Ronald Chesney.

Chesney married Vera Bonner in 1928, and the following year he inherited £50,000 – a fortune in those days – £8,400 of which he put in trust for his wife. The idea was that she should enjoy the interest on it until her death, when it reverted to her husband. The next twenty-odd years were occupied in spending money, acquiring more illegally (usually as an ocean-going smuggler), and spending that. By 1953 he was penniless and separated from his wife. Which reminded him of a certain £8,400. Chesney was at the time living in Germany, while Vera was running a small home for the elderly with her mother 'Lady' Menzies (a title to which she had no right). On 10 February 1954 Chesney slipped into England using a false passport and turned up on their doorstep bearing two bottles of gin.

Having managed to get in to see his wife without his mother-in-law knowing, and having rendered her unconscious through drink, Chesney drowned her in the bath. Unfortunately, the 'tragic accident' plan fell apart when he encountered Lady Menzies in the hall on his way out, and was obliged to strangle her. Ronald Chesney (using the name

'Leslie Chown') made it back to Germany, but it was quite clear he would be followed, and there was no chance of a 'not proven' verdict this time. When the British police arrived on 16 February, his body had just been found, a bullet fired by his own hand lodged in his head.

17 February

1978 (Northern Ireland) On 17 February 1978, police received a telephone warning about a bomb at the La Mon House Restaurant at Castlereagh Hills, near Belfast, only minutes before the explosion, which occurred as they arrived. The blast caused a fireball sixty feet high and forty feet wide which turned the building into a blazing inferno within seconds. The restaurant was packed with diners, including many attending a motorcycle club dinner-dance. Panic-stricken guests, children looking incongruous in bright fancy dress, rushed for the doors and leapt from the windows. People staggered from the blaze with their clothes on fire, many suffering severe burns. The fire brigade, when it arrived at the scene of the blast, was able to do little to bring the blaze under control. Twelve died and thirty were injured.

On 28 September, Edward Manning Brophy, an unemployed shot firer aged thirty-nine, was charged with the murder of the twelve victims and with being a member of the Provisional IRA. He was subsequently charged with causing eleven other explosions.

After a forty-five-day trial at Belfast Crown Court which ended on 1 April 1980, Mr Justice Kelly acquitted Brophy of the murder and explosives charges because it was impossible to be sure that confessions allegedly made by Brophy at the Royal Ulster Constabulary holding centre at Castlereagh had not been induced by 'torture, inhuman and degrading treatment'. Brophy in his evidence claimed that detectives had ill-treated him and concocted confessions between themselves. The judge said the evidence of three doctors showed that some kind of ill-treatment had been suffered, and while he accepted Brophy may well have fabricated the allegations, in law he needed to be sure; and he was not sure. Mr Justice Kelly convicted Brophy on the charge of being a member of the Provisional IRA on evidence he gave during the trial as to the validity of his confessions. Brophy was jailed for five years.

Edward Brophy appealed to the Northern Ireland Court of Appeal, which finally quashed the conviction on the grounds that his admissions were in a 'trial within a trial', and could not be used in the full hearing. In June 1981, the Crown appealed this decision to the House of Lords, who unanimously upheld the Court of Appeal ruling.

While the case against Brophy was continuing police arrested another man, twenty-three-year-old Robert Murphy, and charged him with twelve counts of murder in the La Mon case and with causing four other explosions in Belfast. He appeared for trial at Belfast Crown Court in September 1981 before Lord Justice Gibson. On 28 September, the fifteenth day of the trial, Murphy, a self-confessed IRA member, changed his plea to guilty to manslaughter of the La Mon victims and admitted the other charges. Murphy was sentenced to life imprisonment for manslaughter with a concurrent term of fourteen years on the other charges.

On 7 November 1991, Brophy was shot and seriously wounded by a masked gunman in a store near Belfast city centre. It was thought that responsibility for the shooting lay with the loyalist Ulster Freedom Fighters.

18 February

1963 (USA) On 18 February 1963 seventeen-year-old Harry 'Butch' Hebard skipped school after telling a friend he planned to run away. When he arrived home, his stepmother told him he would not be allowed to eat with the family that night. Later, Butch explained that he felt so frustrated with his family that he took a .22-calibre pistol and a rifle from his father's gun collection and killed them. First he shot his father in the head as he lay sleeping on the couch, then he rushed into the kitchen, where he shot and killed the eleven-year-old twins Janice and Joyce and his fifteen-year-old stepbrother John. When his stepmother came into the kitchen carrying groceries, Butch shot her dead too.

After the bloodbath, Hebard changed his clothes, left the house and went to a friend's home where he persuaded the family to let him stay for the night. The following morning neighbours noticed there were none of the usual signs of activity at the Hebard home and called the police. As well as the bodies of Butch's family, police searching the house found a list made out by him of his preparations for running away, including the name of his friend and the address where, within the hour, Butch Hebard was arrested.

On 20 February, Hebard was charged with first-degree murder, but with only four counts; a cautious district attorney held one charge back so that in the event of Butch being cleared, he could be tried again on the fifth.

On 25 February, the trial judge ordered a routine psychiatric examination, and on 13 March Butch Hebard was certified insane and ordered to be confined to a state mental hospital. The psychiatrists diagnosed him as suffering from schizophrenia rendering him unfit to plead, and therefore incompetent to stand trial. However, in 1967 Hebard was re-examined and declared sane and fit to stand trial. He was subsequently convicted of the murders and jailed for life.

19 February

1951 (Australia) This was the day it ended; ended on the gallows at Pentridge Jail, Melbourne. It had begun almost exactly a year earlier, when Jean Lee and her two unsavoury sidekicks Bobby Clayton and Norman Andrews appeared for the first time before the Melbourne Criminal Court charged with the murder of William Kent; on 26 March 1950, the jury found all three guilty.

During the Second World War, Jean Lee instinctively sensed the advantages that could be had in a country which was playing host to all manner of uniformed personnel from the allied nations. To an enterprising girl in the 'entertainment' business the world, or at least its soldiers, was her oyster. So Jean ditched her husband, hived off her child to relatives and departed Sydney for Brisbane, and 'work' in the canteens of the army camps. When the war ended Jean's source of income dried up, and she found herself in need of a new angle to her chosen occupation. In this endeavour she was helped by Bobby Clayton, a petty crook who 'looked after' her during her nocturnal efforts to fill their coffers. The scam was as old as it was simple and effective. Jean would attract a client back to her room and, having secured her fee, entice him into a compromising position. In walks Bobby Clayton, every inch the enraged husband, and threatens to call the authorities if the bewildered man does not hand over something by way of compensation. Sometimes Clayton would beat the client up; just for fun. In 1949 Norman Andrews joined the business.

In November of that same year Jean was working the lounge of the University Hotel, Calton, when she picked up William Kent, a seventy-three-year-old bookmaker in town for a bit of fun. Which is what Jean offered him. Back at Kent's lodgings he continued to drink, while she tried to prise him away from his money. The problem was, the drunker he got, the tighter he hung on to his wallet; until Jean was obliged to whack him over the head with an empty wine bottle. In came Clayton and Andrews and tied the hapless bookie by his feet and by his thumbs before torturing him to death and ransacking the room.

Unfortunately for them, Jean Lee's distinctive red hair had attracted the attention of fellow residents and her description was confirmed by bar staff at the University Hotel; by way of a bonus, the hotel detective also gave the police the name of Norman Andrews, who had been seen with Jean. Meanwhile, Jean, Clayton and Andrews had skipped town and returned to Sydney. Which is where they were arrested and charged with murder. Clayton accused Jean and Andrews of the killing; Jean made a confession; Andrews did not. Nevertheless all three were arraigned on charges of murder and robbery, and throughout their trial continued alternately to blame each other and to confess. Despite their successful appeal, the threesome were again convicted at retrial and eventually executed.

20 February

1956 (England) When he died, at the age of eighty-nine on 20 February 1956, Sir Travers Humphreys left behind him a lifetime of unrivalled service to the administration of the law; for twenty-three years as one of the country's most celebrated King's Bench judges.

Travers Humphreys was born in 1867, the son of the senior partner in a well-known London firm of solicitors. He was called to the Bar in 1889, and advanced ever upwards through a succession of legal appointments – Counsel to the Crown, Senior Treasury Counsel, Chief Senior Treasury Counsel, and so on. During his time at the Bar, Travers Humphreys prosecuted some of the most notorious murder cases ever to come before the Old Bailey: Dr Crippen, George Joseph Smith (the 'Brides in the Bath' killer), Frederick Seddon and his wife, Lieutenant Douglas Malcolm . . . He received his knighthood in 1925, and was elevated to the Bench three years later. During his term as a High Court judge Sir Travers presided over the trials of Chung Yi Miao, Wallace Benton, Elvira Barney, Ernest Brown, and John George Haigh (the 'Acid Bath Killer'). He retired from the Bench in 1951, at the age of eighty-four.

21 February

1932 (England) In the early hours of this February morning a resident in one of the apartments at Lanark Villas, in London's Maida Vale, was awakened by the sound of a taxi drawing up outside and the slamming of the vehicle's doors. Looking at the clock he noticed that it was 1.30 a.m. It was only a short time afterwards that noises began to be heard in the flat below, the sounds of fighting and of a woman's cries. After five minutes or so, the upstairs lodger heard the front door bang shut and the sound of heavy footsteps retreating into the distance.

Investigation into the nocturnal disturbance next morning revealed the dead body of prostitute Dora Alicia Lloyd lying strangled on her bed. Dora was known to work the Air Street beat in Piccadilly, and that was where the police investigation began. Prostitution is a risky profession, where the majority of clients are total strangers, entirely unknown quantities who might be either saint or psychopath. And for this reason the girls tend to become 'clubby', to keep an eye on each other. Air Street was such a club, and the girls who worked it had a lot to say about Dora Lloyd's last client. In fact he had been along the street and spoken to several of her business rivals before deciding to spend his money on Dora. He had been drunk and talkative and told a couple of the girls that although he was temporarily unemployed he had fifteen shillings that he wanted to spend on a good time (this is 1932, remember). They were also able to provide detectives with a remarkably detailed description of the man: he was aged about thirty-five, tall and slim, clean-shaven, and wearing horn-rimmed spectacles. He was dressed in a dark overcoat and wore a soft felt hat.

However good the description, and however enthusiastic the investigation, Dora Lloyd's killer was never found. At the inquest held by Westminster's coroner, Mr Ingleby Oddie, a verdict was recorded of 'wilful murder by some person unknown'. Dora had become a tragic statistic in a profession with more than its share of tragic statistics.

22 February

1864 (England) It is rare to read of multiple executions of 'pirates' taking place in the middle of the nineteenth century, but just such an event came about on 22 February 1864. However, it would be true to say that although they were called pirates, 'mutineers' would be a more suitable word.

The crew of the *Flowery Land* was as mixed a bunch of tars as any to be found on a merchant vessel of the 1860s – a rag-bag collection of Spaniards, Chinese, Turks and every other nationality under the sun. Before the 900-tonner had left England for Singapore on 28 July 1863, Captain John Smith had already expressed his anticipation of problems with 'a dago crew like that'. Nor was he proved wrong. Within a bare month of setting out, Smith had found it necessary to punish physically several of his crew – including 'Watto the Turk' and a Greek called Carlos, both of whom were to play leading roles in the drama to come.

This drama opened in the early morning of 10 September, as the *Flowery Land* approached the Cape of Good Hope. While the first mate, a man by the name of Karswell, was on watch, the Spanish faction of the crew decided to mutiny. Forcing Karswell to the deck, they mercilessly bludgeoned him to within an inch of his life, and threw him screaming into the waters below. Captain Smith, aroused from his sleep by the disturbance, was grabbed as he came on deck to investigate and forced face to face with Watto the Turk, the man he had savagely flogged just weeks before. Without hesitation, the Turk plunged a knife into his captain's heart. Smith's brother – on board only as a passenger – along with other officers, was also slain that day. The one surviving officer, second mate Taffir, fared better, though hardly well. Being the only one now on board capable of navigating, he was subjected to a salutary beating and put to the task of returning the ship and its mutinous crew to South America.

It is only fair to point out that not all the crew were in mutiny. The Chinese had refused any part in the outrage, and in their turn faced the same brutal, sometimes fatal, treatment which had met the officers. At the end of the nightmarish voyage to Brazil, the hapless Chinese were battened into the hatches and holes were drilled in the sides of the ship below the waterline. While the mutineers and captive Taffir took to the boats, and the safety of Brazil, the *Flowery Land*, and the Chinese, sank and drowned. Had the crew left the second mate behind to share the fate of the Chinamen they may well have escaped the consequences of their actions. The Brazilian authorities were sympathetic to their story of shipwreck and days spent in the water in open boats without food, drink or sleep. Sympathetic, that is, until Taffir found the one official who could speak English and hear the true story. After shipment back to England, and subsequent to their trial at the Old Bailey on 3 February 1864, five of the mutineers were publicly hanged (among them Watto the Turk), thus providing yet another treat for thousands of spectators.

23 February

1885 (England) One of the most extraordinary incidents in the annals of capital punishment occurred on 23 February 1885, when hangman James Berry attempted to execute the murderer John Lee. At the age of fifteen, Lee went into service with Miss Emma Keyse, of Babbacombe. About eighteen months after joining the household, John Lee left to join the Royal Navy. Alas, a weak chest made him fit for only the lightest of duties and finally he was invalided out. Back on shore, the formerly open, honest lad became a changed person. John began to steal – and was eventually rewarded with six months' hard labour. However, Miss Keyse got to hear and persuaded the governor of the prison to release Lee back into her service. An act of generosity which she paid for with her life.

In the early hours of Saturday 15 November 1884, one of the maids woke to the smell of smoke. It was discovered that there was not one but five separate fires, all accelerated by paraffin. The body of Miss Keyse lay in the dining room; her head had been terribly bludgeoned and her throat cut through to the vertebrae. Around the body were smouldering newspapers soaked in blood and paraffin. When John Lee's bloody knife and towel were found next to the body he was immediately charged with murder. He admitted later that the killing had been revenge for having his weekly wage reduced by sixpence on account of some minor lapse.

John Lee was scheduled to be executed for his crime by the official hangman James Berry. He was led to the drop, positioned over the trap and the noose was secured around his neck. As he had done scores of times before, Berry pulled the lever to release the trap. It remained stuck fast with Lee standing on it. Berry pulled the lever again. And again. James Berry stamped several times on the doors of the trap, and so did the warders; still they remained firmly together. With some embarrassment, prison officers removed James Lee from the gallows. The executioner and his assistant tested it – and it worked perfectly. Until they tried to hang John Lee for the second time. A very bewildered Berry again completed a successful test drop; and was once again unsuccessful in launching John Lee into eternity. The only person not surprised by this bizarre turn of events was John Lee himself who had predicted: 'The Lord will never permit me to be executed.' And, indeed, He did not. In recognition of his ordeal Lee's sentence was commuted to life imprisonment and he was released in 1907.

There was considerable speculation over the cause of this apparent miracle – including more than a few invoking Divine Intervention. The most rational explanation was that the flaps of the trap had become swollen as a result of soaking up the recent heavy rain, and when a weight was put directly on them the edges bound.

24 February

1767 (England) An experiment was made to bring to life a convict named Patrick Redmond, who was hanged for a street robbery. It appeared that the felon had hung twenty-eight minutes before the mob rescued his body and carried it to an appointed place, where a surgeon was in attendance to try the experiment 'bronchotomy', an incision in the wind-pipe, which in less than six hours produced the desired effect of reviving the man. A collection was made for the poor fellow, and efforts made to obtain his pardon, for it must be remembered that the law insisted that the condemned should hang 'until he be dead'; consequently men like Redmond, who recovered, were liable to be hanged again – until they were dead. He was spared the full penalty of the law; later, perhaps, to face a higher judge.

25 February

1879 (England) Charlie Peace was one of those rare villains who, bad as he was, squalid and murderous as he was, succeeded – following his execution on 25 February 1879 – in entering British folklore. Indeed, he became quite a hero; transformed, like Dick Turpin, into that figment of romance, the 'lovable rogue'.

Charles Peace was born in Sheffield in 1832, and following his marriage in 1859 fell very easily into a life of crime – mostly burglary around the Manchester area. And when Manchester became too hot for him and he had suffered a few spells of imprisonment, Charlie and family moved back to

Sheffield, to 40 Victoria Place. The Peaces' next-door neighbours were Arthur Dyson, a civil engineer, and his wife. It was not long before Mrs Dyson had attracted Charlie's amorous attentions, and the lady, despite Charles Peace's shambling appearance and the gap of nearly twenty years in their ages, fell, temporarily at least, for him. When Arthur Dyson became aware of this liaison, he made his disapproval loudly known to Peace, and Peace responded characteristically by attacking Dyson in the street and threatening to shoot dead both him and his wife.

Later, both families left Victoria Place, the Dysons to Banner Cross Terrace, Sheffield, the Peaces to an address in Hull. On the first day that Arthur Dyson and his wife took up their new residence, who should appear on the doorstep but Charlie Peace. 'You see, I am here to annoy you wherever you go!' he boasted. And so he was. On the evening of 29 November 1876, Mrs Dyson popped out of her back door on a visit to the privy; out of the darkness leapt Charlie, revolver in hand. Mrs Dyson screamed, her husband ran out of the house and Charlie Peace shot him dead.

Wisely, the Peace family decamped again, this time for south London where Charlie adopted the name 'Thompson'. However, he did not adopt a new profession, and in the early morning of 10 October 1878 he was arrested in the course of a burglary by PC Edward Robinson.

Stripped of his alias, Charlie Peace was put under escort on a train back to Leeds where he was to be tried for the murder of Arthur Dyson. On the journey, Peace made a futile attempt at escape by leaping, handcuffed, through the carriage window. He succeeded only in cracking his skull quite badly on the permanent way.

Charles Peace was found guilty of Dyson's murder, and later paid the supreme penalty at Armley Gaol; the executioner was William Marwood, who later published his memoir on the hanging.

26 February

1952 (England) The death of Sir Patrick Hastings KC, on 26 February 1952, marked the end of a legend of the English Bar. A man described as 'a great and glittering figure', Sir Patrick was one of the foremost jury advocates of any era. In his book *Defender's Triumph*, crime historian, the late Edgar Lustgarten, refers to his 'sophistication': 'More than any other counsel of comparable eminence, Hastings was a sophisticated advocate – in fashionable practice when fashionable people were setting new standards in advanced sophistication.'

Patrick Hastings was born in 1880, the son of a solicitor, and started his education at the prestigious Charterhouse school. However, the family fortunes took a sudden turn for the worse, and at the age of sixteen young Patrick was forced to leave and turn his hand to work. He spent some time as a construction worker in Wales, and then joined the army, seeing active service in the Boer War. On his discharge, Patrick Hastings financed his study of law with what he earned as a journalist in Fleet Street, finally being called by the Middle Temple in 1904. In 1906 he was privileged to be invited to join the chambers of Mr Horace (later Lord Justice) Avory. Hastings had a brief, and by all accounts bitter, flirtation with politics as Labour MP for Wallsend. In 1926 he gave up his seat and returned to full-time practice at the Bar. Although he is remembered best as a luminary of the courts, he was also at home writing about, and especially for, the theatre, with several notable successes to his name, including *Scotch Mist* and *The Blind Goddess*.

Although Sir Patrick Hastings was involved in many of the most celebrated criminal trials of his day, he is perhaps best remembered for the Vaquier and the Barney (see 12 August and 31 May) cases.

Sir Patrick Hastings retired from the Bar in 1948 in failing health, and died in 1952 at the age of seventy-two.

27 February

1781 (England) On this Tuesday morning Mr Powell, an apothecary, was summoned to Lawton Hall, in Warwickshire, and on his arrival found Sir Theodosius Boughton lying dead on his bed; Mr Powell estimated that the twenty-year-old baronet had expired some half hour earlier. According to his mother he had 'died in convulsions'. A subsequent post-mortem, conducted by Dr Rattray of Coventry, led to the conclusion that Sir Theodosius had died of poisoning effected by the administration of a noxious infusion of laurel leaves.

As the only direct beneficiaries of the young man's death were his immediate family – most notably his sister – an inquiry was made as to who might have taken the baronet's life. The most recent addition to the Boughton household was one John Donellan, a captain in the army. Though apparently Donellan's military career had been tainted by some underhand dealings which had earned him a court martial, he had married Sir Theodosius's sister in June 1777. The household was completed by Lady Boughton, the deceased's mother. According to her, Sir Theodosius was a delicate young man and was in the habit of taking daily medicine, what was known as a 'purging draught'. On the morning of 27 February, her son had taken his 'physic' as usual, but complained that it smelled of bitter almonds (a characteristic of laurel-water). Within minutes, according to Lady Boughton, the youth 'struggled very much, and made a prodigious rattling in his stomach and gurgling'; he subsequently died. Shortly afterwards, John Donellan came into the room and removed the medicine bottle, emptied it and washed it thoroughly; he then summoned a servant and ordered the bottle to be disposed of. This already suspicious behaviour was seen in an even blacker light when it was learnt that the bulk of the victim's estate would pass to his sister – Donellan's wife.

Despite Captain Donellan's persistent denial that he had any part in the death of his brother-in-law, he was put up for trial at the Warwick Assize charged with murder and convicted. On 2 April 1781, Donellan mounted the steps of the scaffold, still swearing before God that he was innocent. After praying for some time he let the handkerchief in his hand fall – a signal agreed with the executioner – and he was, as they say, 'launched into eternity'. After his body had hung the prescribed hour it was put into a black coffin and conveyed to the Town Hall to be dissected.

28 February

1760 (Scotland) To avoid the ignominious death of a common felon on the public gallows, Mungo Campbell, capitally sentenced for the murder of the Earl of Eglinton, took his own life. He was found in his prison cell dangling from a silk handkerchief; close to his body was a paper bearing these words:

> Farewell, vain world, I've had enough of thee,
> And now am careless what thou say'st of me,
> Thy smiles I court not, nor thy frowns I fear
> My cares are past, my heart lies easy here,
> What faults they find in me take care to shun,
> And look at home, enough is to be done.

March

1 March

1989 (Australia) The first victim in the series that was to be labelled the 'Granny Murders' was found close to her home in a Sydney suburb. Eighty-two-year-old Gwendoline Mitchelhill had been bludgeoned to death. Over the following twelve months, the 'granny killer' claimed the lives of five more elderly Sydneysiders. Then on 19 March 1990, John Wayne Glover was found by police in the home of his latest victim; Glover had attempted to kill himself with a cocktail of pills and whisky. On 30 November 1991, Glover was found sane and guilty on the murder charges; his sentence is such that he will never see freedom again.

2 March

1921 (England) George Arthur Bailey was executed for poisoning his wife with prussic acid. His trial at Aylesbury Assizes was the first in the country in which a woman served on the jury. As a concession to this, the judge courteously adjourned the court every afternoon so that the jury might take tea.

3 March

1961 (England) Edwin Albert Bush bludgeoned and stabbed to death Mrs Elsie Batten in a London antique shop. Bush stole a dress sword which he attempted to sell to a similar establishment on the opposite side of the road. He was arrested not far from the scene of the crime by a policeman who recognised Bush from an Identikit portrait based on witness descriptions. It was the first time that the

British police had identified a criminal using the American Identikit system.

4 March

1974 (Canada) It is only with the second or third victim that a killer becomes a potential serial killer; at that stage he (or more rarely she) has embarked on a path of destruction that will stop only with capture or death. The problem for investigators is always to identify individual killings as part of a series. Sometimes the *modus operandi* is so idiosyncratic – method, location, victim trait, etc. – that there is no doubt; other times it is more obscure. On some rare occasions a death will pass without even being considered a murder.

Such was the case of Russell Johnson. His third victim died on 4 March 1974. Eleanor Hartwick was found at her home in London, Ontario, and her untimely departure from this world was attributed to an adverse reaction to a prescription drug. The previous November forty-two-year-old Alice Ralston was also found dead in her bed with no visible sign of violence. It was known that she was suffering from hardening of the arteries and this was certified as the cause of death. A month before that, on 19 October 1973, twenty-two-year-old student Mary Hicks had been found dead in her bed. There were no obvious marks of violence on her body and a pillow partly covering her face was not considered suspicious. There was no sign of forced entry to the apartment, so Miss Hicks' cause of death was given as suffocation due to a reaction to a prescription drug. The fourth death was that of forty-nine-year-old Doris Brown in August 1974. It happened that the pathologist carrying out the autopsy did observe some minor abrasions and small quantities of blood in her throat and rectum. However, the police were not alerted, and death was certified as from pulmonary oedema.

Four victims and not a shred of suspicion; had Russell Johnson been able to give up then, he could have remained undetected indefinitely. Even if he had stuck to the same *modus* he could well have clocked up a greater tally without anybody being the wiser. But Johnson was not quite right in the head (surprisingly, perhaps, most serial killers *are* perfectly sane). On 31 December, in the City of Guelph, Diane Beitz was strangled with her own brassiere and sexually assaulted after her death. There was no doubt that this was a murder. Nor was there any doubt in the case of Louella Jeanne George, who had been strangled and robbed. Items of her underwear and jewellery were later found abandoned in a trash can. Then twenty-two-year-old Donna Veldboom was found strangled in her apartment not far from where Louella George breathed her last.

This was the point at which the police got a much-needed break. A check of the other tenants of the apartment block in which Miss Veldboom died revealed that one of them, Russell Johnson, had a record of sexual deviancy; indeed, he had been admitted to a psychiatric hospital diagnosed as a compulsive sex attacker. He had also previously resided at the block where Louella George had been strangled. At his trial in February 1978, Johnson was charged with the Beitz, George and Veldboom murders; it was only later that the police released information connecting him with the four 'undiscovered' killings. Found not guilty by reason of insanity, Russell Johnson was committed to the maximum-security wing of the Ontario Mental Health Centre.

5 March

1840 (England) In the House of Commons, arch-abolitionist William Ewart rose in his seat to advance the earliest resolution for the total abolition of capital punishment; no other recommendation for such wide-sweeping changes in the capital punishment laws had ever been made. Ewart spoke eloquently of the 'Saturnalia of the gallows', and gave in evidence the findings of the Reverend J. Roberts of Bristol, who claimed that of the 168 criminals he had accompanied to the scaffold, 164 had themselves witnessed public executions.

6 March

1922 (England) The question of insanity, in the legal sense of mitigation, has always been hotly debated, and the case of Ronald True showed just how difficult it can be to approach a satisfactory definition. True murdered prostitute Gertrude Yates on 6 March 1922, and his subsequent behaviour left no doubt that he was nothing if not eccentric; however, did this behaviour provide the proof of insanity required by a court?

Brought up in comfortable circumstances, Ronald True nevertheless displayed early tendencies towards petty crime, cheating and lying. These inclinations remained with him, and at the age of seventeen his parents sent him abroad – New Zealand, Argentina, Canada and then Mexico. Any hopes that this might improve the lad's attitude to life were forlorn ones, and he was dismissed from a succession of jobs on grounds of incompetence and dishonesty. It was while he was abroad that True became addicted to morphine.

The outbreak of the First World War saw Ronald True back in England and training with the Royal Flying Corps. It was a short-lived glory and he was invalided out after a serious flying accident resulted from his incompetence. This ignominy, however, did not prevent True from going to New York and posing as an injured air ace. It was here that he married an actress named Frances Roberts and, to his parents' dismay, brought his new bride and his old morphine addiction back home. His distraught mother was prepared to try anything, and Ronald was shunted around a number of nursing homes, none of which seemed to affect his appetite for drugs. This, of course, was hardly surprising, because True would often absent himself to London on a morphia binge, leaving a string of unpaid bills, gambling debts, forged cheques and petty thefts in his wake. True's mind was also becoming increasingly unsettled, and he developed a conviction that there was another person calling himself Ronald True who was trying to kill him. It was this other Ronald True, he insisted, who was forging the cheques and running off without paying bills. True also became involved with a call-girl named Gertrude Yates (though she also used the name Olive Young) who lived in a flat in Finborough Road, Fulham. While True developed a fixation for the woman, she developed a dislike of him, a feeling not helped when True stole money from her.

On Sunday 5 March 1922, Ronald True visited Gertrude at her flat and was let in. Presumably he got up to no mischief, because he was still there the next morning. He rose at 7.30 to make a cup of tea and, returning to the bedroom, unexpectedly hit Gertrude Yates three times over the head with a rolling pin as she innocently sipped her tea, and strangled her with her own dressing-gown cord. True then helped himself to £8 from Gertrude's handbag and a few items of her jewellery. Around the time Miss Yates's body was being discovered by her daily, True was in a gents' outfitters buying a suit to replace the bloodstained one he had on, explaining to the shop assistant that its state was due to a flying accident – he had just flown in from Paris! Then he pawned his unfortunate victim's jewellery and spent the evening at the Hammersmith Palace of Varieties; where he was arrested.

Ronald True was put in Brixton Prison to await his trial, where medical staff lost no time in concluding that he was insane. And this was the defence which was advanced by Sir Henry Curtis Bennett on True's behalf at his Old Bailey trial. It was an opinion quite naturally opposed by the prosecution, and, it seems, by the jury, who found Ronald True sane and guilty. While True was under sentence of death the customary panel of medical men was looking into the matter of his sanity. And it was their conclusion that he was, so to speak, as mad as a hatter. Which is how Ronald True came to find himself in Broadmoor; where he stayed until he died of natural causes in 1951.

7 March

1733 (England) Sarah Malcolm, whose execution took place near Fetter Lane on this day, was at the time just twenty-two years of age and the victim, if it can be said in mitigation, of the most stringent misfortune. Sarah was born in 1711, of respectable parents in the county of Durham. However, her father having, through extravagance, spent all the family's money and property, Sarah was obliged to go into service. Her last post (before her fall) was at a low drinking house in London's Temple Bar, called the Black Horse. From there she was recommended to Mrs Lydia Duncomb, an octogenarian living in a set of chambers at the Temple along with two other servants. Having insinuated herself (in the belief that her employer was very wealthy), Miss Malcolm saw fit to arrange, with a man named Alexander whom she hoped to marry, to rob the old lady. In this enterprise she was joined by a fellow servant named Martha Tracy.

On the night of 3 February 1733, Sarah, by means of a stolen key, let in her murderous band and killed and robbed the unhappy and blameless Mrs Duncomb. The following day, a Sunday, several of Mrs Duncomb's friends and family, unable to raise her, became greatly alarmed, and several of the company forced admittance to her home, thus finding her strangled, her servant Harrison strangled, and the servant girl Price with her throat cut from ear to ear. In the course of the day, following a hue and cry, suspicions began to centre on Sarah Malcolm, and upon her lodgings being searched, a silver tankard was found smeared with blood. Taken immediately into custody, Sarah Malcolm was examined before the magistrates and committed to Newgate. As soon as she entered the jail she was searched by Johnson, one of the turnkeys, who relieved her of a considerable sum of money in gold and silver coin, which Malcolm admitted was Mrs Duncomb's. 'But,' she said, 'I'll make you a present of it if you will say nothing of the matter.' The jailer, however, handed the money to his superior officers.

In the weeks which followed, Sarah Malcolm conversed frequently with this same turnkey on the subject of Mrs Duncomb's murder, and in time confessed that it had been she who had arranged the robbery, though she had had nothing personally to do with the unfortunate woman's death, nor those of her servants; she, so she claimed, merely kept watch on the stairs.

At her trial, Sarah Malcolm made a similar declaration and told the court that Martha Tracy and Alexander were her accomplices. However, a verdict of guilty was returned against her, and the wretched woman was ordered to be executed. On the morning of the execution Sarah Malcolm appeared composed, and joined the Ordinary in prayers; in the cart she wrung her hands and wept most bitterly. At the place of execution she quite fainted away, and it was only with difficulty that she was made to regain her senses in order to face death.

8 March

1982 (Australia) It was the night of 8 March 1982, when neighbours alarmed by the sound of what could only be gunfire, called the police to the Tweed Heads, Sydney home of twenty-seven-year-old Mrs Margaret Ann Ross and her four children.

When the police broke into the house they found the

bodies of the four children, Petrina aged seven, Natalie (six), Clinton (five) and Vicki, just fourteen months; they had been shot through the head while lying in bed. The corpses of twenty-six-year-old Craig Alexander Ross, his wife Margaret Ann, and a man named Philip Layton were discovered in another room. A .22-calibre rifle was found on the floor beside Layton's body.

Neighbours told police that Layton had been having an affair with Mrs Ross, who had been separated from her husband and had been living in the flat with her children for around seven months. It also came to the notice of the investigation team that Mrs Ross had complained to friends that Layton had threatened to 'shoot them all' – and this, from a man who had already been charged with assaulting Craig Ross and slashing his car tyres, needed to be taken seriously.

9 March

1953 (USA) On 9 March 1953 Barbara Graham, in company with three other petty crooks, broke into the home of an elderly widow living in Burbank, California. Although, like many elderly recluses, Mrs Monohan was rumoured to keep a fortune in the house, the thieves found nothing of value. In a fit of pique, Graham battered their victim to death with the butt end of a pistol.

Barbara Elaine Wood was born in Oakland, California, in 1923, and there followed a childhood of unbearable squalor and neglect, seasoned with regular beatings from a mother rarely out of trouble with the authorities. To nobody's great surprise this lifestyle rubbed off on Barbara and eventually she too was a guest of the local reformatory. On her release in 1939, Barbara met and married a small-time crook named Henry Graham, became hooked on drugs, and turned to prostitution to feed the habit. And when the proceeds of prostitution became insufficient, then Barbara Graham and her lacklustre cronies turned to robbery and, eventually, murder.

There is little honour among thieves, especially petty crooks who get caught up in a killing. Within days of the murder of Mrs Monohan, John L. True was in police custody and telling his story to anybody who would listen. Barbara was taken in for questioning and predictably protested her innocence. While she was in a police cell, Barbara Graham was approached by a man who claimed he was a gangster and, for the sum of $25,000, could provide her with an alibi. Barbara jumped at the offer of course; after all, how was she to know her benefactor was a shrewd undercover police officer?

All in all, Barbara Graham's chances in front of a jury were about nil, and on 3 June 1955, she was introduced to San Quentin's gas chamber.

10 March

1682 (England) Christopher Vratz, the youngest son of a Pomeranian gentleman, having distinguished himself in military prowess (notably at the siege of Vienna) but being financially insecure, took to highway robbery in the countries of Austria and Hungary. A daring thief, Vratz had soon saved sufficient to purchase a captain's commission in a regiment in the Emperor of Germany's service. It was while he was in this post that he became acquainted with Charles John, Count Coningsmark, and came over with him to England. Here the count found himself thwarted in his amours with a certain Lady Ogle by one Thomas Thynn, Esquire. He so highly resented his lack of success with the lady that nothing would pacify the count but the very death of his rival. Captain Vratz procured two other assassins – John Stern and George Borosky – who, at a quarter after eight in the evening of Sunday 12 February 1681, met Esquire Thynn riding in his coach up to St James's Street.

Borosky, a Pole, shot him with a blunderbuss, which injured him in such a barbarous manner that Mr Hobbs, an eminent surgeon, found in his body four bullets, which had torn his guts, wounded his liver, stomach and gall bladder, broken one of his ribs, and cracked the great bone below, of which wounds he died.

These murderers being taken the next day, and carried before Justice Bridgman, he committed them to Newgate, from whence being brought to the Old Bailey on 28 February following, they were tried before Lord Chief Justice Pemberton, before a jury half English and half foreigners (all three prisoners being foreign). The jury, after retiring half an hour, brought in the three principals guilty, but acquitted the count of procuring the others to commit the murder. He was ordered, however, to provide three sureties that he would appear at the next sessions and answer any appeal that might be brought by Mr Thynn's relations ... Sentence of death was pronounced by the recorder.

All three condemned men were taken to the place of execution in a cart on 10 March 1682. It was written of Captain Vratz by the chaplain, Dr Gilbert Burnet: 'It is certain that never a man died with more resolution and less signs of fear. His carriage in the cart, both as he was led along and at the place of execution, was astonishing; he was not only undaunted, but looked cheerful and smiled often.'

(*The Newgate Calendar*)

11 March

1942 (England) Harold Dorian Trevor was one of those pathetic crooks; one of those utterly incompetent crooks. When he died on the scaffold at Wandsworth Prison on 11 March 1942 he was sixty-two years old; in the previous forty-two years he had spent less than one out of prison.

That is how incompetent Harold Trevor was. And when it came to murder, the ultimate crime after a lifetime as a petty crook and swindler, he did no better.

It was on 14 October 1941 that Mrs Theodora Jessie Greenhill was found dead in the living room of her apartment in Elsham Road, West Kensington. Mrs Greenhill was sixty-five years old and the widow of an army officer; she also desperately wanted to get out of the noise and danger of wartime London. To this end she had hoped to rent out the Elsham Road flat and move to the country. And this might well explain the fact that on the top of her small bureau lay a sheet of paper bearing the incomplete text: 'Received from Dr H. D. Trevor the su . . .' It must have been at this point that the bottle had shattered over her head knocking her unconscious; Mrs Greenhill had then been strangled.

Police officers investigating the murder found the apartment ransacked, but bearing witness to a rather reluctant killer. There was, to begin with, the handkerchief laid carefully over Mrs Greenhill's face; a murderer not used to murdering, perhaps, a killer unhappy with the presence of the dead! Then there was the fact that whoever killed this unfortunate widow had tried to clear up the glass of the broken beer bottle and put it in a waste basket. And that was a big mistake.

It was a *fatal* mistake. Because the man sent in by Scotland Yard to investigate the scene-of-crime was none other than Detective Chief Superintendent Frederick Cherrill, their leading fingerprint expert. In no time at all Fred Cherrill had the fragments of glass under the microscope for fingerprint comparison with the prints held at the Criminal Record Office. They belonged to Harold Dorian Trevor. '*Dr H. D. Trevor.*' He had fingered himself. Literally.

Trevor was picked up by the Welsh police at Rhyl four

days later and returned to London. In a sad attempt to explain his actions – to himself, one feels, as much as to the police – he began his statement: 'It wasn't murder. There was never any intent to murder. I have never used violence to anyone in my life before. What came over me I do not know . . . something seemed to crack in my head . . .'

At his trial the following January, Harold Trevor tried an insanity plea. He should have known that for an old lag like him it wouldn't wash. This time he had been even more careless than before; and he paid for it with his life. Standing in the shadow of the gallows, perhaps Trevor recalled the words he had spoken before sentence of death was passed on him. He told the court: 'I pray that God in His mercy will gently turn my mother's face away as I pass into the shadows . . .'

12 March

1980 (USA) Despite the numerous confessions that he had made, retracted and made again, John Wayne Gacy, arguably America's most notorious serial killer, did not take the witness stand at his trial. Whether it would have made any difference is a matter for conjecture, but on 12 March 1980 the jury rejected his plea of insanity and convicted him of murder with a recommendation for the death penalty.

Or rather, not murder, but *murders*; thirty-three of them, all young boys, all sexually assaulted, all disposed of around Gacy's home at 8213 West Summerdale Avenue, in Des Plaines, Illinois between 1972 and 1978. And now he was going to die – or, as the placards outside the prison insisted: 'Say goodbye, the time has come for you to fry.' (Of course 'frying' in the electric chair was not an option, the state of Illinois executes by means of lethal injection.) As 10 May approached the atmosphere became more festive as a veritable fever of eager anticipation gripped Chicago. As many as a thousand people occupied a floodlit field close to the prison, many wearing clown costumes in parody of Gacy's alter ego as Pogo the lovable clown, throwing confetti and streamers; others wore black 'grim reaper' hoods and danced about yelling and singing slogans and rhymes. Among the most popular of these were: 'Turn that frown upside down – they have just fried the clown' and 'Goodbye Gacy' to the tune of *Hello Dolly*. On one main Chicago street a group had lined up thirty-three body bags, one for each of the 'Clown Killer's' victims.

Meanwhile, on Death Row, John Wayne Gacy seemed to be enjoying things as much as anybody. He had received over the years an estimated 27,000 items of fan mail (each of which he had diligently replied to), television interviewers were queuing up for the privilege of an on-air chat, and Gacy himself had rented a public telephone line so that, for the price of a couple of dollars his fans could call in and listen to a recorded message protesting his innocence. Gacy's lawyer observed in a stunning understatement: 'I think he denies the reality.'

As the time approached for him to die, Gacy, now a rather tubby fifty-two-year-old, was puffiing away on a cigar and joshing with prison staff and the Roman Catholic chaplain – for all the world like a man getting ready for a party. Inside the execution chamber he was hardly a scrap less jolly, climbing on to the trolley with a smile and offering himself for pinioning. As he was linked through an intravenous needle to the execution machine, he was seen to wink at one of the guards and remark with a grin: 'You can kiss my ass.' Those were his last words before the three drugs were pumped into the vein at one-minute intervals. Or rather, that is what should have happened. In reality it was yet another in a long series of bungled executions over the years. There was a blockage in one of the poison lines. As guards pulled a blue curtain across to prevent observers witnessing the scene, the apparatus was rerun. The curtain opened again and the execution continued. It took eighteen minutes to kill John Wayne Gacy – twice as long as it should have done.

13 March

1992 (USA) Olan Randle Robinson was executed by lethal injection in Oklahoma state – their second execution in a week (the other had been Robyn Leroy Parks on 10 March).

In June 1980, Robinson, his nephew and another man broke into the home of Robert Swinford intent on theft. During the robbery Mr Swinford, his fiancée and another woman friend were shot dead. Robinson received the death sentence and his partners in crime picked up life. As forty-six-year-old Robinson was being given the injection at McAlester Prison, the minister read the prisoner's choice of biblical text, from I Timothy 1:12–17, part of which reads:

> And I thank Jesus Christ our Lord, who hath enabled me, for that he counted me faithful, putting me into the ministry; Who was before a blasphemer, and a persecutor, and injurious: but I obtained mercy, because I did it ignorantly in unbelief.

Even in death Olan Randle was generating news. One of his last requests was that, to save distress to his wife and children, no autopsy should be performed on his body. Unfortunately, even though the state knew quite well how he had died – they poisoned him! – it is a legal requirement that all deaths which 'occur' within prison walls must be investigated by the Medical Examiner's office and, arguably, that is impossible without a post-mortem examination. While the Robinson family were taking their case to law, Judge Robert Leydon issued a temporary restraining order on the autopsy, and Olan Randle Robinson's mortal remains were transported to the refrigerated mortuary store in Oklahoma City, conveniently close to where the Medical Examiner's office is located, which meant that the body was now in a different legal jurisdiction. Therefore to prevent the autopsy the Robinsons would be obliged to reapply to a different court for a restraining order. Exhibiting far more dignity than the state could obviously muster, Mrs Robinson decided not to continue her legal action. And so they autopsied Olan Robinson – and certified that he had died as the result of execution by lethal injection.

14 March

1912 (USA) The Allen family, headed by Floyd, had been a thorn in the side of law enforcement officers in the Blue Ridge Mountains area of Virginia for as long as anyone could remember. They considered themselves above the law and openly practised the traditional mountain-folk's pastime of moonshining; needless to add, they also refused to pay taxes. In many ways this kind of naughtiness was at least containable, but on 14 March 1912 in the Carroll County Courthouse at Hillsville, Floyd Allen escalated the scope of their activities into a bloody battle.

Allen had been convicted of assaulting a peace officer and preventing the arrest of another member of the clan. The court was packed with members of the Allen family and as Judge Massie pronounced the relatively modest sentence of one year's jail on Floyd Allen, he announced plainly: 'I don't aim to go.' And he and the other members of the family produced guns and began firing. It was later estimated that at least seventy-five shots were fired during the shoot-out, including those fired by the heavily armed representatives of law and order. When the smoke cleared, six people lay dead – the judge, Sheriff Lew Webb, Prosecuting Attorney W. M. Foster, a juror named C. C. Fowler, a witness named Betty

Ayers and an innocent spectator; eight others were wounded. Floyd Allen was so badly injured that he was unable to escape from town, and was arrested the following day at a nearby hotel. The other members of the Allen family scattered, but were gradually hunted down and dealt with, leaving the Blue Ridge Mountains a wholly more peaceable place.

Floyd Allen was convicted of murder, and following unsuccessful appeals was sent to the electric chair on 28 March 1913. Sidna Allen received two terms of fifteen years and one of five, and the other members of the family, who claimed they only loosed off their guns to create a diversion, were given various lesser prison sentences. Sidna Allen was released in 1926 through a pardon from the state governor. He later wrote his memoirs which were published in 1929 and in which he claimed the shootings were unpremeditated and only intended as an attempt to free Floyd.

15 March

1977 (England) On 15 March 1977, the mummified body of James Finlay was found in the refuse area of a block of flats in Rochdale, Lancashire. He was able to be identified only by a remarkable fingerprinting procedure developed by DCI Tony Fletcher of Manchester police for use on fingerprinting Egyptian mummies. James's wife, Mrs Eileen Finlay, through lack of evidence, was not charged with any crime, though speculation is still rife.

16 March

1925 (USA) On 16 March 1925 George Sack and his wife were sitting in the back of a cab on their way to George's delicatessen when Edna was shot dead and George was wounded in the arm. Although no gun was found in the taxi, George Sack was arrested and charged with his wife's murder. Now, on the face of it, this might seem a little hard on poor George; to lose his wife and his liberty both in one day. However, the police knew something about George that we didn't – this was the second Mrs Sack to meet an untimely end. The death of his first wife, Julia, occurred in 1923, when George was a struggling Chicago shopkeeper. When Julia died in an inexplicable fire at their home, George didn't have to struggle any more, the five thousand dollars' insurance money saw to that.

Perhaps money had gone to George Sack's head, or perhaps he was just desperate. At any rate he employed one of America's most celebrated defence attorneys to handle his case – the legendary Clarence Darrow, the man who only the previous year had prevented Nathan Leopold and Richard Loeb from going to the electric chair for a 'thrill murder'. Darrow's task now was no less difficult – he had to prevent George Sack from possible judicial execution. This he did by the simple expedient of persuading the jury that George was as mad as a hatter; which he probably was.

When George Sack was released from the hospital for the criminally insane in 1932 he went on the kill again. First there was a business associate named Joseph Young who disappeared without trace. That was in Seattle. Then one of George's tenants in an apartment block he bought was found battered to death; coincidentally just after a row with George. In September 1952, schoolteacher Goldie Goodrich became the third Mrs Sack, and early in 1954 she became the third late Mrs Sack. George had pushed his luck too far this time, and a post-mortem examination proved that Goldie Sack had been drugged with barbiturates and then asphyxiated. George was put on trial, he was convicted and he was sentenced to death. In July 1957, the sentence was commuted to life imprisonment in the Oregon State Prison. Six years later, with nobody else around to kill, George Sack took his own life.

17 March

1976 (South Africa) Ronald Frank Cooper's diary entry for this date reads: 'I have decided that I think I shall become a homosexual murderer, and shall get hold of young boys and bring them here where I am staying. I shall rape them and kill them. I shall not kill all the boys in the same way; some I shall strangle with my hands, others I shall strangle with a piece of cord. Others again, I shall stab to death, others I shall cut their throats. I can also suffocate or smother others.' Cooper is a rare case of the prospective serial killer being stopped after his first murder.

18 March

1789 (England) Christian Murphy became the last woman to be burnt alive. She had been jointly convicted with her husband of coining, at the time regarded as treason, and therefore a capital offence.

19 March

1934 (England) On Monday 19 March 1934, forty-six-year-old livestock farmer John Dawson was on his customary hike home from the comforts of the Edisford Bridge Hotel. It was shortly before nine o'clock and dark, cold and windy. As he passed the entrance gate to Tommy Simpson's farm, Dawson experienced what he described later as a light tap on the back followed by a faint click. Thinking no more of it, farmer Dawson continued his journey and arrived back at Bashall Hall around 9.20 p.m. and ate the hearty supper that his sister Polly had left for him. At eleven o'clock Tommy Kenyon, the stock-hand, came in, and after a brief exchange of words with Dawson went to bed.

Kenyon and young Albert Pickles (Polly's son) were, as usual, up before dawn to attend to milking duties. Dawson's sister Annie was also up attending to the men's breakfasts. 'I don't like the look of our John,' she announced, 'when I took him in his tea he asked me to have a look at his back where he had a bit of pain. He's covered with blood, Tommy! There's a wound in his back and everything's covered with blood!'

John Dawson was a stubborn man, and he refused to see a doctor. So Annie called for one. And he objected to the doctor's suggestion of an X-ray. So Annie bullied him into going to the local hospital. Here the X-ray revealed a foreign body about the size and shape of a small bird's egg lodged just below John Dawson's liver. It had entered through the gaping wound below his shoulder-blade. When it had been removed (much against Dawson's wishes), the 'foreign body' proved to be a strange kind of home-made bullet, fashioned from a short length of hard steel rod rounded at both ends with a file. Predictably, John Dawson refused all offers of treatment and so died three days later of gangrene and septicaemia.

When he arrived in the village of Bashall Eaves, Detective Chief Superintendent Wilf Blacker faced a blanket of silence; it was, he said, 'like talking to a brick wall'. If the locals knew anything they certainly weren't sharing it with him. But if he had no cooperation, then Wilf Blacker did have the singular home-made steel projectile. And, like any detective with a ballistics puzzle, he called in the celebrated London gunsmith Robert Churchill. Blacker and Churchill started off by calling in all local guns, whatever the age or type; garages and workshops were searched for signs that the 'bullet' had been made there. Without result.

For all the tight-lipped secrecy, a few wagging tongues did provide Wilf Blacker with some local gossip – for what it was worth. Like the dog which was found shot dead on Tommy Simpson's farm, with no bullet in its carcass. And who had made seventeen-year-old Nancy Simpson pregnant? Tom

Kenyon? Was that why he and Simpson were seen brawling in the lane outside Simpson's farm? Was the bullet meant for Kenyon, then? Or was Dawson the father of Nancy's child? Was revenge the motive? And why did Tommy Simpson hang himself ten days after John Dawson died? All these questions remain unanswered to this day. The villagers' code of silence had successfully protected somebody; but who?

20 March

1927 (USA) It was on the morning of 20 March 1927 that neighbours were awakened by cries of distress from ten-year-old Lorraine Snyder. When they went next door it was plain to see why. Albert Snyder was lying on his bed, his head and face battered beyond recognition; his wife Ruth was lying outside the bedroom door bound and gagged, but otherwise unharmed. According to Ruth her husband had been attacked by a man 'looking like an Italian', who had also tied her up. Mrs Snyder's opinion was that the motive for the crime had been robbery; some valuable jewellery was missing.

Suspicions were aroused when that jewellery was found under the mattress of the Snyders' bed. It was compounded when the autopsy report revealed that Albert Snyder had not died from a frantic bludgeoning by a disturbed burglar, but as the result of a carefully calculated murder. In addition to the head wounds, a length of wire had been tied tightly round his neck, and chloroform-soaked wads had been forced into his mouth. It was when the police found the torn-up scraps of a letter to Ruth from 'Judd' that the dime dropped.

Ruth Snyder and Judd Gray were jointly charged with first-degree murder. Although there was every indication that Ruth had been the dominant – even manipulative – partner, both were found guilty as charged. In January 1928 they were judicially electrocuted at Sing Sing.

There is an interesting postscript to the executions. A

reporter named Thomas Howard working with the *Daily News* smuggled a camera into the execution chamber strapped to his ankle. Just as the surge of electricity hit Ruth's body, Howard activated the shutter by remote control and immortalised the final moment of her life. It remains one of the most powerful images in the history of crime.

21 March

1984 (Australia) On 17 August 1983, Douglas Crabbe was refused a drink in the bar of the Ayers Rock motel; the staff thought he had had enough. As if to prove them right, Crabbe left the bar, climbed into his articulated truck and drove it through the motel. He killed four people instantly and seriously injured twelve more, one of whom later died in hospital. On 21 March 1984 Douglas Crabbe was found guilty on five counts of murder and jailed for life.

22 March

1962 (USA) By dint of the lengthy American appeals procedure, Vincent Ciucci received several stays of execution following his conviction on charges of familicide in January 1955 and his lawyers kept him alive until Thursday 22 March 1962. At his trial, Ciucci had pleaded not guilty to the indictments, and insisted that somebody else must have entered his apartment and killed the family. The jury, perhaps not entirely surprisingly, found the story more difficult to believe than that Ciucci, in a tight spot, had killed them himself; so he was convicted and sentenced to death in the electric chair. On 22 March he held a press conference during which he told journalists a new and even more preposterous story: that he had seen his wife shoot the children. After this he had snatched the rifle away and shot her. The reality was rather more prosaic.

At the time of his crime, Vincent Ciucci lived with his twenty-eight-year-old wife Anna and their three children, nine-year-old Vincent, eight-year-old Virginia and four-year-old Angeline at their grocery store on West Harrison Street, Chicago.

It had been on 5 December 1953 that a fire had broken out in the shop below the Ciucci apartment and Vincent was the only one to survive the blaze. As the firefighters arrived, he stumbled from the burning building claiming he had been initially overcome by the fumes, but managed to drag himself out. Autopsies carried out on the victims' bodies established that they had been chloroformed and then shot in the head with a rifle. It did not take the subsequent police investigators long to discover that Vincent Ciucci had a mistress, an eighteen-year-old named Carol Amora, who had recently had a baby by him. Ciucci was charged with the murder of his family and his reply was: 'I admit I'm a gambler and I like to fool around with women but I wouldn't do a thing like that . . . How could a man kill his own children? He would kill himself instead.'

23 March

1807 (England)

JOHN MAYCOCK

Executed 23 March 1807, on the Top of the New Jail, Horsemonger Lane, Southwark, for the Murder of an old lone Lady, Mrs Ann Pooley, in company with John Pope, who was admitted Evidence for the Crown

At the trial of Maycock and Pope it was stated by her sister that Mrs Pooley lived a reclusive life in a house in Free School Street, Horsleydown, the dwelling being almost constantly shut up and there being no servants. The last time the victim was seen was on 26 July 1806, when her sister took her the dividend on her stock, which amounted to £12. This was paid in six new £2 notes of the Bank of England.

In evidence, Mr John Mackrill Garrett said that he had entered Mrs Pooley's house on 20 August, there being some concern for the old lady's welfare, and found her dead and the body becoming putrid. All the drawers and boxes in the house had been ransacked.

Tom Griffin, a corn porter, told the jury that John Maycock had, about two months before the crime, told him: 'I know an elderly lady who lives by herself in a house which is shut up, and she is worth a good deal of money; you and I and a stout young fellow who works for Mr Burgess, will do her out of it.' Griffin refused to have anything to do with the robbery, and when he heard of the murder he informed the authorities against Maycock. Pope [the 'stout young fellow'] then confessed and gave evidence against Maycock.

At this stage of the prosecution some discussion arose respecting the acquittal of Pope, for it was contended by his counsel, Mr Guerney, that he was entitled to his acquittal, and that in fact he should not have been put upon his trial, he having confessed under the inducement of being pardoned. Mr Knowles for the prosecution contended that he ought to have been made a party to the crime along with Maycock; but the judge ruled that Pope stood in the same situation as any other prisoner: that he had confessed under the promise of being pardoned, and that he was entitled to it. Pope was accordingly acquitted.

For John Maycock there was an altogether grimmer conclusion; he was convicted of his dreadful crime and duly sentenced to death. From the dock he responded: 'Thank you for that; I'm done snug enough.' He was executed at Horsemonger Lane Jail.

(*Old Bailey Records*)

24 March

1984 (England) The body of Miss Hilda Murrell was found at Moat Copse, about six miles from her home in Shrewsbury; she had been repeatedly stabbed and left to die. As well as being a famous rose grower, Miss Murrell was known as a vociferous opponent of nuclear energy. This added a sinister touch to the crime when it was realised that the only article missing from Miss Murrell's home was a manuscript that she intended to present at a public inquiry into the construction of the Sizewell B power station. Another fact to fuel the conspiracy theory was Miss Murrell's possession of potentially embarrassing information on the controversial sinking of the Argentinian cruiser *General Belgrano* during the Falklands conflict. Her nephew, who worked in naval intelligence, had apparently been the source. Although there has been no shortage either of suspects or theories, the death of Hilda Murrell remains a mystery.

25 March

1990 (USA) On Sunday 25 March 1990, thirty-seven-year-old Julio Gonzalez, a refugee from Cuba, dropped into the Happy Land social club for a few drinks with friends. On the way out he got into an exchange of angry words with a former girlfriend named Lydia Feliciano, resulting in Gonzalez being manhandled out of the club by one of the bouncers. Enraged with Lydia and humiliated by being publicly thrown out, Gonzalez walked down the block and bought a dollar's worth of petrol. He returned to the Happy Land, soaked the entrance with gasoline and set fire to it. Only five people survived the resulting holocaust; ironically, one of them was Lydia Feliciano, the target of Gonzalez' crazed arson attack.

The trial of Julio Gonzalez opened in the Bronx County Courthouse on 8 July 1991. The heated debate that took place during the six-week hearing centred on Gonzalez' culpability for the crime, because he had pleaded not guilty on grounds of insanity. By the end of the first week, one might have been forgiven for thinking that the long-awaited trial of one of America's worst mass killers had not yet begun. The only time the courtroom was crowded was when Lydia Feliciano took the witness stand. Although she was there as a prosecution witness to testify that on the night of the fire, during their row, Gonzalez had told her: 'You'll see. Tomorrow you're not going to work here any more. I told you and I swear to it,' Ms Feliciano was rated by many as only marginally less guilty than the defendant himself. The reason for this was that as soon as she became aware of the fire, it was alleged that instead of raising the alarm she called herself a cab and disappeared into the dark. It is only fair to add that, according to her own recollection, Lydia Feliciano shouted 'Fire' before she left.

Then the series of psychiatric specialists appearing for the defence presented their opinions as to Julio Gonzalez' sanity, and it soon became clear that the matter pivoted on alleged brain damage suffered by Gonzalez during childhood aggravated by the severe beatings he claimed he was given when he was imprisoned for deserting from the Cuban army. The prosecution then exercised its right to refute the defence's medical evidence, and Dr Jose Valciukis entertained the court with allegations that, according to Gonzalez' own words, he and a fellow-employee had once planned to burn down the factory after a disagreement with their boss. Then a Dr Berger laid the foundation of any prosecution's refutation of a diminished responsibility plea – the fact that the arson attack was *premeditated*. He reminded the jury that Gonzalez had been specific in asking the garage for just one dollar's worth of petrol, because it was all the money he had on him; and when the pump attendant was reluctant to sell him such a small amount, Gonzalez invented a car which had just run out of gas. Dr Berger also pointed out that if Gonzalez was being instructed by 'voices', as he claimed, then they were very sensible voices, because by his own admission Julio Gonzalez had waited outside the Happy Land until a trickle of patrons who were leaving got out of sight.

It was on the afternoon of Monday 19 August 1991 that the foreman of the jury, after three days of deliberation, rose to deliver their unanimous verdicts – guilty on all 176 counts. Eighty-seven counts of second-degree murder (one for each victim) resulting from depraved indifference to the lives of other people; eighty-seven counts of felony murder, where death results from the commission of another felony (in this case arson); one count of first-degree arson, which involved causing serious injury or death; and one count of assault, which was the injury sustained by the club's disc jockey who survived the fire. At a separate hearing on 19 September, Julio Gonzalez was given the maximum sentence possible under state law, twenty-five years to life.

26 March

1916 (USA) Robert Franklin Stroud, who became known as the 'Birdman of Alcatraz', had already earned himself a twelve-year stretch for manslaughter when, on 26 March 1916, he attacked and stabbed to death one of the prison officers at Leavenworth Prison, Texas. The killing was apparently quite motiveless and unprovoked and Stroud found himself facing a charge of murder. Although he offered the bizarre defence that the guard had died of a heart attack (in fact he had been stabbed in the heart) Robert Stroud was convicted and sentenced to death.

Thanks to his mother's intercession with President Woodrow Wilson's wife, Stroud's sentence was commuted to life in solitary confinement. The one concession was that he was allowed to continue the ornithological studies, which would lead to his becoming the country's leading authority on diseases of the canary. The Birdman was later transferred to Alcatraz where he was given a specially enlarged cell to contain his livestock and scientific apparatus, and where he published *The Digest of Bird Diseases* in 1943. Stroud was subsequently moved to Springfield Jail, Missouri, where he died in 1963 at the age of seventy-six.

27 March

1905 (England) The rain was teeming down on that early morning of 27 March, and young William Jones was glad for a change to be going to work. He was, then, puzzled and annoyed to find the colour merchant's shop closed and shuttered. Jones tried knocking, but could not raise either the manager, Thomas Farrow, or his wife. Cursing the weather, Billy Jones sped off to Greenwich, where the shop's owner had his own business. George Chapman sent one of his assistants back with the lad, and between them they forced an entry at the back. And then ran out again as fast as their legs would carry them; straight to the police station.

It was seventy-year-old Mr Farrow that the officers saw first. He had been beaten to death in the back parlour. Ann Farrow was in the bedroom, still alive but with such severe injuries that she died in hospital. Before long Murder Squad detectives from Scotland Yard were in charge, and a painstaking search by experts revealed two vital clues. A pair of home-made masks fashioned from ladies' stockings seemed to indicate that the men were local, because hiding their identity had been important. The second clue was a cash box lying close to Mr Farrow's body. The box had been forced, and later revealed a thumbprint which was likely to have been left by the killer.

As police began to make inquiries round the known criminal haunts, the names of Alfred and Albert Stratton cropped up with sinister regularity. Albert's 'wife' recalled him asking for an old pair of stockings, and Alfred's that he had recently burnt a coat he had been wearing on the night of

26–27 March. When the Strattons were taken into custody they were met by Inspector Charles Collins of the Yard's Fingerprint Department, and before long it was established that the thumbprint on the cash box belonged to Alfred Stratton.

The problem was convincing a court. It was, after all, the first time that a fingerprint had constituted major evidence in a British murder trial. Despite an obvious cynicism on the part of the prosecution and the judge, Charles Collins patiently introduced the jury to the technicalities of finger-printing with the aid of giant enlargements of the prints in question. They were obviously impressed, because after a brief retirement they found both prisoners guilty. And so the end of Alfred and Albert Stratton – hanged by a fingerprint – was the beginning of a new era in the fight against crime.

28 March

1905 (England) It came as something of a surprise to the desk sergeant to be confronted by a man confessing to a murder he claimed had been committed twenty-three years previously. The date was 28 March 1905, and the police station was in Great Yarmouth, a fishing port on the Norfolk coast. The man was clearly much the worse for drink, which did not help the believability of his barely coherent story. And so fifty-year-old stonemason John Appleton found himself in a police cell being advised to sleep it off.

The following morning a rather more sober Appleton was still adamant that he was a murderer, and was invited to make a statement. It had been in the summer of 1882, he said, when in company with a man named Joseph Earnshaw they had beaten a man to death outside Newcastle-upon-Tyne. After robbing him, they threw the unfortunate stranger's body into a dyke. Of course, after the lapse of so many years there was little likelihood of finding any evidence to confirm Appleton's claim, but the Chief Constable at

Yarmouth did contact his colleagues at Newcastle to see if they could shed any light on the matter.

It so happened that they could. Records still existed of an unsolved murder which had occurred at a place ironically named Pity Me, near Newcastle; the date had been July 1882 and the victim had been a miner called William Ledger. Armed with this information the Yarmouth police charged John Appleton with murder and he duly appeared at the Durham Assizes in July 1905. His associate, Joseph Earnshaw had seemingly died in the intervening time.

Between being charged and standing his trial Appleton had withdrawn his confession. He now claimed that he and Earnshaw had been in Newcastle looking for work. He had read about the murder at Pity Me and it had so affected him that over the years he had come to believe himself responsible. It was a pretty preposterous defence, and the jury, whether rightly or wrongly, brought in a verdict of guilty. However, having passed the mandatory death sentence, Mr Justice Grantham made it clear that the circumstances of the case would be brought to the attention of the Home Secretary; the result was that John Appleton was reprieved and his sentence reduced to life imprisonment.

29 March

1896 (England) This is the day on which a particularly sordid and unnecessary murder played a huge part in the development of one of the most enigmatic literary talents of the late-nineteenth/early-twentieth century. It was the date on which Trooper Charles Thomas Wooldridge cut the throat of his wife Laura. This is the way the local newspaper reported it:

> A painful sensation was occasioned at Windsor on Sunday night in consequence of a deliberate and cold-blooded murder, which was committed about nine

> o'clock; the victim was Mrs Laura Ellen Wooldridge, aged twenty-three. She was, it is said, married to a trooper in the Royal Horse Guards. This man came to Windsor in the course of the evening and went to 21 Alma Terrace, where Mrs Wooldridge was residing, and under the pretence of signing a paper was allowed to enter the house. Mrs Wooldridge thereupon asked a young woman who was sitting with her in the parlour to fetch her hat and coat, and while the latter was proceeding to the back room, the man and the woman went out the street door . . . There he seems to have attempted to cut the throat of the unfortunate woman, who cried 'Murder!' and ran into the middle of the road, where he threw her down and accomplished his dreadful work. The murderer fled, but is now in the hands of the Windsor police . . .

The following morning Wooldridge was taken before the magistrates and subsequently tried for his wife's murder by the justices of the Berkshire Petty Sessions in April 1896; Trooper Wooldridge was, quite rightly, found guilty. He was sentenced to be executed at Reading Gaol on Tuesday 7 July 1896. Shortly before 8.15 a.m. on that day the death penalty was carried out. The *Reading Mercury* reported: 'It was curious to note how little interest was apparently taken by the public in this execution . . . few even glanced at the black flag which was hoisted over the entrance to the gaol.'

One man who did take a great deal of interest in the fate of Trooper Charles Wooldridge was a fellow-prisoner in Reading Gaol named Oscar Wilde. Wilde was at the time serving a two-year sentence for homosexuality. So affected was he by the Wooldridge case that he composed one of his best known and most moving poems, 'The Ballad of Reading Gaol', in lamentation for the young soldier's passing.

30 March

1975 (USA) Easter Sunday 30 March 1975; this was the date on which one of the worst cases of familicide in American history took place. Charity Ruppert, a sixty-five-year-old grandmother, had planned a family gathering, and invited her elder son Leonard, his wife Alma and their children to join her and her other son James, who was unmarried and lived with her in Hamilton, Ohio, for a special Easter dinner. Everybody was in good spirits, except forty-one-year-old James Ruppert, who had recently lost his job and had been very depressed.

Leonard Ruppert and his family arrived early and spent some time playing games in the garden. James had been out drinking the night before and was still sleeping it off. He got up around four in the afternoon and came down from the bedroom armed with an arsenal of three pistols and a rifle. As the rest of the family came back into the house, James drew a gun and started firing. Leonard Ruppert was the first to drop, then his wife. Charity Ruppert made an attempt to stop her son, but she was the next to be shot down. The children, Leonard, Michael, Thomas, Carol, David, Teresa and John, all fell in a fusillade of shots. Ruppert fired a total of thirty-one shots, hitting most of the victims in the head. Three hours later he called the police with the laconic phone message: 'There's been a shooting here.'

James Ruppert was arrested and charged the same day with eleven counts of aggravated homicide. He refused to talk to the police and made it clear that he was going to plead a defence of not guilty by reason of insanity. When his trial opened in June, the prosecution alleged that Ruppert had planned the killings of his family for the purpose of inheriting the family money, property and life insurance valued at over $300,000. He had been prepared to be sent to a mental hospital, where he was convinced he would eventually be declared sane and able to inherit the family estate. In his defence, Ruppert's attorney told the court that his client had suffered from an unreasoning obsession that his family and the authorities were conspiring to persecute him. Ruppert was described as a 'gun freak' and the state prosecutor pointed out that, a month before the shootings, he had been inquiring about getting a silencer for his guns. The case was heard by three judges who at the end of the trial declared him guilty on all eleven counts of murder and sentenced him to life imprisonment. On appeal James Ruppert was granted a new trial on legal grounds. At the re-trial, he was found guilty of murdering his mother and brother but not guilty by reason of insanity of the other nine deaths. The sentence remained the same, and Ruppert was returned to prison to serve his life sentence.

31 March

1935 (Canada) It was Lizzie's third husband; dead husband, that is. At five o'clock on the morning of Sunday 31 March 1935, Tyrrell Tilford died in his bed.

Lizzie and Tyrrell had met at choir practice in the little town of Woodstock, Ontario. Rather against the advice of his parents (Lizzie was old enough to be his mother) Tyrrell Tilford married her on 10 November 1930. The Tilford clan were notable by their absence, and a certain chilliness grew up between the family and their son over the coming few years. Tilford built a pleasant home for his wife and her two children on Cronyn Street, and all appeared on the surface to be going well. That was until the night of 29 March 1935. Responding to the frantic knocking on his front door, old James Tilford opened it to find his son on the step, doubled up with pain, black in the face and muttering something about being full of arsenic. When he had recovered slightly, Tyrrell told his father that Lizzie and her two sons had been feeding him capsules of the poison in his food. The doctor was less impressed, and couldn't find much wrong with him.

The following day Lizzie arrived at the Tilford home and announced that she had come to nurse her husband. When the parents awoke in the morning, Lizzie had taken their son home. Where he died.

Despite the distinctly odd circumstances surrounding the death, Tyrrell was recorded as having perished from 'influenza and a weak heart'. However, his parents were not finished yet. Finding they got little sympathy from the local police, Mr and Mrs Tilford took their suspicions to the provincial attorney-general in Toronto; he ordered a post-mortem, and Professor Joselyn Rogers found evidence of a fatal dose of arsenic in Tyrrell's stomach. The most damaging evidence presented at Lizzie Tilford's subsequent trial was that two ounces of arsenic had been delivered to her house on her instructions on 20 March. Lizzie Tilford was found guilty of her husband's murder and was hanged at Oxford County Jail on 19 December.

Whether Lizzie killed her other husbands we will never know. One had already died before she arrived in Canada from England in 1928 with number two, a former coal-miner named William Walker. Walker died on 19 February of the following year, apparently of a brain tumour. His body was exhumed in June 1935, though no trace of poison was found. However, it was recalled that in 1929 Lizzie had passed on a 'folk remedy' to a friend with a troublesome husband, with the words 'That will fix him; you'll soon be rid of him.'

April

1 April

1820 (England) The following cautionary tale was published as a broadside by that undisputed king of the broadsheet, James Catnach of Monmouth Street in London's Seven Dials, home to so many of the low-life printing establishments of the eighteenth and early nineteenth centuries.

THE LIVERPOOL TRAGEDY

A few days ago a seafaring man, who had just returned to England after an absence of thirty years in the East Indies, called at a lodging house in Liverpool and asked for supper and a bed. The landlord and landlady were an old couple, and apparently poor. The young sailor entered into conversation with them, and learned that they had one of their sons at sea like himself, but whom they had not seen in many years and, in truth, had given over for dead.

On that night of 1 April 1820, the landlady showed the seaman to his room, and as she left saw him take a large purse of gold and put it on the bedside stand. She returned to her husband and they mutually agreed to murder the traveller in his sleep. In the dead of night, when all was still, the couple crept to their guest's room, approached his bed and cut his throat, almost severing his head from his body. Then they put a washing-tub under the bed to catch his blood. Plundering the unlucky man's boxes they found more gold, and many handsome and costly articles from the Indies, along with a wedding certificate.

Early the following morning an elegantly dressed lady came to the door of the lodging house inquiring for a traveller who had arrived the night before. The old couple were greatly confused and said that he had risen and left early. 'Impossible,' said the lady, and insisted they go and check again, adding: 'You will know him by a mole he has on his left arm in the shape of a strawberry. Besides, he is your long-lost son come to surprise you, and I am his wife. Your son has come to make you happy in the evening of your days, and resolved to lodge with you one night as a stranger, that he might see how you behaved to wayfaring mariners.'

The old couple went upstairs to examine the corpse, and they found the strawberry mark on its arm, and then they knew they had murdered their own son, and were seized with horror. Each taking a loaded pistol, they blew out each other's brains.

2 April

1832 (England) On the bleak edge of Saddleworth Moor where it comes close to the outskirts of Oldham, where the railway line out of Greenfield runs parallel with the river Tame, lies the parish of Uppermill. The area now boasts some of the best golfing in the Midlands, and its abundance of natural beauty spots makes it difficult to relate to a night of horror that occurred on 2 April over one hundred years ago. Along the ribbon of road which crosses the moor joining Greenfield with Holmfirth stood the Moorcock Inn, owned by Bill Bradbury and his forty-six-year-old son Tom, who also had the shooting rights around Greenfield and turned a tidy profit from annual game licences. It was Tom's responsibility to police the reserve and see off would-be poachers – a job for which his prodigious size and strength were perfectly suited.

Three other locals need to be introduced to make the cast of this tragedy complete. First, Reuben Platt, an habitué of the Moorcock and a shadowy character whose part in the events to come was never satisfactorily established. Then there were the 'Red Bradburys' – James and his son Joe – poachers and general ruffians, no relations of Bill and Tom, but regular adversaries of Tom in his position as gamekeeper.

The dreadful sequence of events which was to bring these tough moorsmen together in one instant of terror took place on 2 April 1832. The crime was not discovered until half-past ten, when Bill Bradbury's granddaughter stumbled across the bodies of Bill and Tom – according to one contemporary description: 'weltering in their blood, the walls and flagstones streaming with gore'. Although both men were still just alive, it was more than any doctor could have done to save them. Thomas had fifteen frightful gashes in his head and his skull was fractured; his octogenarian father had suffered wounds to many parts of his body. Bill Bradbury, before he died, described the attackers as five Irishmen, who had also robbed them. The shifty Reuben Platt claimed to have seen three Irishmen behaving suspiciously in the neighbourhood earlier on the day of the murders.

Despite the evidence relating to these citizens of the Emerald Isle, it was the 'Red Bradburys' who were picked up on suspicion. This seems to have been mainly on account of young Tom catching Joe Bradbury poaching and reporting him to the authorities. However, they were taken before the magistrates in Huddersfield (where they had been arrested), and were able to prove an alibi with the help of Reuben Platt. Cleared by the law they may have been, but to the people of the dales they remained branded as brutal killers, and not a single one of the locals would say a word to them from the day of their return. Joe Bradbury eventually left the district, though 'Red Jamie' remained, an outcast till he died around 1850. Reuben Platt, who almost certainly fabricated the controversial alibi, disappeared from the locality inside two years. The murders at the Moorcock Inn were never solved. All that remained as a reminder were the graves of William and Thomas Bradbury in Saddleworth churchyard, where those who cared to look could find their epitaph:

One house, one business, and one bed,
And one most shocking death they had;
One funeral came, one inquest pass'd,
And now one grave they have at last.

3 April

1924 (England) In common with most murders, the shooting of William Hall was a cowardly act; like most murders it was quite unnecessary. On the morning of 3 April 1924 Hall had been sent by the manager of his bank's main branch to attend to business at the firm's local branch in the Hampshire village of Bordon. It was (though rarely is now) a courtesy for such banks to open for one or two days a week to take care of what custom there was in the remoter areas; consequently, when the armed robber entered the bank William Hall was alone. One might have thought all that was necessary was to menace the luckless clerk with a gun and demand the money; this killer decided to use his weapon. He then locked the bank door after him and made off with his swag – a few hundred pounds in notes and silver.

Locking the bank door was an inspired move, for by the time anybody thought to question its closure, William Hall's killer was long gone. But if he had been provident in making his escape, the gunman had been less than careful with his choice of weapon. Ballistics experts brought in by detectives investigating the case lost no time in identifying the ammunition as government issue; as the district played host to a significant army base, it was not unlikely that the bullets had been issued to the army. And so began the painstaking task of interviewing all the personnel in the camp. One soldier, a private with the East Lancashire Regiment named Abraham Goldenberg, volunteered the information that early in the afternoon on the day of the murder he had been in that very branch of the bank cashing a cheque. Oddly enough, three days later the same young man wandered into a police station with the gratuitous information: 'No further developments have come to my knowledge. If anything does crop up, I will notify you.' Strange indeed, especially as Private Goldenberg was already known to the police for petty misdemeanours.

Meanwhile, a thorough search of the army base had turned up a brown-paper parcel hidden in one of the lavatories; it contained the best part of the money stolen from the bank. Abraham Goldenberg was taken in for further questioning on 8 April, and confessed to killing William Hall. He said: 'I have been with my girl for some time, and I would not marry her unless I had enough money. There was no chance of making any in the army.' He then told police where they could find the murder weapon and the remainder of the bank haul. When he was searched, Goldenberg was found to have £37. This he adamantly insisted was his own money and had not been stolen – had nothing to do with the robbery at the bank.

Private Abraham Goldenberg was tried and convicted at the Winchester Assizes; he had advanced a defence of insanity, which had been rejected. However, there were many in court that day who must have had second thoughts. Having been sentenced to death, Goldenberg's only reaction was to ask: 'Can I be assured that the £37 found upon me will be declared to be my property?' He was hanged at Winchester Prison on 30 July 1924.

4 April

1968 (England) The first evidence of Suchnam Singh Sandhu's terrible crime was discovered by two train drivers coming off duty after the London to Wolverhampton service had arrived at 12.52 a.m. on 5 April 1968. The men had been walking back through the carriages when they saw an abandoned suitcase. The torso which the luggage contained was taken to Wolverhampton Royal Hospital and given into the care of Dr Richard Marshall.

Later that morning, anybody crossing Wanstead Flats, in east London, might have seen a man on a moped stop and dump a duffel bag in some bushes by the roadside before riding off. A little more than twenty-four hours later a woman alerted the police when she saw a suitcase, apparently dumped, beneath a bridge over the River Roding in Ilford. This contained some more human fragments which had been part of the same body as the Wolverhampton torso. All that was missing was the head, and that was forthcoming as soon as Mr Howard Petty, cycling across Wanstead Flats, saw a duffel bag that was in better condition than his own and picked it up.

Pathologist Professor Robert Warwick's report stated that the victim was an Asian woman, aged between eighteen and thirty; she was not a virgin, and had recently undergone an inexpert gynaecological operation. After consultation with specialists on Indian culture it was deduced from her clothing that the woman probably came from the area around Jullundor in the Punjab. A police team was immediately put to the task of sifting through hospital medical files in the search for Indian women who had recently had gynaecological problems. It was at Barking Hospital that they found the name of Sarabjit Kaur, later identified by her general practitioner from the decapitated head. Sarabjit Kaur was subsequently traced to the house of her father, Suchnam Singh Sandhu, in Fanshawe Road, Barking. Having first claimed that his daughter had left home, Suchnam Singh afterwards stated at Ilford police station that Sarabjit had taken an overdose of barbiturates and fallen and struck her head; in panic at finding her dead body he had cut it up and disposed of it.

Suchnam Singh Sandhu was tried at the Old Bailey in November 1968. His story of his daughter's suicide was not believed and Singh was convicted and sentenced to life imprisonment. One of the most gruesome medical revelations was that Sarabjit Kaur was alive as her father dismembered her body as proved by the cut injuries to her fingers – known as 'defence wounds'.

5 April

1722 (England) Previous to the passing of the Coventry Act it was common practice for thieves and robbers to maim their victims, usually by cutting the sinews of their legs, in order to prevent them escaping or giving chase. It was after Sir John Coventry had suffered such treatment that Parliament decreed that maiming should be a capital crime. On 5 April 1722, Arundel Cooke and John Woodburne became the first to suffer execution under the Act.

Cooke was born into a family of some fortune, and after the finest of educations became a lawyer. He eventually married a young woman named Crisp, whose brother so took to the new addition to the family that he made his will in Cooke's favour. A fatal mistake, as it turned out, because once having got the scent of money, the wretched Cooke found himself unable to wait for his benefactor's death in order to inherit. He determined, therefore, to relieve Mr Crisp of his life prematurely, and for this purpose engaged the assistance of one John Woodburne. Woodburne was a labourer who, having fathered six children, was very much in need of the hundred pounds offered for his services.

It was decided between them that the murder should take

place on Christmas Eve. Arundel Cooke invited his brother-in-law to dinner, while Woodburne lay in wait in a churchyard along the route from one house to the other. Cooke was to give a loud whistle as a signal to attack. Mr Crisp, duly wined and dined, left Cooke at about nine o'clock in the evening, followed at a discreet distance by his treacherous relative. At the appropriate spot Cooke gave the signal and both he and Woodburne set about the unhappy Crisp, cutting and maiming him most terribly. Thinking that they had dispatched him, the two villains left him lying in his own blood.

Before a quarter of an hour had passed, Crisp appeared at Cooke's door almost dead from his wounds and was immediately put to bed and attended by a surgeon. At the end of a week he had recovered his strength sufficiently to be removed to his own house – with a strong suspicion that his brother-in-law had been one of the men responsible for his plight. So it was that Cooke and Woodburne in due course faced trial at the next assizes. Despite a spirited defence on his own behalf by Arundel Cooke, both men were found guilty under the Coventry Act and sentenced to death.

A contemporary report adds that a short time before the date of execution, Cooke wrote to the sheriff asking that he might be hanged at night, 'to prevent his being exposed to the country people, who were expected from all the adjacent towns and villages'. As a consequence of this plea, he was hanged at Bury St Edmunds at four o'clock on the morning of 5 April 1722; John Woodburne was executed in the afternoon of the same day.

6 April

1944 (England) When James William Percey, forty-eight-year-old chief radio officer of the motor vessel *Pacific Shipper*, took a drink it was a long drink. In fact, there was nothing he liked better than to step off the ship and spend a few days pursuing his favourite hobby. It was Thursday afternoon, 6 April 1944, and James Percey was on just such an errand of pleasure when he fell into company with James Galbraith; they had both been in one of the many houses which dispensed liquid comfort to the docklands of Salford, Lancashire.

Galbraith was a chief steward in the mercantile marine, and apart from their mutual attachment to the sea, he and Percey apparently shared a similar taste for other liquids – the ones that come in bottles and glasses. By evening Percey – who had started his drinking day early – found himself temporarily out of funds, and suggested they return to his ship for an injection of capital and a few more drinks on board. Whether he already had his thoughts on the sixty pounds that his companion boasted of having, or whether at that point he just wanted to carry on with the party, Galbraith followed eagerly, if unsteadily, back to the *Pacific Shipper*.

On board the host rustled up a half-dozen bottles of beer from the second steward, and bore them back to the cabin where waited his 'dear old friend Jimmy'. Generous in drink he threw out an invitation to the second steward to join them; preoccupied at present, he had promised to drop by 'shortly'. Shortly was over an hour later, and when the steward arrived to join the celebrations he found the door to Percey's cabin locked, and the man nowhere to be seen. Assuming James William had gone ashore for a little more of the same, the steward went off to make his own amusement.

So accustomed had the crew become to Percey's three- or four-day binges that nobody paid much attention to his disappearance, and it was not until 11.00 p.m. on 8 April that anyone even thought about their radio officer. That was the time when the third mate noticed the dark brown stain that seemed to be spreading over the ceiling of the lavatory immediately below James Percey's cabin. Of course, it was blood, as the third mate had guessed; and when they opened up his cabin they found that it had come from James's head, savagely smashed with blows from an axe. Of his sixty pounds there remained but four shillings and a few coppers.

Thanks to Galbraith's carelessness in leaving fingerprints about the place, the hunt for Percey's killer was a brief one; he was detained on 12 April, and in July 1944 he faced Mr Justice Hilbery at the Manchester Assizes; upon his wig the judge wore a black silk square. On 26 July James Galbraith was hanged.

7 *April*

1964 (England) There are some parts of the country where it is difficult to imagine a murder happening (though violent death is no respecter of landscape). Equally, there are those places where one would not be in the least surprised to find the Grim Reaper lying in wait – hardly shocking, one might think, to know that Jack the Ripper chose the East End of Victorian London.

Take Workington. It is not that there is anything intrinsically wrong with the town – it was once a thriving jewel of industrial progress. But that glory has passed, and left behind it a layer of soot that seems indelible. Workington, if not its people, is drab; and its suburbs no less. Seaton is one of those suburbs. On the night of 7 April 1964, Joseph Fawcett and his wife were sleeping soundly in their beds at King's Avenue, Seaton, when Joseph was awoken by heavy thuds from next door followed by what sounded like a scream. Still drowsy, he got up to investigate and as he walked downstairs heard a car engine start up and the vehicle moving off down the street.

When Mr Fawcett knocked on the door of No. 28 there was no response; by now he had been joined by another neighbour, and between them they decided to call the police.

By the time Sergeant Park arrived, Joseph Fawcett had retrieved the spare key from its hiding place in the next-door garage and cautiously he and the officer let themselves in the front door.

The body of John Alan West lay on the floor at the foot of the stairs. It was obvious that he had been badly battered about the head, and it was equally obvious that he was dead. At 4.30 Inspector Gibson arrived to begin the police inquiry. A search of the house revealed a raincoat that did not belong to Mr West; in one of the pockets was a medallion inscribed 'G. O. Evans, July, 1961'. With it was a scrap of paper on which was scribbled the name and address of Norma O'Brien of Liverpool. Miss O'Brien identified Evans as Gwynne Owen Evans (whose real name was John Robson Welby), and it was not long before he was in custody. Along with his friend, Peter Anthony Allen, who still had in his pocket a gold watch inscribed to John West for long service.

When they stood trial at Manchester Crown Court in July 1964, Allen and Evans were blaming each other. It appeared that Evans had once worked alongside John West and they had gone along to his house to borrow money; they had even taken Allen's wife and children along for the ride.

It was a squalid, easily forgettable crime. A crime such as one might expect, perhaps, to take place on the grey outskirts of a faded industrial town. And it might easily have been forgotten by all but those who grieved John West's death. But, whether it would have been any comfort to them or not, Peter Allen and Gwynne Evans were going to make legal history – as the last people ever to be executed in Britain, Allen at Liverpool's Walton Prison, Evans at Strangeways, Manchester.

8 April

1927 (South Africa) It is a matter of some wonder the lengths to which some individuals are prepared to go for a comparatively small amount of money. Huibrecht de Leeuw was one of those people for whom no amount of cash would ever meet his expenses. He was employed in the capacity of clerk to the town of Dewetsdorp, in the Orange Free State; and in that capacity had for some time been busily converting the town's finances to his own. Juggling the accounts books with the money kept in the exchequer safe was becoming increasingly difficult, and it was clear that this state of affairs could not go unnoticed for ever. And indeed it did not. On 8 April 1927, Mayor P. J. von Malitz, accompanied by two representatives of the town's finance committee, arrived to conduct his own inspection of the accounts.

So it was all up. Huibrecht de Leeuw had already exasperated the patience of his friends (not to mention emptied their pockets), and there was no way in which he could repay in time the frequent 'loans' from the exchequer. Desperate measures were clearly required; and desperate measures were what de Leeuw employed.

As the mayor's party pored with increasing bewilderment over the columns of incomplete and inaccurate figures, it seemed suddenly as though the whole world had come to an end. In fact, it was not quite as serious as that, only their part of the world had. In the wake of the tremendous explosion which ripped through the building, tearing off the roof and setting the fabric ablaze, Mayor Malitz was found dead and his financial advisers lying amid the scorched rubble with fatal injuries.

Fortunately, it was not long before Huibrecht de Leeuw was in custody where he could cause no more mischief. It seems that he had forgotten to provide himself with matches with which to ignite his home-made contraption of dynamite and petrol, and in something of a panic had been obliged to borrow a match from a local tradesman. After the briefest of trials, de Leeuw was convicted and sentenced to death. With the simple message on his lips 'I am prepared to meet my

Creator', he was hanged on 30 September 1927. Whether he ever did get to meet the Creator, or whether he went to the other place we can never know; but whichever it was, Huibrecht de Leeuw would never again be troubled over money.

9 April

1992 (South Africa) After a trial lasting several months Louis van Schoor was found guilty of seven counts of murder and two of attempted murder. Although he was, incredibly, released on bail van Schoor was back in court for the sentencing hearing on 16 June where he received twenty years.

It had been a strange case and one, perhaps, that could only have emerged from the racial tensions of late 1980s South Africa. Louis van Schoor, an Afrikaaner, had enjoyed a modestly successful if undistinguished career in the South African police force; and that is the way it might have remained had he not become aggrieved by his lack of promotion. Van Schoor left the force, but after finding even less success as a salesman, he went back to policing; not in the conventional sense, but as a security guard protecting business premises around the south coast port of East London. And in this career he was, in his terms at least, *very* successful. Whenever a break-in was reported, Louis would be first on the spot, armed with his trusty 9mm pistol. It was a peculiarity of South African law that it allowed any citizen to shoot dead a person who might otherwise escape from the scene of a 'serious crime'; and petty theft was considered a serious crime if it involved trespass. Louis van Schoor was in paradise. As he was a prominent supporter of apartheid and of the South African National Party, and as the vast majority of his suspects were black, he could mix business with pleasure. Between 1986 and 1989 he shot at least 101 blacks, killing thirty-nine – many were children. In 1989 a coroner's court cleared him of responsibility for twenty-five deaths, even though the pathologist had testified that the shots had been fired to the chest at close range – when it was claimed the victims were running away.

It was only with the political changes which followed the release from prison of Nelson Mandela that the van Schoor case was reviewed, and Louis found himself in the uncomfortable position of having to defend himself against nineteen charges of murder and thirteen of attempted murder. These were later reduced by a closed sitting of magistrates and then reinstated by the prosecutor. In the end, though, the charges on which he was found guilty were sufficient to keep Louis van Schoor's own brand of apartheid off the streets for some time to come.

10 April

1955 (England) A great deal has been written about the murder by Ruth Ellis of her boyfriend David Blakely, but it is as 'The Last Woman to be Hanged in Britain' that she is most often remembered.

Ruth was the unremarkable, rather brassy manager of The Little Club, a London drinking house – and a not very salubrious place even by the standards such establishments set themselves. It was in 1953 that Ruth met Blakely, a good-looking racing driver with an above average appetite for drink; they were instantly attracted, and for nearly a year all seemed to be going as well as such a match might reasonably be expected to go. And then things began to sour. Blakely had started seeing other women; Ruth had started objecting. Blakely decided to make his escape.

He moved in with friends at Tanza Road, on the edge of London's Hampstead Heath, for a few days. Ruth tracked him down and smashed all the windows of his car. Two days later Ruth intercepted Blakely as he was coming out of the Magdala Tavern in South Hill Park. On this Easter Sunday,

10 April 1955, she emptied the chamber of a Smith and Wesson handgun into the body of her former lover.

Ruth made no attempt to escape, and scant attempt to defend herself at her Old Bailey trial. The jury were in retirement for only fourteen minutes before finding her guilty. There was no appeal and, petitions having been rejected, Ruth Ellis became the last woman to hang in Britain, at 9.00 a.m. on Wednesday 13 July 1955.

11 April

1937 (England) Leslie George Stone raped and strangled his former fiancée, Ruby Ann Keen, in a coppice outside Leighton Buzzard. Despite being an obvious suspect, Stone denied killing the girl, and it required painstaking and imaginative forensic work to link a minute fibre sample from Ruby's underwear found on Stone's jacket. Furthermore, soil samples recovered from the scene of the crime matched samples on Stone's trousers. He was executed at Pentonville on 13 August.

12 April

1749 (England) One of the problems with having the death penalty as part of a nation's legal system is that it is always possible to execute an innocent person. As far as we know, this has happened rarely in England, and thankfully can never happen again. There are though, some well-established instances in our comparatively recent past. Such as the case of Richard Coleman, hanged on Kennington Common on 12 April 1749.

Coleman was indicted at the Kingston Assizes in March 1749 for the murder of Sarah Green on 23 July of the previous year. According to a contemporary account: 'she had been junketing with some acquaintances in Kennington Lane, stayed to a late hour, and on her return towards Southwark she met with three men, who had the appearance of brewers' servants, two of whom used her in so inhuman a manner as will bear no description'. Indeed, so inhuman was this usage that the hapless victim was later confined to St Thomas's Hospital, where she afterwards died. However, before breathing her last, Sarah Green was able to claim that the clerk in Taylor's brewhouse was one of the parties who had treated her in such an infamous manner. That clerk was taken to be Richard Coleman.

Some little while afterwards, Coleman was taken before the magistrate who, with nothing positive against him, would almost certainly have discharged the prisoner. However, at this time Miss Green was still alive and able, from her hospital bed, to identify Coleman as her attacker (drunk though she was on the occasion of that attack and despite the landlord who served her drinks on the fatal night claiming never to have seen Coleman in his life). By the following day, Sarah Green was less certain in her identification, but the justice nevertheless detained Coleman. And thus he came to be lodged in Newgate before being transferred to the New Jail at Southwark, till he was tried, convicted and executed.

At the place of execution, Coleman, with great dignity, faced his fate, delivering a paper to the chaplain in attendance in which he declared that he was altogether innocent of the crime alleged against him.

And it was true. Richard Coleman, by now two years deceased, was exonerated when, in 1751, two villains named James Welsh and Thomas Jones confessed that it was they, in company with another, who had committed the crime upon Sarah Green.

13 April

1905 (England) At the end of January 1905, an elderly woman walked into the Kensal Green furniture repository and asked after a trunk that had been deposited in the name of Devereux. It proved to be a large, battered old tin trunk secured by a new leather strap. Asked what her interest in the piece of luggage was, the woman said calmly: 'My name is Mrs Gregory; I believe my daughter is in there.' The warehouseman tapped and sniffed his way around the trunk, assumed the woman was mad or senile, and showed her the door.

On 13 April the tenacious Mrs Gregory made an application to the North London magistrates for an order to open the trunk, a trunk placed in storage by her son-in-law it turned out. Asked why, the good lady repeated her story – she thought it might contain the body of her daughter and her twin babies. Well, magistrates are clearly more imaginative than warehousemen, and the order was granted with immediate effect.

It was as Mrs Gregory feared. There, in the battered old tin trunk were three bodies – one large and two small; all were proved to have died from morphine poisoning. But why, after all this time, did this human shambles not smell? Arthur Devereux, whose wife and children the trunk contained, was a chemist's assistant, and the wooden cover which fitted over the corpses in the trunk had been soaked in a special solution of glue and boracic acid, which had had the effect of forming an airtight seal.

Devereux had met Beatrice Gregory in Hastings in 1898, and both she and her mother had been impressed by this apparently cultured young man. The match, in the parlance of the times, was a good one. Or was it? Beatrice became pregnant; and sure as eggs are eggs Arthur fled back to the metropolis. Which was just as well, because the Gregory family was bent on revenge and were making every effort to track him down. To compound Beatrice's misery, her baby did not survive and, heartbroken and humiliated, she left Hastings in the same direction as her errant lover.

Miss Gregory was soon working hard and earning a respectable, if modest, wage as a barmaid. In her spare time she scoured both high street and low in the search for a chemist's shop; the chemist's shop where Arthur Devereux had come to roost. You see, silly girl that she was, Beatrice Gregory really wanted the rascally Arthur back, desperately wanted her Arthur. Arthur, however, was less than keen, and one can only imagine the panic with which he watched Beatrice stride across the shop. Call it persistence, or for that matter you might call it genuine affection, but before long Beatrice Gregory became Mrs Devereux. Then along came little Stanley, the child who was to become the apple of Arthur's eye, and the only one to be spared the massacre to come. To Arthur's alarm, Stanley was quickly followed by twin sons Lawrence and Evelyn. Then Mrs Gregory added herself to the Devereux ménage. Things were sliding decidedly downhill, for not the least of his worries was that Arthur had become disengaged from his employers, and his poverty was not helped, nor his temper improved, by looking at what must have seemed to him like a veritable horde of dependants making noisy claims on his dwindling finances.

Quite when his resolve to reduce his burden hardened it is impossible to know, but it was early in 1904 that Devereux moved the family to a flat in Stonebridge Park. On the first day of their occupancy Mrs Devereux disappeared; according to Arthur she had taken the twins to the country. In reality, no one would ever see any of them alive again.

After the revelations of the tin trunk, an immediate manhunt was launched and Devereux was traced to Coventry and returned to stand his trial at the Old Bailey. In his defence Arthur claimed that he had arrived home to find that his wife had killed the twins and then committed suicide. He had thought it best to pack them into the trunk and say nothing. The jury showed their contempt for Arthur Devereux's story by remaining in retirement a bare ten minutes before finding him guilty. He was hanged at Pentonville Prison on 15 August 1905.

14 April

1913 (England) Jeannie Baxter, when she came to public notoriety in 1912, was in her early twenties. She had been, how to say ... 'looked after' by a Northern gentleman of some substance, and matters would almost certainly have continued along these lines had a charismatic Londoner named Julian Bernard Hall not come into her life. Hall and, let us call this blameless man 'Jennings', were as different as chalk from cheese. And as long as they stayed in their respective parts of the country there was no reason why Jeannie could not have double rations. Hall had set her up in a comfortable flat in Carlton Mansions, Maida Vale, while he lived in a luxury apartment just behind London's Piccadilly. Mr Jennings had thoughtfully provided a pleasant country cottage for her use.

The snag was, both these suitors became uncomfortably demanding; the result of which was that in December 1912, Jennings journeyed to London to visit Jeannie at Carlton Mansions. Unhappily for all concerned, Julian Hall arrived just ahead of him. Hall opened the proceedings by swigging down a magnum of champagne and loosing off a few random shots around the room from a revolver he was carrying. At this point the doorbell rang and Jeannie let Mr Jennings in. Jennings, sober as ever, found himself confronted by a drunken gun-toting Hall, who produced another gun and challenged him to a duel. Wisely, Mr Jennings declined, and with a few accompanying oaths, Julian (or 'Jack' as Jeannie called him) fired a few shots into a photograph of his rival on the sideboard. In a gesture of defiance, Hall swore that if Jeannie would ditch her other lover, then he would marry her. And with that he staggered out of the front door, firing a final shot over his shoulder.

Now most girls might have found the prospect of being manacled to a drunken psychopath who had just shot up their flat offputting; in fact, definitely to be avoided. But Jeannie was not most girls. So she said goodbye to nice Mr Jennings and started planning her wedding day. Julian had said it would be the following spring, on 15 April – and he would make all the arrangements. So it was with great excitement that the prospective bride turned up on the prospective groom's doorstep on 14 April to find out what those arrangements were exactly. She was irritated, though by no means surprised, to find her fiancé propped up in bed guzzling brandy. And when Jeannie learnt that there were no arrangements, the irritation turned to fury. Minutes later a friend of Julian Hall's who had been staying at the flat heard the loud report of shots from behind the bedroom door followed by a woman's voice crying: 'Come here! I have shot Jack!'

And that is exactly what she had done. And that is why, in June 1913, Jeannie Baxter found herself in the dock of the Old Bailey. She had as her defender the celebrated Edward Marshall Hall, and the story that he told the court, of Julian Hall's drunken threats to shoot himself, and Jeannie gallantly trying to wrest the weapon from him before he could do any damage, was one of his finest orations. Of course, according to Jeannie, the gun went off accidentally. A tragic accident. But the jury didn't go all the way in following Marshall Hall's silver tongue. Why they might have wondered, if the fatal shot had been accidental, was Jack Hall also shot in the arm? And why had Jeannie, on her own admission, fired a couple of shots into the bedroom ceiling? Their compromise was to find Jeannie Baxter guilty of the lesser charge of manslaughter, and she was sentenced to a comparatively modest three years.

15 April

1936 (New Zealand) It was a time when emigration to the fresh challenge of the Commonwealth countries seemed an attractive proposition compared to depression-gloomy Britain; and that was at the forefront of Eric Mareo's mind when he set sail for Australia in 1931. He was exchanging a none too promising job as the conductor of a none too promising orchestra for ... what? Adventure? Fame and fortune? Whatever it was it couldn't be worse; or so Eric thought.

At first things looked promising, the new immigrant found work and, two years after his arrival, a wife, Thelma. Thelma was an actress whom he met through their mutual involvement in the theatre, and ever on the lookout for new avenues of success, the couple travelled on to New Zealand. Here things looked so rosy that Eric was able to send for his two daughters by a previous marriage.

However, every silver lining has a cloud, and the Mareos' fortunes began to slide steadily downhill. Work started to dry up, and alcohol and drugs began to fill its place. Within no time, it seemed, both Thelma and Eric were heavily dependent on the barbituric acid veronal, and Thelma, who had been exhibiting neurotic tendencies moved closer towards mental collapse. A doctor reported finding her 'likely to commit suicide', and a friend visiting later had to use sal volatile to rescue Thelma from a veronal haze. Within days, she was dead. It was 15 April 1936.

The post-mortem findings were entirely in keeping with Mrs Mareo dying from a self-administered overdose of veronal. However, for some unaccountable reason, on 16 April Eric was charged with her murder. Worse still, he was tried, convicted and sentenced to death (though the sentence was later commuted to life imprisonment). Eric Mareo found himself in the middle of a nightmare from which, try as he might, he would never escape.

It was not that Eric was short of supporters, many eminent lawyers, physicians and toxicologists had spoken out in his favour. Sir William Willcox, England's leading toxicologist, had done work on the effects of the drug veronal. The basis of these findings was that a large dose would induce a coma with no return to consciousness, whereas a small dose would result in coma followed by a confused state of mind during which the victim might well take further doses without remembering or knowing what they were doing. At the request of Eric Mareo's solicitor, Sir William agreed to sign any papers necessary in support of his own belief that Eric was innocent. Tragically, Willcox died just days before the affidavit was prepared, a statement which would probably have had the influence to overturn Eric Mareo's conviction. As it was, he was granted leave to appeal some years later, but the appeal was dismissed. Following another two years of legal wrangling Eric Mareo was finally released in 1948. With almost no doubt an innocent man, he had spent twelve years in prison, and died shortly after his release.

16 April

1984 (Scotland) It was a little after midnight on Monday 16 April 1984, when the fire brigade was called out to a council block in Backend Street, Glasgow. The top-floor flat, where the Doyle family lived, was ablaze. They found fifty-two-year-old Lilian Doyle perched on a window ledge ready to jump; she was eventually persuaded to come down by ladder. Mrs Doyle's son Stephen had already jumped, and amazingly had survived the fifty-foot drop on to concrete. The cause of the fire was not difficult to find: petrol had been poured through the letterbox and ignited. In all, six members of the Doyle family perished in the inferno, including Lilian's husband, daughter, three sons and grandson.

At the top of the list of suspects for this dreadful arson attack was thirty-one-year-old Thomas Campbell – or 'TC' as he liked to be known. Campbell's target, if he were guilty, would have been eighteen-year-old Andrew Doyle. Doyle, called 'Fat Boy', had worked as a 'minder' for the Marchetti

Brothers, protecting their ice-cream vans as they plied their lucrative trade around Glasgow. Specifically, they needed protection from the rival firm of Fifti Ices, which was beginning to muscle in on Marchetti territory. Vans had been smashed up, a manager had been threatened – and worse was to come. On 29 February 1984, a masked man had stepped out of a Volvo car and blasted two holes in Andy Doyle's windscreen with a shotgun.

On 3 September 1984, seven men stood before the Glasgow High Court. They were charged variously with murder, attempted murder, attempted robbery, fire-raising, assault and malicious damage. Between all the lies, the contradictions, accusations and retracted statements aired in court, a seemingly coherent picture at last began to emerge. 'TC' was a villain with a reputation for violence. During a ten-year stretch in Barlinnie jail he had devised a scheme for ruining the Marchetti Brothers and capturing their trade. On his release he drew George Reid into the conspiracy as a 'money man', who financed Campbell and led the legitimate £250,000 negotiations for Fifti Ices.

In the autumn of 1982 the campaign to warn off the Marchettis began, and TC was delighted to find a little intimidation went a very long way. Only Doyle proved obstinate, and so Tommy Campbell set his henchman Thomas 'Tamby' Gray on to him. It was Gray who had ambushed Doyle's van and shot at him. But TC, along with a petty thief named Joseph Steele, was the one who had driven to Backend Street and laid the trail of petrol; TC who sat in his car and watched the blaze. And it was TC who received a life sentence, with a recommendation that he serve not less than twenty years. Joseph Steele was sent down for life, and Tamby Gray was given fourteen years. Other foot soldiers in the ice-cream wars received various lesser sentences.

But was that 'coherent picture' the true one? It is

important to ask because eleven years later the accused are still protesting their innocence. Would Thomas Campbell really have kept the baseball bat, three pickaxe handles, six woollen masks and a map with Backend Street circled, lying about the house where the police claim to have found them? Would he have told them: 'The fire at Fat Boy's was a frightener which went wrong'? Would Joseph Steele have said, 'I'm nae the one who lit the match', when arson had not been mentioned in the charge against him? Would William Love, the driver of the Volvo, have confessed to the police and grassed his confederates quite so readily? Or was the case, as Donald Macaulay QC put it, that 'there is something rotten at the core of this investigation. The police officers . . . have completely abused the public trust placed in them – and fabricated evidence'?

17 April

1984 (Canada) The man standing in the dock before the Supreme Court at Kamloops, British Columbia, was David William Shearing. On the previous day, 16 April, he had faced six charges of second-degree murder relating to the deaths in 1982 of the Bentley and Johnson families. He had pleaded guilty as charged and was awaiting sentence. Describing the murders as 'the cold-blooded and senseless execution of six defenceless and innocent victims', Justice Harry McKay sentenced Shearing to life imprisonment without the possibility of parole for twenty-five years. It is believed that this was the first time in Canadian legal history that such a severe sentence had been passed on a second-degree murder conviction.

It had been on 6 August 1982 that George Bentley and his wife Edith met up with their daughter Jacqueline and her husband Richard Johnson at the Wells Gray Provincial Park campsite, near Clearwater. The family party was completed by Richard and Jacqueline's two children, eleven-year-old

Karen and thirteen-year-old Janet. They were seen arriving in a car and a camper, but were never seen alive again, despite a widespread search of the wilderness area.

It was not until 13 September that the Johnsons' burnt-out car was found and inside were the charred corpses of Mr and Mrs Bentley and the Johnson family; indeed, they were so badly burnt that identification was only possible through dental records. All the victims had been shot. In October of the following year, 1983, two forestry workers reported finding the Johnsons' red and silver Ford camper van, which had remained missing since the discovery of the murders. The vehicle had been torched and dumped in a ravine twenty miles from where the victims had been found.

This seemed to the police to indicate a 'local' crime, and house-to-house inquiries were conducted in the Clearwater area. In the course of these interviews, one resident told officers that a man he knew, David Shearing, had told him about a car he owned with a bullet hole in the door. This almost throw-away remark was the piece of information that solved the year-long investigation, because the police had never disclosed the fact that a bullet hole had been discovered in the door of the Bentleys' camper.

Twenty-five-year-old Shearing was taken into custody where he made a full confession to having crept up on the party, reconnoitred the area, and then returned with a rifle and shot them. He had absolutely no idea why he had done it, adding simply: 'I feel really bad about it and nothing else.' David Shearing appeared before the Kamloops lower court on 21 November 1983, where he waived a preliminary hearing and was committed for trial at the Supreme Court.

18 April

1882 (England) A well-qualified doctor, Henry Lamson had seen active service with the French Ambulance Corps before returning to England where, in 1878, he married Kate

John. In the process he inherited £1500. Since Lamson invested his wife's money in a number of unsuccessful medical practices, and squandered the rest on a morphine habit he had picked up while serving in the Balkans, by 1881 his fortunes were in considerable need of replenishment. Mrs Lamson's mother had left her estate in trust to her three sons and two daughters. One son had already died, followed by another in 1879 of a mysterious stomach complaint. This left Lamson's wife Kate and another married daughter, and the youngest son, Percy, who was crippled with paralysis. If he were to die, Lamson would immediately inherit £700 or more through his wife's interest.

Henry Lamson visited fifteen-year-old Percy John at his special school on 3 December 1881, where he took tea with Percy and the headmaster, producing from his bag three slices of Dundee cake. One of these he selected for Percy and one for Mr Bedbrook. Then he quickly took his leave, saying that he had to travel to Paris. Later that night Percy John was taken ill with violent vomiting and after lapsing into a coma, he died. A subsequent autopsy revealed traces of aconitine, and the report of the inquest jogged the memory of a pharmacist who recalled selling a quantity of the poison to Dr Lamson the previous month.

With the kind of short-sighted arrogance displayed by many killers, Lamson, accompanied by his wife, paid a visit to Scotland Yard to protest his innocence. To his chagrin he was immediately put under arrest. The trial opened on 8 March 1882, and lasted six days. The jury, however, took just thirty minutes to find Lamson guilty of Percy John's murder. Before he was hanged by executioner Marwood on 18 April the same year, Dr Lamson made a full confession.

19 April

1971 (USA) An ex-convict and all-round drop-out, Charles Manson is generally considered to have dominated his equally unattractive disciples with a mish-mash of corrupted Biblical philosophy and mistaken interpretations of the lyrics of Beatles songs. This, combined with his magnetic sexual attraction for the female members of his 'Family', ensured Manson's complete physical and spiritual control of the group.

Just after midnight on Saturday 9 August 1969, four shadowy figures were skulking about the grounds of the secluded mansion at 10050 Cielo Drive in Beverly Hills. At this stage, Manson was not doing his own killing; tonight it was the turn of 'Tex' Watson, Patricia 'Katie' Krenwinkel, 'Sadie' Atkins and Linda Kasabian to do their master's will. 10050 Cielo was occupied that night by actress Sharon Tate, who was heavily pregnant, and four friends. In an orgy of overkill, the Family left all five victims horribly butchered. On the front door to the house the word 'Pig' was painted in blood; not one of the murderous gang had the slightest idea of whom they had killed – they were just random victims. Only one person was not pleased – Charlie Manson. When the news of the bloodbath came through on television it apparently offended Charlie's sensibilities that it had been such a messy job. He decided to show everybody how it should be done.

On 11 August, just two days after the Tate murders, after motivating themselves with drugs, Manson led a group on a second murder spree. At shortly after 1.00 a.m. the Family invaded the Silver Lake home of businessman Leno LaBianca and his wife Rosemary; like the Cielo Drive victims, the choice was entirely random. After stabbing and slashing the LaBiancas to death, Manson and his disciples inscribed the mottoes 'Death to the Pigs', 'Rise' and 'Healter [sic] Skelter' in blood on the walls; as a final act of gratuitous violence, the word 'War' was carved into Leno LaBianca's abdomen.

Susan Atkins was later arrested on a prostitution charge

and while she was in custody admitted her part in the Tate murders to a cellmate. The information filtered back to the prison authorities and, on 1 December 1969, the Family were rounded up and charged with murder. Manson, Krenwinkel, Atkins and Leslie van Houten were tried together and, on 19 April 1971, after one of the most extraordinary trials in California's history, they were convicted and sentenced to death for the Tate/LaBianca murders. At a later trial, Manson, Bruce Davis and Clem Grogan were convicted of murder and conspiracy in two other murders.

Although no further charges were brought, there is reason to believe that many other murders could be laid to the account of Charles Manson's Family, including several of their own members. Vincent Bugliosi, prosecutor in the Tate/LaBianca trial, in his book *Helter Skelter* does not dismiss Manson's own claim to have committed thirty-five murders – indeed, he now feels that it may have been an uncharacteristic understatement.

20 April

1934 (Scotland) Jeannie Donald was the thirty-eight-year-old wife of an Aberdeen hairdresser; her victim was eight-year-old Helen Priestley. Helen lived with her parents on the first floor of a tenement at 61 Urquart Road, Aberdeen. Although the Donalds lived on the floor below, Mrs Donald and Mrs Priestley had not spoken to each other for five years, though it is unlikely that either could remember why.

At 12.20 on the afternoon of 20 April 1934, young Helen came home from school for lunch, and after finishing her meal she rushed off to visit a friend, Mrs Robertson. Helen returned home at around 1.10 and was sent out by her mother to get a loaf of bread; she was seen by several people walking back from the shop at about 1.30, but Helen Priestley was never seen alive after that.

When her daughter failed to come home, Mrs Priestley

alerted friends and neighbours and called the police. During the rest of that day and through the night, search parties scoured the district and beyond. At five o'clock in the morning one of the volunteers entered 61 Urquart Road to tell Mrs Priestley he was back after a few hours' sleep to resume the hunt. Here, in the half-light of the communal lobby, his search ended. In a recess under the stairs was a brown sack; inside the sack was the body of little Helen Priestley.

At first it seemed to the police that Helen had been strangled and sexually assaulted. It was only after the post-mortem report had been delivered that it was known that some sharp instrument had been pushed into her body in order to simulate rape. The only reason for this, it was guessed, was that Helen had been killed by a woman who had faked the abuse to deflect suspicion. Cause of death was determined as asphyxia, possibly from manual strangulation.

By the week following Helen Priestley's murder, the investigating team had picked up the gossip about a long-standing feud between Jeannie Donald and the Priestleys (Helen had often taunted Mrs Donald with the nickname 'Coconut'). After lengthy questioning at Urquart Road, Mrs Donald and her husband Alexander were taken into custody. Two weeks later when his alibi had been checked, Alexander Donald was released; Jeannie was committed for trial. The prosecution case was an impressive array of scientific evidence from pathologists, chemists and bacteriologists. In her own defence, Mrs Donald said only that she had nothing to do with the killing, and saw no reason why she should go into the witness box and repeat it. The trial occupied six days, at the end of which the jury returned a majority verdict of thirteen 'guilty' and two 'not proven'.

Jeannie Donald was sentenced to death, though it was

subsequently commuted to life imprisonment. She was released on special licence on 26 June 1944.

21 April

1972 (USA) On Friday 21 April 1972, twenty-five-year-old Charlie Simpson, a farm-hand out of Holden, was driven into Harrisonville, Missouri, by a friend. With his shoulder-length black hair and a waist-length army fatigue jacket Simpson cut a bizarre figure as he jumped from the car and ran across Independence Street into Pearl Street. As he ran he spotted two young officers from the local police force, Donald Marler and Francis Wirt, approaching him. Without any hesitation, Simpson pulled an M1 semi-automatic carbine from under his jacket, dropped into a crouch position and opened fire on the policemen. The officers never had a chance to return fire, they dropped to the pavement, both badly wounded. Simpson ran over to where they were lying and stood over them lining up his gun for more shots. Marler managed to scream: 'Don't shoot me. God. Oh God', before Simpson fired two further bursts into both men. Marler was hit twice in the chest, the abdomen and through each hand and Wirt twice in the abdomen and three times in one arm. Horrified passers-by threw themselves to the ground and cars in the street crashed into one another. Charlie Simpson ran into a nearby bank building and indiscriminately fired another burst of shots into a wall. Two book-keepers were wounded by ricochets. Then he ran from the bank, down the street in the direction of the local sheriff's office. On the way Orville T. Allen, the manager of a dry-cleaning store, was getting out of his car on the other side of the street; Simpson fired a burst from his carbine and Allen fell into the gutter riddled with bullets.

From inside his office sheriff Bill Gough heard sounds, but did not immediately associate them with gunfire; so he went outside to see what the noise was about and caught one of

Simpson's wild shots in his right shoulder before managing to duck back into his office and take cover. Simpson made no further move towards the sheriff, but simply turned on his heels and walked back towards the main square where he stopped, put the barrel of the M1 into his mouth and blew the back of his head off.

22 April

1930 (England) On this bright Tuesday morning William Henry Podmore, a petty crook turned killer, breathed his last on the scaffold at Winchester Prison. It was the final act in a sordid crime which would, but for the ingenious use of a means of photographic testimony, have remained uncelebrated by either historian or criminologist.

It was on 10 January 1929 that the body of fifty-seven-year-old Vivian Messiter was found at the Southampton depot of the Wolf's Head Oil Company, of which Messiter was the local agent and a director. He had been missing since the previous October, so the remains were in a badly decomposed condition. In fact it was not until a detailed post-mortem examination had been carried out that it was discovered that he had not been shot through the head, but rather bludgeoned to death with a hammer. Messiter's premises had been robbed, but his business documents had been left; it was these papers that would provide the clue to his killer.

A receipt book was found from which the first nine pages had been torn, leaving it blank. However, on the tenth page a blind impression was clearly visible of the writing on the previous receipt. Dated 28 October 1928, it read: 'Received from Wolf's Head Oil Company commission on Cromer and Bartlett, 5 gals at *6d* = *2/6d* W. F. Thomas.' Routine investigation revealed that the firm of Cromer and Bartlett did not exist. To detectives, the implication was clear: 'W. F. Thomas' was claiming commission on bogus sales. The signature on the receipt was found to be identical to the one at the foot of a letter found at Messiter's lodgings; it was an application for a job as salesman at the Wolf's Head depot. The man calling himself William Thomas had long flown from the address on the letter, and had been up to mischief in London, where he was arrested. Now it was learnt that Thomas was in reality William Henry Podmore, a criminal hailing from Manchester, in which city he was wanted for a number of car and motorcycle frauds. So, while the Southampton police were busy linking Podmore to the murder of Vivian Messiter, their Midlands colleagues obligingly kept him under lock and key for the Manchester jobs.

On his release from prison on 17 December 1929, William Podmore was immediately rearrested and charged with murder; later that same month he made his appearance at Winchester Assizes. Despite a spirited insistence on his own innocence, the case against Podmore was by now watertight. The fact of his dishonesty in charging Messiter commission on sales which he had not made was demonstrated to the court in a series of photographs made by the police photographic laboratory. By taking the pictures at an angle to a strong light, it was possible literally to 'read' the indented words. On top of this, two of Podmore's fellow-prisoners gave evidence that he had confessed the murder to them. He was convicted, sentenced to death and later hanged.

23 April

1992 (USA) Billy Wayne White was executed in Texas, the forty-seventh since reintroduction of the death penalty in 1976. White had been convicted of the fatal shooting of a sixty-five-year-old furniture store owner, Martha Spinks, during a robbery. In his appeal against sentence, Billy White's defence attorney claimed that White was mentally retarded and that, as the victim had sprayed mace into his eyes, this had provoked him. Neither of these justifications had been offered at the original trial (through which White mostly slept) and the appeal was dismissed. The execution at Huntsville Prison was delayed for more than half an hour while officials searched for a suitable vein to give the lethal injection.

24 April

1650 (Ireland) Patrick Fleming was executed in Dublin for a series of horrific murders and mutilations: 'In particular, Sir Donagh O'Brien, whose nose, ears and lips he did cut off for making some small resistence when he robbed him' (*The Newgate Calendar*).

25 April

1958 (USA) In 1957, during the time David Early was serving a term in Leavenworth Penitentiary, he warned a prison psychiatrist that he would commit murder as soon as he was released. He said: 'I will get back at my landlady. I will get back there when I get out and I will stomp her over the head, tie her up and rape and finally kill her. I will make it to Death Row yet. I have an uncle-in-law who is a corporation lawyer. I have a scheme for holding him up for ransom money and I would kidnap his family and threaten to kill his children for ransom. Right now I am doing an illegal sentence and when I get out of this I am going to kill people to get money if necessary.' Not a great literary speech, but clear enough to anyone with half an ear that David F. Early needed watching. Instead, on 22 April 1958 they released him on parole. Early travelled back to Denver, Colorado, though he did not look for his former landlady; instead, on 25 April, he went to the home of his uncle-in-law, the lawyer, and walked in through an unlocked door. Once inside Early found a rifle and a pistol, and as the family arrived home separately, he held them up at gunpoint and bound all four – father, mother, son and daughter.

Originally Early had planned to leave the house with the money he had stolen but on a whim, he changed his mind and shot and killed the lawyer, his wife and fifteen-year-old daughter. The seventeen-year-old boy succeeded in freeing himself from his bonds and escaped. As he was running away, Early shot at him but missed.

David Early was captured while driving away from the house, and when questioned later he said: 'I killed three people. I killed them with no compunction. It didn't mean any more for me to kill them than to turn off the lights.' He added that he had resented the family's wealth and respectability ever since he was a child. Early was tried and convicted on three counts of first-degree murder and sentenced to death. He was executed in the gas chamber at Colorado State Penitentiary on 11 August 1961.

26 April

1928 (USA) Described variously as a 'gin-guzzling flapper' or a 'fun-loving wife', the real Eva Rablen probably fell somewhere between the two. The reason why she married the much older, deaf and retiring Carroll Rablen is a mystery, though it makes why she killed him easier to understand. Given his nature and inclination, Carroll excluded himself from most of his wife's 'fun-loving' activities, being content to drive her to whatever dance-hall or speakeasy took her fancy, sitting in the car outside until she had finished enjoying herself, and then driving her home.

The Friday evening of 26 April 1928 had followed the regular pattern, and Carroll Rablen was sitting outside the Tuttleton school-house in Tuolumne, California, while Eva was inside stretching her legs on the Charleston. At midnight Eva took her husband a cup of coffee which he accepted gratefully; that is, until the first convulsion shot like lightning through his body and he fell unconscious across the seat.

It is a curious fact that what seemed like such an obvious homicide at first exhibited no sign of foul play. An autopsy had revealed no trace of poison in the body, and a search of the school-house and the surrounding areas could not turn up anything like a poison bottle. Indeed, the investigation might well have ground to a halt had it not been for Carroll's father. Never a great fan of his daughter-in-law, the old man had been convinced Eva was just after Carroll's money. Now, thanks to his persistence, another search was made of the school building, and what should be found but a bottle of strychnine. Strychnine sold by a local pharmacist to Mrs Rablen 'to kill rats'. A second post-mortem was carried out on Carroll Rablen's body, this time by the legendary forensic chemist Dr Edward Heinrich. Heinrich found traces of strychnine in the internal organs as well as in the coffee cup the victim had drunk from and the stains where the contents were spilled in the car.

The trial of Eva Rablen was such a sensation that the preliminaries were transferred from the courtroom to an open-air dance pavilion to accommodate the thrill-seekers. However, the trial proper took place in the rather more dignified surroundings of the Superior Court – where Eva Rablen pleaded guilty and received a life term in San Quentin.

27 April

1911 (England) This was the night on which George Baron Pateman lay in wait for his girlfriend outside her employer's house. As Alice Linfold turned in at the front garden gate in north-west London, Pateman cut her throat, almost severing her head from her body. Pateman, after protesting his innocence, was found to have bloodstains on his clothes. Despite the comparatively basic state of the science of serology at the time, the stains were shown to be from an anaemic person. Such as Alice Linfold.

28 April

1919 (England) When thirty-seven-year-old soldier Henry Perry returned from active service in the Middle East, he was offered temporary accommodation in the home of Walter and Alice Cornish, Mrs Cornish being a sister of Perry's stepfather. There had been friction for some time, and towards the end of April 1919 Perry was asked to leave. On the 28th of the month he returned to the house and Alice Cornish rather unwisely let him in. What happened next is detailed in Henry Perry's subsequent statement to the police: 'She gave me two or three rough words and I lost my temper. I knocked her down with the kitchen poker and carried her to the shed at the bottom of the garden. She was not dead . . . I hit her with a pickaxe and then went back to the house, got a carving fork from the drawer and stabbed her in the throat. That would be between 2 p.m. and 3 p.m. I covered her with some boards and rubbish.'

Perry also cut off Mrs Cornish's finger with a knife in order to get hold of her wedding ring. Then he lay in wait until young Marie and Alice Cornish returned home from school and battered them to death with a hammer before throwing their bodies down into the cellar. When Walter Cornish returned from work and found Perry there he threatened to call the police and he too was killed – felled with an axe.

Henry Perry's trial opened at the Old Bailey on 27 May 1919, before Mr Justice Darling. In Perry's defence, one of the foremost specialists in mental illness Sir Robert Armstrong Jones presented expert testimony in support of his plea of insanity. Sir Robert told the court that during his war service, Henry Perry had been wounded in the head and taken prisoner by the Turks. During this incarceration, he had been beaten on the soles of the feet, banged on the head with a rifle butt and kept in a dungeon. The implication was that this had unsettled his mind; Perry himself had claimed that 'voices' instructed him to murder Mr and Mrs Cornish and their children.

For the prosecution, Dr Higson, the Medical Officer at Brixton Prison, claimed that although he was of low intelligence, Perry could not be called a mental defective in the legal sense; that he had not been insane at the time of the killings. It was a view with which the jury clearly concurred, because they found Henry Perry guilty of murder. He was hanged on 10 July 1919.

29 April

1955 (England) On the evening of 29 April 1955, forty-six-year-old Mrs Elizabeth Currell made her daily pilgrimage to the Potter's Bar golf course with her pet corgi. It was almost a ritual – the path along the railway embankment, past the wartime pillbox and on to the links. But tonight it would be different; lurking in the shadows of the pillbox was the last person who would see Mrs Currell alive. As she reached the seventeenth tee, the man pounced, trying ineffectually to strangle her, then punching, struggling, till his hand reached out and grabbed the heavy iron tee-marker . . .

At dawn the following day a police constable found Elizabeth Currell's body. Pathologist Dr Francis Camps confirmed that she had been battered to death; rape had clearly been considered, but abandoned. The killer had left one clue – a fragmentary palmprint on his weapon, a mark that, but for his youth, would have hanged him.

It is often rightly assumed that the rapist thought to be on foot, lurking in a particular dark and isolated place, will be a local. It was based on this assumption that a decision was made to carry out a mass palmprinting in the Potter's Bar area, including all the male occupants of close on 7,000 homes, plus the employees who travelled into the area to work. A team of fifty-seven detectives was mobilised to take the prints, while twelve experienced officers from the fingerprint branch were responsible for the work of comparison.

By the middle of August 9,000 palmars had been taken and the experts were half-way through comparing them. On the 19th of the month, print 4,605, taken from seventeen-year-old Michael Queripel, matched. As profiled earlier, Queripel was a local youth, living with his parents and brother in a house close to the golf course. In fact, he had already been questioned by the police five days after the murder. On 3 July he had refused to have his palmprint taken, claiming that it was 'against his principles'; only the intervention of his brother persuaded Queripel to comply.

After insisting that Mrs Currell was already dead when he found her on the golf course, Michael Queripel confessed to her murder. His trial lasted a bare five minutes and he was ordered to be detained during Her Majesty's pleasure.

30 April

1986 (England) It is usual in Great Britain (and in most other countries which adopt the 'English' system of law) for it to take approximately one year for a case to come to trial after an accused has been charged. So it was not until April 1987 that the British public heard the full story of the tragic death of Jeanne Sutcliffe and her daughter Heidi on 30 April of the previous year. The following entry is derived from trial reports.

> *1 April 1987*: A jury at Bristol Crown Court was told how Paul Sutcliffe, a teacher, arrived home to find the bodies of his wife and baby daughter lying side by side in the sewing room of their home at Westbury, Wiltshire. In the dock, Mrs Heather Arnold, a mathematics teacher and a colleague of Paul Sutcliffe, had pleaded not guilty to two counts of murder. The court was told that Mrs Sutcliffe had probably let her killer into the house in

order to sell her some dressmaking cotton (she ran a small business from home), and as she bent down to get the item, was struck on the back of the head; afterwards, baby Heidi was also slain. Mr David Elfer QC, prosecuting, said that a household axe had been used in the attack, the head of which had been found in Mrs Arnold's possession. Flakes of red paint from the handle had been found on Jeanne Sutcliffe's body and in the accused's car.

6 April 1987: Mrs Arnold's solicitor daughter gave evidence that during the May Bank Holiday [1986] her mother confided that she had found a small axe in her garage and had cut up the handle, but kept the head. Mrs Arnold, clearly distressed, had said: 'I didn't do it.'

Next, a detective constable who had been working undercover on the case, posing as a council refuse collector, told the jury that he had taken a white carrier bag from Mrs Arnold which was later found to contain three charred pieces of an axe handle.

7 April 1987: Further police evidence told how, in custody, Heather Arnold had confessed to the double murder and signed the notes; however, on the advice of her solicitor she had later denied going to the Sutcliffe home on the day of the killings.

8 April 1987: Mrs Arnold took the witness stand to claim that she had innocently found the murder weapon, but had felt some 'inexplicable' need to dispose of it . . .

15 April 1987: The jury – reduced to eleven members after one of their number was incapacitated – retired to consider their verdict, though it was not until the following day that they were able to return a unanimous judgement of guilty. Sentencing her to life imprisonment, Mr Justice Henry told Heather Arnold: 'The jury has rightly convicted you of these two terrible murders, murders which have shocked and horrified the community . . .'

May

1 May

1868 (England) Nineteen-year-old railwayman Thomas Wells shot stationmaster Edward Walshe over some minor and apparently well-deserved reprimand concerning his work. Quickly arrested near the scene of the crime, Dover Priory station, Wells was tried, convicted and executed. The only thing to elevate this sordid crime to forensic interest was that Wells was the first capitally convicted felon to be hanged behind prison walls (13 August 1868) following the abolition of public executions.

2 May

1924 (England) 'We are police officers, is that your bag?'

'I believe it is.'

'You will have to accompany us to the police station.'

'Rubbish!'

The indignant captive is one of Britain's most notorious murderers; the bag contains an assortment of clothing heavily stained with blood and grease, a large cook's knife and a racket bag with the initials E.B.K. The date is 2 May 1924.

Patrick Herbert Mahon was a ladies' man; he liked them and they liked him. Which was a pity, because Mahon was already married. He was married when he met Emily Beilby Kaye, a secretary at the firm he visited in his capacity as a salesman. It is certain that Miss Kaye took the affair of the heart which followed a great deal more seriously than Patrick Mahon; in fact she was all for marriage. It was in the early days of April 1924 that Emily insisted on what she called a 'love experiment'. This briefly meant that they would spend a length of time together in preparation for their future life together. To this end Mahon was badgered into renting a bungalow on a lonely stretch of shingle beach called the Crumbles. While they were at the house, Emily decided that they should emigrate to South Africa; Mahon refused. Emily decided that Mahon should travel up to London and get a passport for the purpose; he refused. This had the effect of infuriating Emily Kaye, and she no doubt spoke some harsh words; they were to be her last. On that evening of 15 April 1924, Patrick Mahon battered poor Emily over the head and set about dismembering her corpse with a cook's knife and a saw bought specially for the purpose. Then he disposed of the body, a great deal of it on the living-room fire, crushing the bones with a hammer and scattering them on the beach outside the cottage. When he later visited the scene in his capacity as pathologist, Sir Bernard Spilsbury described the carnage as the worst it had been his misfortune to examine.

Meanwhile, back in London a suspicious Mrs Mahon had gone through her husband's pockets and found a left-luggage ticket. And that is how detective-sergeants Frew and Thompson came to be waiting for Mahon at Waterloo railway station.

In a celebrated trial Mahon was found guilty and sentenced to death. On 9 September he faced the hangman in the execution shed at Wandsworth Prison.

3 May

1957 (England) A doctor summoned by Kenneth Barlow to his home in Bradford, Yorkshire, was told that Barlow had found his wife lying dead in the bath. Thanks to meticulous examination by pathologists, two tiny needle-marks, consistent with hypodermic injection were discovered. This was also consistent with Barlow's boast to a work colleague that insulin injection was the perfect murder method. Barlow was tried, convicted (the first for this type of poison) and imprisoned. He was released in 1984 at the age of sixty-five.

4 May

1957 (England) Thirty-four-year-old Polish art student Ginter Wiora stabbed his girlfriend Shirley Marguerite Allen with a sword at a house in Bayswater where they both had rooms. When police arrived after Miss Allen's screams had roused a neighbour, they found Wiora in a gas-filled room having also stabbed himself with another sword and cut his wrists with a bread-knife. Even so he lived, was convicted of manslaughter, and confined to Broadmoor.

5 May

1960 (Wales) It was, to say the least, a bit of a shock when, on 5 May 1960, Leslie Harvey prised open the landing cupboard in his mother's house at Rhyl. Mrs Sarah Jane Harvey was sixty-five years old and had been taken into hospital for routine observation so her son and his wife were taking the opportunity to decorate the house for her. Leslie recalled that when he was a child, that particular cupboard had been out of bounds. Inside was the dusty corpse of a long-previous tenant named Frances Knight. The body was in a doubled-up position, and clothed in a now-faded and cobweb-encrusted nightdress and dressing gown. The skin was shrunken and leathery, and what flesh remained was as hard as stone. The whole body had, by the natural process of warm dry air rising and circulating around the cupboard, become mummified; which is how it had remained undetected for so long without the tell-tale odour of decomposition. It was clear that Mrs Harvey would have a bit of explaining to do.

The police, not surprisingly, were treating the incident as

a murder investigation – particularly in view of the pathologist's revelation that the body appeared to have a ligature round its neck. There was no record of a death certificate being issued in Mrs Knight's name, and more puzzling still, Rhyl council were still paying out her maintenance cheque – to a Mrs Harvey, who claimed her lodger was housebound. She was certainly that. On 9 June Sarah Jane Harvey was arrested on a charge of murder.

At trial it was the prosecution's case that Mrs Harvey had strangled her lodger some time in 1940 in order to avail herself of Mrs Knight's weekly £2 maintenance money. In her defence Mrs Harvey insisted that the victim had died of natural causes and she had panicked and hidden the body. As for the stocking found round her throat, it was suggested that she was employing an old folk remedy for a sore throat – perhaps she had accidentally strangled herself.

It was all very uncertain, and it must be seen as an act of compassion towards this elderly, frail woman, accused of a twenty-year-old crime, that the trial was stopped after three days. She was instead convicted of fraudulently obtaining money and sentenced to fifteen months.

6 May

1927 (England) The cabbie had picked up the military-looking gentleman with the trunk practically opposite the Rochester Row police station in south-west London. It was just after midday on Friday 6 May 1927. Man and trunk were ferried to the left-luggage office at Charing Cross station where the luggage was deposited. It was only on the following Monday that things began to step out of the ordinary. For a start, the trunk had begun to smell most offensively; and when a policeman was summoned to open it, it was found to contain the piecemeal body of a woman neatly wrapped in brown-paper parcels.

It was Sir Bernard Spilsbury whose job it became to piece

together the dismembered parts of the unfortunate victim, and found he had the remains of a plump lady of about thirty-five who had been asphyxiated after being beaten. The first clue to the woman's identity was the name tag 'P. Holt' on a piece of underwear in the trunk. Although Mrs Holt clearly had no connection with the tragedy, she did recall that one of her previous employees, Minnie Alice Bonati, had stolen some of her clothing. Mrs Bonati, a prostitute, had last been seen on 4 May. A routine search of the premises from which the trunk had been driven revealed that one of the occupants of the offices was John Robinson, who had not been seen for a few days. One other clue which would prove significant was a bloodstained matchstick caught in a wicker basket.

When John Robinson was finally located he denied all knowledge of the crime. It was the bloody match that broke his confidence. And then he had a story to tell; though not, of course, the truth. He had picked Minnie up, he said, at Victoria station and taken her back to the office. She had become abusive, demanding money and threatening violence; they struggled, the woman fell, knocking herself unconscious on a coal-bucket. Then, in a panic, he fled. Next morning Robinson was horrified to find the body still lying on the floor where it had fallen and decided to get rid of it. He made no attempt to deny the business of the dismemberment, or of the trunk – only the killing.

That, however, was not the version offered by the prosecution at Robinson's trial; no unfortunate accident, but cold-blooded murder and grisly dismemberment. It was certainly the version the jury preferred, and John Robinson was sentenced to death. It is a measure of the man's character that, when asked by the judge why he did not seek help when Mrs Bonati fell, he replied: 'I did not see it in that light.' Robinson was executed at Pentonville Prison in August 1927.

7 May

1992 (USA) Justin Lee May was executed by lethal injection at Huntsville, Texas. May had been convicted of shooting a shopkeeper during a robbery in 1978, although he had consistently claimed that he was framed. May's final appeal failed just minutes before his execution.

Meanwhile, on the same day, Arkansas was pumping a lethal cocktail into Death Row inmate Steven Douglas Hill. Hill was accused of the murder of an Arkansas state police investigator in 1984. At the age of twenty-five he had been the youngest prisoner awaiting the death sentence. A second man charged with Hill, Michael Anthony Cox, claimed after the trial that it had been he, not Steven Hill, who fired the fatal bullet. Unfortunately, Cox's testimony was considered too unreliable to amount to grounds for Hill to appeal. On the morning of 7 May, Arkansas governor Bill Clinton denied a clemency plea and the Supreme Court rejected a final appeal by Hill's lawyers. He died at Little Rock.

8 May

1968 (England) Ronald and Reginald Kray, leaders of a notorious east London gang, were arrested and subsequently tried and convicted of crimes of violence including murder. The twins were sentenced to life; Reggie remains in prison, Ronnie was later committed to Broadmoor, where he died on 17 March 1995.

9 May

1923 (England) The following description of one of London's most controversial murder cases was given in court by a milliner named Jessie Findlay:

> I was returning home along Acre Lane [Brixton] at about 9.40 on 9 May. I heard someone moaning and, as I got to the top of Bay-Tree Road, I could see two

> people struggling, but I could not detect whether they were men, women or boys until one cried out: 'Save me! He is killing me!' He repeated that twice, and then I saw the other one throw him to the ground and shoot him twice. The man who was shot was lying on the ground, apparently on his side; the other man was crouching close to him. There were no lights in Bay-Tree Road except just one by the bend, and it was nearly dark. I did not see anyone else near the two who were struggling. The last I saw of the man who fired the shots he was running round the bend of Bay-Tree Road towards Brixton Hill. The man who had been shot began to stagger up and come towards Acre Lane. I ran for a policeman.

The man later identified as cab-driver Jacob Dickey died a few moments later from head wounds. Lying in the road close to Dickey's taxi were a number of items that would later prove significant, among them a walking-stick of a distinctive design which was identified as the property of one James (called 'Eddie') Vivian. Vivian was picked up and made a statement that led to the immediate arrest of a twenty-two-year-old man named Alexander Campbell 'Scottie' Mason. Both men were convicted criminals, and when Mason came to trial in July 1923 Vivian was the chief prosecution witness.

The story Vivian told was this. He and 'Scottie' had been jointly convicted of burglary in January 1922, though Vivian had been released early. When he was let out on 5 May 1923, Mason went straight to Vivian who put him up and lent him some money; with which, so the tale went, he bought a gun 'to stick-up a taxi-driver'. Although they had planned another joint burglary on the night of the 9th, Vivian claimed he was ill and had to remain at home. Mason went out on his own mischief and returned to the house in a dishevelled state complaining: 'I have made a terrible mess of things. I have shot a taxi-driver.'

Of course, 'Scottie' Mason denied every word of this. According to him Vivian was with him that night, and had picked up Dickey's cab outside the Trocadero because he might be willing to join them as a get-away driver in the burglary. The plan was for Mason to meet Vivian and the cabbie at Bay-Tree Road. When they arrived Vivian and Dickey were already in some kind of dispute which spilled out of the cab on to the road where Vivian shot the driver. Mason had run off followed by Vivian.

It was quite clear that the truth had never been any great priority of either of these men. However, it was the version told by Eddie Vivian that the jury chose to buy, and 'Scottie' Mason was sentenced to hang. It was always the view of Superintendent Francis Carlin, who was prominent in the case, that the evidence of Vivian was too unreliable for a safe conviction, and although the then Home Secretary declined to set up the called-for inquiry, he did reprieve Mason. After spending fourteen years in prison, Mason was released in 1937 and was reported killed on active service during the Second World War.

10 May

1982 (England) Sixty-six-year-old Margaret Johnson and her friend Ann Lee usually walked their dogs every afternoon on a common near their homes at Aldershot, Hampshire; the afternoon of 10 May was no different, except that this would be the last time.

It was in the latter part of the afternoon that passers-by on the common saw the two dogs, the red setter and the labrador. Not an unusual sight considering the location. What *was* unusual was that this particular pair were keeping guard over the dead bodies of their owners; Mrs Johnson had been stabbed five times, Mrs Lee eleven times. There had been no sexual motive, nor did it look as if either of the victims had been robbed.

Within hours of the discovery, the local police received two telephone calls, both sounding as though they were from the same person, both accusing 'Peter Fell' of the murders. Naturally police officers paid a visit to the twenty-three-year-old former soldier's bedsitter, but he was not at home. A check with employers revealed that he had been at work at the time of the murder and the telephone caller was put down as a crank.

It was more than a year later, and the murders on the common remained unsolved, when the Bournemouth police had a series of no fewer than eleven telephone calls accusing the same Peter Fell of being the Aldershot killer. Fell was arrested at a Brighton hotel where he was employed as a porter. Transferred to Farnborough police station, near Aldershot, Peter Fell confessed that he had killed the two women because they had laughed at him – and besides, one of them looked like his mother whom he had always hated for getting divorced from his father. As for the alibi, the factory rechecked its records and found that they had made a mistake – Fell had not turned up at work on 10 May until *after* the killings.

In July 1984, Peter Fell appeared at Winchester Crown Court charged with murder. There was no forensic evidence linking him to the crime, and he had retracted his confession. The difficulty faced by the jury was illustrated by the fact that it took them more than twenty-five hours to convict Fell, and even then it was only by a majority. Peter Fell was sentenced to two terms of life imprisonment.

11 May

1812 (England) On the evening of 11 May 1812 a furtive figure could be seen skulking in the House of Commons, just behind the folding doors which lead into the body of the

House. At five o'clock the Prime Minister, the Right Honourable Spencer Perceval, advanced up the lobby. As he did so the hidden assassin stepped out of the shadows and aimed a pistol squarely at Perceval's heart. Unable to utter more than the word 'Murder!', the Prime Minister staggered and fell dead to the floor.

The gunman made no attempt to escape as he was taken. Already there were those present who knew the villain to be John Bellingham, a deranged individual who had been bombarding Members with complaints about some real or imagined injustices suffered while working in Russia. Bellingham was repatriated back to Britain in 1809 and spent the next three years demanding compensation from the British government. On 23 March 1812 he had sent one final letter, to the magistrates at Bow Street, advising them that he hoped to get his demands met 'in order to avert so abhorrent but compulsive an alternative'. On 11 May he felt compelled to the abhorrent alternative.

John Bellingham's trial at the Old Bailey on 15 May was a spectacle if not of law then of the quantity and quality of those in attendance. One description describes how 'The judges at ten o'clock took their seats on each side of the Lord Mayor; and the recorder, the Duke of Clarence, the Marquis Wellesley and almost all the Aldermen of the City of London occupied the bench.' But Bellingham's cause, as ever, was a lost one, and an attempt at an insanity defence was a forlorn hope. After only fourteen minutes the jury came to the conclusion that he knew quite well what he was doing, and he was ordered for execution on the following Monday.

12 May

1961 (England) 13 May 1961 was a beautiful spring morning; a morning that made David Pilcher pleased he was a milkman. Until he got to his regular delivery at Pantile Bungalow, where what he saw would spoil his days for a long time to come. Lying across the porchway was the savagely battered body of an almost naked woman. There was blood everywhere, and beside the corpse was the bloody double barrel section of a broken shotgun. Inside the house police would later find the body of a man. The victims were Mr Hubert Buxton and his wife Alice.

Soon Pantile Bungalow was playing host to some of Scotland Yard's finest detectives, headed by Detective Chief Superintendent John Du Rose, whose legendary speed in solving crimes had earnt him the nickname 'four-day Johnny'. The Buxtons, he learnt, were a well liked, if quiet, couple – certainly not the kind to end up as murder victims. It was John Du Rose's painstaking search of the house that solved that riddle. On the floor of the bedroom he found some scraps of a torn-up letter which had been written to Alice Buxton at an address in Belgium. It was a letter of some passion which ended 'bye bye, Hendryk, kiss you. XXX'.

It had been about a year after their arrival at Aldington that the Buxtons and the Niemasz family became entwined. Alice had met Grypa Niemasz on a bus and she had introduced her husband – Hendryk. Things were beginning to make sense to the murder team, and before long they were talking to Mr Hendryk Niemasz himself. From the first he denied he had even been near the Buxtons' home on the night of 12 May; then he passed off the letter to Alice as one of friendship: 'Everyone puts kisses!' However, a check of the smallholding to the rear of the Niemasz house turned up the broken stock of a shotgun buried beside some cartridges.

Niemasz was eventually convicted on overwhelming evidence of the double murder and received the death penalty. But why had he killed the Buxtons? According to Mrs

Niemasz, Alice was demanding that Hendryk run away with her. However, Hendryk told the police another version – that Alice had given him a pistol and insisted that he not only shoot Hubert, but Grypa as well. The exact truth of what went on in Hendryk's mind we will never know. He was hanged on 8 September 1961.

13 May

1748 (England)

This sinner, William York, was but just turned ten years of age when he committed the dreadful crime. He was a pauper in the poorhouse belonging to the parish of Eyke, in Suffolk, and was committed, on the coroner's inquest, to Ipswich Gaol for the murder of Susan Mahew, another child, of five years of age, who had been his bed fellow. The following is his confession, taken and attested by a Justice of the Peace, and which was, in part, proved on his trial, with many corroborating circumstances of his guilt.

He said that a trifling quarrel happening between them on the 13th of May 1748, about ten in the morning, he struck her with his open hand and made her cry. That she going out of the house to the dunghill, opposite the door, he followed her with a hook in his hand with an intent to kill her. But before he came up to her he put down the hook and went into the house for a knife. He then came out again, took hold of the girl's left hand, and cut her wrist all round to the bone with his knife. Then he threw her down, and cut her to the bone just above the elbow of the same arm. After this he set his foot on her stomach, and cut her right arm round about, and to the bone, both on the wrist and above the elbow. Then he thought she would not die, and therefore took the hook and cut her left thigh to the bone. His next care was to conceal the murder. For this purpose he filled a pail with water at a ditch and washed the blood off the child's body, buried it in the dunghill, together with the blood that was spilt on the ground, and made the dunghill as smooth as he could. Afterwards he washed the knife and the hook and carried them into the house. He washed the blood off his own clothes, hid the child's clothes in an old chamber, and then came down to get his breakfast.

This boy murderer was found guilty and sentence of death was pronounced against him; but he was respited from time to time, and, on account of his tender years, was at length pardoned.

(*The Newgate Calendar*)

14 May

1968 (Scotland) Maxwell and Sheila Garvie were married in 1955 and had worked the farm at Carnbeg, Kincardineshire ever since. Although the farm kept him busy, Max Garvie still found time to fly light aircraft around Europe and establish the local branch of the Scottish National Party. He also founded a naturist club, which gives some indication of his other interests. Twenty-two-year-old Brian Tevendale and his sister Trudie Birse met Garvie through the SNP, and were regular house guests at the farm. What went on between the foursome would later emerge in court, but it can be said here that it had little to do with fatstock prices and milk yield. By 1968 the Garvie marriage was beginning to find itself in serious difficulty; Sheila had run off with Brian Tevendale at one stage, and though she had now returned to the farm things were very uneasy. On 14 May, Max Garvie left a meeting of the SNP at around ten o'clock and simply disappeared. It was not until a week later that his sister reported him missing.

For reasons best known to herself, Sheila Garvie hinted to her mother that Max was dead and that Brian Tevendale had something to do with it; her mother, wise woman, took the story to the local police. Not long afterwards Sheila and Tevendale were in custody, soon to be joined by a friend named Alan Peters. In August Maxwell Garvie's body was found bludgeoned and shot through the head. And in November Sheila and her two co-defendants appeared before an Aberdeen court.

It was Tevendale's claim that Sheila had called him to the farm after a row with Max over his 'unnatural demands' (a coy reference to anal intercourse) because he had threatened to kill her if he didn't get his way. As they struggled for the gun Garvie was accidentally shot. According to Tevendale Garvie was lying dead on the floor when he arrived. However, Sheila and Alan Peters had a different narrative. This involved Peters and Tevendale arriving at the farm together and, after Mrs Garvie had gone to bed, Brian Tevendale murdering her husband.

It was difficult to decide who was telling the truth, if any of them were. It was only left for the jury to convict Sheila Garvie and Brian Tevendale of Max Garvie's murder. But to everybody's disbelief, the case against Alan Peters was found 'not proven', that uniquely Scottish verdict.

15 May

1948 (England) In the early morning of this Saturday, Peter Griffiths abducted three-year-old June Ann Devaney from her cot in the children's ward of Queen's Park Hospital, Blackburn, and savagely murdered her. In one of the most remarkable fingerprinting operations in police history, 47,000 sets of prints were taken from every male over the age of sixteen who had been in Blackburn over 14/15 May. Griffiths was eventually charged with murder on 13 August, put on trial on 15 October, and executed on

19 November. On 3 November all the fingerprints of local residents were ceremoniously pulped.

16 May

1878 (USA) It was a long and busy life for Lydia Sherman, the 'Queen of Poisoners', and when she died in prison on 16 May 1878 the world lost one of the most prolific and successful poisoners in the criminal history of America. According to her own estimate she had killed at least eleven people, all for profit, though there could, she added, have been a dozen or so more.

The first murder that we are aware of was that of her husband, a policeman named Edward Struck, some time in the 1860s. There was a dual purpose in disposing of Mr Struck – the obvious one was insurance money, but after giving birth to six of his children, Lydia decided to undertake a bit of serious birth-control. In fact this was a very successful venture, and there was enough rat poison left over to dispose of the six children as well. Thus Lydia Sherman became at one and the same time wealthy and free. By 1868 Lydia had remarried to a rich, elderly farmer called Hurlbrut, out of New Haven, Connecticut. Within two years she was the widow Hurlbrut, and just squandering her way through the last of the poor man's hard-earned savings. In the case of Nelson Sherman, Lydia had to work her way up from housekeeper to wife, though this simply prolonged the process, and along the way she managed to poison Sherman's teenage daughter and his baby. On 12 May 1871 Nelson himself succumbed to a cup of Lydia's special hot chocolate.

Perhaps she was getting careless. But this time the local doctor called in a second opinion on Nelson Sherman; and the second opinion called in a third. The children were exhumed and also found to have died from arsenic poisoning. Dr Beardsley lost no time in passing his findings on to the police; and they lost no time in hauling Mrs Sherman back from her hidey-hole in New York to face trial in Connecticut. The Queen of Poisoners was eventually found guilty only of second-degree murder, which is perhaps a reflection on the mainly circumstantial nature of the evidence; it was, anyway, sufficient to earn her a life sentence.

17 May

1929 (South Africa) Ntimane Sandwene, a Zulu working on a farm in Natal, claimed his first victim on 17 May 1929, when he shot dead a storekeeper and robbed the till of his meagre takings. For the next seven years, Sandwene would carry out a series of murder-robberies that would claim eight lives and often bring only the most pathetic financial reward. On 27 January 1933, Sandwene killed another shopkeeper, and then another. It was around this time that the local police actually interviewed Sandwene, who agreed that the crimes were scandalous, and promised to help all he could.

On 13 June 1934 he was at it again; this time the victim count was higher. The two shop-owners, Ismail Hajet and Hassan Mayat, were shot, followed by the murder in cold blood of a fourteen-year-old boy who had told Sandwene where his masters' money was. In December the assassin struck again, this time only wounding his victim, but in the following year he killed and robbed shopkeeper Abraham Hlatshwayo. So elusive was the unknown serial killer they called the 'Killer of the White Mountain' that the local Indian population were in a state of panic – particularly those who kept shops.

In the end it was not clever police work but careless killing that put Ntimane Sandwene in custody. His wife had been molested and Sandwene had followed the man to Bergville. On the way he fitted in a little financial enterprise when he attacked two Zulus on the road to rob them. He killed one, but left the other only wounded; this was the man who would identify Sandwene as his companion's killer. In police custody Ntimane Sandwene freely, and quite casually, admitted the shootings, pointing out in no uncertain terms that he did not *enjoy* killing people, he had simply done it in pursuance of a more secure financial future. The Native High Court sentenced him to death. Ntimane Sandwene was hanged at Pretoria Central Prison in May 1937.

18 May

1835 (England) Execution of Patrick Carroll, a soldier from Ballihoy, Ireland, who stabbed innkeeper Mrs Browning with his bayonet, for the insolence of repulsing his unwanted and unwelcome advances. This is the first case reported to have been tried at the Old Bailey under its new title of 'Central Criminal Court'.

19 May

1968 (England) It was the day of the 1968 Football Association Cup Final and, as is usual, the best part of the nation's male population (and more than a few women too) were glued to their television sets. The village of Buckden was no exception. In fact, it seemed on this bright afternoon that the place was deserted. Except for Richard Nilsson and eight-year-old Christopher Sabey, out riding his bicycle.

Nineteen-year-old Nilsson was a building labourer with an unhealthy attraction to young boys; indeed he had already come to the attention of the local police after trying to strangle a lad. And when, after failing to return home from his trip, Christopher Sabey's strangled body was found dumped close to a sandpit, Nilsson was the first to be questioned.

Not surprisingly, perhaps, Richard Nilsson denied any knowledge of Christopher's death. However, the police are very good at making the most of what they have, and experience has taught them that any clue is better than no clue. The forensic team had found three fawn-coloured dog hairs attached to the victim's clothing. It was the first time that such a piece of evidence had played a vital role in a murder inquiry, and a police team was dispatched to gather samples from every light-coloured dog in the vicinity. These were then sent to the Home Office Forensic Laboratory at Aldermaston and tested against the samples recovered from Christopher's clothes. After subjecting the hairs to Neutron Activation Analysis, it was found that they could have come from only three dogs – one of which belonged to Richard Nilsson. Nilsson was subsequently tried for murder, convicted and sentenced to life imprisonment.

20 May

1797 (England) By early 1797, four years into the French Wars against Napoleon, that envy of the world – the British Navy – was reduced to its lowest depth of demoralisation. The French appeared to be winning the war, Britain's allies had deserted her, and the conditions of service aboard ship were unspeakably bad.

As the conflict had escalated, the Service found itself in need of ever-increasing numbers of recruits; press gangs were prowling everywhere, tearing men from their families and loved ones, and consigning them to floating hell-holes where as many as 1,600 men were crowded cheek by jowl in a space 186 feet long by 52 wide.

Sailors' pay had not been increased by a single farthing in the years since 1652, and stood at four shillings and ninepence a week for an ordinary seaman. Pay was deducted for time spent away from duty as the result of illness, injury or wounding in battle. Not that this made much practical difference to the hapless tar, for in all but the most minor cases all illness was terminal, all wounds fatal, either as a result of the verminous living conditions or the notable lack of interest from barely qualified surgeons. To this was added the savagery of physical punishments inflicted for the most minor, or imagined, infringement of rules having no purpose by officers of unparalleled barbarity. Flogging was meted out so brutally that often hanging was offered as an alternative. Suicide frequently cheated the captain of his entertainment.

The Admiralty had been receiving complaints at least since the beginning of 1793; complaints that were ignored until, in the spring of 1797, the Fleet stationed at Spithead rose in mutiny, forcing the Admiralty, on 17 May, to implement a package of concessions including pay increases, improved conditions, the dismissal of officers accused of unnecessary brutality and a free pardon for all those engaged in the mutiny (mutiny, needless to add, was a capital offence).

A subsequent, related outbreak of mutiny was carried out by ships resting at the Nore, a sandbank in the Thames estuary, and occupied the days between 20 May and 13 June, and was a far more serious and widespread problem, extending to almost the whole Fleet. By the beginning of June, twenty-six vessels were blockading the River Thames, and the mutiny's leader, Richard Parker, had declared himself president of the 'Floating Republic'. This time the mutiny was mercilessly suppressed. One by one the crews surrendered, and when Richard Parker was taken while aboard the *Sandwich* and hanged from the yard-arm on 14 June, the affair was over. Twenty-nine of Parker's fellow-conspirators were also hanged, nine were flogged and twenty-nine imprisoned for up to eight years.

21 May

1939 (England) On the night of 21 May 1939, Walter Dinnivan was found unconscious and bleeding from head wounds in his ground-floor apartment in a house at Poole, in Dorset. He had been viciously bludgeoned and an attempt had been made to strangle him. Dinnivan was rushed to hospital by his family who had discovered him injured, but despite emergency treatment he died the following morning. Joseph Williams, a friend of the dead man for forty years, had been seen drinking with him shortly before the attack. Saliva stains found on cigarette ends in the murder flat proved to be of the same group as Williams, and his right thumb-print was matched with a print deposited on a tumbler. Despite this strong forensic evidence, Joseph Williams was acquitted at trial, but gave a free and full confession to the *News of the World*'s ace crime reporter Nicholas Rae just after leaving court; he claimed he was the new John Lee of Babbacombe – 'the man they couldn't hang' (see 23 February). There was nothing that the newspaper could do with this information until Joseph Williams died in 1951, when they printed the admission.

22 May

1992 (USA) On 22 May 1992 Robert Black was executed by lethal injection at Huntsville, Texas. Black, a former Marine Corps captain, was convicted of hiring a man to kill his wife in 1985. His grounds for appeal had been that he had taken out the contract on Mrs Black's life while suffering from post-traumatic stress disorder resulting from active service in Vietnam but his appeal was dismissed.

A curious side issue was the accusation of murder made against a *magazine*. Robert Black had hired his hit-man, John Wayne Hearn, from an advertisement in *Soldier of Fortune*, a journal used by military mercenaries to exchange information on 'commissions'. In 1988, a federal jury in Texas ruled that the magazine *was* liable for Sandra Black's death; however, the following year an appeal court over-turned the ruling. John Hearn, whose finger pulled the trigger and who had testified against Black in exchange for immunity from the death penalty, is serving life.

23 May

1701 (England) Captain William Kidd, the 'Wizard of the Seas', suffered penalty of death at Execution Dock, Wapping, for the crime of piracy. It was a multiple hanging – Kidd being dispatched along with several of his jolly jack tars – and like many such events was badly bungled. Kidd, incapably drunk, was turned off the first time, the rope snapped, and he plummeted to the ground. He was fastened for a second attempt and this time the knot loosened and again the bewildered buccaneer hit the dust. Ignoring the superstitious crowd's fear of divine intervention the hangman, who was probably no less inebriated than Captain Kidd, finally brought things under control and, for him if not for his client, it was third time lucky.

24 May

1934 (England)

> Sir, Have you ever heard of a wife poisoning her husband? Look further into the death (by heart failure) of Mr Major, of Kirkby-on-Bain. Why did he complain of food tasting nasty and throw it to a neighbour's dog, which has since died? Ask the undertaker, if he looked natural after death? Why did he stiffen so quickly? Why was he so jerky when he was dying? I myself have heard her threaten to poison him years ago. In the name of the law I beg you to analyse the contents of the stomach. (signed) 'Fairplay'

This curious anonymous letter was received by Inspector Dodson of the Horncastle police on Monday 26 May 1934, and like most good coppers he didn't throw it in the wastepaper basket before he had checked. Sure enough, just two days before, on 24 May, a lorry driver named Arthur Major had died a very painful death. What was more, a neighbour's wire-haired terrier had died during the night in much the same way.

Inspector Dodson was in time to stop the funeral of Mr Major taking place and both his body and that of the unfortunate canine were entrusted to the redoubtable Dr Roche Lynch, the Home Office analyst. In both cases death had been the result of strychnine poisoning.

What then of 'a wife poisoning a husband'? This could only refer to Mrs Ethel Lillie Major, who seemed in no way sorrowful at the loss of her husband; indeed, she claimed to be 'much better in health since he has gone'. Mrs Major was also anxious to disassociate herself from the purchase of corned beef – the last meal Arthur Major ate, and which almost certainly was the vehicle for the poison. When Chief-Inspector Hugh Young of Scotland Yard began to look into the background of the Majors he realised that they could no longer stand even the sight of each other. In fact, Ethel, a cantankerous, arrogant woman was pretty much disliked throughout the neighbourhood. An aggravating factor was that Arthur had recently been receiving compromising letters from a neighbour, Rose Kettleborough. In showing the missives to their doctor, Ethel is quoted as saying: 'A man like him is not fit to live, and I will do him in.' Said in the heat of passion, perhaps, but after all her husband *was* dead; had been poisoned. Besides, by now the police had found the key in Mrs Major's handbag that fitted her gamekeeper father's work-box containing a bottle of strychnine.

After one of the most damningly watertight prosecutions ever to be heard in the old Lincoln Assizes, the jury found against Ethel Major. She died on the scaffold at Hull Prison, on 19 December 1934. There can be few who mourned her passing; perhaps including her son whom she deliberately sent out to purchase the fatal corned beef.

25 May

1968 (England) On 25 May 1968 Martin Bell, aged four, was murdered by eleven-year-old Mary Bell (no relation). Eight weeks later the child killer struck again, strangling three-year-old Brian Howe. Mary Bell was found guilty of manslaughter and sent to a special approved school as no mental hospital would accept her. Mary escaped briefly from Moor Croft open prison in an attempt to prove she could live a normal life on the outside. She was eventually released in 1980.

26 May

1947 (England) In May 1947 Dr Robert George Clements was fifty-seven, while his wife, his fourth wife, Amy Victoria (called 'Vee'), whom he had married in 1940, was forty-seven. She would never reach forty-eight, for on the night of 26 May Mrs Clements had to be removed to the Astley Nursing Home where she died the following day.

One should not be unsympathetic to the bereaved, but this was becoming something of a habit. Clements' first wife died, apparently of sleeping sickness after ten years of marriage; the second Mrs Clements died of endocarditis after seven years; and the doctor's third bride died of cancer after they had been married ten years. And now Vee had had her seven.

Clements had earlier diagnosed myeloid leukaemia, and the young pathologist who performed the post-mortem saw no reason to disagree. So Mrs Clements was consigned to the earth. Only one man had any suspicion. Dr Andrew Brown at the nursing home had been very aware of the dilated state of Amy Clements' eyes in her last hours; this, he knew, was not a symptom of myeloid leukaemia. It was, however, indicative of morphine poisoning. Such internal parts of Mrs Clements as had not been disposed of following the first autopsy were now entrusted to Dr J. B. Firth, Director of the Home Office Forensic Laboratory at Preston. For two weeks the tiny remains were tested for virtually every known poison. Then a microscopic portion from the spinal cord tested positive for morphine.

When the police arrived to arrest Clements, he was found dead from a self-administered overdose of morphine. Beside him lay an audacious note reading: 'I can no longer tolerate the diabolical insults to which I have been recently exposed . . .'

27 May

1817 (England) After a local dance, wealthy farmer's son Abraham Thornton raped and murdered Mary Ashford near her home at Erdington. As the result of bribing witnesses, Thornton was acquitted of his obvious crime, but a private prosecution was taken out by Mary's relatives. In response, Thornton invoked the ancient law of Trial by Combat – battle to the death. Clearly so uncivilised a spectacle could not be permitted in the year 1817, and Abraham Thornton was allowed to walk free yet again. Wisely, he set sail for America to start a new life.

28 May

1942 (Australia) The third death was on 28 May 1942. Gladys Hoskins had followed Ivy McLeod and Pauline Thompson in the succession of strangled corpses to be found, where they had fallen, on the streets of Melbourne.

It was to be the last in the series thanks to an observant sentry at the local US army base who remembered challenging a shaken and dishevelled GI returning to camp late on the night of the murder. The description happened to match that of a soldier who had been reported for threatening violence to a young woman only a few days previously; both descriptions fitted Edward Joseph Leonski, a big Texan who had recently confided to a camp buddy the alarming news that 'I'm a Dr Jekyll and Mr Hyde! I killed! I killed!'

There was not much need to search for evidence against him, Leonski provided his own; sure he had killed all those ladies: 'It was to get their voices.' He recalled with particular affection that Pauline Thompson had sung to him as he walked her home, a soft, sweet voice: 'I could feel myself going mad about it.'

Nutty as a fruit-cake? The court martial didn't think so. The 'Singing Strangler', or the 'Melbourne Jack the Ripper', was hanged on 9 November 1942, at Pentridge Gaol; it is said that in the hours before his execution, Leonski sat in his cell singing softly to himself.

29 May

1753 (England) William Smith was a farmer in good circumstances at Great Broughton, in the county of York. His mother had married a second husband, one Thomas Harper, of Ingleby Manor, who already had two children. Smith therefore wished to rid himself of those whom he considered obstacles between him and his prospects from his late father's estate.

One day in an apothecary's shop the evil spirit whispered to Smith that the means were at hand, and he immediately asked for a little arsenic to kill the rats in his barn. The apothecary, not suspecting a man of Smith's respectability meant the deadly powder for any other use, sold him twopennyworth.

The day chosen by this now-determined sinner to administer the poison was 29 May 1753, when, observing a large cake being prepared, of which some of the neighbours had been invited to partake, he unperceived, as he imagined, mixed the arsenic with the flour, and thus it was served up to the table. It happened that the neighbours did not come to dinner, and none ate of the cake except Thomas Harper and his two children, William and Anne.

Having made preparations for flight, the murderer, the moment he found his wickedness had taken its desired effect, set off for Liverpool, from which a suspicion arose that he was the perpetrator of the horrid deed. The unfortunate people languished in excruciating torments until the next day, when they expired.

No sooner had Smith reached Liverpool than his conscience began to rebuke him, and having no kind of employment his existence became a burden to him. Nor could he find the least respite until he returned to the very spot where he committed the murder. He was immediately apprehended, and confessed to his crime.

At the next assizes for the county of York, before Mr Serjeant Eyre, Smith was found guilty, on his own confession, the evidence of the apothecary, and a maid-servant who saw him tamper with the flour, and other corroborating circumstantial evidence. He received the sentence of death.

(Derived from a contemporary account)

30 May

1832 (England) Mr Paas carried on the business of manufacturer of brass instruments for the bookbinding trade at High Holborn, London. James Cook was a bookbinder working in Leicester and using Mr Paas as one of his suppliers. On Wednesday 30 May 1832, Mr Paas, according to his custom was visiting the city of Leicester for the purpose of collecting the accounts due to him there, including £25 owed by James Cook. Accordingly, after having booked in at the Stag and Pheasant Inn, he took himself off to the bookbinder's workshop in Wellington Street – an address he would never leave alive.

On the night in question a milkman named Sawbridge, who had a cow-house beneath Cook's business premises, saw a large fire blazing in the workshop, but, knowing that strong heat was occasionally necessary in the trade, he thought little of it. At about eight o'clock James Cook was in the Flying Horse ale-house where he was seen to be in possession of a large amount of money; again no attention was paid to it, despite his apparent change in fortunes. Cook returned to the workshop at around ten, where he was heard moving about by Mr and Mrs Sawbridge. It was not until late the following evening that the fierce fire which was still blazing in Cook's premises, despite his absence, began to cause neighbours some alarm – there being the fear that the building might catch alight. As a consequence Mr Timson, a broker who lived two doors away, climbed the stairs to Cook's workshop and burst open the door. He saw that the fire had spread beyond the grate and a large piece of flesh was burning on top of it. The flesh was taken off and the fire extinguished. Cook, who was found at his home, insisted that the meat was horseflesh, bought, he said, to feed a dog. However, examination by a physician revealed it to be part of a human body.

The non-return of Mr Paas to the inn, meanwhile, had aroused some suspicion of foul play which was linked to the odd goings on at the Cook workshop. An examination of the premises proved this to be the case, for in the chimney was found all that remained of the unfortunate tradesman. Two thighs and a leg were discovered suspended from a nail by a cord in the chimney. There were also, scattered about the room, many bloodstained clothes and other property later identified as belonging to the late Mr Paas. A coroner's jury, convened on 3 June, returned a verdict that Paas had been wilfully murdered by James Cook.

On 8 August 1832, Cook stood his trial at the Leicester Assizes and pleaded guilty to murder. After execution in front of the gaol in that same city, Cook's body was hung in chains as a warning to all others minded to kill.

31 May

1932 (England) On the night of 30 May 1932, Elvira Barney was doing what she did best – or at least what she did most of – and that was drinking. Elvira, to be honest, was a gin lush whose affection for the bottle had ravaged her looks far beyond her twenty-seven years. The night had started with one of Elvira's parties which was attended by the usual rag-bag of idlers, ne'er-do-wells and hangers-on. When they had tired of that, Elvira and her current boyfriend, a lazy and impecunious young man named Michael Scott Stephen, drifted on first to the bar of the Café de Paris and then to the Blue Angel Club. They left around midnight while just able to stand, and went back to Elvira's flat in Williams Mews where they continued drinking and squabbling loudly. Neighbours later recalled hearing a woman's voice yelling: 'I will shoot you', followed by a couple of shots. If they hadn't heard it all before, the long-suffering neighbours might have called the police; but they had, and they didn't. It would have been too late to save Michael Stephen's life anyway.

On 3 June Mrs Barney was arrested and charged with murder. According to her statement Stephen had threatened to leave her; then she, in a characteristically histrionic gesture threatened to kill herself with the revolver she kept beside the bed. There followed a brief struggle for the gun during which Stephen was shot. One thing Elvira Barney could thank her lucky stars for was that she had secured the services of Sir Patrick Hastings to present this defence. Because despite the medical brilliance of Bernard Spilsbury, who claimed that the angle of entry of the bullet wounds

UNDER THE PATRONAGE

Of the NOBILITY.

INSTANTANEOUS COMMUNICATION,

Between PADDINGTON and SLOUGH, a distance of nearly Twenty Miles, by means of The

ELECTRIC

TELEGRAPH

Which may be seen in operation Daily, from Nine in the Morning till Eight in the Evening, at The

GREAT WESTERN RAILWAY,

Paddington Station—and The

TELEGRAPH COTTAGE,

Close to the Slough Station.

Admission. — ONE SHILLING,
Children and Schools Half-Price.

Since this very interesting Exhibition has been opened to the Public, it has been honoured by the visits of His Royal Highness Prince Albert, the Emperor of Russia, the King, and Prince William of Prussia, the Duke de Montpensier, His Royal Highness the Duke of Cambridge, the Duke of Wellington, Sir Robert Peel, the Foreign Ambassadors, and most of the Nobility, &c.

In no way has the Science of Electricity been made so subservient to the uses of man, as in its application to the purposes of Telegraphic Communication, which is now brought to the height of perfection. The working of this beautiful Apparatus is not in the least degree affected by the weather, intelligence can be sent by night equally well as by day; distance is no object; by its extraordinary agency communications can be transmitted, to a distance of a Thousand Miles, in the same space of time, and with the same ease and unerring certainty, as a signal can be sent from London to Slough. According to the best authorities, the Electric Fluid travels at the rate of

280,000 Miles in a Second.

The Electric Telegraph has been adopted by Her Majesty's Government, and the Patentees have just completed a line of communication between London and Portsmouth, agreeably to directions received a short time ago, from

The Right Hon. the Lords of the Admiralty.

In the late trial of John Tawell, at Aylesbury, for the Murder at Salt Hill, near Slough, the Electric Telegraph is frequently mentioned in the evidence, and referred to by Mr. Baron Parke in his summing up. *The Times* Newspaper very justly observes, "That had it not been for the efficient aid of the Electric Telegraph, both at the Paddington and Slough Stations, the greatest difficulty, as well as delay, would have been occasioned in the apprehension of the prisoner." Although the train in which Tawell came to town was within a very short distance of the Paddington Station, before any intelligence was given at the Slough Telegraph Office, nevertheless before the train had actually arrived, not only had a full description of his person and dress been received, but the particular carriage and compartment in which he rode were accurately described, and an officer was in readiness to watch his movements. His subsequent apprehension is so well known, that any further reference to the subject is unnecessary.

The Telegraph Office, at Paddington Station, is at *the End* of the Up-Train Platform, where a variety of interesting apparatus may be seen in constant operation.

T. HOME, *Licensee.*

S. G. Fairbrother, Printer, 31, Bow Street, Covent Garden.

After murdering Sarah Hart, John Tawell was apprehended as a result of a message sent on the newly installed electric telegraph – the first time it had been so used. See 1 January.

Artist and parricide Richard Dadd at work in Bethlem Hospital. See 8 January.

Gary Gilmore, executed by firing squad in 1977. See 17 January. (*Popperfoto*)

A wedding photograph of Wills Eugene Boshears, whose trial for murder resulted in the verdict 'guilty but asleep'. See 4 February.

PRICE SIXPENCE
THE MAN THEY COULD NOT HANG
THE LIFE STORY OF JOHN LEE
PUBLISHED AT 17 AND 18, HENRIETTA STREET, LONDON, W.C.

Murderer John Lee claimed to have been saved by God when the trap doors failed to open. He went on to publish the story of his life on his release from prison in 1907. See 23 February. (*Rocky Stockman Collection*)

Robert Stroud, the famous 'Birdman of Alcatraz'. See 26 March.

Cuban refugee Julio Gonzalez, who set fire to the Happy Land social club and so became one of America's worst mass killers. See 25 March. (*Popperfoto*)

Scenes from the Arthur Devereux case. See 13 April.

The Kray twins, Ronnie and Reggie, with their mother Violet and grandfather Jimmy Lee. See 8 May. (*Hulton Deutsch Collection*)

Spencer Perceval, the only British Prime Minister to have been assassinated, lies dying inside the entrance of the House of Commons. See 11 May. (*Rocky Stockman Collection*)

John Bellingham, Perceval's assassin, in the dock at the Old Bailey. (*Rocky Stockman Collection*)

Edward J. Leonski, the 'Singing Strangler'. See 28 May.

GENERAL HEADQUARTERS
SOUTHWEST PACIFIC AREA
A.P.O. 500

4th November, 1942.

In the foregoing case of Private EDWARD J. LEONSKI, 32007434, Headquarters Company, 52nd Signal Battalion, the sentence having been approved by the Reviewing Authority on 30 September, 1942, and confirmed by me as the Confirming Authority on 14 October, 1942, and Article of War 50½ having been complied with, the sentence will be duly executed. The Commanding General, United States Army Services of Supply, Southwest Pacific Area, is directed to cause the execution of the sentence to be effected without undue delay, at such place as determined by him.

Douglas MacArthur
DOUGLAS MacARTHUR,
General, U. S. Army,
Commander-in-Chief.

Authorisation of the death sentence passed on Private Edward J. Leonski, signed by the then United States Army Commander-in-Chief, Douglas MacArthur.

James Cook languishing in gaol awaiting sentence of death. See 30 May.

Elvira Barney. See 31 May.

Elvira Barney's lover and victim, Michael Scott Stephen.

The scene outside the Old Bailey during Mrs Barney's trial.

Discovery of the unidentified victim of the first Brighton trunk murder. See 17 June.

and lack of close-up scorch burns mitigated against Elvira's story, and despite the ballistics brilliance of gunsmith Robert Churchill, who claimed that the gun's trigger was unlikely to go off by accident, the jury set Mrs Barney free. She went to Paris shortly after her acquittal where she died four years later.

June

1 June

1948 (England) Mr Rome was about his leisurely occupation of milk roundsman when he reached the home of ninety-four-year-old Mrs Freeman Lee in the exclusive Ray Park Avenue area of Maidenhead. He was surprised to see that the previous day's delivery was still on the doorstep, and popped his head over the adjoining fence where Arthur Hillsdon was at work building a caravan. Mr Hillsdon had not seen his neighbour for a couple of days, but as she was of reclusive habits he had not thought a lot about it. Nevertheless, curiosity being what it is, he needed no second invitation to take a look through Mrs Freeman Lee's front-room window. Nothing unusual. Next the amateur sleuth peered through the letter-box; on the hall floor he noticed a couple of cushions and a large black leather trunk, a bunch of keys and a woman's shoe. It was strange enough, he thought, to alert the police.

Mrs Lee was eventually found in the black trunk in the hallway – dead. It was left to Dr Keith Simpson to break the worst news. Although Mrs Lee had been viciously bludgeoned, that was not the cause of her death; she had perished not from head injuries but from asphyxia – the old lady had been crammed into her black leather coffin and left to suffocate to death. Like many elderly eccentrics living alone, Minnie Freeman Lee had acquired the reputation of a miser sitting on a fortune in gold. When detectives learnt this, it at least made the motive clear. In reality, though, Mrs Freeman Lee was living on a small monthly stipend from a benevolent society.

On Thursday 3 June 1948, Chief Superintendent Frederick Cherrill, head of Scotland Yard's Fingerprint Bureau arrived at the scene of the crime to begin his own specialised search. He wrote later:

> My search was coming to a close and I felt my hopes fading. I stood for a moment gazing around me. The only thing I had not examined was the actual bed . . . First, I picked up the eiderdown quilt, and as I did so there fell from among its folds the bottom of a small cardboard box . . . But it turned out to be devoid of a finger-mark in the true sense of the word. Then I had a peculiar feeling – which I often experienced on an investigation – that at last I was going to find something tangible. This box *must* have had a lid, and that lid might furnish the clue which had so far evaded me. With great care I removed every article of bed-clothing separately. There was no sign of the lid, but still I felt that it must be somewhere about. And then at that very moment I saw something white lying on the floor half hidden by the bed. I stooped down to see what it was. It was the lid of the box! . . . Carefully I placed it on a clean sheet of paper and tested it for finger-marks. On the edge appeared to be two faint fragments of finger-marks. And they *were* fragments, for they were on the outside of one side of the lid . . . I knew at once these marks had not been made by Mrs Lee.

In fact they had been left by an habitual housebreaker and thief called George Russell. Within days Russell was taken into custody and among his scant possessions was a scarf which had belonged to Mrs Lee. Confronted with Fred Cherrill's evidence, George Russell made a confession, though not a truthful one. He had only been to the house to apply for a job as a gardener, he said. 'I was told she had a lot of money by another man. Did I murder this poor aged woman for something she was supposed to have, and had not?' That was George's big mistake. How, after all, was he to know that Mrs Lee was poor if it had not been he who ransacked her house? And that is what the jury thought too; Russell was found guilty of murder and sentenced to death. Some weeks later his miserable life ended, unmourned, on the scaffold at Oxford Gaol.

2 June

1967 (USA) Luis Jose Monge went to the gas chamber in Colorado State Penitentiary at 8.00 p.m. on Friday 2 June 1967 – the last man to suffer the death penalty in America until the execution of Gary Gilmore in Utah on 17 January 1977 heralded the return of capital punishment to the United States. Monge, a salesman of Denver, Colorado, and his wife Dolores had always wanted a large family. By early 1963, they had more than achieved their ambition by producing ten children ranging between the ages of eighteen years and eleven months; the eleventh child was due later that same year. Not surprisingly, Luis Monge was considered by most to be the perfect family man. However, the façade of loyal husband and loving father concealed a terrible secret – for several years Monge had indulged in sex games with his daughter Janet, now thirteen years old. His wife had found out about the illicit liaison and quite understandably had put pressure on him to stop; for his part, Monge had promised to control himself.' Unfortunately in Luis Monge's case the flesh proved as weak as his resolve. On the night of Friday 28 June 1963, he found himself irresistibly drawn to Janet's bedroom, where she slept with her sister Anna. Believing Anna to be sleeping, Monge climbed into Janet's bed and began fondling her in his very unfatherly manner. As he did so, Anna woke, saw what was going on, and threatened to tell her mother. If she did, then Luis Monge, the 'perfect father', would soon be exposed as a child abuser.

He panicked and decided he would kill his family and then himself. First, he laid hold of a poker and hit his wife four or five times over the head with it. When she was dead he cleaned up the body and then got out his stiletto-bladed knife and plunged it into eleven-month-old Tina; when she cried out, he covered up her mouth until she suffocated. Monge then almost ritually cleaned the baby's body and laid her in bed beside her mother. Next it was four-year-old Thomas's turn; he was choked before being placed by his dead sister. The last victim was Monge's favourite son, six-year-old Freddie, whom he struck twice with the poker and covered his mouth until he stopped breathing. The cleansing ceremony followed, and the body was laid in bed with the others. In his statement, Monge said that at that point he could not go on, and thought of killing himself. Instead, he called the police, saying: 'I've just killed my wife and three of my kids. You'd better come over before I kill somebody else.'

When Luis Jose Monge appeared in court, he stood charged only with the murder of his wife. Although he pleaded guilty, Monge was routinely transferred to the Colorado State Hospital for psychiatric assessment, and following two examinations was declared sane and fit to plead. On 23 October 1963, Monge again entered a formal plea of guilty to the court and signed a statement admitting responsibility for the murder of his wife. Before the penalty hearing, the judge arranged for Monge to have a reunion with his remaining children, where he was completely reconciled with the family who, with remarkable compassion, told him they forgave him everything.

The penalty hearing began on 23 November, by which

time Monge had already instructed his lawyers that he did not intend to fight for his life. Obligingly, the jury returned a recommendation for the death penalty, but before a judge could formally pass the death sentence, on 18 December Monge changed his mind and instructed his attorney to lodge an appeal; which the Colorado Supreme Court rejected. In January 1966, the state governor issued a stay of execution to all condemned prisoners in advance of the referendum which was to be held on the whole issue of capital punishment. After a hard-fought campaign on the issue, Colorado voters elected to retain the death penalty by a margin of two to one.

In early 1967 Luis Monge decided on another appeal and took on a new lawyer. The attorney did put in the appeal, but he also proposed an alternative motion that, if Monge was to be executed, then it should take place outside Denver City Hall and be televised. This was clearly an attempt to demonstrate capital punishment as being degrading and repugnant, but the scheme misfired badly and received such heavy publicity that Monge was obliged to abandon the whole appeal in order to protect his family from the pressure of media attention.

3 June

1928 (USA) This was the day on which the man calling himself Frank Howard arrived like the tooth fairy at the front door of the Budd family's apartment in New York City. He was there, he announced, to offer young Paul a job. Paul Budd, it should be explained, was looking for work and had placed an advertisement in the newspaper. Howard said he had a farm out on Long Island and would be pleased to give the boy a try out. Then he remembered that his sister, who lived close by, was holding a children's party that very day – why didn't he take twelve-year-old Grace over there while Paul was packing his grip. And so

Mrs Budd entrusted her daughter to the kindly Mr Howard, and off they went hand in hand.

But his name was not really Howard; his name was Albert Fish. And there was no Long Island farm. There was no party. Instead Fish took young Grace over to an empty house in Westchester. Mrs Budd never saw her daughter again – alive or dead.

Six years later, in November 1934, the Budds received an unexpected piece of mail. It read:

> Dear Mrs Budd
> Some years ago a friend of mine, Captain John Davis, shipped from California to Hong Kong, China, where at that time there was a great famine. It was dangerous for children under the age of twelve to be on the streets, as the custom was for them to be seized, cut up and their meat sold for food. On his return to New York, my friend seized two boys, one six the other eleven, killed, cooked and ate them. So it was that I came to your house on 3 June 1928, and under the pretence of taking your daughter Grace to a party at my sister's I took her up to Westchester County, Worthington, to an empty house up there, and I choked her to death, I cut her up and ate part of her flesh. I didn't fuck with her. She died a virgin.

It is impossible to imagine the anguish that letter caused Grace's parents; but to the police it was a godsend. On the back of the envelope was an imperfectly erased address; it was Albert Fish's address in a grubby New York boarding house. And so at last the 'Cannibal Killer's' career was at an end; a career that had included the violent assault of more than one hundred young girls and the murder of twelve of them.

Fish died in the electric chair at Sing Sing on 16 January 1936, a look of genuine anticipation on his face.

4 June

1935 (England) They found the body of Alma Rattenbury caught up in the weeds on a lonely backwater of the river Avon known locally as Three Arches Bend on 4 June 1935. Looking at the sodden, dishevelled corpse it was hard to imagine that this was a woman whose intrigues had been on the lips of the nation for months. The so-called Murder at the Villa Madeira is one of history's most celebrated crimes of passion. The Villa was the home of retired architect Francis Mawson Rattenbury and his considerably younger wife Alma. Oh, not to forget the eighteen-year-old chauffeur George Percy Stoner. It is important to remember Percy, because he is Alma's lover. If Rattenbury knew of the affair then he seems to have found enough comfort in his whisky decanter not to mind.

In the small hours of 25 March 1935, Alma came downstairs, so she claimed, and found her husband lying in a pool of his own blood on the drawing-room carpet, still alive, but bleeding heavily from head wounds. When the police arrived they found Alma Rattenbury, almost incapably drunk and blurting out what appeared to be a confession: 'I did it with a mallet . . . He's lived too long . . .' That sort of thing. She later made other admissions, seemingly to protect Percy Stoner. Percy had also begun to make statements, these to the effect that it was he and not Alma who was responsible for the attack on Francis Rattenbury.

And so it went on, and by the time poor Rattenbury had succumbed to his injuries both Alma and Percy were jointly charged with murder. Their trial opened before Mr Justice Humphreys at the Old Bailey on 27 May 1935. With a little persuasion from her attorney, Alma had stopped protecting

Percy, but he, loyal lad, was still protesting her innocence. And whatever the truth of it, that was what the jury accepted. On 31 May Percy Stoner was convicted of murder and sentenced to death. Alma was acquitted, but was so heartbroken that she took her own life. Which was a waste, because Percy's appeal against sentence was upheld and he was reprieved. He served seven years of his life sentence and was released in 1942. However, the question remains – who *really* killed Francis Rattenbury?

5 June

1797 (England) Believed to be innocent of a charge of murder, Martin Clench and James Mackley were, nevertheless, executed before Newgate Gaol on 5 June 1797. The following account derives from one version of *The Newgate Calendar*.

> Sydney Fryer, Esq., a gentleman of considerable property, on Sunday 7 May 1797, called, by appointment, on his cousin, Miss Ann Fryer, who resided in Shepherd Street, Oxford Street, in order to take a walk with her into the environs of London, to pay a visit to their aunt. When they had proceeded across the fields to the back part of Islington Workhouse they heard, as they thought, a female voice in distress; upon which Mr Fryer, contrary to his cousin's advice, leaped over the hedge into the field whence the voice seemed to proceed, but instead of seeing a woman he met with three men, who, upon his rashly drawing his tuck-stick (the sword of which dropped out), fired, and wounded him a little above the left eye, and he fell into a small pond. One of the villains took the watch out of his pocket and a purse from the lady, and another took her cloak. Mr Fryer died two hours after.

Several were taken up on suspicion and strictly examined in the presence of Miss Fryer, but dismissed for want of evidence. On 27 May the Worship Street officers apprehended Martin Clench, James Mackley and a man named Smith, a chip-hat maker; however, no criminality appearing in the latter, he was discharged. The two committed prisoners were most impartially tried, and no ingenuity was wanting in their defence. Indeed, there was no positive evidence except Miss Fryer's, who swore the identity of the prisoners. The jury, retired for half-an-hour, returned a verdict of guilty. The two men were accordingly executed and their bodies publicly exposed in a stable in Little Bridge Street, near Apothecaries' Hall.

A short time before their caps were drawn over their eyes the platform, by some improper management, suddenly went down with the two clergymen, the executioner and his man. The Catholic priest who attended Clench, being very lusty, suffered most, but fortunately not materially. When the two men died most of the people were of the opinion that their fate was just; but soon after, the confession of three separate criminals, who could have no interest in taking the crime upon themselves, threw a different light on the transaction, and recalled to mind the strong assertions which Clench and Mackley had made of their innocence; for Clench, upon retiring from the bar, returned thanks to the court for the fairness of his trial, but observed (in a rough way) that, though they were condemned to die, and be teased afterwards (referring to their dissection), they were no more guilty of murder than their prosecutrix.

One Burton Wood, who was afterwards executed on Kennington Common, and another, while under sentence of death, wrote a letter to Carpenter Smith, Esq., magistrate of Surrey, declaring the innocence of Clench and Mackley, for that they were, with another not yet in custody, the murderers. Soon after the third man suffered for another offence at Reading Gallows, and made the same confession. His name was Timms.

6 June

1961 (England) This was the date on which a man, hearing that his wife of two months had made a complaint about him to the authorities, wandered into the police station at West Ham, London, carrying a loaded hand-gun in his pocket. He had arrived in a sports car, giving an appearance of affluence, and announced himself as John Hall. It was as Hall had suspected: in his interview with officers Philip Pawsey and George Hutchins they pointed out that it had only been Hall's foresight in surrendering himself that had prevented his arrest on a charge of causing grievous bodily harm.

That was all John Hall wanted to hear. He had no intention whatever of being arrested, and none of remaining in custody. Pulling the gun from his pocket, Hall kept the officers at bay while he backed towards the door. As he fled, Inspector Pawsey and Sergeant Hutchins, along with PC Charles Cox, were quickly in pursuit. The result was that Pawsey and Hutchins were shot dead, and PC Cox was badly wounded.

For the next eight hours, officers and dogs from various Metropolitan Police areas joined in the hunt for John Hall; more shots were fired, but there were no further casualties. Eventually Hall was cornered in a telephone box and decided that it was better to take his own life than let the hangman take it for him. Although the shot he put into his body was not immediately fatal, John Hall died in hospital eight days later.

7 June

1753 (England) Dr Archibald Cameron, the Jacobite rebel, was ordered to be hanged, drawn and quartered at Tyburn for High Treason; the following is a contemporary account:

> Dr Cameron, a well-respected physician, was the youngest son of Evan Cameron, chief of one of the Highland Clans who made his escape to France with the Pretender. At the persuasion of his elder brother Lochiel, an active general in the service of the Pretender, Cameron joined the rebels in the year 1745, and after the battle of Culloden fled in a small boat to Bologne. Here Lochiel was given a regiment by the King of France, and Archibald was made the king's physician. When Lochiel died, the doctor was appointed physician to Lord Ogilvie's regiment.
>
> In 1750, Archibald Cameron returned to England to receive his share of a fund set up to help those persons who had been forced to flee abroad. This dangerous mission was made the more hazardous by the doctor's writing many letters, which eventually led to the suspicion that he was returned. Accordingly a detachment of soldiers from Lord George Beaumont's regiment was sent to seek him out and take him prisoner. He was lodged first in the Castle at Edinburgh and then removed to the Tower of London.
>
> At his examination in the Cockpit, Cameron denied his identity. Brought before the court of the King's Bench he then acknowledged who he was, upon which Lord Chief Justice Lee pronounced this sentence: '[that you] be removed from hence to His Majesty's prison at the Tower of London, and on Thursday 7 June next, your body to be drawn on a sledge to the place of execution, there to be hanged, but not till you are dead; your bowels to be taken out, your body to be

quartered, your head cut off, and affixed at the king's disposal; and the Lord have mercy on your soul'.

In the end, Cameron was granted the mercy of hanging long enough to extinguish life. The executioner cut off the head and took out the bowels, but did not quarter the body. The head and body were put into a coffin and a hearse was ready to convey it to the undertaker. Dr Cameron was executed in his forty-sixth year.

8 June

1957 (England) Emily Pye was one of a breed now long extinct, the elderly lady who kept the local corner shop and could always be relied upon to be open all hours; and if she was not, then she would jolly well open up. Miss Pye had never married, and at the time of the tragedy which took her life she was eighty years old. It was the afternoon of 8 June 1957, and it is recorded that there was a thunderstorm over Halifax at the time she was battered to death in her little business in Gibbet Street – O ominous name! The killing was clearly in the furtherance of theft because the till had been plundered; it was also, presumably, an impulsive, hurried crime, because the much larger amount of money in Miss Pye's modest accommodation above the shop was untouched.

The body had been found by the victim's niece and her husband, who were visiting, and a police statement issued later repeated the pathologist's view that Emily Pye had been struck many times with fists, before her skull was crushed in a frenzied attack with a fire-iron. Not surprisingly, the local force requested the assistance of Scotland Yard, and this was sent in the person of Detective Superintendent Herbert Hannam. It was Hannam's view that the perpetrator of this grotesque crime was a local, and something like 15,000 statements were taken during the course of the investigation. Although few details emerged of the inquiry, it was known that a request was made to Interpol regarding three people who had been in Halifax at the time of the murder, but had since left the country. One point of interest did emerge in that Superintendent Hannam was collaborating with Yorkshire police on the possibility of linking the death of Emily Pye with two other, similar cases in the county – though it must be said that they were separated by a number of years.

In August 1957 the 'wanted' list numbered eight men, all of whom, it was thought, could help the police with their investigation into the Halifax murder – which seemed promising. Subsequently there were optimistic noises being made by Scotland Yard about 'promising results'. And then there was silence. Police silence, press silence; it was as if the inquiry had never been launched. And there it remains – Miss Emily Pye was beaten to death on 8 June 1957 . . .

9 June

1958 (England) Among the many thousands of American service personnel who crossed Britain's shores during the Second World War and the post-war years, there were few really troublesome ones. A number of drunks, perhaps, womanisers too, that is part of the traffic of war. But not many killers. One was a man named Carl Hulten, who thought he was a Hollywood gangster and with his 'moll', Londoner Betty Jones, murdered a cab-driver in cold blood. Hulten was considered so odious even by his own people that they waived the right to try him by court martial and left him to be convicted by a British jury and then hanged.

Marcus Marymont was another killer. Perhaps it was the fact that he killed his own wife that kept him out of the English courts, but it was one of those rare cases of a US serviceman (Marymont was a Master Sergeant with the USAF) being tried for murder by his own countrymen, abroad.

It was on 9 June 1958 that Mrs Mary Marymont was rushed to the US Air Force hospital at Sculthorpe, Norfolk. As it turned out it was a one-way trip; she died shortly afterwards. Sudden, unexplained deaths are always the subject of post-mortem examination – and the greatest proportion of them reveal some natural cause. In the case of Mary Marymont it revealed poisoning by arsenic – a quaintly old-fashioned death for the late 1950s.

Not surprisingly, Sergeant Marcus Marymont was at the head of the list of suspects, and not surprisingly he had a very good reason for wanting to be widowed. Her name was Cynthia Taylor, a twenty-three-year-old woman separated from her husband, who had swallowed Marymont's story that he was divorced and agreed to marry him. Mrs Marymont had found out about the affair and was beginning to make a fuss.

Because Marymont was tried by a court martial in closed session we are unaware of most of the details of the proceedings. However, it is known that evidence for the prosecution included testimony from a chemist from whom Marymont tried to buy arsenic, and evidence of him questioning two cleaners at the USAF base about the same subject. In Master Sergeant Marymont's defence there was little to be said; however, in one embarrassing blunder his attorney, seeking to discredit the Home Office pathologist Dr (later Professor) Francis Camps, asked him in a supercilious tone exactly how many post-mortems he had undertaken. The pathologist, with customary deference to the dignity of the court, apologised for not being specific, but thought it must be somewhere around sixty thousand!

Marcus Marymont was convicted first on a charge of

murdering his wife, and secondly on a charge of adultery (an offence under American military law); he was sentenced to life imprisonment to be served at Fort Leavenworth, Kansas.

10 June

1919 (England) When seventeen-year-old William Nelson Adams, homeless, penniless and hungry, met George Jones on a bench by the Thames Embankment he would never have believed the price he was going to be asked to pay for Jones's friendship. At least that is what he told the jury at Guildford Assizes in July 1919.

Adams's story was that after taking him back to his modest room for a meal, the ageing ex-con began to regale his guest with desperate tales of huge income-tax demands that were 'worrying him out of his life'; Jones ended his pathetic story: 'I've done you a good turn, now you do me one. Will you kill me?'

One week later, on 10 June 1919, Adams and a man called Charlie Smith travelled by tram to meet George Jones at a pub in Tooting. After a few drinks, the odd trio set out on foot for Jones's home at Sutton. *En route* Jones, perhaps the worse for drink, cried out: 'God help me; will you kill me?' Adams reluctantly indicated that he would 'try', and they turned into a field behind Ridgeway Road. According to Adams, Jones pressed a shoemaker's awl into his hand and renewed his plea to be put out of his misery: 'The best way is to stab me on the left side of the neck.' Despite his best efforts – a generous three blows with the awl to the neck and three in the stomach – William Adams failed to dispatch his victim beyond the reach of the Inland Revenue. Then he tried, but failed, to drag Jones to a nearby pond to drown him. In the end both he and the no doubt thoroughly bewildered Charlie Smith fled in panic, having first helped themselves to the few shillings Jones had in his pocket. As for Smith he simply vanished, and despite a police hunt was never heard from again. Jones was found where he had fallen, but in a strange state of undress. He was wearing just trousers and a string vest, and somebody – either Adams or, perhaps, Jones himself – had tied his shirt round his stomach in an attempt to staunch the blood from his wounds. Jones was rushed to hospital where he lingered for three days on the borderline of life and death. During this time of grace he expressed considerable puzzlement at his predicament, wondering the while why Adams should have wanted to attack him: 'I had done nothing to him!'

This was exactly what the jury wondered as well, before they rejected William Adams's ludicrous story and convicted him of murder. Adams was not, however, asked to pay the ultimate penalty for his crime. The then Home Secretary, Mr Edward Shortt, commuted his death sentence to one of life imprisonment.

11 June

1930 (England) On 11 April 1930 a young woman named Edith May Parker was walking on Dartford Heath, Kent, with her sister Eva, when she was suddenly attacked from behind and stabbed in the back. The man responsible for this outrage was a twenty-three-year-old labourer named Albert Edward Marjeram, and he was taken into custody within a few hours of the attack. Marjeram seemed rather confused, but made no attempt to deny stabbing Miss Parker. He told police: 'I bought the knife for two shillings. I was on the heath and the two girls came along. I never spoke to them – I just up and done it with the knife.' As an afterthought he added: 'I forgot to add the motive. It was robbery. I was out of work and wanted money.'

Albert Edward Marjeram's trial opened at the Old Bailey on 22 May 1930, where the judge was Mr Justice Humphreys. Not surprisingly the defence tried to advance a plea of insanity and to this end Marjeram's long-suffering mother was brought in to court as a witness in his favour. Mrs Marjeram told the jury that when he was five years old, Albert developed an abscess on his brain and it was necessary to strap him down – partly because of the excruciating pain, and also to prevent him from acting violently. He also apparently acquired an unhealthy obsession with knives, just gazing at them mesmerised him and then he would draw them across his throat.

However, sad as his case might have been, counter medical evidence on behalf of the prosecution – expert testimony that Marjeram was, in the legal sense, sane – clearly impressed the jury and they returned a verdict of guilty. Mr Justice Humphreys pronounced sentence of death from beneath the black cap, and the execution was duly carried out on 11 June at Wandsworth Prison.

12 June

1960 (England) On Sunday 12 June 1960 the body of sixty-year-old William Arthur Elliott was found in Clod Hill Lane, which crosses the moor near Baslow; incongruously he was wearing no shoes. This was not as strange as it may have seemed, for in a separate incident the previous day, police had found a 'bubble' car in Chesterfield which had crashed and was bloodstained. It also contained a pair of men's shoes. As the murder hunt got underway, Detective Superintendent Leonard Stretton found out that a week before Elliott was killed, a bus cleaner named William Atkinson had been attacked close to where the bubble car was found. Mr Atkinson bore a remarkable likeness to Elliott; a case of mistaken identity perhaps?

Despite an inquiry during which no fewer than 10,000 statements were taken it was clear that the killer had slipped through the net. This is why police could hardly believe it when they learnt that another man had been found dead at almost the same spot on the moors as William Elliott; the date was Wednesday 29 March 1961. The murder team had a carbon-copy killing on their hands. The victim was an industrial chemist named George Gerald Stobbs. Once again DS Stretton was given charge of the investigation, and once again it must have seemed to him as though a fiction writer was scripting his inquiry. It was discovered that a man named Gillespie, bearing a great resemblance to victim George Stobbs was attacked shortly before the latest killing. Was Dr Gillespie a victim of mistaken identity too?

It was when the two killings were linked that certain underlying similarities emerged, notably that both men were closet homosexuals. However, over all, a frustrated team of investigators seemed to be getting absolutely nowhere. But they were not giving up yet. One of the suspects questioned during the Elliott inquiry was Michael Copeland, on National Service in Germany but home on leave in Chesterfield. He had boasted to his girlfriend that he was the killer, but apart from that there was nothing to link him with the Elliott killing. But now Copeland was back in Chesterfield; in fact he arrived shortly before the murder of George Stobbs. It was Chief Inspector Thomas Peat who first made the connection, and wondered whether the victims' homosexuality might not also be a factor. In a risky piece of police undercover work a local officer got to know Copeland and won his confidence. It was a long and tedious job, but after two years Michael Copeland confessed to the two murders – and it *was* because they were homosexuals ('It was something I really hated'). Copeland also confessed to the quite gratuitous killing of a German youth while he was on service.

Michael Copeland was put on trial in March 1965, when he claimed that he had only made the confessions in order to force a trial and prove his innocence. The court did not believe a word of it, and Copeland was found guilty and sentenced to die. At the time the whole issue of capital punishment was under review and his sentence was commuted to life.

13 June

1943 (England) In 1943 pretty Caroline Traylor was eighteen years old, already a bride of six months with a husband away on active service, and, like many of her friends, bored. The war had been going on just too long.

It was 13 June 1943, Whit Sunday. And for Caroline it might have been just another Sunday evening spent with her parents behind the black-out curtains. But she was determined that she would get some pleasure out of this holiday. That is why she was in the Mechanics Arms; and it was probably the same combination of boredom and determination that persuaded her to leave at closing time on the arm of an off-duty soldier. The darkness swallowed them up; Caroline never emerged from it.

The search for missing Caroline Traylor ended in an empty shop in Folkestone's Foord Road. A cursory glance at the body was enough to tell the police that strangulation had been accompanied by violent sexual assault. As in so many of those wartime murder cases, the forensic pathologist's expertise was given by Professor Keith Simpson, who arrived with representatives of Scotland Yard's Murder Squad within hours. Simpson's reconstruction suggested that the sexual element almost certainly began with Caroline's consent. Whether she changed her mind, or whether her partner began to get sadistic was impossible to tell. The bruising around Caroline's throat indicated that her killer had tried unsuccessfully to strangle her from the front, then turned her over and completed the job from behind.

But who was this brutal killer? This was in part to be answered by Keith Simpson's minute examination of the victim's body. He found half a dozen dark hairs stuck to Caroline Traylor's thighs which contrasted sharply with her own auburn colouring. Beneath her fingernails the pathologist found rusty-brown fibres, in all likelihood from the assailant's clothing. All that was needed was a suspect to match them.

Dennis Leckey, a serving Artillery gunner chose the day Caroline's body was found to go awol; not a very sensible thing to do if you want to avoid suspicion. Leckey was finally picked up in London ten days later and was required to give samples of his body hair; they matched those found on the victim. The fibres matched his uniform shirt. It was as watertight a case as any prosecution could have wished for, and quite rightly Dennis Leckey was convicted and sentenced to hang.

It is unfortunate that the highly experienced Mr Justice Singleton made one error which allowed a vicious killer not only to escape the gallows, but to evade justice altogether. In addressing the jury, the judge told them: 'Of course he [Leckey] is not bound to say anything [in his defence], but what would you conclude?' Dennis Leckey's right to remain silent without it being assumed he was guilty had been compromised. And so he walked free.

14 June

1962 (USA) A reign of terror haunted the city of Boston between June 1962 and January 1964, leaving thirteen women dead, and providing the state capital with a modern legend. This maniac's first murder was back on 14 June 1962, when a fifty-five-year-old divorcée named Anna Slesers was found by her son, naked, raped and strangled with the belt of her own blue housecoat. The killer's method became unvarying. After targeting his victim, the 'Boston Strangler' (as he became known) gained admission to her home by posing as a workman. All his victims were women, all were sexually assaulted and all were strangled – usually with an item of their own clothing, often a pair of stockings or tights which he tied with a bow under the chin. In some cases strangulation had been accompanied by biting, bludgeoning and even stabbing. Despite the customary false confessions, and a blanket police response to the city's mounting panic, the Strangler remained an enigmatic object of terror.

After the murder of sixty-eight-year-old Helen Blake on 30 June, the police enlisted the expertise of forensic psychiatrists in order to help build a profile of the killer. In the opinion of the experts he was a youngish man, eighteen to forty, suffering delusions of persecution and with a hatred of his mother (so far only elderly women had been attacked). This 'word portrait' was run alongside police records of known sex offenders, and although a number of suspects emerged from the files and were interviewed, the Strangler remained free to kill seventy-five-year-old Mrs Ida Irga on 19 August. On 5 December 1962, the psychological profile of a 'mother-hater' collapsed when Sophie Clark was murdered; she was twenty years old, just three years younger than two of his next three victims. The killing ended on 4 January 1964 with the discovery of the body of nineteen-year-old Mary Sullivan. Like all the other victims of the Boston Strangler, she was found in her own apartment. She had been stripped and bound, raped and strangled; and in a final sadistic gesture, Mary's killer had left a New Year's greeting card wedged between the toes of her left foot.

Finally, it was for the Strangler to make himself known. On 27 October 1964 he entered, as he had done before, a young woman's apartment posing as a detective. The intruder tied his victim to the bed, sexually assaulted her, and then inexplicably left, saying as he went, 'I'm sorry.' The woman's description of her assailant led to the identification of Albert De Salvo, and the publication of his photograph led to scores of women coming forward to identify him as the man who had sexually assaulted them.

But De Salvo was still not suspected of being the Boston Strangler. It was only in 1965, while he was being held on a rape charge and confined to the Boston State Hospital that De Salvo confessed in detail to the Strangler's crimes. His knowledge of the murders was such that at the time no doubt could be entertained as to the truth of his confession. Nevertheless, there was not one single scrap of direct evidence to support these claims, and in a remarkable piece of plea-bargaining, De Salvo's attorney agreed that his client should stand trial only for a number of earlier crimes unconnected with the stranglings. Albert De Salvo never stood trial for the crimes of the Boston Strangler, but was instead convicted of robbery and sexual offences and sent to prison for life. On 26 November 1973, Albert De Salvo was found dead in his cell, stabbed through the heart; he was forty-two years old.

15 June

1936 (USA) On 15 June 1936 Mildred Bolton took the elevator to her husband's office on Chicago's West Jackson Street, strode through the door and emptied the six chambers of a revolver into his body. As Charles Bolton floundered and groaned in agony on the floor, Mildred is reported to have told horrified onlookers: 'Don't pay him any mind, he's putting on an act.'

It's not often that you hear 'battered husband syndrome' being discussed, but Charlie Bolton could tell you all about it – and then a bit more. He was one of the prototype henpecked husbands. Charlie married Mildred, a vivacious Michigan girl in 1922. What he only learnt later was that she was also insanely jealous; she was spiteful and short-tempered too, but that wasn't so bad. Although he was always the mild-mannered industrious businessman, never giving Mildred the slightest cause for anxiety over his fidelity, she accused Charlie of having romantic affairs with every woman who crossed his path. When he protested his innocence she got mad; and when she got mad she beat him up a bit. It got so that there was a patrol car almost permanently outside the house to break up the fights. Finally, the violence took Mildred over; and the jealousy. So she shot Charlie dead.

At her trial Mildred was sentenced to 199 years without possibility of parole. She still had 192 to go when she slashed her own wrists in Dwight Penitentiary.

16 June

1919 (Wales) In 1919 Harold Greenwood was living in the village of Kidwelly with his wife Mabel, son Kenneth and daughter Irene; he practised as a solicitor in nearby Llanelli, and to all appearances life was suiting them all very well. The only problem that might raise its head from time to time was Harold's inexplicable attraction for some of the local women; that and Mrs Greenwood's rather poor health.

Even so, it was somewhat of a surprise when Mabel Greenwood died at 3 a.m. on 16 June. The previous day had been a Sunday, and Mrs Greenwood had spent the best part of the morning before lunch in the garden writing letters. The family lunched together, and according to the parlour-maid Greenwood drank whisky, the children drank water, and Mrs Greenwood had some Burgundy wine. They all ate meat and vegetables and gooseberry tart and custard. After lunch Mabel returned to the garden until tea was served at 4.30. At 6.30 Mrs Greenwood complained to her husband about pains around her heart, and after he gave her some brandy she vomited violently. Helped by Irene, Harold Greenwood got Mabel upstairs to bed and then called for Dr Griffiths who lived opposite; he paid several visits during the evening to check on progress. The district nurse, Elizabeth Jones, joined the household at about eight. The nurse heard Mrs Greenwood praying at one o'clock, and shortly afterwards she went into a coma and died at three. Dr Griffiths certified death due to valvular disease of the heart.

There is always some smoulder of gossip surrounding a sudden death, especially in small villages, but usually it dies down of its own accord. However, in Harold Greenwood's case he fanned the fire. On 1 October 1919, barely four months after Mabel's death, he married again. And although there was not the slightest blemish on either the lady concerned or their propriety before Mrs Greenwood's decease, the very fact of the wedding was enough for the wagging tongues of Kidwelly. And it is a certain fact that if tongues wag long enough and loud enough, people will take notice. On 30 October, Greenwood was asked permission to exhume his wife; which he gave. After his examination of the remains Dr William Willcox estimated that before her death Mabel Greenwood had ingested at least two grains of arsenic.

Harold Greenwood stood trial at the Carmarthen Assizes in November 1920. It was alleged that he had laced the Burgundy drunk by his wife with weedkiller. And this might have seemed possible if her daughter Irene had not been adamant that she had taken a glass from the same bottle with her supper. Indeed, so fine a young witness was Irene Greenwood that the jury accepted the truth of her statement; at any rate, they acquitted Harold Greenwood. Sadly, the years of gossip and suspicion that followed took its toll of his work and his health and he died at Ross-on-Wye on 17 January 1929.

17 June

1933 (England) It was on that Sunday the luggage attendants really began to be concerned about the smell. It was 17 June 1933, and the trunk had been left at Brighton station almost a fortnight before. In fact, to be precise it was deposited on 6 June, easy to remember because it was Derby Day. And there it had remained. But not any more; this was the kind of smell that cried out for investigation, and that is the police's job. And so the stinking luggage was transferred from railway station to police station and opened.

It contained the trunk of a woman, minus head, arms and legs. It had been wrapped in brown paper and tied with window cord. Written on the paper in blue pencil were the letters 'ford'; what had obviously been a first syllable was obliterated with blood. With their customary thoroughness the police circulated a general request around the nation's left-luggage offices to be on the lookout for malodorous baggage. The plan paid off, because at King's Cross station in London a stinking suitcase contained the legs and feet of the Brighton torso. At this point Sir Bernard Spilsbury took charge of the remains and passed on his observations: 1. She was dismembered by somebody with a rudimentary appreciation of anatomy; 2. No other injuries to body except points of dismemberment; 3. Aged under thirty years; 4. Time of death about three weeks before discovery; 5. Victim in fifth month of pregnancy; 6. From the state of care of the hands and feet, it was likely the victim came from a middle-class background and had not engaged in any strenuous or dirty occupation.

None of which really helped to identify the unfortunate woman. Nor did the best efforts of spirit mediums or newspaper rewards. And the trail was growing colder. In fact it froze over; and that is the situation today – the Brighton trunk torso remains a mystery woman.

But let us not leave Brighton just yet, because a most odd thing happened just a month after the station discoveries. On 15 July the police removed a black leather trunk from a house in Kemp Street. When Sir Bernard Spilsbury was seen arriving the whole town was waiting in eager anticipation to be told that the arms and head had been found. The truth was more bizarre than that – *they had found a whole new body*. Brighton had its second Trunk Murder.

18 June

1895 (New Zealand) It was one of the country's most unusual trials when Minnie Dean appeared in the dock at Invercargill Supreme Court on 18 June 1895, because of the rarity in New Zealand of 'baby-farmers'. Perhaps it reflected the official odium at such a practice that Minnie achieved the doubtful distinction of being the first and the last woman to be hanged in the country.

Scottish-born Minnie (or Williamina) was barely eighteen years old when she arrived at East Winton just outside Invercargill in 1865. She was not a lot older when she met and married Charles Dean and settled down to family life. She took up gardening, and soon had a little plot the envy of the neighbourhood. But gardening puts no butter on the bread, and as Charles's income was less than reliable (and always less than enough) Minnie decided to turn her hand to baby-farming. Unfortunately for business one of her little charges, May Irene, died while in her care. And in 1891 so did six-year-old Bertha. There was never any accusation of foul play, and death certificates were made out indicating natural causes. However, the local authorities were not entirely happy with the hillbilly state in which the children were being kept; 'squalid' was one word that was bandied about.

Minnie Dean used to advertise her services in the *Timaru*

Herald, and in April 1895 received a reply from a Mrs Hornsby. After suitable terms had been agreed, Minnie took charge of a one-month-old baby. When the baby disappeared after being seen in Minnie Dean's care on a train, awkward questions began to be asked. Minnie's reply that she had never set eyes on the child was exposed as a lie when the mite's clothing was found at her home. At this stage both Minnie and Charles were put under arrest while officers rooted about the Dean property. It was beneath the recently turned soil of the chrysanthemum bed that searchers found two small bodies – one of which was the missing baby; an infant's skeleton was unearthed from the dahlia patch. Subsequent post-mortems proved that one of the deaths had been due to morphia poisoning. It was soon quite clear that Charles Dean had no idea what was fertilising his wife's prize blooms and he was released from custody. Minnie faced her trial alone. And she faced her execution alone, one reporter from *The Times* remarking that she went to the scaffold 'without a flinch or falter; she died a brave, a wonderful woman'.

19 June

1928 (England) Chung Yi Miao was twenty-eight years old at the time he stood in the dock at the Carlisle Assizes in November 1928. He stood charged that, on 19 June of the same year he murdered his recent wife in a wood at Borrowdale. Both Chung Yi Miao and Wai-Sheung Siu were cultured, well-educated individuals from wealthy families of the Mandarin class. Wai-Sheung Siu was just a year older than her husband. They had met in New York, and married in a Christian church in the United States on 12 May 1928. As part of a leisurely honeymoon that would eventually take them back to China, the young couple had visited first Scotland and then the northern parts of England.

Shortly after lunch on 19 June Chung Yi Miao and his wife set off from the Borrowdale Gates Hotel, in the heart of Lakeland, on a walk that would take them alongside the River Derwent. At four o'clock Chung returned alone telling the maid that his wife had gone shopping in nearby Keswick and would be back around six. Wai-Sheung had not returned by ten-thirty, and her husband dined alone.

Meanwhile, to the south of the hotel along the Borrowdale Road, strange things were happening. At about seven-thirty that evening a local farmer had seen a woman in a fur coat beneath an open parasol, apparently sleeping beside a pool known locally as Kidham Dub. On his way home the farmer fell into conversation with a fellow traveller and happened to mention the woman with the parasol; that fellow traveller just happened to be Detective Constable William Pendlebury of the Southport police who was holidaying in the Lake District. And so the unfortunate Wai-Sheung Siu was found a little earlier than she might otherwise have been. She had been strangled with a thin white cord and there were abrasions where her wedding rings had been pulled off.

Chung Yi Miao was in bed snoozing, apparently unconcerned, when Inspector Graham arrived at the hotel at 11.00 p.m. Told that he was being held on suspicion, the sleeper feigned shock and surprise – which didn't wash very well when a search of the room revealed the victim's rings hidden in a roll-film container and cord of a similar type used in the murder.

Needless to say, Chung Yi Miao had a story. It involved being shadowed by a pair of 'sinister Orientals' who were after his wife's jewellery; and there was something about members of a secret 'tong' organisation. But it didn't fool the jury any more than it fooled Mr Justice Humphreys, who had no hesitation in passing sentence of death. Chung

Yi Miao was hanged in Manchester's Strangeways Prison on 6 December 1928.

20 June

1920 (England) This was the date on which Ronald Light stood trial at Leicester Castle for the murder of twenty-one-year-old Bella Wright at Gartree – what came to be known as the Green Bicycle Murder. The court heard how they had met while cycling near the village of Stoughton. Or rather, Light had been cycling and Bella was crouched over her bike trying to mend a puncture. Ronald Light stopped to help and afterwards accompanied her to her uncle's house at Gaulby. While she went in to see her relatives Light waited outside. When he got fed up with waiting Light mounted his bicycle and made his way back home to Leicester. However, he too had a puncture, and during the hour it took to fix it, Bella had not passed.

A farmer, Mr Cowell, was going along the Gartree Road later that night when he came across a girl lying on the ground next to a bicycle; when he examined her he found she was dead. After arranging for someone to guard the body, Mr Cowell went to summon the police and a doctor who ordered the body removed to an empty cottage nearby. On the following day a police officer returned to the scene and after a careful search found a bullet in the road, and when he washed some congealed blood from the face of the girl he found a bullet wound.

After speaking to Bella Wright's relatives at Gaulby a hue and cry went out for the man who had been waiting outside the house – 'The Man on the Green Bicycle'. Ronald Light claimed he read about the girl's death some days afterwards, and alarmed by the tone of the publicity he decided to dispose of his green bicycle, first filing off the serial number on the saddlebar, then throwing it into the canal.

In January 1920 Ronald Light left the district to take up a teaching job, and was unaware that shortly afterwards a barge dragged his bicycle from the canal. A cycle dealer examined the frame and found a second serial number on the front forks which quickly identified Light as the owner. It is, then, no surprise to find Ronald Light standing in the dock. What is a surprise is that, in part thanks to the brilliance of his defence attorney Edward Marshall Hall, Ronald Light was acquitted. To this day there is controversy among crime historians over the verdict of the trial; but there it is, we must accept the verdicts of juries or we must find another system.

21 June

1931 (England) In June 1931 Lieutenant Hubert George Chevis, a young artillery officer, was occupying a bungalow on the Blackdown Camp, near Aldershot. He also kept a family house in London where his wife and two children resided during the week and the family was reunited at the bungalow at weekends.

On the 21st of the month the Chevis's cook, a Mrs Yeomans, took delivery of a brace of partridges which Mrs Chevis had ordered from a local poulterer. The cook had hung the birds in the ventilated meat safe outside the house where they remained until mid-afternoon, when they were transferred to the oven to roast. That evening Lieutenant and Mrs Chevis sat down in anticipation of their evening treat, served, in accordance with quaint military protocol, by the Lieutenant's batman, Private Nicholas Bulger. Mrs Chevis took care of the carving.

Hubert Chevis lifted a forkful of bird to his lips expectantly . . . chewed, and grimaced: 'It tastes horrible!' Mrs Chevis, less adventurously, merely touched a piece of partridge flesh with her tongue. 'Fusty!' was her verdict. Within minutes Hubert was feeling very unwell, within fifteen minutes he had lost the use of his legs and was in the grip of strong convulsions; within the hour he was in the military hospital, by morning he was dead. Mrs Chevis suffered milder symptoms and eventually responded to treatment. As in all cases of violent or inexplicable death a post-mortem examination was ordered.

On the following day Sir William Chevis – Hubert's father – was arranging the funeral when the telegram boy delivered a message. It read, simply: 'Hooray Hooray Hooray', and was signed on the back 'J. Hartigan, Hibernia [a Dublin hotel]'. It seemed clear to both Sir William and the police that 'Hooray' was a celebration of Lieutenant Chevis's death, but how could that be when no information had been released. Could it be that Hartigan had first-hand knowledge? As it turned out no investigation of the telegram either in Eire or England would materially advance a solution to the case.

In the meanwhile the post-mortem had confirmed that Hubert Chevis had been poisoned and identified the poison as strychnine. And Sir William had received another telegram; this time postmarked Belfast and reading: 'It is a mystery they will never solve. J. Hartigan. Hooray.'

There was very little that could be added by witnesses at the coroner's inquest and it was left to the coroner simply to sum up for the jury – that Lieutenant Hubert Chevis had died from asphyxia following strychnine poisoning. Also that the poison had been administered in the flesh of the partridge, though there was no evidence as to how or by whom the birds were poisoned. It was therefore impossible to form an opinion as to whether the death had been accidental or murder. The jury took just five minutes to return an open verdict. Which is where the case still stands: an unsolved and apparently motiveless killing.

22 June

1954 (New Zealand) It was Tuesday afternoon, 22 June 1954, when two hysterical teenage girls rushed into a tea-shop in Canterbury with a story that the mother of one of them had suffered a fall and hit her head on the pavement. When police officers arrived they found Mrs Honora Parker lying on a pathway in the park; she was dead. And what was more, the injuries she had suffered were not consistent with a simple fall.

Now the girls changed their story. Sixteen-year-old Pauline Parker maintained that her mother had fallen just as they said, but added that they had thought it best to drag the prostrate woman to help. Pauline taking one leg, fifteen-year-old Juliet Hulme taking the other, they made their slow way along the path, and as they did so poor Mrs Parker's head kept 'bumping and banging'. The police were not convinced. So Pauline had another try. She and Juliet had lured Mrs Parker to the secluded spot and battered her to death with a brick. Almost certainly this was the true version – but why?

The two girls were, it turned out, very close. Close may not even be the best word to describe it – they bathed together, they slept in the same bed whenever possible, and they discussed sex endlessly. Whether they had embarked on a serious lesbian relationship has always been in doubt. It seemed unhealthy enough to the girls' mothers, though, to make a plan whereby the Hulmes were to emigrate to South Africa taking Juliet with them. Pauline asked Mrs Parker if she could go too. Mrs Parker said no; so they killed her. And that is really all there was to it.

At their trial in Christchurch High Court, they presented themselves as arrogant and unrepentant, which almost certainly turned the feelings of the jury away from them, and Pauline and Juliet were convicted and sentenced, as juveniles, to be detained during Her Majesty's pleasure. They were released in 1958.

23 June

1903 (England) Samuel Herbert Dougal was a man both attracted to and attractive to women, an unashamed womaniser with a string of illegitimate children dotted around the world like markers charting his career with the Royal Engineers.

In 1869 he married for the first time, and despite the inevitable infidelities the marriage lasted until 1885, when Mrs Dougal died in Nova Scotia where her husband was stationed. Within months the second Mrs Dougal had also perished – after a bout of severe vomiting. Dougal married for the third time in Dublin in 1892. In 1896 he was imprisoned for forgery (Samuel Dougal's second weakness was money – other people's money). On his release in 1898 he set about cultivating an attachment to a fifty-five-year-old spinster named Camille Holland. Miss Holland, though well educated, was rather unworldly, and seemed oblivious to the clear fact that Dougal simply wanted to get his hands on her modest fortune.

In 1899 they moved to a lonely farmhouse outside Saffron Walden called Moat Farm. Dougal, up to his old tricks, was discovered by Camille trying to seduce the maid and she ordered him to leave the house immediately. Shortly after this episode, on 19 May, Camille Holland and her lover set off on what they announced as a shopping trip; only Samuel returned. It was to be four years before anybody saw Camille Holland again – or what was left of her after spending that time buried in a drainage ditch.

Meanwhile, Dougal was making free with her money by the simple expedient of forgery; his wife (explained away to the neighbours as his widowed daughter) came to stay at the farm, and the couple settled into a life of comfort and ease underwritten by Camille Holland's bank balance.

But four years is a long time to spend on holiday (Dougal's explanation for Miss Holland's disappearance), and rumour became so strong that the local police were eventually obliged to make serious inquiries. Which was how they found the body in the ditch; it had been shot through the head with a revolver belonging to Samuel Dougal. He fled with what money and portable valuables he could lay his hands on, but was identified in London and detained.

On 30 April 1903, Samuel Herbert Dougal was charged with the murder of Camille Holland. His trial opened before Mr Justice Wright at the Shire Hall in Chelmsford, and by the evening of 23 June the jury had reached a verdict of guilty. Under sentence of death, Dougal made a number of preposterous 'confessions', among which was one that may have been close to the truth – characteristically it was made to a newspaper for money. On the morning of 8 July 1903 Samuel Dougal was hanged at Chelmsford Gaol by executioner Billington.

24 June

1806 (England) This story begins in 1806, at a time when much of the Church's revenue came from tithes; this was a levy exacted at ten per cent of the annual produce of land or labour, and was clearly not designed to be popular with the small farmer. It was particularly unwelcome when pursued with the aggressive disregard for circumstances that characterised the collecting technique of the Reverend Mr Parker, rector of Oddingly, just south of Droitwich. He was, in short, a very unpopular man.

On 24 June, Midsummer's Day, a shot was heard to come from the rectory garden, followed by the cry 'Murder!' When villagers reached him the Reverend Parker lay dead, his clothes still smouldering from the gun wadding. As one of the villagers gave chase the assassin turned and levelled a gun at him; having scared his pursuer into flight the gunman threw his weapon over a hedge and made good his escape. But not before he had been identified as Richard Hemming, a carpenter and wheelwright of Droitwich. It is no doubt indicative of Parker's unpopularity that the fifty guineas 'for information' remained unclaimed; and the mystery of why a comparative stranger with no connection with the rector should want to kill him remained unsolved.

It was in the year 1830 that the answers to this puzzle were uncovered. Since the relaxation of Parker's strangling grip on the collective agricultural purse, local farmers had been enjoying modest prosperity. Thomas Clewes, though, seemed happy to exchange one master for another, and now he gave the greater part of his profits to the brewer or innkeeper. When through drink he became incapable of following the plough his Netherwood Farm was sold; it was the new owner who found the skeleton under the barn floor. And it was Mrs Hemming from Droitwich who identified the teeth – heaven knows how – as those of her missing husband Richard.

It was far too late now, and unnecessary, to punish Hemming for the Reverend Parker's death; but it was in time to arrest Clewes for the murder of Richard Hemming. The terrified farmer was quick, however, to give credit where credit was due, for it was not his hand alone that cut Richard Hemming off in his prime. It transpired that a consortium of six local farmers had hired Hemming to dispose of the hated rector, and had then – whether as a precaution against exposure or because Hemming was trying to blackmail them on his own account – disposed of him in his turn. Of the guilty six, only Clewes and two others were still alive, and as the two others were by now prosperous and influential members of village society, it was thought best to put the skeletons back in the cupboard, so to speak, and withdraw any allegations and charges that had been made. Which seems to be a curiously satisfying conclusion.

25 June

1906 (USA) It was on 25 June 1906 that New York's Madison Square Roof Garden ironically played host to the murder of its own, and one of America's most famous, architects, Mr Stanford White. The occasion was the opening of a new review at the garden theatre, and among the audience, apart from White, were Harry Thaw, son of a Pennsylvania railroad millionaire, and 'Mad' Harry's wife, the twenty-year-old chorus girl Evelyn Nesbit. The aggravating factor on this particular evening was that Evelyn, before her marriage to Harry Thaw had been 'associated' with Stanford White. In order, presumably, to protect what little good name she had left, Evelyn had told her prospective husband that White had drugged and seduced her. Now, Stanford White was a notorious womaniser, attracted to the young nymphs of theatreland's chorus lines and would no doubt have been quite capable of drugging and seducing his prey; it just happened that in Evelyn Nesbit's case it was not necessary. In fact he was keeping her in some degree of luxury even at the time she was seeing Mad Harry.

However, it was Evelyn's story that Harry chose, loyally, to believe. And so, during the performance of the uninspired musical *Mamzelle Champagne* on that hot June evening, Harry Thaw left his seat, crossed between the maze of tables and chairs to where Stanford White was sitting (waiting for one of the chorus girls) and shot him through the head.

In a sensational New York trial, Thaw's defence depended upon the jury accepting an 'unwritten law' which absolved 'all true Americans' from the consequences of avenging the violation of their womenfolk. Despite large amounts of the Thaw family's fortune being spent buying lawyers, bribing witnesses and underwriting a campaign to vilify publicly the reputation of Stanford White, Harry Thaw was found guilty but insane and committed to an asylum.

In 1915, after a dramatic escape from the custody of the hospital, Harry Thaw successfully applied for a retrial and was this time acquitted. Which all went to confirm that old Broadway adage – 'You can't convict a million dollars!'

26 June

1992 (USA) It had taken three trials to get her pinned down – the first fell on a technicality, the second on a hung jury; at the third trial the jury returned a unanimous verdict of guilty. On 26 June 1992 Carolyn Warmus, having been convicted of second-degree murder and possession of an illegal weapon, was sentenced to twenty-five to life.

To anybody who knew her well this would have come as no surprise, to anybody who had been on the receiving end of her obsessional spite it would have come as a relief. Carolyn had those two failings which so often end up in court – she was promiscuous and she was vindictive. And the curious thing is that she might be thought to have had all the advantages in life: she was young, attractive and outgoing, she had a bachelor's degree from the University of Michigan and a master's from Columbia, and she had a good career as a teacher. Carolyn Warmus clearly wanted more – she wanted the power to destroy. In 1983, for example, she tried to sabotage the engagement of an ex-lover to another girl – sending threatening letters until the police were obliged to warn her off. Then she hired a private detective to check on the fidelity of her current lover and ended up sleeping with the detective.

The real trouble started in 1987, when Carolyn began an affair with Paul Solomon. Solomon was married, but that didn't worry Carolyn – she would simply get rid of Betty Jeanne Solomon. First she thought she might hire a detective to prove that Mrs Solomon was being unfaithful to her husband; then she told another investigator that a woman named Betty Jeanne was threatening her family. In the end she opted for the simple approach and bought a .25-calibre Beretta pistol. At midnight on 15 January 1989 Paul Solomon telephoned the police to tell them that he had just arrived home and found his wife dead. She had been shot nine times in the head and chest. The story that he and Carolyn had concocted was simple. They had spent the evening together at a Holiday Inn in New York, had a few drinks and parted at 11.30. Easy.

But within six months both Carolyn and Solomon were up to their old tricks. He was vacationing in Puerto Rico with a new woman, Carolyn was sabotaging their relationship with messages sent to the hotel, anonymous phone calls to the woman's family . . .

The end of the line came for Carolyn Warmus in November 1989; that was the month that the police learnt of her purchase of a gun of the type used to kill Betty Jeanne Solomon. On 1 February 1990 she was indicted for second-degree murder.

27 June

1981 (England) As eternal triangles went, this one had nothing very special going for it. Susan and Michael Barber had been married long enough to have produced three children, and the relationship had long since soured.

Susan had worked her way through a succession of lovers and had left home twice, only to return for the sake of the children. In May 1981 Michael Barber returned home inconveniently early from a fishing trip and found his wife and his best friend, Richard Collins, in bed together. Furious, he beat his wife and threw Collins out of the house. The following day Susan made her husband one of his favourite meals, steak and kidney pie. This time it had an extra ingredient – a dose of weedkiller containing paraquat.

Now paraquat is as lethal to human beings as it is to weeds, producing fibrosis of the lungs with symptoms identical to pneumonia and kidney disorder. On 27 June 1981 Michael Barber died in Hammersmith Hospital, London. Fortunately for justice, the obligatory post-mortem was carried out by an observant pathologist, Professor David Evans who, suspecting poison, removed samples from the organs for analysis before releasing the body for disposal. The results from the National Poisons Unit at New Cross Hospital confirmed that Michael Barber had been poisoned with paraquat.

It was not until April 1982 that Susan Barber, now in possession of her husband's £15,000 insurance was arrested and charged with murder. At Chelmsford Crown Court in November of the same year, Mrs Barber was joined in the dock by Richard Collins; she received a life sentence for murder, he collected two years for conspiracy. But by now Susan Barber had a new lover, and in July 1983 she was briefly released from Holloway Prison in order to marry him.

28 June

1964 (England) It was 28 June 1964; a fine day to look for maggots, the two thirteen-year-olds thought as they scouted through Bracknell woods in the hope of finding a dead pigeon or a squirrel, any dead meat that might be home to the fat white maggots they needed for fishing bait. Then they found them; thousands of the things. The excitement ended as soon as the boys saw what the maggots were feeding on, as soon as they saw the arm. 'There's a dead body buried in the woods!' the horrified youngsters told police.

For forensic pathologist Keith Simpson the call-out was routine – a body discovered in suspicious circumstances. Beneath the covering of moss and leaves was the body of a man lying on his back, his head wrapped in towelling. The corpse was too far decomposed to allow any normal time-of-death tests – in fact the police thought it might have been up there a couple of months But they had reckoned without a very special study that Simpson had made his own. He put the time of death as at least nine or ten days – 'but probably not more than twelve; it's astonishing how quickly maggots will eat up flesh'.

The pathologist had routinely collected samples of the insect infestation and identified the maggots as those of the common blue-bottle (*Calliphora erythrocephalus*): 'The larvae I was looking at were mature, indeed elderly, fat, indolent, third-stage maggots, but they were not in pupa cases. Therefore I estimated that the eggs had been laid nine or ten days earlier. Adding a little more time to allow for the blue-bottles getting to the dead body, I reckoned death had occurred on 16 or 17 June.'

The victim had been identified as Peter Thomas, reported missing from Lyndney on 16 June; he had died from blood seeping into his windpipe from a crushed larynx. It was also known that Thomas had lent a sum of money to a man named Brittle. Under questioning William Brittle admitted that he had met with the victim on 16 June and had repaid the money. It came to light during the interview that Brittle had been trained in unarmed combat – which was just what Keith Simpson wanted to know. Peter Thomas's neck injury was entirely consistent with a karate chop to the throat.

The problem with all of this was that the police had a very inconvenient independent witness who insisted that he had seen Thomas, alive and well, in Gloucester on 20 June. At William Brittle's trial, Keith Simpson's entomological evidence effectively destroyed this 'alibi', and Brittle was convicted of murder and sentenced to life imprisonment.

29 June

1959 (Canada) Twenty-one-year-old Bobby Cook was arrested in Stettler, Alberta, on a charge of using his father's identity card to obtain a car by fraud. Cook, who already had a previous record for auto theft insisted that his father had given him the ID in order to get the car. The following morning, Royal Canadian Mounted Police Sergeant Roach went to Cook senior's home to check on his son's story, but found nobody in. Returning the next day, 29 June 1959, the police decided to search the house and found in the garage, concealed in a grease pit, no fewer than seven bodies, all of which had been shot and bludgeoned. The victims were Ray Cook senior, his second wife Daisy Mae and their children, Gerald Rae, Patrick William, Christopher Frederick, Kathy Vern and Linda Mae. Inside the house, officers noticed that attempts had been made to scrub the walls clean of bloodstains. Hidden beneath a mattress in the master bedroom was a bloodstained prison-issue blue suit and tie which had been allotted to Bobby Cook.

Cook was charged with his father's murder and remanded to a mental institution for psychiatric examination. When he was refused permission to attend his family's funeral, Cook escaped but was recaptured four days later, without any resistance, less than an hour's journey from the cemetery where his family had been buried.

Robert Cook's trial opened in Red Deer in November 1959 before Mr Justice Peter Greschuck. The prosecution presented a strong but circumstantial case, with some contradictory evidence about the guns found in the case. Cook's defence was an alibi; simply that he was not in Stettler at the time of the murders. After a ten-day trial, the jury found him guilty and he was sentenced to death. Following an appeal to the Alberta Court of Appeal, the justices by a 3–2 majority ordered a new trial. The second trial opened in Edmonton on 20 June 1960, and followed a similar course to the first, except that the jury deliberated for less than half an hour before returning with their guilty verdict. Mr Justice Harold Riley passed sentence of death. A second appeal to the Alberta Court of Appeal was dismissed, and an application for leave to appeal to the Supreme Court of Canada was refused. Bobby Cook was hanged at the Fort Saskatchewan Correctional Institute on 14 November 1960.

In the intervening years many people have confessed to the Cook family murders but none convincingly enough to be believed. Nevertheless, despite a lack of evidence to support their claim, there are still some Canadians who are convinced of Robert Cook's innocence.

30 June

1716 (Scotland) The Maiden is a very particular kind of execution machine looking and acting like a guillotine and confined to Scotland. It has a very long history and the original apparatus can still be seen in the Edinburgh Historical Museum. On 30 June 1716, John Hamilton was beheaded by the Maiden, said to be the last felon who was. The following is derived from a contemporary account.

Hamilton was born in Clydesdale and his parents sent him to Glasgow to study the law; but the young gentleman's disposition leading him to the profession of arms would have secured a commission, but for the intervention of this crime.

He soon became connected with some abandoned young men in Edinburgh and lost considerable sums in gaming. Having borrowed more money from his parents, Hamilton went to a village near Glasgow to meet his companions at the public house kept by Thomas Arkle. Having been drinking and gaming for several successive days and nights Hamilton's companions crept out as he slept and left him to discharge their bill. A quarrel arose over the matter with Arkle and, as they quarrelled, Arkle stripped Hamilton's sword from his scabbard. The latter immediately ran away, but finding he had no sword he instantly went back to the house, when, on Arkle calling him several scandalous names, he stabbed him so that he instantly expired. The daughter of Arkle attempted to seize her father's slayer and in doing so tore off the bottom of his coat as he escaped a second time. However, the purloined sword and the piece of coat proved the means of bringing the assassin to justice.

Having fled to Holland to escape the consequences of his murder, John Hamilton, hearing of the death of his parents two years later, returned to Scotland, where he was taken in custody. At his trial, John Hamilton pleaded that he was intoxicated at the time of the incident, and that he was provoked by the ill-usage he had received from Arkle. The jury, dismissing these arguments, found him guilty, and he was sentenced to be beheaded on the Maiden.

July

1 July

1909 (England) If you had been watching the Tottenham Court Road shooting gallery during the first half of 1909 you couldn't have missed him; he was there three days a week for target practice with his Colt automatic revolver. He was distinguished from the other budding marksmen by his dark complexion and serious look. He was getting good, too.

Today is 1 July 1909, and it is twenty-five-year-old Madar Lal Dhingra's last visit to the gallery. Of his twelve shots, eleven have hit the target; the target is about the size of a man's head. That same evening there is a concert at the Imperial Institute, and Dhingra has received an invitation from the secretary of the National Indian Association, a charitable group committed to helping and advising Indian students studying in England; Madar Lal Dhingra is completing an engineering course at University College, London. Unlike the other students, Indian or otherwise, attending the Imperial Institute concert, Dhingra is taking along his trusty Colt, a pistol of Belgian origin and a knife. One man there who is most *un*likely to be carrying an arsenal with him is the honorary treasurer of the National Indian Association, Sir William Hutt Curzon Wyllie KCIE, for many years a servant of the Crown in India; he is there with his wife . . .

The concert finished at around 11.00 p.m. and the audience were beginning to disperse in an orderly and good-natured manner when Sir William is approached by Madar Lal Dhingra who exchanges a few words with the diplomat before pulling the Colt from his pocket and firing five shots at him from point-blank range. It should not need saying that given Dhingra's marksmanship and the closeness of range, Sir William died instantly with four bullets in his brain. At first there was the paralysis of utter shock, utter horror. Then one of the crowd, an Indian doctor from Hong Kong, leapt forward to seize the assassin and was, for his trouble, fatally shot. With the final bullet Dhingra now turned the gun on himself, but the mechanism misfired and before he could retrieve the other gun from his pocket he was disarmed.

Not the sort of behaviour that one would have expected of an Indian student at a National Indian Association concert attended by its distinguished honorary treasurer. It was not until his trial opened at the Old Bailey that we got an insight into this madman's mind. Dhingra, in a statement which was read to the court, declared: 'English people have no right to occupy India and it is perfectly justifiable on our part to kill the Englishman who is polluting our sacred soil.' Dhingra seemed conveniently to have forgotten the unfortunate Indian doctor whom he had also slain. Not that it made any real difference to anybody in the end. The jury had no alternative but to convict, nor the judge to pass sentence of death, nor for that matter the hangman to pull the lever. For Madar Lal Dhingra the loss of his miserable life was nothing compared to the privilege of dying for patriotism.

2 July

1669 (England) Stephen Eaton, George Roades and Sarah Swift, in company with several others, conspired to rob and kill the Reverend John Talbot at Aniseed Clear, near Shoreditch, east London. There is a lengthy and bloodthirsty account of the attack on Mr Talbot in *The Malefactors' Register*, from which the following extracts are taken:

Not long after Mr Talbot had got into the fields he perceived the same persons at his heels who had dogged him before. He was now more alarmed than ever, it being eleven o'clock at night. The most probable method of escaping was by breaking through a reed hedge to a garden house; but before he could reach the place one or more of the villains seized him and began to pick his pockets. They found about twenty shillings and his knife, with which they attempted to kill him, by cutting his throat.

Whether it was by chance, or these wretches have acquired extraordinary skills in butchering men, is uncertain; but they first cut a piece of his throat, about the breadth of a crown-piece, without touching the windpipe, and then, in the dependent part of the orifice, they stabbed him with the knife so deep that the point almost reached his lungs. However, Providence so far overruled their cruelty that they did not cut the recurrent nerves, which would have stopped his speech, nor the jugular veins and arteries, which if they had done he had instantly bled to death without remedy, and then possibly no discovery would have been made. While the wretches were committing their butchery the dogs barked and the beasts bellowed in an uncommon manner; so that several gardeners rose out of their beds supposing it to be daylight. Some bricklayers who had been alarmed by the noise discovered Mr Talbot lying in his shirt and drawers all bloody . . . The care of Mr Talbot's wounds was committed to one Mr Lichfield, an able surgeon, who was helped by many eminent volunteers. By their joint direction he was in a fair way to be cured. About noon on Sunday he was dressed. The wound looked well, and he seemed more cheerful than lately; but within two or three hours after, a violent fit of coughing seized him which broke the jugular vein, and caused such an effusion of blood that he fainted, and his extreme parts were cold, before anyone could come to his assistance. The flux was once stopped, but upon coughing he bled again, so that his case was almost past hope . . . The doctor prayed with him and departed, and within two hours he expired . . .

It should be added that the whole gang who attacked the reverend gentleman so fatally were taken into custody, and on 14 July 1669 they were transported by cart to the gallows at Tyburn and hanged.

3 July

1993 (USA) 'RAMBO RAMPAGE' was a typical newspaper headline reporting middle-aged property developer Gian Ferri's second visit to a San Francisco office block on Friday 3 July 1993. His first visit to the legal company on the 34th floor had been over a law suit he was engaged in, and had apparently ended in him storming out very angry indeed.

On this second visit Ferri had two 9mm semi-automatic pistols strapped to his braces, a .45-calibre revolver in his hand and a bag full of ammunition. He entered a conference room and opened fire on the legal staff present. Twenty-eight-year-old lawyer John Scully died when he threw himself on top of his wife to protect her. Several other people engaged in the conference were hit as Ferri sprayed bullets around the room. Then he made his way through the offices shooting at anyone he saw. For nearly an hour Gian Luigi Ferri rampaged over four floors, leaving eight dead and seven wounded, two critically.

The shootings created a state of terror among the more than 6,000 staff employed in the building, many of whom locked themselves in their offices. Ferri's murder spree finally came to an end when he was making his way down the stairs to the 29th floor, presumably to continue the carnage. Fortunately, perhaps, he met an armed police team on their way up. Before they could take any action, Ferri put a gun under his chin and fired a single shot which killed him instantly.

A police statement afterwards said 'No one was suspicious because he was wearing a business suit and a shirt and a tie. He kept his weapons hidden under his jacket.'

4 July

1770 (England) Execution of James Attaway and Richard Bailey at Tyburn. They had broken into the home of Thomas Le Merr, Esquire, in Bedford Row, London, stabbed the butler through the stomach, bound and gagged him and then locked him in the cellar before robbing the house. With his last breaths the loyal retainer gnawed through his ropes and shouted for help, which led to the speedy arrest of the felons.

5 July

1589 (England) Joan Coney, Joan Upney and Joan Prentice, collectively known as the Chelmsford Witches, were executed within two hours of being capitally sentenced for the crime of bewitching to death. This was the third major witch trial to have been held in the Essex town, the first taking place in 1566.

6 July

1984 (USA) When they finally caught up with Bizarre Bob Berdella officers of the Kansas City police force could hardly believe their ears. They knew he was weird – possibly dangerous – but they listened dumbfounded when he began to catalogue the imprisonment, torture, sexual abuse and murder that had been going on under their noses between 6 July 1984, when Bob claimed his first victim, and 5 August 1987 when the last one died. And when a police team raided

Berdella's home there was no doubting the truth. There they found packs of photographs showing explicit scenes of the mutilation and degradation of his victims and a diary recording details of his captives and the injections of animal tranquillisers he used to subdue them.

Robert A. Berdella was already known to the police as the crazy who ran a weird emporium in the city called Bob's Bizarre Bazaar, a throwback to the hippie cults of the 1960s, specialising in the macabre mumbo-jumbo such as replica skulls so beloved of ageing hippies, pill-poppers, pot-heads and weekend Satanists. He used to hand out business cards saying he had 'poison' in his head. But if a little something was being smoked out back then who cared – when you have a place like Kansas City to patrol you ignore the antics of people like Bizarre Bob.

That was until 1 April 1988, when officers of the Kansas City police force found a young man wandering the streets wearing nothing but a studded dog's collar round his neck. Down at the station the man said his name was Christopher Bryson, that he was twenty-two years old, and that he had been picked up by a man named Robert Berdella. Berdella had invited him back home, jumped him and bound and gagged him. He then suggested sex. When Bryson rejected his indelicate advances, and absolutely refused to cooperate, crazy Bob threatened that he would 'end up in the trash like the others'. After five days of sexual abuse, Chris Bryson had taken advantage of Berdella's temporary absence to make his escape through a second-storey window.

On 4 April, Robert Berdella was arraigned on seven counts of sodomy, one of felonious restraint and one of first-degree assault. Safely out of mischief, the police could now make further investigation into the more serious possibilities – like murder. Berdella said he had killed six times, and officers digging around his house unearthed a number of skulls as well as other bone fragments. In the end they were able to list the victims as Larry Pearson, Gerald Howell, Robert Sheldon, Walter Ferris, Mark Wallace and Todd Stoops.

In court on 13 August 1988, Robert Berdella pleaded guilty to the murder of Larry Pearson, though as the result of a technical fault on the part of the prosecution in not informing the prisoner that they would be seeking the death penalty, Berdella was sentenced only to life imprisonment. On 20 December he officially pleaded guilty to the other five killings and received a further five concurrent life sentences.

7 July

1856 (England) On 7 July 1856 the Select Committee on Capital Punishment presented its recommendation to Parliament that: 'execution should in future be carried into effect within the precincts of the prison . . .' (See also 1 May.)

8 July

1921 (Wales) That juries are fallible is obvious from their very constitution. It would be a miracle if errors of judgement were not occasionally made by these twelve ordinary citizens; but there are occasions when the consequences reach far beyond the jury box. The case of Harold Jones is one. Cleared of one murder, on 8 July 1921 Jones committed a second.

On the evening of 5 February 1921, eight-year-old Freda Burnell walked into an oil and seed merchant's in Abertillery on an errand for her father. Mr Burnell kept a few chickens in the back yard at home, and it had been Freda's duty and pleasure to shop for the poultry grit. She would never feed the chickens again.

On the morning of the following day Freda Burnell's body was found in a lane near to the seed shop; the girl's hands and feet had been bound and some attempt had been made at rape. Death had resulted from partial strangulation and shock, probably occasioned by a savage blow to her forehead.

It was in the shed behind the shop that investigating officers found little Freda's handkerchief – the clue which was to put Harold Jones, shop assistant, and only fifteen years old, into the dock at Monmouth Assizes. Despite strong evidence in favour of a conviction, some spirit of the perverse seemed to infect the seven men and five women of the jury. We will never know what debate passed between them in the retiring room on that late June afternoon, but whatever it was produced the astonishing verdict of not guilty.

Now, if the jury had seemed perverse, it was left to the general public – not least the good citizens of Abertillery – to add caprice to the case. No sooner had Jones's acquittal been announced, and he had been released by the court, than he was elevated to that position of popular approbation normally reserved for conquering heroes. After his slow – almost majestic – return to his home town in an open deck bus with bunting, Harold Jones addressed the jubilant crowd from a hotel balcony.

On 8 July in that same year of 1921, Florence Irene Little, aged eleven, was found at the end of a trail of blood leading to the attic of the Jones family house. Her throat had been cut with a kitchen knife over the downstairs sink.

Harold Jones, by the time that he had been indicted at Monmouth for the second time in six months on a charge of murder, had confessed not only to the killing of Florence Little, but also to that of Freda Burnell. His reason for such cruelty? 'My desire to kill.'

In November 1921, Jones was found guilty. That he evaded the sentence of death was due solely to his youth; sentenced before his sixteenth birthday, Jones was ordered to be detained during His Majesty's pleasure. The final word went to Mr Justice (later Lord) Roche, who observed that the quite undeserved adulation showered on Jones after his previous acquittal almost certainly contributed to his arrogance in killing again.

9 July

1923 (England) Madame Marie-Marguerite Fahmy shot her husband, Prince Ali Kamel Fahmy Bey, at London's Savoy Hotel. At her Old Bailey trial before Mr Justice Swift, Madame Fahmy's counsel, Edward Marshall Hall, gave graphic descriptions of his client's life of brutality, humiliation and sexual degradation at her husband's hands. The jury, clearly moved by this impassioned speech, gave Marshall Hall what he wanted – an acquittal.

10 July

1782 (England) Joseph Wall, Esquire, was descended from a good family in Ireland, and entered the army at an early age. He was of a severe and rather unaccommodating temper; nor was he much liked among the officers.

Mr Wall was Lieutenant-Governor of Senegambia, but acted as chief, the first appointment being vacant. It was an office he held but a short time – not more than two years – during which he was accused of the wilful murder of Benjamin Armstrong, by ordering him to receive eight hundred lashes, on 10 July 1782, of which he died five days afterwards. His emoluments were very considerable, as, besides his military appointments, he was Superintendent of Trade to the colony.

As soon as the account of the murder reached the Board of the Admiralty a reward was offered for his apprehension. But having evaded justice in 1784, he lived on the continent, mostly in France but sometimes in Italy under an assumed name, where he behaved respectably and was admitted into good company.

In 1797 he returned to Britain as if by a kind of fatality. He was frequently advised to leave again but seemed unable to, saying sometimes he had a distant intention of making a surrender in order to take his trial. He was allied by marriage to a noble family and his wife frequently visited him in his concealment in Lambeth. But for a short time he lived in Bedford Square, where he was apprehended.

At the trial it was proved by witnesses that Armstrong was far from being undutiful in his behaviour. He was, however, tied to a gun carriage, and black men, brought there for the purpose – not the drummers, who in the ordinary course of things would have to flog this man, supposing him to have deserved flogging – were ordered to inflict on him the punishment ordered. Each took his turn and gave this unhappy sufferer twenty-five lashes until he had received the number of eight hundred; and the instrument with which the punishment was inflicted was not a cat-o'-nine-tails, which was the usual instrument, but a piece of rope of great thickness.

The prisoner in his defence urged that the deceased was guilty of mutiny, that the punishment was not so severe as reported. The jury nevertheless pronounced a verdict of guilty and the recorder proceeded to pass sentence of death: that he should be executed the next morning and that his body be afterwards delivered to be anatomised, according to statute.

11 July

1980 (USA) Alvin King, a forty-eight-year-old former schoolteacher, drove from his home to the First Baptist Church in Dangerfield, Texas on the morning of Sunday 22 June 1980, carrying an arsenal of weapons including an M1 carbine, an automatic rifle, two revolvers and 240 rounds of ammunition. Bursting into the church, he shouted 'This is war' and opened fire with the carbine. With the first shots, Gina Linam, aged seven, and seventy-eight-year-old Thelma Robinson fell dead and Mrs Gene Gandy, aged forty-nine, took a bullet near the heart and died later the same day.

Another member of the congregation, Christopher Hall,

grappled with King and succeeded in knocking the rifles out of his hands and dislodging his spectacles. No doubt the loss of King's glasses was responsible for saving Chris Hall's life; at least as he fled after the struggle he was not hit by shots from the gunman's revolver. James McDaniel and Kenneth Truitt were the next people to try to tackle King. First, McDaniel managed to pull King to the ground but in the struggle was shot dead; Truitt charged at King while he was on the floor, but was also killed by revolver fire. Ten other members of the Dangerfield First Baptists' congregation received gunshot wounds of greater or lesser severity. Alvin King ran from the church, dropping one of the guns as he did so; once outside he made an ineffectual attempt to shoot himself in the head.

The day after the shootings, King had been due to face trial on a charge of incest involving his nineteen-year-old daughter; he had also been a suspect following the stabbing to death of a local minister who had persuaded the daughter to contact police regarding the incest allegation.

On 11 July, Alvin King was charged with five counts of first-degree murder and ten of assault with intent to kill. On 28 July a jury found him to be of unsound mind and he was sent to a State Hospital for the criminally insane until he was judged to be 'rehabilitated'. On 24 November 1981, he was certified fit for trial which was fixed for 25 January 1982.

Alvin King never did face trial; on 19 January he hanged himself in the Dangerfield town jail with strips torn from his towel.

12 July

1898 (Scotland) John Watson Laurie, a Glasgow pattern maker, was masquerading under the name of 'Mr Annandale' at Rothesay during the Fair week in July. On the 12th of that month he struck up an acquaintance, during a sail from

Rothesay to Arran on board the *Ivanhoe*, with a London clerk named Edwin Rose, who was also on holiday. The upshot of this was that they both agreed to return to Arran and climb Goatfell together. For this purpose they engaged a room at Invercloy, and returned to Rothesay.

They set out for Arran as arranged on 13 July. In the meantime, Rose had introduced his friend to two acquaintances who took against Annandale, and warned Rose – a man who had plenty of money – to have nothing more to do with him. Rose, however, did not act upon this advice, and they climbed Goatfell together. Annandale returned to his lodgings that evening alone and told the landlady that his friend had been called back to London.

Rose's relatives, who became alarmed at his non-appearance at the end of his holiday, instituted inquiries. It was established that he had not left the island, so numerous search parties scoured Goatfell for the missing man, who seemed to have veritably vanished into space. After some time his mangled remains were found lying under a boulder at the foot of a precipice on Goatfell. Rose's pockets were empty, while under a stone were a stick and a cap which belonged to him. Annandale (or perhaps now we should call him Laurie) had earlier been seen wearing some of the dead man's clothes but had now disappeared. A warrant was issued for his apprehension on the charge of murder. He was at length run to earth, on 3 September, near Larkhill, after an exciting chase. He attempted suicide – when hotly pursued – by cutting his throat with a razor.

In court it was alleged that Laurie had thrown Rose over a cliff, beaten him to death, then buried his body under a heap of stones. For the defence it was maintained that the injuries could easily have been accounted for by a fall. The jury returned a verdict of guilty, and the Lord Justice-Clerk passed sentence of death to be carried out at Greenock Prison.

Petitions for a reprieve were at once set in motion, stating that the prisoner was not fully responsible for his actions and that there had been insanity in the family. In consequence of the petitions the capital sentence was commuted to penal servitude for life in view of a medical report on his soundness of mind. Laurie was removed to Peterhead Gaol where a few years later he tried to escape, but was quickly recaptured. Latterly his mind gave way and he died on 4 October 1930.

(Account based on the *Scots Black Kalander*)

13 July

1959 (England) It was while his blackmail victim kept him talking that Guenther Fritz Podola was pulled from a public telephone box by Detective Sergeant Raymond Purdy and Detective Sergeant John Sandford on 13 July. As they attempted to take him into custody, Podola escaped, and in the chase that followed, he shot DS Purdy dead and ran off. Podola was traced to the Claremont House Hotel, Kensington, on 16 July. Although he claimed total amnesia for the time of the shooting, it took the jury only thirty minutes to find Podola guilty of murder. He was hanged at Wandsworth on 5 November 1959.

14 July

1966 (USA) On the night of 14 July 1966 Corazon Amurao and five friends were at home in their Chicago nurses' residence. In response to a knock, Corazon opened the front door and the six girls found themselves captives of Richard Speck, who reeked of alcohol and waved a gun in one hand and a knife in the other. Speck ordered the girls to lie on the floor and bound them with strips torn from a bed-sheet. At intervals of twenty minutes Speck dragged the girls one by one into another room and stabbed and strangled them. All, that is, except Corazon Amurao, who managed to wriggle under a bed and was miraculously overlooked by the killer.

When Speck finally left, Miss Amurao raised the alarm and it was not long before the murderous Speck was identified by fingerprints left at the scene of his crime.

After a brief trial Richard Speck was sentenced to die in the electric chair on 6 June 1967. However, the United States Supreme Court had suspended the death penalty and Speck was resentenced to a term of 400 years' imprisonment. He maintained his innocence until 1978, when he made a full confession. Richard Speck died in prison in 1991.

15 July

1953 (England) On this date one of the country's worst serial killers, John Reginald Halliday Christie – the Monster of Rillington Place – kept his appointment with the hangman at Pentonville Prison. It was too late, however, to save Timothy Evans who, in 1949, was executed for one of Christie's murders.

John Christie and his wife Ethel had occupied the ground floor of No. 10 Rillington Place since 1938 and he was regarded by the neighbours as a rather superior sort of fellow, with pretensions to education. The house had enjoyed its brief period of notoriety when the tenant of the flat above the Christies, Timothy Evans, had been hanged for the murder of his wife and child; Christie was the chief prosecution witness at his trial.

Around December 1953, Mrs Christie stopped being seen about her domestic duties, and when neighbours inquired John (or 'Reg' as he liked to be called) told them she had gone north on medical grounds. Then John Christie disappeared, and the rooms passed to Mr Beresford Brown. While Mr Brown was exploring his new kitchen he was struck by the strange combination of smells, first it was disinfectant, then something rather unpleasant. Having traced the origin of the smells to a small papered-over cupboard, the new tenant tore the paper from over a cut-out section of the door and shone his torch in. What he saw were a woman's legs. When the police arrived they found more than one woman's legs in the cupboard, they found three whole women. And another one – later identified as Mrs Ethel Christie – beneath the floorboards in the living room. More detailed searching in the back yard provided evidence of two more deaths.

Meanwhile Mr Christie had been picked up by a beat bobby at Putney Bridge and gone quietly to the local police station. In conversation with Chief Inspector Griffin, Reg Christie told how one night in December he had been awakened by his wife who was convulsive and unable to breathe. He could not, he said, bear to see her suffer so he strangled her. Then he put her under the floorboards: 'I thought that was the best way to lay her to rest,' he said. After that Christie described the meetings with and murders of a succession of other women, lured to the house while Ethel was away. There was Rita Nelson, Hectorina MacLennan and Kathleen Maloney who ended up in the kitchen cupboard; and Ruth Fuerst and Muriel Eady who were buried in the back yard. Oh yes, and there was Beryl Evans, for whose murder poor Tim Evans had already been executed.

Christie's trial was a formality, and despite his confession to multiple murder he was charged only with the killing of his wife. Mr Derek Curtis-Bennett QC advanced a plea of insanity on Christie's behalf, but the jury found him sane and guilty. There was no appeal.

16 July

1952 (England) On the evening of 16 July 1952, Mr Cuthbert Wiltshaw returned to his luxury house at Barlaston to find his wife lying in the hallway, her skull smashed, her jaw broken and her face gashed open. Beside the body lay a metal poker, heavily bloodstained. Realising their own limitations, it was not long before the local police summoned help from Scotland Yard. When it arrived, in the persons of Detective Superintendent Reginald Spooner and Detective Sergeant Ernest Millen, they found that the local force had already turned up a number of potentially valuable clues. A bloody footprint on the kitchen floor, for instance, and a pair of bloodstained chamois leather gloves found beneath a tree in the garden, and probably accounting for the absence of alien fingerprints in the house. On the thumb of the left glove there was a small tear and the little pearl button torn from it was found beneath the body of Mrs Wiltshaw. Inexplicably missing was Mr Wiltshaw's old blue gardening raincoat. The fact that a large amount of jewellery and other valuables had disappeared suggested robbery as the motive; and to Superintendent Reg Spooner's mind, the way the items were selected suggested a person who knew the inside of the house. This meant former staff had to be traced, and soon only Leslie Green, the chauffeur had not been accounted for. One sinister fact was that Green had recently been dismissed from his post for making personal use of the car.

When Leslie Green was finally interviewed he claimed that on the day of Mrs Wiltshaw's murder he was in Stafford, and gave a very elaborate itinerary by way of an alibi. The only problem was that it was not nearly tight enough. It would have been possible, Reg Spooner calculated, for Green to have caught the 5.10 from Stafford to Barlaston and have fifteen minutes to commit the crime before returning on the 6.05. Which coincided with the unverifiable time Green claimed he was snoozing in the park.

One significant breakthrough came in an interview with Leslie Green's girlfriend to whom he gave two of Mrs Wiltshaw's rings on the evening of the murder. Then the railway police turned up Mr Wiltshaw's old raincoat, bloodstained now, from along the Stafford/Barlaston line. Leslie Green was invited to try on the chamois gloves found in the Wiltshaw garden – not only did they fit, but the cut in the left thumb corresponded exactly with a recently healed cut on Green's thumb. And of course his rubber-soled shoe was a perfect match for the bloody footprint.

Never was such a complete case brought against a killer. For three relentless days the damning evidence was paraded before the jury at Stafford Assizes; two days before Christmas 1952 Leslie Green stood on the drop at Stafford Gaol.

17 July

1942 (England) A case that was to prove fundamental to the development of that branch of forensic medicine called odontology (or forensic dentistry) was revealed in 1942. A labourer who was clearing the bomb-damaged crypt of Vauxhall Baptist Church on 17 July had lifted a stone slab and found beneath it a human body reduced almost to a skeleton. The first suggestion was that it was just one more victim of the Luftwaffe's attacks on London. It was not dismissed so lightly by Dr Keith Simpson, the pathologist who was called to the scene.

War victims, in Simpson's experience at least, do not bury themselves under stone slabs. Nor do they dismember themselves and jump into a fire covered with quicklime! No, Dr Simpson thought there must be some other explanation for the remains – one that the police were not going to like very much. The pathologist's estimate of the time of death was between one and one and a half years before. A check of the police records for that area showed that a Mrs Rachel Dobkin, former wife of a fire-watcher, had been reported missing fifteen months previously by her sister. Harry Dobkin, it was learnt, was employed to keep a lookout for fires by a company of solicitors whose offices had been located next to the Baptist chapel.

Although the corpse's lower jaw had become detached and was missing, the upper jaw showed evidence of extensive dental repair. An interview with Mrs Dobkin's sister, Polly, provided two vital clues. The first was that Rachel had been suffering from a fibroid tumour (evidence of which had been found in the remains); the second was that Rachel's regular dentist was Dr Barnett Kopkin of Stoke Newington. Dr Kopkin, a meticulous practitioner, had kept records of the treatment undertaken on Mrs Dobkin's teeth and was able to draw a chart which corresponded exactly with the upper jaw of the corpse. On 26 August 1942, Harry Dobkin was arrested and charged with the murder of his wife. Three months later he was tried, convicted and sentenced to hang. The execution took place behind the walls of Wandsworth Prison on 7 January 1943.

In as far as one should say such a thing, it transpired that Mrs Dobkin could not have been too surprised that Harry wanted to get rid of her. They had married in 1920, through the traditional Jewish custom of a marriage broker. Three days later they separated, but unfortunately nine months afterwards a baby boy was born. In 1923 Mrs Dobkin obtained a maintenance order for the upkeep of the child. Dobkin was a spasmodic payer and spent several short terms in prison for it. In addition, Rachel had unsuccessfully summonsed him four times for assault. She was in the habit of pestering Harry in the street to get her money – and it should be remembered that she was still demanding cash in 1941 when the 'child' was twenty years old. Dobkin also hinted that she was blackmailing him over some undisclosed indiscretion at work. So when the bombs started to fall on London, it is easy to see why Harry thought 'one more victim of the Blitz' might go unremarked. It was an unlucky day for Harry Dobkin when Keith Simpson was assigned to the case.

18 July

1981 (USA) When Jack Henry Abbott first came to the attention of American author Norman Mailer he was thirty-seven years old. He had spent most of those years – twenty-one of them – in prison, fourteen in solitary confinement. In

1966 he stabbed a fellow prisoner to death and was sentenced to an additional fourteen years. Mailer was at the time engaged in writing *The Executioner's Song*, an analysis of the life and crimes of double-killer Gary Gilmore (see 17 January). When Abbott learnt of the Gilmore project through a newspaper article, he wrote a letter to Mailer offering the benefit of his own experience of violence in prisons. It was his contention that only a person who has endured a decade or more of incarceration can fully appreciate the principle and practice of institutional violence.

The result was an extraordinary series of letters in which Norman Mailer recognised 'an intellectual, a radical, a potential leader . . .' Those letters were to constitute the basis for Abbott's best-selling autobiography, *In the Belly of the Beast*. As a result of this success Jack Abbott was released on parole and became the darling of the New York literati. But the years of institutionalisation had ill-equipped him for life outside prison.

In the early hours of the morning of 18 July 1981, Abbott became involved in an argument with twenty-two-year-old Richard Adan, an actor and playwright then working as a waiter in New York. Abbott had taken strong exception to being told that the men's lavatory was for staff use only, and reacted in the only way that seemed natural to him – he stabbed Adan to death. After two months on the run, Jack Abbott was arrested and sentenced to be confined to the maximum-security prison at Marion, Illinois.

In 1981, shortly after Adan's death, his wife Ricci had begun proceedings to extract financial compensation for the 'wrongful death' and 'pain and suffering' caused to her husband by his killer. Abbott had been found liable to pay damages in 1983, and on 5 June 1990, he was back in court again. Ten days later, after six hours of deliberation and considerable use of an electronic calculator, the jury, to the apparent delight of everyone in court except Jack Abbott, awarded Mrs Ricci Adan $7.575 million damages ($5.575 million for loss of her husband's potential earnings and $2 million for the pain he suffered). Before he was returned to prison to continue his sentence, Jack Abbott commented: 'It is a little excessive, your honour, I would say.'

19 July

1768 (England) Sarah Metyard was a milliner and her daughter, also Sarah, was her assistant, working at Bruton Street, London. At that time the mother had five apprentice girls from different parish workhouses, among whom were Anne Naylor and her sister. Anne, being of a sickly nature and unable to work so hard, was the object of much barbarity from both her mistresses. Indeed the cruelty became so great that she attempted to abscond, but being brought back was confined to an upper room with no more sustenance than a small piece of bread and a little water. The child was later soundly beaten and tied to a door in such a manner that she could neither sit nor lie down, except at night. On the fourth day of this treatment Anne Naylor died, and the Metyards concealed her body in a box.

The body remained in the box two months, during which time the garret door was kept shut, lest the offensive smell should lead to a discovery. The stench became so powerful that they judged it prudent to remove the remains of the unhappy victim of their barbarity. On the evening of 25 December they cut the body in pieces and tied the head and trunk up in one cloth and the limbs in another. These were taken to Chick Lane where it was proposed to throw them over a wall into the sewer, but not having the strength the two women left the bundles where they were in the mud.

At around midnight that same day a passing watchman found some of the pieces and alerted the constable, who himself summoned the coroner who examined the pieces and supposed them to be parts of a corpse taken from a churchyard for the use of a surgeon, and declined to summon a jury.

It was not until four years later that this cruel crime was avenged, for mother and daughter were disagreeing constantly, the daughter threatening to confide her mother's dark secret to the magistrate. In the end information of the affair was laid before the overseers of Tottenham parish and mother and daughter were committed to the Gatehouse. At the ensuing Old Bailey sessions they were both sentenced to be executed the following Monday 19 July 1768, and then to be conveyed to Surgeons' Hall for dissection.

The mother, being in a fit when she was put in the cart, lay at full length till she came to the place of execution, when she was raised up, and means were used for her recovery, but without effect, so she departed this life in a state of insensibility. From the time of leaving Newgate to the moment of her death the daughter wept incessantly. After hanging the usual time the bodies were conveyed in a hearse to Surgeons' Hall where they were exposed to the curiosity of the public, and then dissected.

20 July

1736 (Scotland) On 20 July 1736, Captain John Porteous was convicted of murder at the Edinburgh High Court of Justiciary, and sentenced to death; death by judicial hanging. But a mob, so angry at his treatment of their fellows, broke him out of the Edinburgh Tollbooth and did the job themselves. This was his crime:

Captain Porteous, widely regarded as a coarse, brutish man, and his City Guard, many of whom were no better, were ordered by the Lord Provost to keep order at the execution of Andrew Wilson, a smuggler. Wilson, on account of his rather colourful exploits, was held in particular affection among the city's low-life, and a massive and sympathetic crowd turned out to watch him die. Porteous managed to show at one and the same time his total inability to read the mood of the crowd and his innate sadism when he began the proceedings by crushing Wilson's hands in the iron cuffs before setting off on the journey to the scaffold. Arriving at that place, the execution took its grim course without interruption, then, as the hangman cut Wilson's body down, the mob burst into a loud jeering and stones were thrown which hit several of the City Guard. The Guard made ready their rifles, firing into the screaming rabble. Six people in the crowd were shot dead and many others were wounded.

Porteous was arrested, charged with murder and tried on 19 July; the following day he was found guilty and sentenced to death. On 26 August, the sentence on Captain Porteous was respited for a period of six weeks on the order of Queen Caroline. This was not calculated to appease local feelings, and an angry mob deprived the hangman of his wage.

21 July

1924 (USA) One of the most famous trials in the world opened in Cook County on 21 July 1924. In the dock sat two young men charged with the murder of a fourteen-year-old boy. Hoping to save them from the death penalty was the legendary defender Clarence Darrow.

In Chicago in the summer of 1924 seventeen-year-old Richard Loeb and eighteen-year-old Nathan Leopold were indicted for murder. Apart from the youth of the two killers and the apparent pointlessness of their crime, the case shot to prominence in large part because of the wealth and social standing of the families involved. The victim, little Bobbie Franks, had not returned home from school, nor did he return later that night. Early on the following morning, his father, Jacob Franks, received a letter stating that his son was safe and would be returned for a ransom of $10,000. The letter also contained detailed instructions on how the money should be handed over. Mr Franks was to wrap it in a parcel and stand on the rear platform of a specified train out of Chicago at four o'clock that same afternoon. The money was to be thrown off the train at a specified spot. However, before Franks could set off on his journey, the afternoon papers led with the discovery of a dead body lying naked in a culvert under a railway crossing twenty miles south of the city. It was that of young Bobbie Franks.

An examination of the spot where the body was found yielded a couple of vital clues. One of them was a pair of spectacles, identified by his optician as having been made for university student Nathan Leopold. Asked to describe his movements on the night that Bobbie Franks died, Leopold said that he had just been driving round town with his buddy Dick Loeb. Prudently, one of the detectives checked with the Leopolds' chauffeur, who told him that the car was in for repairs that night and nobody could have used it. After two days of intensive questioning the boys broke down and confessed to murder. Their motive, it seemed, was to commit the perfect crime.

As well as their own confessions, the evidence against Leopold and Loeb was more than enough to convince a jury, and the callousness of their crime would ensure they got no sympathy votes. Their only chance of escaping the death penalty lay with their defence counsel. Clarence Darrow, who had become a legend in his own lifetime, had been persuaded out of retirement. At the end of the trial, Darrow rose to address the judge and jury. First he spoke of the boys' ages, commenting: 'If Your Honour can hang a boy at eighteen, some other judge can hang him at seventeen, or sixteen, or fourteen . . .' He ended his impassioned speech: 'I am pleading for the future; I am pleading for a time when hatred and cruelty will not control the hearts of men. When we can learn by reason and judgement and understanding and faith that all life is worth saving, and that mercy is the highest act of man.' It is recorded that a deathly silence locked the court for two minutes after Darrow had resumed his seat. The great defender had saved two more lives from an untimely meeting with the Grim Reaper.

22 July

1928 (England) Beatrice Annie Pace was committed for trial at the Gloucester Assizes on 22 July 1928, charged with the murder of her husband. The facts as laid before the court were these: Harry Pace, a sheep rearer with a farm on the edge of the Forest of Dean, had been taken ill while dipping sheep in the early summer of 1927. He was suffering so acutely from stomach pains that it was thought wise to confine him to hospital for observation. He was discharged, but readmitted after a similar attack in December. He died on 10 January 1928.

Although the funeral was scheduled for 15 January, Harry's brother Elton obtained a coroner's order to stop the service and submit the body for autopsy. After a painstaking examination, Professor Walker Hall told the coroner that he had found no signs of natural disease in Harry Pace's body, but the stomach lining showed evidence of a strong irritant poison; changes to other organs such as the liver pointed to arsenic. In reply to a question from the coroner, Professor Hall thought it impossible that the poison could have been absorbed through the skin (arsenic is a major ingredient of sheep-dip) unless there is a lesion. Having been told by the coroner that in his opinion there was no evidence for accidental poisoning, the jury returned a verdict of 'arsenical poisoning by some person or persons other than himself'. Mrs Pace, sitting in the body of the court, was arrested on the coroner's warrant.

So Mrs Pace sat patiently in another court, in the dock of the Assize. In her favour it can be said that there was such sympathy for her plight that a public subscription had enabled Mrs Pace to retain the services of no less an advocate than Mr Norman Birkett KC. It is customary in cases of poisoning for one of the Law Officers of the Crown to lead the prosecution, and in this instance the Solicitor-General Sir Frank Boyd Merriman presented the Crown case. He called a total of seventeen witnesses, just about equally divided between medical experts and Harry's relatives, none of whom seemed ever to have had a good word to say for poor Beatrice Annie. Much of the evidence they gave was informed by that dislike rather than any real proof of foul play. In cross-examination Norman Birkett persuaded Sir William Willcox to agree that it is possible for arsenic to enter the body in any number of ways (remember Harry frequently used sheep-dip) including: 1. From the hands or clothing to the mouth; 2. Through the skin if it is broken; 3. By self-administration.

When Sir Frank had closed for the prosecution, Norman Birkett rose to take one of the biggest gambles of his long and distinguished career at the Bar. He submitted to Mr Justice Horridge that there was insufficient evidence for the trial to continue further. The scientific evidence was, he said, as consistent with self-administration as with any other possibility. Amid general surprise, the judge replied: 'My opinion is that it would not be safe to ask the jury to proceed further with it.' He instructed them to return a formal verdict of not guilty.

23 July

1928 (USA) The notion that money is the root of all manner of evils would have been most enthusiastically supported by Mr Franklin J. Bradshaw, late of Salt Lake City, Utah. Having made a lot of money (over $60 million as a matter of fact) from his own hard work, and believing in hanging on to what he had, Bradshaw was frequently heard advising his family that if it was wealth they wanted then they should take a leaf out of his book.

Youngest daughter Frances, however, having twice failed to marry into money and being left with a family of her own to rear, was unenthusiastic about so monotonous and time-consuming a route to the riches to which she felt entitled. Fortunately her teenaged son Marc was as unscrupulous as herself, and in him Frances Schreuder Bradshaw found a willing weapon.

Although she had for some time been receiving welcome, if modest, handouts from Mrs Bradshaw, Frances had already openly declared that 'This family can't keep going much longer; not unless somebody kills father,' and on 23 July 1928 Marc was dispatched with a loaded Smith and Wesson .357 magnum to take care of the job.

After a protracted investigation, Marc Schreuder stood his trial in 1928, when he freely admitted killing his grandfather for the simple reason that his mother had asked him to do it as a favour. Frances Schreuder, who had never handled a gun in her life, was tried, convicted and sentenced to life imprisonment for the shooting of her father, while the worthless Marc, whose finger had been on the trigger, escaped with a token five years.

24 July

1800 (England)

James Brodie, a blind man, was indicted at the assizes for the county of Nottingham for the murder of a boy, named Robert Selby Hancock, who acted as his guide, on 24 July 1800.

John Robinson, a warrener, said he went to his warren on Sunday 24 July 1800, about two o'clock in the afternoon. He saw the prisoner, as he supposed, fishing in a rivulet. On approaching him he found him lying on his belly, upon which he called out: 'Hullo! What are you doing?' The prisoner said he was a blind man, and had been wandering about all night, for he had lost his guide, who was dead; and that he had stayed with him till he had taken his last gasp. The warrener went with two men to seek the boy, and they found him about three miles from the place where the blind man was, covered all over with ling, or fern, as much as would fill a cart. The skull was found fractured in two places, the head covered with blood and torn at the ear, and the shoulders and arms beaten to a jelly. The blind man had a stick with which it was supposed he committed the murder.

The prisoner, in his defence, said they had lost their way, and that the boy had got up into a tree, with his assistance, to see if there was any road near; that the boy fell from the tree and hurt himself very much; that just before he had tumbled over a log of wood; that finding the boy was hurt, and could not stand, he covered him over with ling in order to keep him from the cold; and that he stayed by him till he was dead.

Not one word of this defence was admitted by the jury, who instantly found him guilty, and execution, in the short time allowed to murderers, followed, at which time this culprit of darkness was but twenty-three years of age.

(*The Newgate Calendar*)

25 July

1980 (Ireland) It was the conclusion of one of the strangest cases of murder in modern Irish legal history; a case where an incredulous space-age jury was brought face to face with witchcraft and devil worship they might have thought more appropriate to the Middle Ages. The date was 25 July 1980 (remember that, 1980 – not 1480), and in the dock were Phoebe and Verren Brady, two self-confessed High Priestesses of the Devil Worshippers, and Michael Harmsworth, a petty criminal who would join anything. The jury had found all three guilty of the murder of Eric Willmot, a man who had become entranced by Phoebe Brady and found himself enmeshed in a medieval nightmare.

Thirty-six-year-old Eric Willmot had been working the fairs and markets as a tinker, when he had come under the spell of Phoebe Brady in 1973. He had gone to her caravan to have his fortune told, fell for her stunning good looks, and ended up in her bed. A bit of casual fun for the tinker, perhaps, but not for the High Priestess of the Devil Worshippers, the title Phoebe Brady had inherited on the death of her mother. She ruled a sect of twenty or thirty members, who put into practice the laws she ordained. And one of those laws was that having slept with her, Eric Willmot had to wed her. Not that Eric was grumbling; in fact he probably thought Santa had been delivering early. He wasn't too sure about the ceremony, though, and it was rather unwillingly that he engaged in a ritual having 'the sanction of the Devil' and carried out 'beneath an arch of crossed clubs'. Still, he received a wedding ring from Phoebe for his troubles. The honeymoon was an extended sojourn in Phoebe's bed, an exhausting effort to satisfy her lusty appetite.

Over the years a disillusioned Eric tried to run away a number of times – as had his several predecessors – only to be returned to the fold with a good beating for his pains. On the last occasion, six months before the murder, he had ended up with a broken arm and three cracked ribs. Wisely, Willmot planned to make a permanent escape. Unwisely, he spread it around the bars in Cork that he was saving his money, was emigrating to Canada, and had sold the sacred wedding ring with which Phoebe had blessed their marriage made in hell. That last indiscretion was a heinous offence against the sanctity of the Devil Worshippers, and Phoebe Brady was compelled to take appropriate action. For this she enlisted the aid of a bland petty criminal by the name of Michael Harmsworth, a thirty-five-year-old with the strength of a bull. Four hundred pounds up front, another four hundred for delivering Willmot, bound and gagged, to the moors on the night of the winter solstice. Harmsworth coshed Willmot in an alley in the city, half dragged and half carried 'my drunken friend' out to the moors, took what money he had and ran. Phoebe and her daughter Verren, Assistant High Priestess, did the rest, carrying out with iron bars the sentence of the Court of the sect, which had condemned the man to death for stealing the ring.

On the morning of 23 December 1979, Eric Willmot's body was found on a desolate, treeless moor on the road from Cork to Dublin, buried in a shallow grave. He had been gagged and bound, beaten with a dog whip on the back and buttocks, and with iron bars on the chest and head, fracturing his skull, smashing his face and rib cage, rupturing several of the vital organs; and, perhaps as a final reminder of where it all started, his testicles were bruised.

26 July

1984 (USA) Ed Gein died today; peacefully, in the geriatric ward of the Mendota Mental Health Institute. He was seventy-seven. How many people who saw that half column-inch remembered Ed Gein, the killer who fifteen years earlier had been the bogey-man to a generation, 'The Cannibal', the one who made lampshades out of human skin? And today, in the mid-nineties, there are probably only a few crime historians and true-crime enthusiasts who have even heard his name. And yet, in a strange way, Ed Gein has been immortalised, though he is remembered under different names – Buffalo Bill, the serial killer who likes to dress up in human skin in Thomas Harris's *Silence of the Lambs*; and Norman Bates in Robert Bloch's *Psycho* (later transformed by Alfred Hitchcock). The real Ed Gein was rather different . . .

Ed and his brother farmed the small family homestead at Plainfield, Wisconsin, constantly watched by their domineering mother. Hard work and no pleasure, they were the rules. And women were never mentioned let alone welcome. Little surprise, then, that when his brother died in 1944 and his mother the following year, this middle-aged sodbuster was left with nothing but his own dark thoughts – and the memory of his mother, enshrined for ever in her room, untouched since the day she died. Ed started to take an interest in sex now, furtively. It started with books. Not the usual sort of 'girlie' books; Ed's books were the kind read by doctors and medical students, the kind which display the human body in all its component parts. Then Ed graduated to grave robbing for some hands-on experience, sometimes removing the skin of the corpse and wearing it around his own body. If it had stopped there nobody might ever have disturbed 'ol' weird Ed'. But Ed grew discontent with the fruit of the grave and began to create corpses for himself. The first had been Mary Hogan in December 1954. Three years later Bernice Worden disappeared from her shop in town; about the same time that Weird Ed had his pick-up truck outside.

It started as a routine visit, and it turned into a day the Plainfield Sheriff Office would never forget. They would never forget the ride out to the lonely Gein farm, now barely more than a crumbling hulk. They would never forget the headless corpse of Bernice Worden hanging by its feet from the rafters of the lean-to, or the ghastly array of artefacts fashioned from human corpses – lampshades covered with skin, the crown of a skull used as a soup bowl, the refrigerator stocked with human organs . . .

Of course Ed was not 'weird', he was criminally insane, and it is some surprise that, in 1968, he was finally considered fit to stand trial. In the event he was found guilty but insane and put back into the psychiatric unit, first at the Central

State Hospital at Waupon, then at Mendota. Where he lived to a ripe old age.

27 *July*

1908 (England) It is a source of never-ending wonder to crime historians that some of the most prosaic, most sordid crimes are the source of elevated legal debate and decision-making. Such a case was that of Thomas Meade.

Meade, a labourer by trade and a drunk by inclination, lived with a woman named Clara Howell in a single squalid room in Crook's Yard, Leeds. The couple frequently quarrelled, especially if Meade had been drinking heavily, which was almost always. The night of 27 July 1908 was no different from any other; except that this time the beating he gave the wretched Clara with fist and broom-handle was fatal.

In due course, Thomas Meade stood trial for murder at Leeds Assizes, where his defence was that he was too far in his cups to be able to form any intent to kill Clara Howell or, indeed, to do her grievous bodily harm. The charge, his counsel suggested, should be one of manslaughter. Mr Justice Coleridge in his summing-up advised the jury:

> Everyone is presumed to know the consequences of his acts. If he be insane that knowledge is not presumed. Insanity is not pleaded here, but where it is part of the essence of a crime that a motive, a particular motive, shall exist in the mind of the man who does the act, the law declares this – that if the mind at that time is dethroned, and the man is incapable, therefore, of forming that intent, it justifies the reduction of the charge from murder to manslaughter.

Whether the twelve good men and true understood that we can never be sure. What is certain is that they found Thomas

Meade guilty of the murder of Clara Howell. However, Meade's counsel lodged an immediate appeal on the grounds that the judge misled the jury into thinking that a person had to be 'insane' with drink, rather than merely incapable of forming an intent through drink. Giving the result of the appeal, Mr Justice Darling pointed out that 'A man is taken to intend the natural consequences of his acts' unless, *inter alia*, 'his mind was so affected by the drink that he was incapable of knowing that what he was doing was dangerous – that is, likely to inflict serious injury'. In the case of Thomas Meade, he had been heard threatening to give Clara Howell 'a good hiding' just before he attacked her; therefore he was capable of forming an intent. In consequence the appeal was dismissed and Thomas Meade was hanged on 12 March 1909.

28 July

1926 (England) This was the date of Edwin Creed's last day among the living. Which was a pity, because by all accounts he was a very kindly man and an unsurpassed cheesemonger. In all probability it is just because he was such a nice man that he lost his life. It was his custom always to stay behind in his shop at the corner of Leinster Terrace and Craven Hill Gardens to clear up after the day's business so that his young assistants could get off home to their suppers.

It was after dark when PC Watts passed the shop on his regular patrol, and he noticed a strong smell of gas wafting up from the pavement grating. Officer Watts shone the beam of his torch down into the cellar and could clearly make out a man's foot on the stairway up to the shop. When they broke in the police found Edwin Creed lying dead on his back on the stairs, his head bloody from a head wound. Judging from the trail of blood, it was clear that Mr Creed had been bludgeoned to death in the shop, his body dragged across the sawdust strewn floor and thrown down the cellar stairs. Quite why three gas jets had been turned on was a mystery.

The motive for the crime became clear when it was learnt that £40 had been stolen from the safe. So Creed must have let his killer into the shop, probably thinking he was a late customer. As for clues, the only object that seemed of any significance was a left-hand wash-leather glove which had been abandoned or dropped on the floor of the shop – presumably by the killer. There was a glimmer of hope for detectives when two letters arrived, both in the same handwriting, both inscribed 'Important. Urgent', and both posted in the Notting Hill district of London. The letters were unsigned, but the text gave the impression that it was within the writer's power to solve the Creed case. However, despite pleas from the police and the newspapers, nothing more was ever heard.

The coroner's jury were left with only one possible verdict: 'Wilful murder against some person or persons unknown'. There has never been any more information with which to solve the case of Edwin Creed's untimely death, and it is as much of an enigma today as it was when the coroner, Mr H. R. Oswald, described it as 'the perfect crime'.

29 July

1986 (England) The media called them the 'Reggie Perrin Murders', after the television series 'The Fall and Rise of Reginald Perrin'. Each episode of the series opened with Perrin, the central character, undressing and leaving his clothes in a pile on the beach to persuade the police that he has drowned himself, and then going off to start a new life. On 29 July 1986, police looking for Robert Healey found his clothes in a pile on the beach at Prestatyn, North Wales. In one of the pockets was a suicide note to his mother saying that his marriage was breaking up and life was no longer worth living.

A search of the Healey home in Stockport aroused fears that some harm may also have come to Mrs Greeba Healey and her daughter Marie Walker. They were missing from the house, where police later found bloodstains that forensic tests proved were of the same blood groups as the two missing women. It was at this stage that Healey's 'suicide' was believed to be faked, a belief confirmed when two videotape recordings of 'The Fall and Rise of Reginald Perrin' were discovered at the Stockport house. Things began to look even more sinister by the weekend of 9 August. Bloodstains on a quilt found in a ditch off the A5117 matched those found at the Healey home, and matching stains were also discovered in the car abandoned by Robert Healey in a Birmingham car park.

Shortly after the bodies of Mrs Healey and her daughter were found in a shallow grave in a wood at Caerwys, North Wales, Robert Healey presented himself at New Scotland Yard. While he was in custody, Healey began a kind of journal in which he tried to rationalise the killing of his family. He writes of being taunted by his wife over his sexual prowess. He describes how, 'as if in a dream', he battered Greeba to death with a rolling pin as she lay in bed; and when his stepdaughter came into the room, attracted by the noise, he grabbed her by the throat to prevent her struggling. That, however, was just Healey's version of events. And in the light of prosecution medical evidence at his trial, a very sanitised version.

The trial opened in Liverpool Crown Court in the last week of March 1987. As a rebuttal to Healey's defence, Mr Brian Leveson QC for the Crown said that both Mrs Healey and Marie had had sexual intercourse before their deaths. As to Healey being 'in a dream', it was quite clear from the meticulous way in which he had cleaned the house of blood that he was acting rationally and with forethought. Dr Donald Wayte, the pathologist who examined Marie's body said that her injuries most resembled those that he had seen on victims crushed to death in road accidents. As Healey crouched in the dock, his hands over his ears, Dr Wayte told the court that Marie could have taken as long as five minutes to die from her massive injuries. At the end of an eight-day trial, the jury needed a bare three hours in which to reach a unanimous verdict of guilty. Robert Healey is currently serving two concurrent life sentences.

30 July

1992 (USA) It happened that in one of the most controversial cases in recent American criminal history, William Andrews was not even at the scene of the crime when his accomplice Dale Selby Pierre shot dead three white people during a robbery in 1977. But on 30 July 1992 they executed him anyway.

Andrews, a black man like his associate, did admit to torturing five people by forcing them to drink Drano, a caustic drain cleaner. Two of the victims survived, though one has permanent brain damage. As for the other three victims, the medical examiner stated in court that the Drano would have killed them within twelve hours anyway – if Pierre had not shot them first. The murders became known as the 'Hi-Fi Killings' because they took place at Ogden's Hi-Fi shop, Salt Lake City.

So brutal and unnecessary were the attacks that the predominantly white local population began to fear an anti-white movement existed among the area's one per cent black citizens. Indeed, it was the racial issue which created the controversy in the case, with a legal representative of the NAACP Legal Defense and Educational Fund going on record as saying: 'I've never seen such a raw case of racism; the entire case was infected with racism.' There is no denying that the jury in the Andrews trial was composed of all whites, most of them Mormons. And it was also true that during sentencing a note was passed to the jury reading 'Hang the Niggers'. However, invoking racism as a ground for appeal against the capital sentence has a long history in the courts of the United States, and it is frequently advanced by lawyers representing black clients. It has also been consistently unsuccessful. In the case of William Andrews, his attorney claimed: 'During the trial people in Utah looked at Bill Andrews and only saw a scary looking black guy; they didn't see a scared nineteen-year-old kid.'

In all, eighteen appeals were made, eighteen appeals rejected. Days before his execution date the last hope failed when the Utah Board of Pardons turned down Andrews' plea. On 30 July 1992 William Andrews died by lethal injection at Utah State Prison; his last words were: 'Thank all those who have tried so hard to keep me alive. I hope they continue to fight for equal justice after I'm gone.'

31 July

1910 (Canada) Nobody can deny that the true story of Dr Hawley Harvey Crippen would defy the fiction writer to invent – and the myth that has emerged epitomises the theatricality of murder as no other has. He murders a spiteful, domineering wife, a lacklustre music-hall entertainer working under the name of Belle Elmore, in favour of a young mistress, Ethel Le Neve, with whom he is desperately in love. He cuts up the body and disposes of it – heaven knows where. Crippen and Ethel put on disguises (he as Mr Robinson, she as his young son) and take a steamship to America, to the New World. Unfortunately the captain is something of an amateur sleuth, and via the newly invented wireless telegraph system alerts Scotland Yard to his suspicions about two of his passengers. Meanwhile, the police have found a few fragments of Mrs Cora Crippen buried under the cellar floor. There is a subsequent chase across the Atlantic by Chief Inspector Walter Dew (also in disguise) who overtakes and arrests the fugitives aboard ship on 31 July 1910. Then follows the ritual of the trial at the Old Bailey – the most famous criminal court in the world – where Crippen is literally fighting for his life in the shadow of the gallows. He loses the battle, and maintaining the atmosphere of high drama to the very last act, Crippen is hanged, and according to his last wishes is buried holding a photograph of his beloved Ethel and surrounded by her love letters. Ethel is acquitted and builds a new life for herself . . . These are the ingredients of a very successful novel.

But consider this: Crippen did not, as his mythology might suggest, kill in a moment of blind passion, his back broken by the final straw. His was a cold, calculated murder, planned over months, certainly never out of his mind from the time he bought five grains of hyoscine on 7 January 1910, until he administered the fatal dose to the unlucky Cora three weeks later.

Then, having rendered her dead, the little doctor set about the gruesome job of cutting his wife's body into pieces. When Inspector Dew prised up the bricks from the cellar floor at Hilldrop Crescent he found the remains of Crippen's handiwork.

It was the young Dr Bernard Spilsbury, on his first major murder case, who was left to describe the putrid mass caked in quicklime which it had been his misfortune to examine: 'Medical organs of the chest and abdomen removed in one mass. Four large pieces of skin and muscle, one from the lower abdomen with old operation scar, 4 inches long – broader at lower end. Impossible to identify sex . . .'

That was all. No head, no limbs, no bones. No bones. Crippen had literally filleted his wife! What he did with the missing parts is anybody's guess. They were never found.

Was it Crippen's undoubted and undying love for Ethel Le

Neve, interwoven with the public's undoubted and undying love of romance, that has transformed this butcher into a hero? Almost certainly.

August

1 August

1966 (USA) 'I've been having fears and violent impulses,' Charles Whitman wrote in a memo of 1 August 1966. 'After my death I wish an autopsy to be performed to see if there's any mental disorder.' Finishing the memo with the words 'Life is not worth living', Whitman left his home in Austin, Texas, and drove to the home of his mother, who had separated from her husband on grounds of his violence. At Margaret Whitman's apartment there was a brief struggle before Charlie stabbed and then put a pistol shot to the back of her head. Back home, Whitman walked into the bedroom and stabbed his wife as she slept. It was 3.00 a.m. Six hours later he packed a trunk with tinned food, water, tools, a radio and all the other accoutrements of a survival kit, an arsenal of seven guns, three knives and 1,000 rounds of ammunition, and drove his Chevrolet to the campus of the University of Texas – to the 307 ft-high tower of the administration offices. In his grey overalls, Whitman passed himself off as a maintenance man and swiftly ascended to the 27th floor. Here he clubbed receptionist Edna Townsley to the floor, before wheeling his heavy trunk out to the observation deck. No sooner had he done so than a group of visitors got out of the lift. Whitman fired three rapid blasts from his sawn-off shotgun, killing Marguerite Lamport and teenager Mark Gabour and seriously injuring Mark's mother and brother. He barricaded the door, shot Mrs Townsley through the head, and went out on to the observation gallery.

The sniping began at 11.45 a.m. Alex Hernandez was the

first, shot through the leg. Three more students fell in quick succession before traffic cop Billy Speed picked up the first reports of a gunman on the roof. He pulled in to the campus and was moving in on the tower when Whitman felled him with a single shot. Over the next fifteen or twenty minutes the gunfire was heavy and deadly. Whitman was an ex-Marine sharpshooter, and most of his victims were hit in or around the heart. Claudia Rutt was strolling up one of the malls when she clutched at her chest and fell, crying 'Help me!' As her boyfriend Paul Sonntag reached down to the girl he too was shot, both victims dying instantly. Harry Walchuk was a good two hundred yards away, browsing at a news-stand, when he was hit in the throat and collapsed on to the magazine rack.

Attempts to get a shot at Whitman from a light aircraft and from a helicopter proved abortive, but three policemen on the ground managed to dash from cover to cover across the plaza to the tower. Here they picked up Allen Crum, an experienced ex-serviceman, deputised him on the spot and gave him a rifle. The four men took the lift to the 26th floor, and inched their way up to the gunman's lair. Crum loosed off a rifle shot which sent Whitman scurrying back into the line of fire of Ramiro Martinez. The sniper managed one wild shot before Martinez emptied the magazine of his pistol into his body. As Whitman fell Houston McCoy shot him twice with a shotgun; he was down, but still moving and still armed. Officer Martinez finished Charles Whitman off with a shot to the head at point-blank range. It was 1.20 p.m. Whitman's killing spree left fifteen dead and thirty injured. As to his self-diagnosed mental illness, an autopsy revealed a small tumour in the back of his brain, but medical authorities have been unable to agree whether this was benign or malignant.

2 August

1830 (England) Captain William Moir was a gentleman, native of Forfarshire, in Scotland. He had joined the British Army at the age of nineteen, and during a period of seventeen years served with great credit in several Regiments of Foot, in France, Spain and America. While in that latter country he married a young lady and brought her back with him to England where, in 1829, he took possession of Shellhaven Farm, in Barking, Essex.

Captain Moir was in the habit of pursuing a strict line of discipline with regard to trespassers upon his farm, and was considerably annoyed by the constant appearance on his lands of fishermen, who resorted there to drag a portion of the river that passed through, and which was supposed to contain an abundance of fish of superior quality and size.

On Wednesday 24 March 1830, a poor man named Malcolm, who resided at Hammersmith, quitted his home in a boat, accompanied by his apprentice and a brother fisherman, for the purpose of fishing. They proceeded to Shellhaven Creek, where Malcolm threw out their nets. Shortly afterwards Captain Moir made his appearance, armed with a knife, and accompanied by a servant named Raven, and ordered the nets to be removed. Malcolm offered some observations of abuse towards him and reluctantly retired. He was proceeding to cross Moir's meadows to go to the house of a man named Baker when he was called back and ordered to go round by the sea wall. He directed some further abuse towards the Captain but at length went away. Captain Moir then went to his house and Malcolm and his assistants went to Baker's cottage. After an hour and a half they returned to their boat, again via Captain Moir's land. Up rode Captain Moir and his servant chastising Malcolm for again trespassing on his land. Whereupon Malcolm told him to be damned. Moir then drew a pistol and shot it straight at him, occasioning such wounds that after a few days he died.

A coroner's inquest was held upon the unfortunate fisherman, and a verdict of wilful murder was returned, and Captain Moir was committed to Chelmsford Jail, to take his trial at the coming assizes. At the Chelmsford Assizes Moir appeared before Lord Tenterden on 30 July, where every effort was used on his behalf, but to no purpose. He was sentenced to death.

Throughout the dreadful concluding scene of his life, which was on 2 August 1830, Captain Moir conducted himself in the calmest manner. At nine o'clock the fatal bolt was drawn, and the ill-fated gentleman died instantaneously.

3 August

1951 (England) It is not often that a national newspaper gets the chance of a scoop, of a totally exclusive murder story, so it must have seemed as though Christmas had come in August when, on the afternoon of the 3rd a voice came through on the *News of the World*'s news-room telephone: 'I've just found a woman's body. It looks like murder.'

Of course it would have been unthinkable for the paper not to call the police immediately, and so having ascertained the location of the telephone box from which the informant was speaking, and its number, the reporter asked him to wait there for a return call. In the meantime, the Nottinghamshire police were alerted that there was a possible murder in their area. Having picked the caller up from the phone box, police officers learnt that he was nineteen-year-old Herbert Leonard Mills, a local lad. He had been right about the body; and judging by the marks of strangulation and bludgeoning he had been right about murder. Mills then gave a rather hazy description of a man with a limp he had seen in the neighbourhood.

After providing samples of blood and fingernail parings, Leonard Mills was released to the eagerly waiting *News of the World*. He explained to their celebrated crime reporter

Norman Rae that he had wanted to write a sonnet and went to the leafy glade to seek inspiration. That was when he encountered the corpse.

Meanwhile, the police had identified the victim as forty-eight-year-old Mabel Tattershaw, a married woman who lived with her daughter and made ends meet by taking in lodgers. Poverty had been unkind to Mabel and had robbed her of what physical attractions she might once have had. Like a shabby spectre on life's periphery, she came and went, unremarked, about her humdrum existence. Who, detectives wondered, even *noticed* poor Mabel Tattershaw, let alone felt compelled to kill her?

Norman Rae, a detective of a different kind, was finding it difficult to stop Leonard Mills from making statements to the paper – each a little more explicit than the last. On 24 August they were to meet at a Nottingham hotel for a very strange episode in criminal history. Mills was going to write, for a journalist, on hotel notepaper, his complete confession to murder. For an hour Mills wrote, and the next morning Rae accompanied him to Nottingham police station. It seems that Mills had lured Mabel Tattershaw to the woods with flattery, and then set about proving that the perfect murder was possible. His statement concluded: 'I was rather pleased. I think I did rather well. The strangling itself was easily accomplished.'

Later, at his trial, Mills claimed that he had just invented the murder confession to get his name in the papers. But for the jury his story was just too good to be untrue; so they convicted him. And so in December 1951 that elusive moment of fame ended for Leonard Mills; on the drop at Winson Green Prison.

4 August

1892 (USA) It was at about eleven o'clock on the morning of 4 August 1892 that Lizzie Borden, a spinster of thirty-two, summoned the local doctor with the news that her father had been killed. When the medic arrived, he found sixty-nine-year-old Andrew J. Borden lying in his study brutally bludgeoned to death. One of the neighbours, who had been attracted by the commotion, asked about Mrs Borden. Lizzie replied: 'I'm sure I don't know. But I don't know perhaps she isn't killed also, for I thought I heard her coming in.' A strange comment, one might think. Anyway, a search of the house proved Lizzie correct when the body of Mrs Abby Borden was found, cut down like her husband, while cleaning a spare bedroom.

The subsequent evidence showed that the two killings had been separated by a time gap of ninety minutes, suggesting that the killer was a member of the household – who else could hang around the house for an hour and a half without being noticed? Lizzie's elder sister had an alibi for the time of the murders, which left Lizzie and the servant. As far as the neighbours were concerned there was no doubt that Lizzie was the killer – after all, it was common knowledge that she did not get on with her stepmother, and that she despised her father for his parsimony in forcing them to live in a poor part of town. A search of the cellar disclosed an axe head which had recently been cleaned, and was a strong candidate for the murder weapon.

Following a private inquest, Lizzie Borden was charged with both murders, and by the time the case reached trial at New Bedford in June 1893, Lizzie had become a household name throughout the nation. Local feeling, as is so often the case, veered backwards and forwards between guilty and innocent on the merest caprice. In court, Lizzie presented the appearance of a demure, refined young woman, quite incapable of mischief; and when she fainted in the dock it was seen as yet further proof of an innocent soul in torment. At the end of a ten-day trial Lizzie Borden was acquitted.

Defiantly, Lizzie moved back into the small Fall River

community where she bought a large elegant house. At first she shared it with her sister, but after she and Emma quarrelled, Lizzie lived alone until her death in 1927 at the age of sixty-six. She left an estate totalling around one million dollars, a third of which was willed to animal charities. Although the case remains officially unsolved, there are many who believe firmly in Lizzie Borden's guilt, attributing the killings to some temporary mental aberration such as epilepsy.

5 August

1723 (England) It was customary for people convicted of acts of piracy to be dispatched at Execution Dock on the Thames bank at Wapping. Philip Roche, an account of whose misdeeds follows, was so executed on 5 August 1723.

Roche was a native of Ireland, and being brought up to a seafaring life, served on several coastal vessels before sailing for Barbados on board a West Indiaman. From there he got himself a station on board a vessel bound for Cape Breton, the captain of which trusted him sufficiently to give him the ship's management. Roche used this privilege to enlist five fellow Irishmen with the intimation that there might be money to be made. They had only been at sea a few days when one night, as the captain and most of the crew were asleep, Roche ordered two of the seamen to furl the sails, which being done Roche and his Irish gang murdered them. At this instant a man and boy at the yard-arm, observing what had passed, and dreading a similar fate, hurried towards the topmast-head, upon which one of the Irishmen followed and hurled the boy off into the sea. The man descended to the main deck, fearing the same, where Roche was waiting to strike him down. The noise created by these transactions alarmed the sailors below and they hurried to the deck where they were seized and murdered as fast as they came up. At length the master and mate came on the quarterdeck, where Roche and his villainous companions seized them and, tying them back to back, committed them to the merciless waves.

This wicked crew had intended to sail up the Gulf of St Lawrence, but as they were within a few days' sail of the British Channel, and finding themselves short of provisions, they put into Portsmouth. Here they gave the vessel a fictitious name, painted her afresh and sailed for Rotterdam, where they disposed of their cargo and took in a fresh one. Also, an English gentleman named Annesley shipped considerable property on board, and took his passage with them to the Port of London. When the ship arrived in the river Thames, Mr Annesley's friends made inquiry after him in consequence that he sent letters describing the ship he was boarding. Roche denied any knowledge of the gentleman and even denied he was Philip Roche. However, he was suspected, and a letter he sent to his wife being intercepted it was shown to him as proof. Roche instantly confessed his crimes and in an attempt to evade justice implicated some of his murderous companions. Nevertheless judgement of death was awarded against him, and he was hanged at Execution Dock on 5 August 1723.

6 August

1967 (Scotland) Although the murder of fifteen-year-old Linda Peacock took place on the night of 6 August 1967, it was not until the following morning that her battered and strangled corpse was found in a cemetery at Biggar, a small town between Edinburgh and Glasgow. The girl had not been raped, though the clothing on the upper part of her body had been disarranged, and the police photographer whose job it was to record the scene of the crime and the victim's position was particularly impressed by an oval bruise-type mark on one of her breasts; consistent, he believed, with a bite mark. The fact was quickly confirmed by the pathologist, and Scotland's foremost forensic dentistry expert, Dr Warren Harvey, was assigned to the team investigating Linda Peacock's murder.

Police officers had already eliminated the 3,000 people so far interviewed in the area, and there remained a single group of twenty-nine youths, all inmates of the local detention centre. Dr Harvey suggested as a first step taking dental impressions of each of the men in an attempt to match a set of teeth to the distinctive bite mark on the victim's body. One mark in particular looked as though it might have come from an uncommonly sharp or jagged tooth.

Dr Harvey was now able, on general observation, to reduce to five the number of impressions that could not yet be eliminated from suspicion. At this point he consulted with that other luminary of forensic dentistry, Professor Keith Simpson, and the two experts concentrated their attention on the 'jagged' tooth. Of the five suspects, only one had a match. He was seventeen-year-old Gordon Hay, who had been proved missing from the borstal dormitory at the time of Linda Peacock's murder; he had been seen returning just before 10.30, dishevelled, breathless, and with mud on his clothes. Equally incriminating was the fact that Hay had met Linda at a local fair on the previous day, and had observed to a friend that he would like to have sex with her. Hay willingly submitted to a further set of impressions being made of his teeth. From these the watertight evidence that would convict him of murder was assembled, for closer examination revealed that Hay suffered from a rare disorder called hypo-calcination, which creates small pits on the tips of teeth. An examination of 342 sixteen- and seventeen-year-old boys revealed none with two pits; Gordon Hay had two pits – the pits that made the 'jagged' marks.

In February 1968, Dr Warren Harvey spent a whole day in

the witness box at the Edinburgh High Court of Justiciary explaining the relevance of bite marks as means of identification. Clearly the jury were impressed. Gordon Hay was found guilty of murder and, on account of his youth, sentenced 'to be detained during Her Majesty's pleasure'.

7 *August*

1977 (USA) A rabid supporter of the American Nazi movement, Joseph Franklin had a particular grudge against mixed-race couples. The first the world knew of this obsession was on 7 August 1977, when he shot Alphonse Manning and his white girlfriend. Franklin went on killing until his capture in 1980.

8 *August*

1935 (England) Arthur Mortimer had a very strange pastime, very strange and very anti-social – his great pleasure derived from driving his motor-car at women cyclists, knocking them off their mounts, and subjecting them to such further indignities as circumstances permitted, or fancy led. On 8 August 1935, one of these attacks was fatal, but he had a trial run on the previous day.

Mrs Alice Series had her unfortunate meeting with Arthur at Stratford Saye, Hampshire. Having forced Mrs Series into the side of the road with such suddenness as to hurl the luckless woman into the ditch, Arthur reversed, wound down his window, smiled, and apologised: 'So sorry, trouble with the steering wheel. Look!' He pointed to the wheel. As Alice Series staggered up and neared the open window, Arthur Mortimer landed her such a punch on the head as to loosen several of her teeth; after thumping her several more times as she lay stunned on the ground, Mortimer made off in a puff of exhaust. Before abandoning the car to its rightful owner, Arthur Mortimer indulged his hobby once more. The victim this time was Nellie Boyes; the location Hartley

Wintney. The plucky Nellie, though, was a more equal match and, after giving her assailant the rough edge of her tongue, frightened him off with threats of the police.

The following morning Arthur was out and about early stealing another car. Driving through Winchfield, the prospect of sport manifested itself in the persons of Phyllis Oakes and her sister Betty. Riding ahead of her sister, Betty Oakes was horrified to hear a crash from behind, and turned in time to see Phyllis bouncing off the bonnet of Arthur Mortimer's car. That afternoon Lillian Rose Harwood was cycling at Crastock, near Knaphill. Mortimer left her unconscious where she had fallen into a ditch, minus her handbag and the thirty shillings it contained. The police caught up with Arthur Mortimer at Guildford, and despite a spirited chase, Arthur eventually crashed into the police road-block. He emerged shaken and bruised, but in a great deal better shape than most of his victims. On the passenger seat of the car was Lillian Harwood's handbag; in his pocket was Lillian Harwood's thirty shillings.

A charge of grievous bodily harm against Miss Oakes was quickly changed to murder when the unfortunate young woman succumbed to her injuries.

After a three-day trial, Arthur Charles Mortimer was found guilty of murder and sentenced to be hanged by the neck. However, there was little by way of punishment that would have made much difference to Arthur. Clearly as mad as a hatter he was reprieved on grounds of insanity and spent the rest of his days in prison under medical supervision, well out of harm's way.

9 August

1991 (USA) The culmination of what the trial prosecutor called Arizona's 'biggest homicide case' came on Monday 12 July 1993, with verdicts of guilty by a Phoenix jury, against a teenaged military fanatic on nine counts of murder, nine of armed robbery and one each of burglary and conspiracy to commit armed burglary.

The scene of the crime was the Wat Promkunaram Buddhist temple at Phoenix on 9 August 1991. The prosecution alleged that Jonathan Doody (aged seventeen at the time) and his co-accused Alessandro Garcia (then sixteen) had planned to rob the temple. They had ransacked the monks' quarters and taken cameras, electronic equipment and $2,790 in cash. In order to eliminate witnesses, Doody had herded six monks, an elderly nun and two male followers into a circle on the floor of the temple's living quarters and methodically shot them all in the head with a borrowed .22-calibre rifle. The bodies of the victims, who ranged in age between sixteen and seventy-one, were discovered the following day by would-be worshippers.

Garcia had entered into a plea bargain arrangement with the prosecution whereby he agreed to plead guilty to murder and give evidence against Doody in a deal to avoid the death sentence. Garcia testified that he had fired harmless shotgun shots between the victims while Doody did the killings.

Doody did not give evidence at his trial but his lawyer, no doubt to his embarrassment, was obliged to present his client's preposterous excuse for being at the temple waving a gun – he was playing a war game to test the building's security! In his defence, it was also suggested that the prosecutors were attempting to influence the jury by the persistent production of bloody autopsy photographs of the victims because they had no direct proof of Doody's guilt. The defence claimed that four men from Tucson who had originally been detained, or a friend, Roland Caratachea, who had lent Doody the rifle, may have been responsible for the killings. Caratachea was called as a witness, but refused to answer any questions by invoking his rights under the Fifth Amendment not to incriminate himself.

After two days of deliberations the jury convicted Doody

on all counts; his defence attorney immediately gave notice of appeal, and the sentence hearing at which he could receive the death penalty was postponed.

10 August

1985 (England) It cannot be stated exactly when Ronald Barton began to interfere sexually with his stepdaughter Keighley. The first time the matter came to the attention of the authorities was in 1980, when, with both Keighley and her mother giving evidence against him, Barton was given a one-year suspended sentence for acts of gross indecency on the child. She was just eight years old.

Mrs Barton, aware of her husband's 'tendencies' continued to live with him and put herself and her daughter at certain risk. Ronald Barton was a very violent, aggressive and domineering man, who thought nothing of keeping his family in a constant state of fear with threats of injury, and worse. Mrs Barton claimed later that both she and Keighley were forced to submit to sexual acts under the direct persuasion of a gun barrel. Mrs Barton made a further complaint in 1982, though at the last minute Keighley refused to testify when Barton put a gun to her head. However, this time she was placed in care.

Unfortunately Keighley was unhappy at the hostel and ran away. However, by now Mrs Barton had obtained an order banning Barton from going within a quarter of a mile of the family home. Although it provided a temporary solution, for Barton's part he felt a bitter resentment at being evicted from his home and separated from his two sons.

On the morning of Saturday 10 August 1985 it was raining, but Keighley Barton decided to take the family alsatian, Rex, out for a walk. Later in the morning the dog returned alone; Keighley would never be seen alive again. Ronald Barton was immediately suspected of being responsible for his stepdaughter's disappearance; however, in the face of his absolute denial, there was no evidence on which to hold him. Then on 23 October Barton was taken into custody and officially charged with the abduction and murder of his stepdaughter. He had made the great mistake of boasting about the killing to a fellow prisoner; in fact he boasted that he had had his old car crushed at the breaker's yard with Keighley's body inside it.

Ronald Barton finally came to court at the Old Bailey on 7 October 1986, and after a jury retirement of two days he was convicted by a ten-to-two majority. Mr Justice Turner sentenced Barton to life imprisonment with a recommendation that he serve at least twenty-five years. Barton did eventually disclose the whereabouts of Keighley's body; he had buried it at Abney Park Cemetery, Stoke Newington. On 25 February Keighley Barton's remains were laid to rest at Manor Park Cemetery, Forest Gate, just at the end of the road where she had lived out most of a frightened and brutalised existence of just fourteen years.

11 August

1703 (England) The killing of a policeman on duty is no new phenomenon. Thomas Cook, who stabbed a constable at Mayfair, was executed on 11 August 1703.

12 August

1924 (England) It was one of the oldest crimes of passion in the history of romance: the love triangle. It began in Biarritz and ended, on 12 August 1924, on the scaffold at Wandsworth Prison.

Mabel Jones met Jean-Pierre Vaquier amid the luxury of the Victoria Hotel, Biarritz. Mabel, escaping from impending bankruptcy, was having one last fling with what was left of her money. Vaquier was retained by the hotel to keep its newly installed radio set working. A French Basque with all the good looks of that aristocratic race, he was difficult not to notice; so Mabel did not try. Despite the fact that Vaquier had no English, they obviously found other ways to communicate, because in no time at all a passionate love affair had developed. And when it came time for Mabel to leave, Jean-Pierre came too. The only problem seemed to be Mr Jones. Mabel had married Alfred Poynter Jones in 1906 and shortly afterwards gave him the money to purchase the Blue Anchor Hotel at Byfleet. This was a great convenience for Alfred, because it meant that he could spend all day drinking without even walking through the front door. It was also a great convenience for Mabel, because it gave her the time to travel and meet new friends. Whatever Mabel may or may not have told Vaquier of her domestic arrangements, when they landed in England he booked into London's Russell Hotel, while Mabel returned to Byfleet. Six weeks later Vaquier moved into the Blue Anchor Hotel as a non-paying guest of the landlord's wife. What Alfred Jones made of all this is anybody's guess, he was usually so drunk that it may have been some time before he even noticed, and by then Vaquier had become as familiar to him as the beer-pumps.

On 29 March 1924 Alfred Jones awoke with a more than averagely stubborn hangover and, as usual, reached over the bar for the bottle of bromo-salts, mixed his seltzer and downed it in one gulp. 'My God,' he shouted, 'that's bitter.' It was the last coherent thing he said. Within seconds he was in convulsions; minutes later he died. The doctor who was called had no doubt that Jones had been poisoned, and from his experience it was most likely strychnine. In fact it was, as the police discovered when they had the sediment in the bottom of Jones's seltzer glass analysed. Vaquier was a strong suspect, of course, but not the only one – what about Mabel? – so it was three weeks before Superintendent Boshier of the Woking force felt confident enough to arrest him.

The trial opened at Guildford on 2 July 1929, where it was learnt that Vaquier had made a couple of trips to London where he had purchased a quantity of strychnine. Questioned on this by Sir Patrick Hastings for the Crown, Vaquier said that Mabel Jones's solicitor had asked him to buy it, though he was reluctant to give the man's name. And if it was, in reality, for Vaquier's use, what could that use be? The jury had no doubt it was to dispose of poor drunken Alfred Jones. They showed their disapproval by finding Vaquier guilty. Mr Justice Avory showed the disapproval of the nation by sentencing him to death.

13 August

1832 (Canada) In the year 1828 Henry Sovereign faced trial at London, Ontario, for what at that time was a capital offence: he had shot a horse. He was rightly convicted and sentenced to death. The severity of the sentence aroused considerable sympathy for Sovereign's case, and served to crystallise many existing pockets of public resistance to the much despised British criminal code. The result was that, prudently, the judge, Mr Justice James Buchanan Morley, recommended clemency and Sovereign was released to return to his wife and family.

Some years later, on a bitter January day in 1832, Henry Sovereign appeared, dishevelled, banging at the door of a relative, bleeding from wounds to his arm and chest. The story he told was that his house had been broken into and he and his family had been attacked by two men. He had escaped and ran to get help for his wife and children. Wasting no more time, the relative armed himself and, with a neighbour, accompanied Sovereign back to his home. On the threshold of the building Sovereign suddenly stopped and said: 'I am afraid they have murdered my family.' He was not wrong, for in and around the house lay the bloody and battered bodies of his wife Polly and seven of their children.

The youngest child, two-year-old Anna, was found alive, crying loudly but unhurt. It was God's mercy that three of the eleven Sovereign children were away from home that night.

It was the sad task of the local constable to investigate this awful crime, and accompanied by an increasingly agitated Henry Sovereign, he set out on the search for clues. Soon the officer found the bloodstained blade of a knife lying on the snow, and not far away was the handle. According to Sovereign this weapon had belonged to one of his children. Acting on intuition, the constable took Sovereign aside and required him to empty his pockets; and that is how the bloody jack-knife was found.

In August of that same year, 1832, Henry Sovereign pleaded not guilty to murder at his trial. It was an irony not missed by the court that this was the second time he had been arraigned before Mr Justice James Buchanan Morley; this time he could expect no similar leniency. As well as the evidence of the knives and a bloodstained maul belonging to Sovereign, hairs found grasped in Polly Sovereign's clenched hand were a perfect match for her husband's. As for the prisoner's own wounds, medical opinion was that they were of a very minor nature and most likely to have been self-inflicted. Sovereign persisted in his story of being attacked by two strangers, but nobody believed him, and he was convicted and sentenced to death. As might have been expected, the judge made it quite clear that he would not be recommending clemency for a second time. Henry Sovereign was hanged in London on 13 August 1832; his body, according to common practice was afterwards given for medical dissection.

14 August

1963 (England) Although sixty-four-year-old William Garfield Rowe was murdered on 14 August, it was not until the following morning that his body was discovered on his remote farm in the village of Constantine, Cornwall. Mr Rowe had suffered multiple injuries including a smashed skull, fractured jaw and cut throat, there were also many less serious knife injuries to his head and chest. The farmhouse had been plundered for valuables, but the killers had overlooked the £3,000 in cash which was hidden there.

On 16 August twenty-three-year-old Russell Pascoe was stopped on his motor-cycle at a police roadblock and questioned about his activities on the night of the murder. Pascoe admitted that he knew William Rowe – in fact he had once worked for him – but claimed that on the night of the 14th he was with his friend Dennis Whitty and three girls at a caravan in Truro. All five of them were taken in for questioning and the girls confided that Pascoe and Whitty had left the caravan on the night of the murder, saying they were 'going to do a job'. They returned in the early hours of the morning. Dennis Whitty told the girls that he and Pascoe had killed Mr Rowe, but that if they mentioned it they would get the same.

Under arrest, Pascoe admitted his part in the crime, though he was adamant that he had 'only' hit the victim over the head with an iron bar. Whitty, he said, then 'went mad with the knife'. Pascoe added that they stole £4, a watch and two boxes of matches. And while Pascoe was blaming Whitty, Whitty was blaming Pascoe: 'He made me stick him. I stabbed him in the chest. Pascoe was going to hit me, so I stuck him in the neck.' And so it went on until this grisly couple came up for trial at the Bodmin Assizes charged with a crime which the prosecution described as 'one of the most horrible and gruesome murders ever known in this county or this country'.

It turned out that Pascoe had already broken into the Rowe farmhouse two years previously, when he had stolen £200 and some jewellery belonging to Mr Rowe's mother. In his defence it was said of Dennis Whitty that he suffered from hysteria, black-outs and 'strange unnatural things' such as winged figures appearing in the sky. None of which cut much ice with the jury, and Pascoe ended up on the scaffold in Bristol, and Whitty in Winchester.

It seems that it was not only the £3,000 that William Rowe's murderers missed. He had also hidden large sums of money about the farm – in a safe buried beneath the cowshed, in a glass jar elsewhere, and so on. The police eventually traced this buried treasure as the result of directions written in a diary – in Esperanto.

15 August

1767 (England) John Williamson, having been made a widower by his good wife's untimely death, contracted an acquaintance with a young woman so deficient in intellect as to border on idiocy. However, her relations had bequeathed her sufficient money for her maintenance, and this circumstance induced Williamson to make a proposal of marriage, which she accepted. On 15 August 1767, the marriage was solemnised, and in consequence Williamson received the money that was then in the hands of his wife's guardian.

About three weeks after the wedding, Williamson cruelly beat his wife, threw water over her, and generally treated her with great severity; and this kind of brutality he frequently repeated. At length he fastened the miserable creature's hands behind her with handcuffs, and, by means of a rope passed through a staple, drew them so tight above her head that only the tips of her toes touched the ground. On one side of the closet wherein she was confined was now and then put a small piece of bread-and-butter, so that she could just touch it with her mouth; and she was allowed daily a small portion of water.

She once remained a whole month without being released

from this miserable condition; but during that time she occasionally received assistance from a female lodger and Williamson's young daughter by his late wife. Williamson released his wife on the Sunday preceding the day on which she died, and at dinner-time cut her some meat, of which she could eat very little. Her hands being greatly swelled, through the pain occasioned by the handcuffs, she begged to be permitted to go near the kitchen fire. When she had sat a few minutes, Williamson, observing her throwing the vermin which swarmed upon her clothing into the fire, ordered her to 'return to her kennel'. Thereupon she returned to the closet, the door of which was locked till the next day, when she was found to be in a delirious state, in which she continued till the time of her death, which happened about two o'clock on the Tuesday morning.

The coroner's jury incriminating Williamson, he was dispatched to Newgate. At the ensuing sessions he was brought to trial before Lord Chief Baron Parker, and sentenced to death. The gallows was placed on the rising ground opposite Chiswell Street, in Moorfields. After he had sung a psalm and prayed some time, with an appearance of great devotion, he was turned off, amidst an amazing concourse of people. His body was conveyed to Surgeons' Hall for dissection, and his children were placed in Cripplegate Workhouse.

16 August

1960 (Australia) Eight-year-old Graeme Thorne's body was found on 16 August 1960, on a stretch of waste ground ten miles from his home in Sydney. He had been abducted on 7 July on his way to school, shortly after his parents had won a large sum of money on the Sydney lottery; the kidnapper later demanded a ransom of A£25,000 for his safe return. Graeme's killer, Stephen Leslie Bradley, was finally snared by the ingenuity of forensic botanists, who proved that the fungus spores breathed into the victim's lungs and identified after post-mortem, could only have come from a rare combination of trees found in Bradley's garden.

17 August

1991 (Australia) The massacre began on the Saturday afternoon of 17 August 1991, at the Coffee Pot restaurant in Sydney's Strathfield Plaza. Fifteen-year-old Roberta Armstrong and her schoolfriend, Katherine File, had been cheerfully chatting when they became aware of the attention being paid to them by the man sitting in the next booth, his eyes fixed, unblinking on them. Suddenly the stranger drew out a long-bladed knife and lunged at Roberta, slashing into her back. As Katherine began to scream, the attacker began to laugh, at the same time picking up an SKS self-loading assault rifle and firing wildly. The manager was shot through the head and terrified diners threw themselves under anything that might offer cover. Then the shooting stopped, and the madman with the gun walked with uncanny calm out of the Coffee Pot and up to the roof-top car park, shooting a bystander on the escalator as he passed.

Catherine Noyes was sitting in her car when the man levelled his gun at her head. She had watched horrified as he sent five bullets ripping into another car and was not arguing. The gunman climbed in beside Mrs Noyes and told her to drive, reaching the bottom of the ramps just as the first police cars arrived. As he jumped from the vehicle, the man turned and said simply: 'I'm really sorry'; he dropped down on one knee, put the rifle barrel beneath his chin and pulled the trigger. So ended thirty-three-year-old Wade Frankum's murderous spree; in just ten minutes, he left eight people dead and dozens injured. At the inquest, forensic psychiatrist Dr Rod Milton told the coroner: 'Frankum led a troubled and lonely life, full of simmering emotional and sexual frustration which finally exploded in an outpouring of rage.' And there was no debating Dr Milton's final words to the court: 'Guns make people like Frankum feel more powerful. If you want to have semi-automatic weapons you will have more killings; it's a simple equation.' The coroner, summing up the seven-day hearing, also expressed alarm to learn that 150,000 SKS semi-automatic rifles, identical to Wade Frankum's, were owned in Australia.

18 August

1959 (USA) There is a kind of morbid acceptance of their own sickness that many serial killers express when they are finally trapped. A recognition that they will go on and on killing until they are stopped. William Bonin, California's 'Freeway Killer' told a journalist after his trial: 'I'd still be killing. I couldn't stop killing.' William Heirens scrawled a message in the home of one of his victims: 'For Heaven's sake catch me before I kill more . . .' And just before he was executed in the gas chamber at San Quentin on 18 August 1959, Harvey Glatman commented: 'It's better this way. I knew this was the way it would be.'

Glatman was like many serial killers in another way, too. He liked to keep 'souvenirs' of his killing as a way of prolonging the pleasure of the act. After his release from prison on a robbery charge in 1951, Harvey Glatman took up photography as a hobby and became interested in 'glamour' shots. Like many another amateur photographer with the same interest, Glatman hired a model (using the alias Johnny Glynn). On 1 August 1957, nineteen-year-old Judy Dull arrived for the photo-session. Once in his 'studio' Glatman raped the girl and tied her to the bed – then he got out his camera to take snaps of his helpless victim. Fearful of the consequences, he killed Miss Dull and buried her body out in the desert. Her bleached skeleton was found protruding from the sand five months later.

Next Harvey (using the alias George Williams) met divorcée Shirley Bridgeford through a lonely hearts club. On their first date, 9 March 1958, he drove her out to the desert where he raped her in the car, bound her, and started clicking away with his camera. The next victim was a stripper and part-time model called Ruth Mercado; and the fourth an amateur model, Lorraine Vigil. Harvey (using the alias Frank Johnson) was driving Miss Vigil out to the desert on 27 October 1958, when he decided to pull a gun on her. During the struggle which followed the weapon went off, wounding the unlucky girl in the leg. With uncontrolled fury, she wrested the gun from Glatman and held him captive at its barrel end until a highway patrol officer rescued her.

In custody, Harvey Glatman was quite happy to admit to the assault on Lorraine Vigil, but insisted to detectives that it was done on a sudden impulse. Which hardly matched the evidence of the team that searched Harvey's home, where the walls were covered with photographs of his trussed-up victims – alive and dead. Glatman was convicted of murder in November 1958 and refused to appeal his death sentence.

19 August

1920 (England) Seventeen-year-old Irene Munro stood cheerfully on the threshold of Mrs Wynniatt's boarding house in Eastbourne in eager anticipation of her holiday. It was the height of the season in the middle of August, and after hastily unpacking her few belongings, Irene took to the promenade in search of romance, adventure and postcards – in whatever order they might come. The postcards came first. The other two did not come at all.

Perhaps Irene was hoping to help them on their way by walking into the seaside pub and ordering a drink. And it certainly did the trick. Soon she was in the company of Jack and Bill. Irene left the bar for lunch at Mrs Wynniatt's promising to meet her new friends later in the afternoon. And that is why, a little after three o'clock, she was standing, dressed up to the nines in her Sunday-best green coat outside the Archery Tavern.

The three companions walked out of the town towards that wide stretch of shingle beach called The Crumbles. A group of workmen on the coastal railway line saw Irene, Jack and Bill walk into the distance, and that is the last time anybody saw Irene Munro alive again; except Jack and Bill.

Her corpse was found by a small boy the next morning, and before long the beach was swarming with policemen. According to the police surgeon, Irene had died after being bludgeoned with a hefty lump of stone which lay by her side, covered in her blood. The fact that the dead girl's handbag was missing provided at least a provisional motive for the brutal attack. It did not take Detective Chief Inspector Mercer very long to identify Irene's last companions; they were two local lads not noted as model citizens. Jack Alfred Field, nineteen, unemployed with a previous criminal record; and William Thomas Gray, twenty-nine, formerly a soldier, now unemployed.

By the time they stood in the dock of the Lewes Assizes on 13 December 1920, Jack and Bill were doomed men. So tightly had the Crown built its case that a conviction was never in doubt. Jack Field made a futile attempt to establish an alibi, but failed; Bill Gray was so fed up he didn't bother. Mr Justice Avory later observed: 'The defence which you concocted has been demonstrated to be untrue . . . you must now prepare yourselves to undergo the penalty which the law enacts for such a crime as you have committed.' They were hanged at Wandsworth Prison on the morning of 4 February 1921.

20 August

1986 (USA) On the hot Wednesday morning of 20 August 1986, Patrick 'Sandy' Sherrill drove to work as usual, and wearing his regulation postman's uniform took two .45-calibre automatic pistols, a .22-calibre handgun and 300 rounds of ammunition and walked towards the post office. He stopped just once, to shoot dead a fellow-worker who was crossing the car park, before passing through the employees' entrance to the single-storey building. After locking several doors in order to maximise his kill, Sherrill began, in the words of the police, 'shooting people as though they were sitting ducks'. Although FBI marksmen were deployed around the building after an employee had escaped and raised the alarm, Sherrill refused to speak with the specially trained negotiators. When police eventually stormed the building, they found the bodies of fourteen men and women, and seven other badly wounded victims. Patrick Sherrill lay dead where he had put a single bullet through his own head, his arsenal of guns and ammunition beside him.

Patrick Sherrill was only one of a number of US postal workers with a grudge who have exacted this kind of revenge (others include Joseph M. Harris and Thomas McIlvane). Sherrill was a part-timer attached to the main post office at Edmond, Oklahoma, and had been warned only the day before his shooting spree that he was facing dismissal for unsatisfactory work. It was not the first time he had been in trouble, and reports claimed that he had already been suspended once since he joined a year before. Sherrill was always prepared to tell anybody who cared to listen that he was a Vietnam veteran, which was quite untrue. However, he was a member of the Oklahoma National Guard, and a considerable marksman in their competition team. In fact it was from this source that he 'borrowed' the two .45s and most of the ammunition. This is a characteristic which Patrick Sherrill shares with many other mass killers – a passion for military or para-military activities and uniform, and a fascination with firearms. Sherrill, again in common with many multicides, was a loner with no known family, no known attachments, and apart from his boasting about service in Vietnam, no past. Indeed it was some days before Sherrill's body could be cremated because nobody could be found to claim it.

He also shared another characteristic. The majority of mass killers take their own lives. The one puzzle is why Sherrill did so when he did. He was under no immediate threat from the outside, and he had plenty of ammunition. But that is one question that will never be answered.

21 August

1911 (England) It was when a milkman stumbled across her body in London's Clerkenwell district on the morning of 21 August 1911, that the police became aware of the murder of Rose Render. It was later learnt, however, that the nineteen-year-old waitress had been killed much earlier in the morning, when a passer-by had heard her scream and then call out 'Don't Charles! Don't!' No good samaritan, he decided to ignore her cries for help.

It transpired that 'Charles' was Charles Ellsome, a man with whom the victim had been living until she left him shortly before her death; in fact Rose had been part-timing as a prostitute in order to keep him. Confronted with Rose's death as he sat in a Soho cafe, Ellsome insisted his name was Brown, but told police: 'It's me you want.' Which he later claimed simply meant that he knew he would be suspected.

It was not much of a case, and even less of a trial – in fact it lasted less than one day. A friend of Ellsome's, a man named Fletcher, claimed that on 21 August, Ellsome had woken him up at about two or three o'clock in the morning and said that he had killed Rose. 'She drove me to it' was his reason. Under cross-examination, Fletcher made a grave error of judgement in boasting to the court: 'I thieve for a living, and I'm proud of it.' With little hesitation, the jury took less than thirty minutes to find Charles Ellsome guilty of murder. Asked whether he had anything to say, Ellsome cast his eyes upwards and muttered, 'I have only one Judge.'

Which in the circumstances seemed hardly true as Mr Justice Avory sentenced him: 'The prisoner has been living the most degraded life that a man can live. I cannot doubt that he took away the life of the girl, not from jealousy that she loved another man, or that another man loved her, but that another man should reap the benefit of her immoral life. For the crime of which he has been convicted, he must die.'

Unfortunately, in reminding the jury that they should not accept the man Fletcher's evidence without its being corroborated, he had intimated that this corroboration was contained in a statement made by Fletcher immediately following the murder. As this statement had not been introduced as evidence, the judge's remarks could be seen as a misdirection. Accordingly the Court of Criminal Appeal overturned the conviction (incidentally, the first time that that court had ever done so in a case of murder) and Charles Ellsome was necessarily released. And so on this occasion it seemed that he did have only one Judge.

22 August

1700 (Scotland) It is comparatively rare to find clergymen taking up arms against their flock, though it seems that the Rev. Thomas Hunter was one of the exceptions, hanged on 22 August 1700 for the murder of two children.

23 August

1961 (England) It was in the small hours of the morning of 23 August 1961, that a murder took place which has kept lawyers, politicians, crime historians and campaigners busily quarrelling among themselves for thirty-four years. The story began on the previous evening . . .

Michael Gregsten sat in his parked car in a field at Slough; beside him sat his mistress, Valerie Storie. Suddenly a man appeared at the door of the car, climbed in, and with a gun to Gregsten's head forced him to drive along the A6 to the appropriately named Deadman's Hill. Here he ordered Gregsten to pull into a lay-by, shot him dead and raped and shot Valerie Storie. By a miracle she survived, though paralysed for life.

An Identikit expert from Scotland Yard visited Valerie Storie at her bedside and between them they created the portrait of her attacker which was published throughout the country. It was accompanied by a second Identikit compiled from the recollections of three 'witnesses' who saw a man on the morning of the 23rd driving Michael Gregsten's car. The problem was that they looked like entirely different people. Only the deep-set brown eyes which Miss Storie remembered so well were common to both.

Meanwhile, the police had rounded up two suspects – James Hanratty and Peter Louis Alphon. Not only did the Identikit pictures look nothing like each other, but they did not look like Hanratty either – not least because he had clear, pale blue eyes. His hair was neither dark, nor was it brushed back. One man who did fit Valerie Storie's Identikit almost perfectly was Peter Alphon.

Then Valerie Storie retracted her description of her attacker's eyes, which became 'icy-blue' and 'saucer-like'. She did not pick Peter Alphon out of a special identity parade, but subsequently she did identify James Hanratty. Hanratty was arrested on the spot. When he was put on trial, Hanratty's defence was one of alibi, though he refused to name the friends with whom he claimed to be in Liverpool. Hanratty then changed his alibi and insisted that he had been in Rhyll (almost certainly true).

James Hanratty was convicted of murder and hanged at

Bedford Prison on 4 April 1962; but not before enormous doubts had been expressed about the safety of the verdict. Those doubts have remained throughout the years, fuelled in part by Peter Alphon's regular confessions.

24 August

1992 (Canada) On 24 August 1992 Professor Valery Fabrikant took a gun with him to the ninth floor of Concordia University, Montreal, where he opened fire on his colleagues; not, it should be added, with any great attention to target selection. Fabrikant killed three people and wounded two others, including a woman, and took a couple of hostages. One student later recalled: 'We were in my teacher's office talking, then we heard noises. I looked out and saw this man walking; my teacher said he had a gun.'

What everybody wanted to know was why this highly intelligent, if eccentric, expatriate Russian engineer should suddenly go berserk in his university, shooting his own colleagues. The problem is that this description masks the truth. Professor Fabrikant was more than eccentric, he was bordering on the insane, with strong feelings of persecution, and he did not suddenly go berserk, his shooting spree was the culmination of a long calculated campaign. As for shooting his own colleagues – that is exactly what he wanted to do; he felt that the only way to avenge himself on those he thought were betraying him was with a gun. The problem was that of the five victims only one was on his 'hit-list' of 'miscreants', and the two men who were the targets of his greatest venom (and law suits) were not harmed.

Professor Valery Fabrikant was a specialist in mechanical engineering, who had emigrated in 1979 from what was the Soviet Union and was at the time of the shooting incident on the staff of the Concordia. For reasons either real or imaginary, Professor Fabrikant was convinced that his academic colleagues were exploiting students and researchers by adding their own names to scientific papers in which they had played no material role. Professor Fabrikant had already taken out law suits against two staff members, in which he insisted both men withdraw their names from upwards of thirty published papers and make a public admission that they had made no contribution to them. The two accused responded with counter law suits of their own. A storm, indeed, was brewing over the groves of Academe. Valery Fabrikant next made use of some truly twentieth-century wizardry – a system of transmitting information internationally through a computer network accessed by most universities around the world – it is called Internet. The professor's exposé began: 'Dear Colleague, the events I will tell you about are so outrageous that you will have to see it to believe it . . .'; he concluded: 'I have little time left, because on 25 August I will be in jail for contempt of court and must do the mailing fast . . . I cannot fight the battle without your help. Speak up.' Far from arousing moral outrage on his behalf, Fabrikant's electronic campaign, supported by copious bundles of printed documentation, was greeted either with knowing winks and taps on the forehead, or irritation. And so there was only one solution . . .

25 August

1928 (England) While police constables Buzzy and Evans were on their midnight patrol of the Outer Circle of London Zoo on 25 August 1928, they heard the unmistakable sounds of a human voice in distress coming from the thick bushes on the zoo side of the railings. Investigation revealed the pathetic sight of a diminutive oriental clutching his ankle and groaning on the grass. He was for the most part incoherent ('Probably foreign,' thought PC Buzzy, sagely) but the officers understood that the oriental and somebody called Ali had been attacked by four men. After alerting the Zoo's

Superintendent, the policemen ran to the Tapir House where the attack was supposed to have taken place, while the injured oriental who thanks to the Superintendent they now knew as San Dwe ('Though we call him Sandy Wee, ha ha') had been removed to hospital. On his bed in the room above the Tapir House the officers found Said Ali, an elephant keeper like San Dwe. Only he would not be keeping elephants any more. Said Ali lay on his bed, his head cruelly bludgeoned, probably from the sledgehammer on the floor beside the bed.

By this time Detective Inspector Walter Hambrook of Scotland Yard had arrived on the scene, and without resort to any of his legendary powers of detection could see that a ferocious struggle had taken place; there was no reason, on the face of it, to disbelieve the little elephant keeper's story about being attacked by four men. It looked as though the sledgehammer had been used to break down the door before being used as a weapon. But nobody could pull the wool over Walter Hambrook's eyes. If the sledgehammer had been used on the door *before* being used on Said Ali's head, then why was there blood on the indentations where the door had been battered down? Somebody had been telling lies; and it could only be San Dwe. An attack by four large men was beginning to look like an attack by one small one.

At the trial of San Dwe in November, the jury was told that at first both men had worked together happily tending the zoo's elephants. San Dwe was the newcomer and when he arrived he and Said Ali shared the job of the children's elephant ride, with all the little financial perks that came with it from grateful parents. However, in 1928 Said Ali was given full charge of the rides, while San Dwe was appointed to care for the baby elephants in the zoo's sanatorium. San Dwe was not best pleased. And so, it would seem, he had decided to eliminate the competition – in a very final way. The jury thought so too and, to cut a long story short, San Dwe was sentenced to death. But he never got to meet the hangman, he was reprieved and after spending four years in prison he was returned to his native land.

26 August

1953 (Australia) Of all the incidents of multiple murder, by far the most common is familicide, and by far the most common within that category is murder within the nuclear family – that is to say within a single household. One of the rarest cases is that of John Balaban in Australia in 1953. Balaban was unusual in that he killed his family *as well*; he was already at least a double murderer before he committed familicide. Despite the fact that he was considered 'sane' enough to hang, on 26 August 1953, there must be serious doubts about his mental condition.

According to his own statement, John Balaban had first killed in Paris; the victim was a prostitute, and until Balaban's confession the French police had the murder on record as unsolved. The second victim was another prostitute, this time in Australia in December 1952. The woman's name was Zora Kusic – her throat had been cut and her stomach ripped open. Although Balaban was arrested and charged, the magistrate judged that there was no *prima facie* case against him and released him. Then Balaban moved on to his family . . .

In the early hours of 12 April 1953, screams were heard coming from the Sunshine Cafe in Adelaide followed by one of the cafe's waitresses hurtling twenty feet from an upstairs window on to the street below. Meanwhile, police had forced an entry into the premises and come upon three people savagely bludgeoned. The victims were later identified as thirty-year-old Thelma Balaban, who was lying dead in bed when the police arrived, her mother Mrs Susan Ackland, aged sixty-six, and Mrs Balaban's six-year-old son from a previous marriage, Philip Cadd. Both Mrs Ackland and the boy were still alive but died later in hospital. Mrs Balaban's husband, John Balaban, was arrested outside the cafe. Under questioning, Balaban made a statement admitting to the attack on his family and the waitress. He described how he had returned to the cafe and decided to kill his wife and mother-in-law, and because the boy had woken he killed him as well. Then he went into the room where the waitress was sleeping and hit her because, so he said, she had been stealing money and 'siding with his wife' against him. After beating the girl, Balaban had sex with her and then went and battered the other victims again, just for good measure. It wasn't much of an excuse, but he said he had killed them because they deserved to be killed.

John Balaban was charged only with the murders of his wife and Zora Kusic. At his trial in July 1953, Balaban's defence was insanity, and a psychiatrist stated that in his opinion he was schizophrenic and was certifiable. The superintendent of government mental institutions, on the other hand, considered that despite an abnormal personality, John Balaban was not mentally disordered. He was eventually found guilty of murder and sentenced to death by Mr Justice Abbott. Balaban's appeal was dismissed and he was hanged.

27 August

1933 (England) On the warm Sunday night of 27 August 1933, the stillness is broken by the tinkle of shattering glass. Mrs Fox snaps awake and nudges the man who sleeps beside her. 'Charlie! Wake up; someone's broken in.' Charlie Fox grunts bad-temperedly as he lights a candle and creeps across the bedroom. Charlie is down in the hallway now, with his wife looking on from the top landing, trying to follow him among the flickering shadows. Suddenly the candle goes out; a scuffling; a moan. Charlie Fox stumbling back up the stairs, tottering through the doorway . . . slumping on to the floor without ever uttering another sound. In the growing light of dawn it is just possible to see the handle of the knife protruding from his back.

But Mr and Mrs Fox were not the only ones to suffer a break-in that night. Mr Newton's butcher shop had had a late shopper. In fact, apart from the few scraps of money he took, the intruder had helped himself to a pint of milk. Which was the worst thing he could have done – without gloves on, anyway; because around the bottle he left a perfect set of prints. It was only a matter of minutes before Fred Cherrill of Scotland Yard's Fingerprint Bureau had identified the prints as belonging to Stanley Eric Hobday.

The result was that an unfamiliar announcement was made by the BBC. For the first time in its history the radio network was broadcasting the description of a criminal 'wanted by the police in connection with a murder'. Hobday by this time was on his way north in a stolen car which he managed to crash in Cheshire, whereupon he was obliged to take to his feet. Outside Carlisle he was jostled in a country lane by a herd of dairy cows.

'Watty' Bowman, the cowman, was the proud owner of a wireless set and an avid listener to the BBC. As he passed Eric Hobday, he realised he had seen him before. He had 'seen' him on the radio! And that is how Police Constable Elder of the Cumberland Constabulary learnt that he had a wanted fugitive on his patch; and how Stanley Hobday came to be taken into custody.

The trial was an unremarkable event, with all the aces dealt to the prosecution. Despite a gallant defence by Sir Reginald Coventry KC, there really wasn't much to be said for Hobday that was positive. The jury thought so too.

The following month, December 1933, Stanley Eric Hobday featured in Thomas Pierrepoint's diary: 'Hobday: 8 a.m., Winson Green Prison, Birmingham.' Pierrepoint was the public hangman.

28 August

1948 (England) In the early morning of 28 August 1948, sixty-four-year-old Nancy Ellen Chadwick was found lying dead in the roadway by a passing bus driver. Nancy was an eccentric old lady well known around Rawtenstall as a fortune-teller. At first it was thought that Old Nancy might have been the victim of a hit-and-run driver, until the pathologist suggested that it was much more likely that she had died from a savage bludgeoning with a blunt instrument.

As Nancy Chadwick had been found practically outside the house occupied by a woman named Margaret Allen, who may have seen something suspicious, she was marked down for routine questioning. Margaret Allen had been born in Rawtenstall in 1909, suffering a miserable childhood and adolescence trying to come to terms with her latent homosexuality. This feeling of being an outsider was carried through into adult life where it manifested itself in a determination to belong. Margaret's difficulty was that she wanted to participate, but as a man. She began to dress in men's clothing, and wear her hair short. She preferred to be called 'Bill'. When she was thirty-three, 'Bill' Allen became a bus conductor with the local corporation; a job which suited her temperament. Sadly her mother died the following year, and Margaret Allen took the loss dramatically, becoming a virtual recluse outside of work. The final blow was struck when she began to have dizzy spells and was forced to give up the buses. Having lost this one link with normality, Margaret Allen cut herself off entirely from society, and took to wandering the streets aimlessly, night and day. It was probably on these wanderings that she encountered old Nancy Chadwick . . .

When a policeman turned up at Margaret Allen's house three days after the discovery of Nancy Chadwick's body, they could hardly have missed the blood caking the walls of the tiny hallway. It didn't really matter now, though, because Margaret wanted to talk about it. Wanted to tell them how Old Nancy had come knocking at the door on the Saturday morning . . . she wanted to come in; Margaret was going out . . . Nancy insisting on coming in. Then Margaret looked round and there in front of her was the hammer. In Margaret's own words: 'On the spur of the moment I hit her with the hammer. She gave a shout and that seemed to start me off more. I hit her a few times, but I don't know how many.' She had intended to dispose of the body by throwing it in the river, but when it came to it the load was too heavy and she simply abandoned it where it fell.

Of the trial at Manchester Assizes there is little to say. Margaret appeared as 'Bill' and her counsel entered a courageous plea of insanity, though he must have known that it would never fit into the narrow confines of the M'Naghten Rules. 'Bill' Allen was found guilty, and was sentenced to death; a sentence which was carried out behind the bleak façade of Strangeways on 12 January 1949.

29 August

1812 (England)

Benjamin Renshaw was convicted on the clearest evidence of the wicked and wasteful crime of burning the hay of Mr Charles Stanton; and, in aggravation of such business, soon afterwards, of wantonly slaughtering a ram, the property of Mr Isaac Dodsley, both of the town of Mansfield, in the county of Nottinghamshire. He was sentenced to death and left by the judge for execution.

About eleven o'clock on the morning of 29 August 1812, he was taken from the prison and placed in a cart, accompanied by the executioner and a respectable gentleman who had daily visited him during his condemnation. The concourse of spectators was unusually great, to witness the awful catastrophe. After he was turned off, the noose of the rope moved under his chin, and it was deemed proper to put him into the cart, that the rope might be adjusted afresh, after which he was turned off again. This circumstance occasioned a considerable sensation among the spectators, who generally expressed abhorrence of the executioner, to whose carelessness they attributed the accident. After hanging the usual time, his body was given to his friends for interment at Mansfield.

(*The Newgate Calendar*)

30 August

1982 (USA) It was 30 August 1982, and Leslie Lowenfield had just bought himself a .22-calibre rifle; now Leslie and his gun were in a taxi heading towards Robinson Avenue, Marrero, Louisiana, where he intended to exact a bloody revenge on his former girlfriend and her family. Lowenfield paid the cabbie off before reaching Robinson, and walked up the street making a mental note of the eight men sitting playing cards in the front garden of a nearby house. Around five-thirty in the evening he burst through the door and opened fire. His one-time girlfriend, twenty-seven-year-old deputy sheriff Sheila Thomas, fell to the ground with gunshot wounds in the head and arm; her four-year-old stepdaughter Shantel was shot in the head, and Shantel's father, Carl Osborne, died from a bullet which entered his right ear and lodged in his brain. Sheila's mother, Mrs Myrtle Griffin was shot twice, once through the heart and once in the lungs. The noise of the shooting aroused Mrs Griffin's husband Owen, who had been outside with the card school, and he rushed into the house scattering cards and loose change as he ran; Owen Griffin got no further than the front porch before he was cut down with a bullet in his face. Lowenfield didn't wait around to see who else his massacre had attracted.

Of the five victims only little Shantel Osborne was alive when the police arrived, and she died shortly afterwards in hospital. Investigations managed to turn up the taxi driver who had brought Lowenfield to Robinson Avenue, and who remembered that the man was carrying what looked like a brand new .22 rifle. A subsequent search of the house revealed the weapon hidden under Sheila Thomas's bed – a bizarre touch was that her name had been written several times on the gun's stock. Also in Sheila's bedroom searchers found a notebook containing a number of obscene death threats. The police learnt later that Sheila had once had a boyfriend, a native of Guyana, called Leslie Lowenfield; they also learnt that Lowenfield had repeatedly uttered threats against the family.

A warrant was issued for the immediate apprehension of Leslie Lowenfield, and on 5 October 1982 he was picked up in Brooklyn by FBI agents who recognised his description from the wanted notices. While he was in custody awaiting extradition to New Orleans, Lowenfield wrote several letters claiming that he had not intended to shoot Shantel, and that it was only because her father had been using her as a human shield when Leslie opened fire that the child had been wounded.

Leslie O. Lowenfield came up for trial in May 1984, when he pleaded an alibi, insisting that he was in Jacksonville, Florida, at the time of the killings. It was an alibi which was effectively shattered when a prosecution witness testified that she had received a telephone call from Lowenfield that same day – from Alabama. On 14 May Leslie Lowenfield was found guilty of the first-degree murders of Sheila Thomas, Carl Osborne and Myrtle Griffin, and the voluntary manslaughter of Shantel Osborne and Owen Griffin; a fortnight

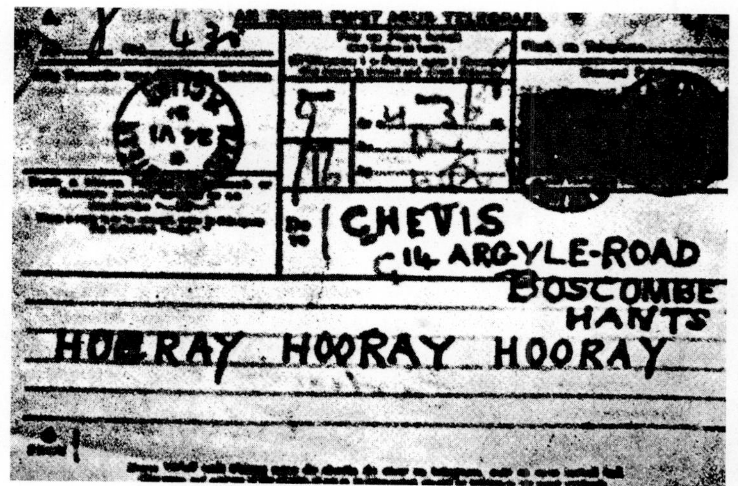

The telegram received by Sir William Chevis four days after his son, Hubert, was murdered. The sender – perhaps Hubert Chevis's killer – was never found. See 21 June.

Pauline Parker (left) and Juliet Hulme. See 22 June.

Samuel Herbert Dougal with lover Georgina Cranwell. See 23 June.

Miss Camille Cecile Holland, the unworldly spinster who became the object of Dougal's attentions.

Camille Holland's body recovered from the ditch at Moat Farm.

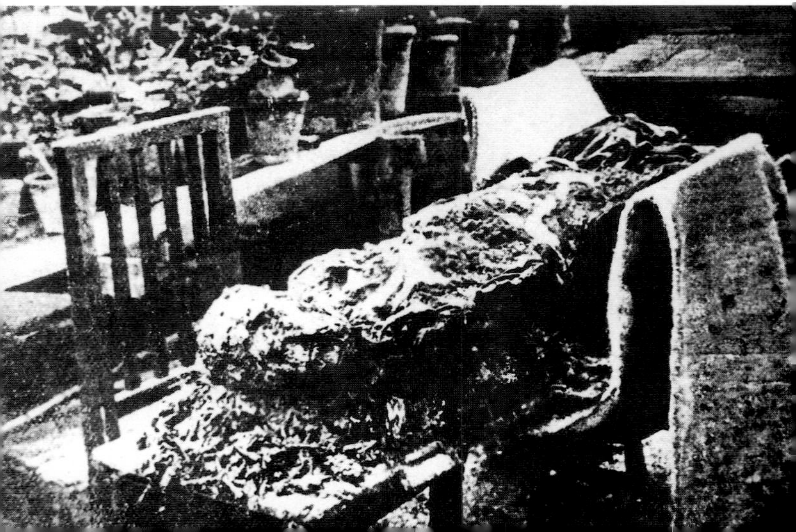

Susan Barber, who laced her husband's food with poison. See 27 June. (*Syndication International*)

Michael Barber, whose post-mortem revealed that he had died from paraquat poisoning. (*Syndication International*)

John Christie with his wife Ethel. See 15 July.

The systematic removal of three of Christie's victims from the kitchen cupboard at 10 Rillington Place.

The cellar at the rear of Vauxhall Baptist Church where the remains of Rachel Dobkin were unearthed. See 17 July.

The mutilated remains of Rachel Dobkin.

'I want somehow to convey to you what it means to be in prison for so long...'

IN THE BELLY OF THE BEAST

JACK HENRY ABBOTT

'Hell is now clear to behold'
NORMAN MAILER IN HIS INTRODUCTION

'Awesome, brilliant, perversely ingenuous'
NEW YORK TIMES BOOKS REVIEW

'Astonishing...a saga, an heroic story'
WASHINGTON POST

The title page of double-killer Jack Abbott's autobiography. See 18 July.

Margaret Allen as her alter ego 'Bill'. See 28 August.

Jonathan Doody in court as the jury gives its verdict. See 9 August. (*Popperfoto*)

Robert Lee Haggart. See 8 September. (*Popperfoto*)

Artillery gunner 3969722 Reginald Sidney Buckfield, known to his friends as 'Smiler'. See 9 October.

Herbert Mullin claimed to hear voices of people begging him to kill them. See 13 October. (*Associated Press*)

Former merchant marine George Hennard went on a vengeful rampage that left twenty-two people dead. See 16 October. (*Associated Press*)

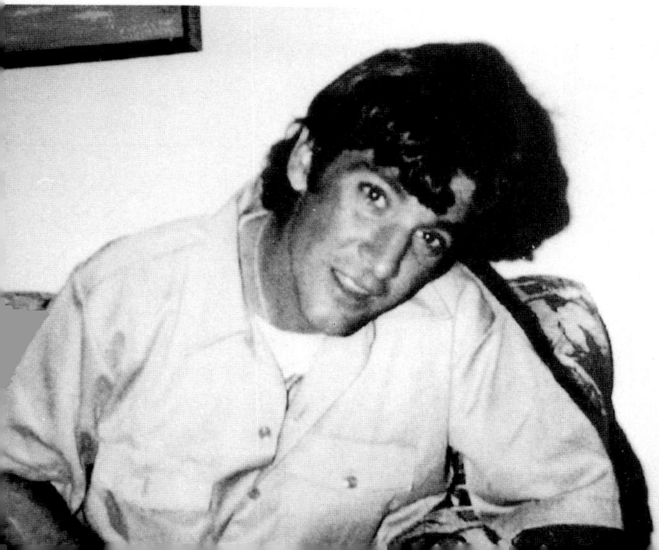

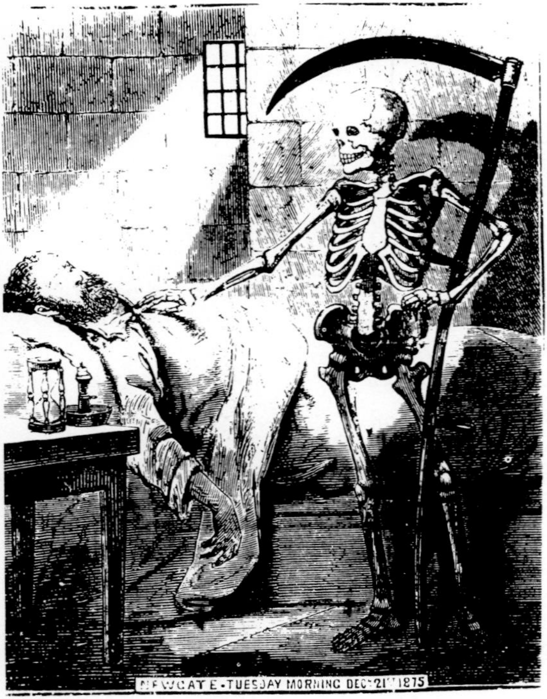

Henry Wainwright on the morning of his execution, as depicted by the *Illustrated Police News*. See 27 November. (*Rocky Stockman Collection*)

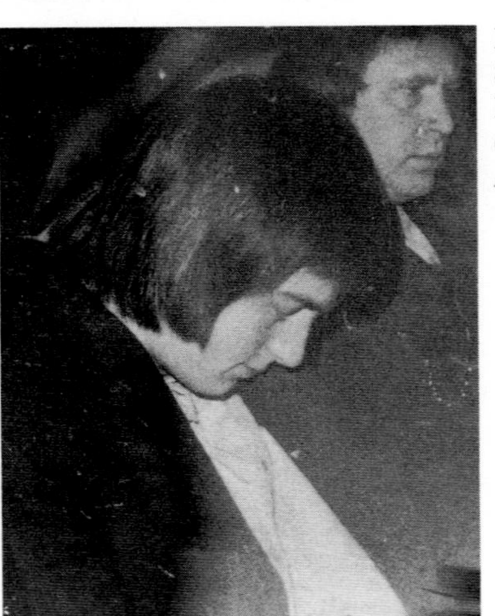

Mark Rowntree. See 31 December. (*Syndication International*)

later he was sentenced to death. Following an unsuccessful series of appeals, Lowenfield went to the electric chair on 13 April 1988.

31 August

1888 (England) Arguably the world's most famous sado-sexual serial killer, Jack the Ripper has remained a household bogey-man since the autumn of 1888, when the Whitechapel area of the East End of London was witness to a series of vicious – and still unsolved – murders. All five victims – Mary Ann Nichols, Annie Chapman, Elizabeth Stride, Catherine Eddowes and Mary Jane Kelly – were prostitutes. They had been attacked from behind and their throats cut, the bodies afterwards subjected to such mutilation and dissection as to suggest a perverted sexual motive. The first of Jack's victims, Mary Ann (or Polly) Nichols, was murdered on Friday 31 August 1888.

September

1 September

1956 (England) Is the perfect murder possible? Some have come perilously close to being perfect. Like the killing of baby Terence Armstrong. Between his death and the arrest of his murderer, on 1 September 1956, a year had elapsed; and the crime was only discovered then because somebody was feeling spiteful . . .

Five-month-old Terence Armstrong died at his home in Gosport, Hampshire, on 22 July 1955. At first it was thought that he had been the victim of infant curiosity in eating poisonous red berries – not an unreasonable assumption in view of the red skins found in the child's throat and stomach during post-mortem examination. However, subsequent laboratory analysis of the contents of the stomach showed that the 'skins' were none other than the soggy gelatine capsules that had once held the barbiturate drug Seconal. By this time the parents, neither of whom seemed particularly distressed, had been given permission to bury their son, and it was necessary to apply for an exhumation order so that a second autopsy could be performed – this time confirming the presence of traces of the drug Seconal.

John Armstrong, the father, was known to have access to the drug in the course of his duties as a naval sick-bay attendant, but as he denied ever having had Seconal in the house, and as there was no proof to the contrary, the inquest on Terence Armstrong's death returned an open verdict.

It remained open for a year, during which time marital

strife between Armstrong and his wife Janet became so intolerable that in July 1956 she applied for, and was granted, a legal separation on grounds of cruelty. Then Mrs Armstrong had quite a lot to tell the police about the tragic death of her son. Her husband had, according to her written statement, brought Seconal capsules home from the hospital where he worked, and after little Terence's death one afternoon when John Armstrong was alone in the house with him, she was made responsible for disposing of the remainder of the drug.

Facing charges of murder at Winchester Assize Court, John Armstrong continued to plead his innocence. From the evidence it transpired that Terence Armstrong was the innocent victim of his parents' inability to cope with the responsibilities of family life. John and Janet Armstrong, twenty-five and nineteen years old respectively at the time of their son's death, already had a three-year-old daughter, Pamela, who had been stricken with a mysterious illness two months earlier, but had recovered in hospital. Mrs Armstrong had also given birth to a second child who died in 1954 at the age of three months, of the same strange symptoms that had brought Pamela so close to death. When his wife had become pregnant with Terence, John Armstrong had made it clear that he could not afford any more children, and when the child arrived it became, quite simply, an expensive nuisance. At the end of the Armstrongs' trial John was found guilty of murder and sentenced to death (though he was later reprieved). Janet Armstrong was acquitted, but in a sensational revelation one month later, admitted she had given a Seconal capsule to Terence to help him sleep.

2 September
1744 (England)

Lydia Adler was tried at the Old Bailey on 2 September 1744, for the wilful murder of her husband, John Adler, by throwing him on the ground, kicking and stamping on his groin, and giving him thereby a mortal bruise, of which he languished in St Bartholomew's Hospital ten days, and then died; she was again indicted on the coroner's inquest for manslaughter.

Hannah Adler, daughter of the deceased, swore that he told her that his wife had given him the wounds which occasioned his death. Benjamin Barton testified that the deceased came to him with a bloody handkerchief about his head, and asked him for a spare bed, saying: 'This infernal fiend will be the death of me'; meaning his wife. When he visited the deceased during his stay in hospital, Adler repeated: 'I wish, Mr Barton, you would be so good as to get a warrant to secure this woman, for she will be the death of me.' Hannah Adler, being further questioned, said that her father died between twelve and one o'clock; that about two hours before he said: 'I am a dead man and this lady [the prisoner] has killed me.' That after this he repeatedly declared that his wife was the person that murdered him, and begged that she might be brought to justice. His last declaration was made only ten minutes before he died.

Mr Godman, a surgeon, deposed that the husband died of mortification, occasioned by a blow; but acknowledged that the deceased had a rupture, and that such a blow as he received would not have hurt a person in sound health.

The prisoner, in her defence, said that her husband had two wives besides her; and that a quarrel happening between her and one of the wives, the husband endeavoured to part them, and in doing so fell down, and the other woman fell on him; but that she herself never lifted hand or foot against him.

Joseph Steel deposed that the deceased had had four wives; that he was kind to them all at the first, but afterwards used to beat them severely; and that he had seen the prisoner and her husband frequently fight together.

The jury gave a verdict of manslaughter, in consequence of which Lydia Adler was ordered to be burned in the hand.

[This punishment involved the felon being branded with a hot iron, usually on the ball of the thumb – colourfully described in Newgate cant as 'Glymming in the paw' – so that the next time an offence was committed a much more severe punishment, usually death, would be imposed. Needless to say, money spoke loudly in such circumstances, and a suitable reward would ensure that the executioner used a cold iron.]

(*Old Bailey Records*)

3 September

1982 (USA) Although Coral Watts was known to have killed at least twelve women (and possibly as many as forty), he was never tried for murder. When, on 3 September 1982, he was sentenced to sixty years' imprisonment it was for burglary and attempted murder following an attack on two young women.

Coral Watts first came to the attention of the police in Michigan in 1974. The body of a young woman called Gloria Steele had been found slashed to death near Western Michigan University. Watts was pulled in as a suspect, but later released. In December 1975, however, he was given a year in prison for an attack on another co-ed just prior to the Steele murder. On Halloween night in 1979 Mrs Jeanne Clyne was stabbed to death in a Detroit suburb; once again Coral Watts was under suspicion. In 1980, while Watts was living in Ann Arbor, he was taken into custody in connection with the activities of the so-called 'Sunday Morning Slasher' who stabbed three women to death in April, July and September of that year. In this, as in all the previous cases, no direct evidence was ever forthcoming to link Watts to the killings.

When Coral Watts moved to Houston, Texas, in 1981, the Michigan police authorities advised Houston of their suspicions and for a period he was kept under surveillance as he had been while he was in Michigan. The watch was eventually relaxed, although at the time a new series of killings, reminiscent of those in Michigan had begun to plague Texas. If one man were really responsible for all ten deaths in the space of a year – from 27 March 1981 to 23 May 1982 – then either he was very clever (or lucky) or the police were very inept (or unlucky). On the same date as the most recent killing – that of Michelle Maday on 23 May 1982 – Coral Watts was arrested and charged with burglary and the attempted murder of two young women.

In advance of his trial, Watts agreed to plead guilty, and in return for a sixty-year jail sentence and immunity from further prosecution, to clear up many as yet unsolved murders and lead police to undiscovered corpses. The deal was finally approved, and Watts admitted to all nine Texas murders plus that of Linda Tilley in September 1981 – previously believed to have been an accidental death. He gave detailed instructions for the recovery of the bodies of three missing Texas women, and confessed to killing Mrs Jeanne Clyne back in Detroit.

4 September

1713 (England) Jack Shrimpton, highwayman, was one of those colourful figures of eighteenth-century crime (along with individuals such as Jack Shepherd) whose exploits, criminous as they were, endeared them to the ordinary citizens of London for whom they became folk-heroes. At this distance it is impossible to say for sure which stories are true and which fable (one thing that is a matter of record is that he was hanged for the murder of a watchman on 4 September 1713).

5 September

1933 (England) Ernest Brown had for some time been engaged as groom to a wealthy Yorkshire cattleman named Frederick Morton. He had also been the lover of Morton's wife Dorothy Louise; though she had tired of the liaison and given him the brush-off. At the beginning of 1933, the Mortons took up residence at Saxton Grange. It was about a year after the move that Brown was asked by his master to mow the lawn. Brown became unreasonably angry at the request and withdrew his services, greatly irritating Mr Brown, but delighting Dorothy Louise. It was not long before a very contrite groom was asking for his job back – he would even mow the lawn. In fact he was offered a job – as odd-job man! – thus sparking off an all-consuming hatred.

On Tuesday 5 September 1933, Morton drove off for the day in one of the family's two cars. Ernest Brown took the opportunity to pester Mrs Morton. The conclusion of the inevitable row was that Brown knocked his former lover to the ground. At around 9.30 that evening Dorothy Louise was in the kitchen with her companion/help Ann Houseman, when they heard a shotgun being discharged, followed by a rattle of pellets against the window pane. Brown burst into the room and announced that he had just shot a rat. The women, unnerved by this activity, locked themselves in an upper room. By midnight, Frederick Morton had still not returned. At three o'clock the house was rocked by a huge explosion, and when the two terrified women looked out of the window, they could see that the garage was an inferno. Finding the telephone dead, they fled to the village for help. Meanwhile, Brown, having failed to round up the frightened livestock, drove into Towton to raise the farm bailiff.

When the flames had been extinguished and the debris cooled, police entered the garage and found the remains of Frederick Morton's car; in the driver's seat they found the remains of Frederick Morton; a post-mortem examination revealed that he had been shot dead before the fire had started.

Ernest Brown's account of events was that his master had arrived home around 11.30 on the previous night, somewhat under the weather through drink, and must have accidentally set fire to himself with a cigarette. However, at his trial, the prosecution had Brown as the villain of the piece – claiming that Morton had arrived home at 9.30, been killed by Brown, who then loosed off another shot at the house in case there was any suspicion. He had then cut the telephone wires to delay help. In this last claim the Crown was helped by a remarkable, for its time, piece of forensics by Professor Tryhorn. Tryhorn had, with the use of greatly enlarged photographs of the cut ends of the telephone wires and the blade of the knife Brown had removed from the kitchen drawer, proved that the latter had cut the former. It was enough to convince the jury anyway, the result of which was Ernest Brown's collaboration with the hangman at Armley Road Gaol, Leeds.

6 September

1971 (Australia) Monday 6 September 1971 was the day that forty-year-old labourer Clifford Bartholomew decided to kill his wife and ended by shooting-up his whole family. It has to be said, though, that the family – or at least Bartholomew and his wife Heather, were in pretty bad shape emotionally anyway, and Clifford had walked out of their home – a run-down farmhouse at Hope Forest, near Adelaide – a few months before.

It had all started back at the beginning of 1971, when Bartholomew lost his job. To help out with the weekly budget the Bartholomews took in a lodger, a Vietnam veteran in his twenties. The already fragile marital relationship was not helped by the mutual attraction which developed between Heather and the lodger. In July 1971 she visited her sister Winnis, and while she was away wrote a passionate letter to him. Clifford Bartholomew opened the letter; the lodger left. Heather returned home shortly afterwards, followed by her sister and her two-year-old nephew Danny. The state of affairs between Mr and Mrs Bartholomew could now best be described as open warfare. The result was that Clifford left home to stay with his stepmother.

On 5 September 1971, Father's Day, Cliff Bartholomew drove back to the farm with presents for the children; they included a .22-calibre rifle for his eldest son. Despite an opening skirmish, Bartholomew calmed down a bit and during the conversation pleaded for a reconciliation. Heather told him she was taking the seven children to Adelaide where their former lodger was arranging accommodation. Dejected and rejected, Clifford Bartholomew left the farmhouse. That night he couldn't sleep. In the early hours of the following morning, 6 September, Bartholomew came to a decision. The plan was this: with all the upset of the previous day he had forgotten to give his children their presents. The gun was still in the trunk of the car. He would drive up to Hope Forest, knock his wife unconscious with a rubber-headed mallet, drag her into the shed and shoot her. This way he would not disturb the rest of the family.

When he arrived at the farmhouse, Bartholomew loaded the rifle, put on a pair of gloves and crept up to his wife's bedroom. It may have been nerves, it may be that he found it difficult to hurt the person he once shared his life with, but Cliff Bartholomew did not bring the mallet down nearly hard enough; that first blow simply made his wife scream, so he hit her again, harder, and she fell back on the pillow. But the screams had woken the rest of the household and Bartholomew panicked and killed them; then he telephoned to tell his stepmother what he had done, and she rang the police. When the squad car arrived Clifford Bartholomew was sitting drunk in the kitchen.

At his trial in the Adelaide Supreme Court, Clifford Bartholomew pleaded guilty and was sentenced to death, though that was later commuted to life imprisonment. He was a model prisoner, and in spite of a public outcry he was paroled on 10 December 1979.

7 September

1929 (England) The expression 'The butler did it' has entered the language to describe corny endings to detective fiction. But in fact butlers (like doctors, lawyers and vicars) occasionally do 'do it'. One butler who did was Charles Houghton who on 7 September 1929 killed his elderly employers.

For twenty-two years, Charles Houghton had been in service as butler to the Woodhouse family in their splendid stately home, Burghill Court, just outside Hereford. In 1929, the family in residence consisted solely of two maiden sisters, Elinor Drinkwater Woodhouse, and her younger sister Martha (May) Gordon Woodhouse. Which was as well, because Houghton was no longer as young as he was, and he saw himself more as the Old Family Retainer – a position of privilege and influence below stairs and with very little to do above. And that, in a way, was the problem. Had he been more usefully engaged he might not have had the time to develop a fondness for the fruits of the wine cellar. But develop that taste he did, to the exclusion of most else. Indeed, he began rather to resent the time spent not drinking his way through the clarets. Of course it was noticeable, particularly at meal times; and the kindly Misses Woodhouse must have had a good many worrying moments as their butler weaved and lurched his way towards them with the soup. As well-bred ladies, they did not at first mention it; indeed they pretended not to notice; besides, most of the time Houghton was out of sight, down in the pantry reviewing the ports. But it was meal times . . .

Eventually, Miss Elinor and Miss May could avoid the inevitable no longer; their Old Retainer could no longer be retained. Upon which decision they gave him twenty-four hours' notice and two months' wages. And upon which Houghton bowed, thanked them with an inscrutably blank look, and repaired to the cellar to check on the malts. The following morning, 7 September, a Sunday, Houghton attended church with the household and returned to serve breakfast. Shortly afterwards he found Miss Elinor in the kitchen discussing menus with cook, crept up behind her, and shot her dead with a fowling piece. Then he tracked down Miss May and dispatched her too. Upstairs in his own billet, Charles Houghton took out his open-razor and made a half-hearted attempt to cut his throat, succeeding only in giving himself a superficial wound and making a lot of mess with the blood.

When the police arrived, summoned by the other staff, Houghton observed mournfully: 'Oh dear, this is a bad job.' He appeared before Mr Justice Swift at the Hereford Assizes charged only with the murder of Elinor Woodhouse. It was said in his defence that he was suffering from symptoms of epilepsy, but this made no difference to the result of the trial. Which was that on 6 December 1929 he was hanged.

8 September

1982 (USA) Family guests calling for supper at the Post farmhouse near Farwell, Michigan, at around 6.30 p.m. on Tuesday 16 February 1982, were surprised to find the place in darkness. The visitors cautiously entered the kitchen and switched on the light; they were horrified to see, lying in pools of blood, the bodies of forty-two-year-old Mrs Vaudrey Post and her twenty-three-year-old daughter Garnetta Haggart. They rushed from the building and drove to the next farmhouse to call the sheriff.

When the sheriff's officers arrived, they proceeded to search the house and the area around it; that was how they found the body of Mrs Post's husband, George, in the basement. In a pick-up truck in front of the farm building were the bodies of another daughter, twenty-nine-year-old Helen Gaffney, three of her children, ten-year-old Angela, Tom, aged eight, and Amy, seven. Lying among the bodies, amazingly unscathed, was Helen Gaffney's youngest child, a one-year-old girl, who had apparently been protected from harm by her mother's body. The pick-up had been riddled by what appeared to be a fusillade from a shotgun. Six of the victims had died from shotgun wounds and one of the children had been killed with a hand-gun. It was subsequently discovered that Mrs Post's car was missing from the farm but, because there was no indication that anything else had been taken, robbery did not seem to be one of the options when it came to motive.

Detectives questioned other members of the Post family and many volunteered the suspicion that Garnetta Haggart's estranged husband, Robert Lee Haggart could be responsible. On the following day, Garnetta had been due in court to sue for divorce from her husband. Haggart was also wanted by the police to answer a charge of fraud and had a previous conviction for a sexual offence. The sheriff decided to issue a warrant for Haggart, who was thought to be driving Mrs Post's missing car.

On Thursday 18 February, a man in Haletown, Tennessee, read a newspaper article about the Post murders, and was amazed to see the suspect named as Robert Lee Haggart; he happened to be sharing an apartment with Haggart. The man took his story to the authorities, telling them that Haggart was currently in Alabama, outside the authority's jurisdiction. He agreed to contact Haggart and arrange to meet on the Tennessee side of the border, so that he could be arrested. When he was later confronted by police officers, Haggart surrendered without offering any resistance, though he had in his possession a loaded .38 pistol. In his Haletown apartment, detectives found bloodstained clothing. Haggart waived extradition and was returned to Michigan, where he was charged with seven counts of murder.

Haggart came up for trial on 8 September 1982. The prosecution case included expert evidence that the bloodstaining on the clothing found in Haletown matched the blood groups of two of the victims found in the pick-up and was of a different group to Haggart's. The bullet that killed one of the children was demonstrated by ballistics experts to have been fired from the pistol found in Haggart's possession when he was arrested. After a trial lasting a month, the jury found Haggart guilty of six counts of first-degree murder, one count of second-degree murder, one of attempted murder and eight of possessing a firearm during a felony.

On 22 October, Robert Lee Haggart was sentenced to life terms on each of the seven murder charges, thirty to fifty years for attempted murder and two years on the firearms charges.

9 September

1990 (Austria) On 9 September 1990, Felix Zehetner was enjoying himself at a barbecue in Vienna. The problem was that he was enjoying himself far too much, eventually becoming so drunk and objectionable that the host had him thrown out.

Twenty-two-year-old Zehetner stumbled home much the worse for schnaps and a bruised ego. From its hiding place in his bedroom, Zehetner took out his Smith and Wesson pistol and, as they provided the nearest targets on which to vent his anger and frustration, shot his parents, killing his fifty-one-year-old father and severely wounding his mother. Felix Zehetner then made his way back to the barbecue, and without a word opened fire on the revellers, killing four and wounding sixteen. The party's host, who had been Zehetner's prime target, died and his twenty-three-year-old sister was critically wounded with a bullet through the lung.

Police were called and engaged Felix Zehetner in a brief shoot-out, during the course of which he seriously wounded two officers before putting a fatal bullet through his own head.

10 September

1953 (England) 'These are pictures of William Pettit. The police are anxious to trace this man, who, it is believed, may assist inquiries into the death of Mrs Rene Brown at Chislehurst on 10 September.' The voice was that of John Snagge, the BBC's chief radio announcer, who had been seconded to their television service in order to give the medium's first police request for the public's help. It was thought that it would be more 'suitable' for a man to read the message rather than the duty announcer Sylvia Peters. The message continued: 'Will anyone who can give information about this man's whereabouts get in touch with their nearest police station.' The pictures of Pettit remained on the screen for several seconds after the announcement had ended.

This unprecedented use of television by the police came about after weeks of official frustration over the brutal stabbing of Mrs Agnes Irene Brown (called Rene) in a field in Kent. Forty-eight-year-old Mrs Brown was known to have been eating in a restaurant with twenty-seven-year-old Pettit, a former lodger of herself and her husband, and probably her lover, on the evening of 10 September 1953. She had not returned home and her husband had eventually reported her missing.

William Pettit was a very sick man – both physically and mentally. He was suffering from tuberculosis and had long-term psychological problems. At around 10.20 on the evening Agnes disappeared, Arthur Brown received a telephone call from Pettit saying: 'Hello, old chap. Your wife is quite all right, and everything should be all right now. We have had an argument about my future, but I am afraid it was all my fault.' He told Brown that he would ask Mrs Brown to call him and then rang off.

The hunt for William Pettit was headline news in the papers for weeks, it seemed almost as if the earth had swallowed him up – and that was the reason for the television announcement. But by this stage he was already dead. His body was found in a war-damaged building in the City of London, and in his hand a piece of paper bore a scribbled note to Arthur Brown: 'Forgive me for what I have done. I could have gone on living with Mr and Mrs Brown, but not without Mrs Brown. I love her, I love her, I love her.' According to pathologist Professor Keith Simpson, William Pettit had died naturally from advanced tuberculosis.

11 September

1907 (England) Bert Shaw, a railway dining-car cook, arrived home off the night shift at around eleven o'clock on the morning of 12 September and found the door of his flat locked. When he had borrowed a spare key and let himself in, he was horrified beyond belief. Lying on the bed, her throat cut almost through to the vertebrae was his partner of nine months, Phyllis Dimmock, a twenty-three-year-old prostitute.

Phyllis, the police soon learnt, was a popular member of the twilight world she inhabited and it was an easy job to piece together her regular movements. She had two pubs which she used as pick-up points – the Eagle and the Rising Sun. Detectives managed to track down one of her regular customers, a ship's cook named Robert Roberts. Roberts admitted to being in Phyllis's company on the three nights prior to the night of her murder. On the last of those she had shown him a letter asking her to meet somebody called Bert at the Eagle at 8.30 on the evening of 11 September. Phyllis also showed Roberts a postcard with the message: 'Phillis Darling, If it pleases you to meet me 8.15 p.m. at the [here was drawn a cartoon sketch of a rising sun with a winking face on it]. Yours to a cinder, Alice.' Roberts thought both the letter and the postcard were in the same handwriting.

The postcard was found in the back of a drawer by Bert Shaw and handed over to the police who released it for publication by the press. The handwriting was recognised by Ruby Young as belonging to her occasional boyfriend Robert Wood, a twenty-five-year-old artist. When she taxed Wood with the business of the postcard and the dead prostitute, he explained that he had indeed written the postcard at the request of Phyllis (she had liked the Mother and Child painting on it) and signed it 'Alice' to allay Bert Shaw's suspicions. At the same time he begged Ruby to say that he spent the night of 11 September with her. Unfortunately Ruby Young was indiscreet enough to mention this conversation to a journalist friend, and the journalist friend passed it on to a policeman friend.

At two identity parades Robert Wood was picked out by a number of people who had seen him with Phyllis. This combined with his attempt to get Ruby Young to lie for him led to Wood's arrest and eventual trial at the Old Bailey. The trial opened on 12 December 1907, and Robert Wood was fortunate indeed to have the services of Edward Marshall Hall as his defender. The most damaging witness, Ruby Young, somehow antagonised the jury, for what in reality was her telling the truth, seemed to them simply a prostitute betraying her lover for money (the *News of the World* had offered £100 to anyone who recognised the writing on the postcard). The end result was a wave of sympathy for Robert Wood, and when the judge summed up in his favour it was in the bag. To public approbation Robert Wood was acquitted.

12 September

1866 (New Zealand) On Wednesday 12 September 1866, the trial of Richard Burgess (also known as Richard Hill), Thomas Kelly and Philip Levy opened at the Supreme Court in Nelson before Mr Justice Alexander Johnston. A member of the same gang, Joseph Sullivan, gave evidence against his former partners in murder. The trial ended six days later with guilty verdicts against all three men.

The misdeeds that had brought this unlovely gang of ruffians to the foot of the scaffold had entirely to do with greed. The sort of greed which stems from easy money; the easy money that some were making in the gold-fields of New Zealand during that boom period of the mid-nineteenth century. It began like this . . .

Four men, Felix Mathieu, John Kempthorne, James Dudley and James de Pontius left Pelorus Bridge on 13 June 1866 with the intention of prospecting for gold in the area of Maungatapu, called the 'Sacred Mountain'. As they departed, the men were unaware that they had been marked out by four hardened criminals who planned to hold the prospectors up at gun point, rob and murder them. The gold-hunters were intercepted as planned and taken into the bush where they were stabbed to death. The assassins – Burgess, Kelly, Levy and Sullivan – then robbed them at leisure, stealing cash, gold and other valuables from their pockets. The prospectors' baggage yielded a little more gold, but the total value of their haul amounted to little more than £300. For the purpose of confusing future investigations, Richard Burgess fired shots into the bodies of Mathieu, Kempthorne and Dudley in order to try to create the impression that de Pontius had killed and robbed them. The body of James de Pontius was buried out of sight, while the others were left to the elements.

Burgess and his murderous band then travelled on to Nelson. It was not for them to know that Felix Mathieu had arranged to meet another man in the same town, but when the prospector failed to arrive, an alarm was raised. The finger of suspicion immediately pointed in the direction of Richard Burgess and his companions, well known in the area as criminals. A reward of £200 was offered for information on the missing men, described as 'presumed murdered'. The four suspects were detained, and with minimum persuasion, the treacherous Sullivan offered to make a full statement on condition he was pardoned. His directions led police to the corpses of Mathieu, Kempthorne, Dudley and de Pontius which were exhumed from their rustic graves. Burgess, Kelly and Levy were charged with their murder.

Burgess, Kelly and Levy were convicted and sentenced to death. Sullivan was put on trial for a separate, earlier, murder, and he too was found guilty and sentenced to death. Two weeks later, the death sentences on Burgess, Kelly and Levy were confirmed but that on Sullivan was commuted to life imprisonment. On Friday 5 October 1866, Richard Burgess, Thomas Kelly and Philip Levy were hanged.

13 September

1707 (England) William Elby (alias Dunn) was executed for burglary and murder on 13 September 1707, at Feltham. The account which follows is from *The Newgate Calendar*:

> William Elby was indicted at the sessions in the Old Bailey for breaking into the house of Mr James Barry, at Fulham, on 9 August 1707, with intent to rob it; and likewise for the murder of Nicholas Hatfield, by giving him a mortal wound with a rapier near the left breast, of which he died soon after.
>
> The evidence deposed that, Mr Barry hearing a noise about his house between twelve and two in the morning, he got up with his wife and man, Nicholas Hatfield. went downstairs, found a window broken open, and espied two men without, about five yards' distance, one of whom was the prisoner. They ran immediately upstairs for arms, but Hatfield, stepping into the kitchen, was met by Elby, who drove him into the pantry and gave him a stab in the breast, of which he died twelve hours afterwards.
>
> Elby was hanged on 13 September 1707, and afterwards hung in chains.

14 September

1901 (USA) The anarchist Leon Czolgosz visited the Pan-American exhibition at Buffalo, New York and, on 14 September 1901 while apparently waiting in line to shake President William McKinley's hand, pulled a pistol from his pocket and shot the President in the stomach. Eight days later McKinley, twenty-fifth President of the United States (inaugurated 1896), died from his wounds; and on 29 October, Leon Czolgosz was executed in the electric chair at Auburn Prison.

15 September
1849 (England)

EXECUTION OF JOHN GLEESON WILSON

At Kirkdale Gaol, on Saturday, September 15th, 1849, the Murderer of Mrs Henrichson, her Two Children, and a Female Servant

One of the most appalling murders which has for years startled and disgusted society took place on Wednesday 28 March 1849. At No. 20 Leveson Street, Liverpool, at mid-day. A miscreant in the most brutal manner murdered two unprotected women and two helpless children. In due course Wilson was committed for trial, which took place before Mr Justice Patteson and a respectable jury, who, in less than five minutes, returned a verdict of guilty.

On Saturday morning the iron gate leading to the drop was opened and the prisoner appeared between two priests. A general feeling of horror seemed to pervade all present, which found expression in the most distant part of the assembly by bursts of execration. Calcraft, the London executioner, was unable to be present from illness, and the office was performed by Howard from York. Thus terminated the life of one of the greatest criminals that ever disgraced the human family. Upwards of 100,000 persons were present, the railway company running cheap trains from all available parts.

(From a contemporary Execution, or 'Gallows' Broadsheet, by J. Harkness of Preston)

16 September
1777 (England)

Captain A'Court, a gentleman of fortune, intending to take his family on a visit to Cheltenham, hired Joseph Armstrong to attend them on such excursion, in the capacity of footman. It appears that his pertness and neglect soon disgusted Mrs A'Court, who requested her husband to discharge him. In revenge, Armstrong determined to poison her; in doing which he had the barbarity to keep her lingering in misery ten days. This he effected by putting arsenic, at different times, into her tea, of which, in that time, she expired in excruciating torment on 16 September.

This being fully proved at his trial, Armstrong was sentenced to death; but when the jailer went to his cell to summon him to his fate, he had contrived to hang himself but a short time before, thus robbing the gallows of its deserved due.

(*The Newgate Calendar*)

17 September
1709 (England)

THE MURDER OF MR ROBERT COLLINS BY AMBROSE GWINNETT
Written by Himself

My sister was married to a man named Sawyer, a seafaring man who had quit his profession and set up a public house outside Deal in the county of Kent. I had frequent invitations to pass a short time with them, and in the autumn of 1709, I left my home in the city of Canterbury on foot on the 17th day of September, though through some unavoidable delays on the road, the evening was considerably advanced before I had reached Deal. So tired was I that, had my life depended on it, I could not have got as far as my sister's that night. I went seeking lodging from house to house to no avail, until in the end I entered a public house and begged to be allowed to sit by the kitchen fire till morning. The landlady, who happened to know my sister, led me into the parlour where an elderly man sat counting a considerable amount of money. 'Uncle,' the landlady said, 'this is a brother of our friend Mrs Sawyer. He is tired after his journey, will you give him part of your bed?' After some hesitation this arrangement was agreed and, collecting up his bag of money and candle, he led me upstairs.

At about three in the morning I awakened with the most violent gripes and had to inquire of my companion directions to the necessary. Having told me, my benefactor added: 'You may have difficulty opening the latch, the string being broken. I will give you my penknife which will open it through a chink in the boards.' I must have stayed in the garden privy near half an hour before returning to my bed; to my surprise my bed-fellow had gone, and I slept alone.

About six o'clock I awoke and found myself still alone. I dressed with haste and, having paid my reckoning the previous night, I departed. I reached my sister's in time for breakfast, and at about eleven, three men strode into the bar parlour and seized me, shouting: 'You are the Queen's prisoner', and dragged me back to my lodging of the previous night. Here I was accused by all who stood there of the robbery and murder of the landlady's old uncle. And there, as evidence it seems, was the blood-soaked bed where we had lain. There was no body and no money. On being asked to turn out my pockets, I produced the knife, at which the landlady shrieked: 'O God! there is my uncle's penknife'. It being supposed that I had thrown the old man's body into the sea, I was taken before a justice of the peace, and at the following Assizes was condemned to die a felon's death on the gallows.

[The report adds that Gwinnett was hanged, but when cut down was found to be alive and later recovered. In fear of being re-hanged, Gwinnett fled overseas and, so it is said, had many adventures.]

18 September

1908 (England) To have a much loved wife and companion snatched from him by an assassin's bullet was grief enough, but when the poisonous letters began to drop through his letterbox, Major-General Charles Luard could stand no more. On 18 September 1908 he rose early in the morning, washed, dressed and walked to the railway crossing at Teston, outside Maidstone, in Kent. He waited patiently in a clump of bushes for the 9.09 a.m. from Maidstone West, and threw himself under the thundering wheels.

It had all begun less than a month earlier, when the major-general and his wife Caroline left their home in Ightham, he to make the hour's walk to the local golf club at Godden Green, she to visit their near-by summer-house in Fish Pond Wood. Charles Luard collected the set of clubs he was after and returned home in the early evening expecting his wife to be there to meet a friend they had invited for tea. She was not.

It was with some anxiety that the major-general entertained their visitor and then hurried off in the direction of the summer-house to look for his wife. He found her lying dead on the floor, gunshot wounds in her head. Mrs Luard's purse was missing and her rings had been roughly pulled off her fingers. It was the first impression of the police that Caroline Luard had been killed and robbed by a passing vagrant.

This, however, did not stop the local tongues wagging, and despite the fact that any number of witnesses could place him far away from the site of his wife's murder, and despite the coroner's statement that Luard could not have committed this terrible act, the campaign of vilification had already begun. On the night before he took his own life, Charles Luard wrote this final letter to his close friend Colonel C. E. Warde:

> . . . I thought that my strength was sufficient to bear up against the horrible imputations and terrible letters which I have received since that awful crime was committed and which robbed me of my happiness. And so it was for long, and the goodness, kindness and sympathy of so many friends kept me going. But somehow in the last day or two something seems to have snapped. The strength has left me and I care for nothing except to join her again . . .

The verdict of the coroner's jury on the death of Mrs Caroline Luard was 'wilful murder against some person or persons unknown'. Although like most classic cases of unsolved murder there has been no shortage of theories over the years, that person, or persons, remains unknown.

19 September

1947 (England) It was certainly the trial of the year, if not of the decade, as three young thugs named Jenkins, Geraghty and Rolt appeared at the Old Bailey charged with the murder of Alec de Antiquis, the man who had tried to prevent their escape after an armed robbery. Charles Jenkins and Christopher Geraghty were hanged at Pentonville on 19 September 1927; Rolt, on account of his youth was ordered to be detained at His Majesty's pleasure.

On 29 April 1947, the men carried out an armed raid on a jeweller's shop in Charlotte Street, in the West End of London. The shop's owner was battered over the head, and the manager, wisely or not, threw a wooden stool at the raider instead of the keys, and at the same time set off the alarm. The three men ran from the shop empty-handed, one of them firing a wild shot into the wall. When they reached their getaway car, the amateur heist-men found it was blocked in by traffic, so they made off on foot. A passing motor-cyclist rode into the path of the robbers in an attempt to stop them; for his troubles, Alec de Antiquis was shot in the head and later died.

It was Scotland Yard's Superintendent Robert Fabian whose lot it was to head the murder inquiry. No fingerprints had been left at the scene of the aborted robbery, and descriptions of the gunmen could have fitted almost anybody. But then a cab driver reported that he had seen two masked men disappear into Brook House, Tottenham Court Road, just after the shooting. From the office block police recovered a scarf, folded to make a mask, and a raincoat that was eventually traced to twenty-three-year-old Charles Jenkins. Later a schoolboy found a gun where it had been dumped on the foreshore of the Thames at Wapping; ballistics proved it to have been the murder weapon which killed Alec de Antiquis.

At an identity parade, more than two dozen witnesses failed to identify Jenkins, but police began to round up his known associates anyway. Among them were Chris Geraghty and Terence Peter Rolt. Both young men confessed their part in the events of 29 April, and for good measure implicated Charles Jenkins. All three were arrested, formally charged and brought to trial at the Old Bailey on 21 July 1947, where they were convicted of murder.

Although the executions of Jenkins and Geraghty provoked considerable public criticism, it was the belief of Robert Fabian and a number of other senior policemen – including the Metropolitan Police Commissioner, Sir Harold Scott – that the summary treatment of Jenkins and Geraghty was responsible for many gangsters giving up carrying guns.

20 September

1946 (USA) In the early afternoon of 15 November, a chambermaid found the body of twenty-five-year-old Virginia Lee Griffin stuffed into the closet of a run-down Skid Row hotel room; she had been choked to death and mutilated with a knife. Almost immediately following this grisly discovery, the body of Mrs Lilian Johnson was found in a hotel room only a few blocks away; she too had been choked to death and hideously mutilated.

Before nightfall, a manhunt was under way, centring on the bars and hotels of Skid Row. Police patrolmen were issued with the description of a man who had booked into the rooms where the victims were discovered. Patrolman Harold Donlan of the city police recalled that he had seen a man answering this description drinking around the local bars, and made a particular point of diverting his route around the liquor dives. At 5.30 p.m. he found Otto Wilson, just about to buy a drink for a new girl he had met. 'I walked over and put the handcuffs on him,' Donlan said later. And in doing so probably saved Wilson's companion from becoming his third victim.

By 7.30 p.m., Wilson had confessed to both murders, pleading that he was searching for love, but had always been mentally unstable and had lost control of himself. The psychiatrists were not so benevolent in their assessment of Otto Wilson: 'He has an urge to kill and destroy women. He may be considered a sexual psychopath and degenerate. His hatred of womankind has unquestionably been built up for years and increased by alcoholic stimulation. If he had not been apprehended, there is no telling how many other victims of his lust and passion there might have been.'

Wilson's trial commenced on 18 June 1945, and he pleaded not guilty by reason of insanity; on 28 June, a jury found him sane and guilty of murder. Otto Wilson was given a capital sentence, and died in the gas chamber on 20 September 1946.

21 September

1953 (England) The date was 21 September 1953. As the clock announced two o'clock, the body of Mary Hackett was exposed, lying face-down in her makeshift grave. At the mortuary it was the little green dress she wore on the day of her disappearance that her parents had to identify her by; her face was unrecognisable.

Mary Hackett had last been seen alive at 12.55 p.m. on 12 August, when she told her aunt she was going out to play near her home. When local searches failed to find any trace of Mary, help was sought from Scotland Yard. That help arrived in Halifax in the persons of Detective Superintendent John Ball and Detective Sergeant Dennis Hawkins. John Ball's initial feeling was that Mary's body would be found very close to the place from which she had been abducted, and one of his first calls was at the Congregational church close to the Hacketts' home. The church and its crypt had already been searched, but John Ball wanted to have a look for himself. It was on this visit that he encountered George Albert Hall, the caretaker. Hall proved suspiciously talkative on the subject of Mary's disappearance, and over the following days the two detectives became convinced that they need look no farther than Albert Hall for a suspect. And so the arc lights and a team of diggers were moved into the crypt to begin excavating a corner where, for no apparent reason, pews and chairs had been stacked in a pile. That is where they uncovered Mary's body, what remained of it.

Acting on his instinct Superintendent Ball had Albert Hall followed. He visited the Scalebor Park mental hospital (where Hall had once been a patient) to visit Dr Valentine, the superintendent. Dr Valentine told the police that Hall had said he was concerned about the corpse being found in his church, but that he was not responsible for the girl's death. He added that it had been Ball and Hawkins who told him about the body at one o'clock on the day it was found, and that the girl had died from head injuries. Which came as something of a surprise to John Ball and his DS, because Hawkins had not even been in the crypt, and the cause of the death was only known after the post-mortem three hours later. When he was arrested, Albert Hall obligingly made a full confession, and was later tried, convicted and executed.

22 September

1900 (England) On 22 September Mrs Mary Bennett was murdered by her husband John, who was condemned to die for his crime. It was customary in former days to fly a black flag above the prison gate following an execution. As the flag was run up after Bennett was hanged in March 1901, a strong gust of wind caused the flagpole to break and the flag to fall; a divine sign, some said, that John Bennett was innocent.

23 September

1920 (England) On 23 September 1920, Mrs Fanny Zeitoun was found lying on her bed with her throat cut. By her side lay her father, fifty-seven-year-old Marks Goodmacher, a Jewish tailor from the Whitechapel area of London's East End.

Marks Goodmacher recovered from his self-inflicted wound, and was charged with the murder of his daughter. The Old Bailey jury heard that there had been bad blood between father and daughter for some time, which was especially distressing as Fanny and her husband were at the time living under Goodmacher's roof. In the end the constant bickering forced the Zeitouns to leave, and the air became distinctly chilly. The jury rejected a defence plea of insanity, and Marks Goodmacher was sentenced to death by Mr Justice Darling.

A number of unsuccessful attempts were made to secure a reprieve, and on 30 December 1920 Goodmacher faced the hangman at Pentonville Prison. For many years the Jewish community of Whitechapel called this the 'Black Fast Murder', because it was believed that the reason that Marks Goodmacher was distressed enough to kill his own daughter was because she and her husband had not been to visit him on the Day of Atonement. It is an ancient tradition among orthodox Jews for those who have quarrelled to seek reconciliation on that day.

24 September

1905 (England) At 10.55 on the night of Sunday 24 September 1905, Sub-Inspector William Peacock and a railway work gang arrived at Merstham Tunnel on the London–Brighton line to continue repair work. Four hundred yards inside the tunnel, Peacock's lamp picked out a large bundle; which was, in reality, the badly mutilated body of a young woman. Since the terrible injuries had rendered the face unrecognisable, it was only a description of her build and her clothing that was published but it soon drew a response from Robert Henry Money, who identified the unfortunate victim as his sister Mary Sophia. Suicide was ruled out when Mary's own scarf was found pushed into her mouth as a gag.

Mary Money was twenty-two years old and was employed as a book-keeper at Clapham, where she lived. At seven on the evening of the 24th, Mary Money had told her flatmate that she was going for a walk. When she had not returned by one in the morning the friend assumed Mary had stayed over with friends. Subsequent investigations by the police placed Mary in the sweet-shop in Clapham Junction station approach at 7.00 p.m., where she mentioned to the owner that she was going to Victoria. In fact a ticket collector was traced who remembered her checking the platform number with him. For what purpose Mary went to Victoria station we will never know; it was most likely that she went to meet somebody, probably a man and possibly her killer.

What happened between the time she arrived at Victoria, around 7.45, and the time she was found dead is anybody's guess. However, a study of the railway timetable suggests that, since the body was warm when it was found, the train from which Mary Money was launched was the 9.33 from London. The police learnt from the train's guard that in one of the first-class compartments he had seen a man and a woman. His description of the woman fitted Mary Money. A little farther down the line the guard saw the couple again, and thought they looked 'furtive'. When the train stopped at Redhill, the compartment door was open, the carriage was empty, and the man was walking down the platform alone. A signalman at Purley Oaks remembered seeing a man and a woman struggling in a first-class compartment.

So what are we to make of all this? Perhaps Mary's unknown companion had started off gallantly escorting her back to Croydon after a couple of drinks. Perhaps around Purley the young man started to demand more than a last kiss and cuddle, they struggled, she screamed, he forced her scarf into her mouth to keep her quiet. It would be interesting to know whether there was evidence of a recent sexual assault on Mary's body. This would open the possibility that the man panicked about the consequences of rape and bundled Mary Money, alive and struggling, out of the window. Or perhaps it was different . . .

25 September

1930 (England) On 25 September 1930, eighty-two-year-old Margery Wren finally succumbed to her injuries. It had been five days before that little Ellen Marvell had been sent to Miss Wren's general shop in Ramsgate on an errand for her mother. She was accompanied by her friend Jessie Langton and when they reached the shop the door was locked. Ellen banged on the door and Miss Wren came and unfastened it; when she opened the door, the children could see blood trickling down Miss Wren's face. The old lady seemed confused, so Ellen called her father who came over and sent the children for a doctor and the police.

Despite conflicting accounts given by Miss Wren herself (such as 'I came over giddy and down I went') it was quite clear that she had suffered a brutal bludgeoning. Nevertheless, although she clearly knew who it was, she refused to give police the name of her attacker, leaving Chief Inspector Hambrook from Scotland Yard with an uncooperative victim and not much else. Indeed, it was worse than that, because Miss Wren deliberately misled the inquiry by giving the names of perfectly respectable, quite innocent local people.

The question of motive was puzzling as well. Although the house had been methodically searched (indicating a killer who knew the layout of the building), nothing was missing. Was the intruder disturbed? Or was what he was looking for not there? Or did he take something that Miss Wren would not disclose?

Following Miss Wren's decease, Sir Bernard Spilsbury conducted a post-mortem examination on her body and found seven lacerations to the top of the head, and a further eight wounds and bruises on the face, consistent with having been inflicted by a pair of fire tongs (such as those found in the room where Miss Wren was attacked, and which had human hairs adhering to blood on them. There had also been an attempt at strangulation.

Understandably the coroner's inquest could be no more definite in its conclusions. A verdict of 'murder by some person or persons unknown' was returned. And there the investigation stopped; the case remains unsolved, and Miss Wren's refusal to cooperate remains one of crime's enduring mysteries.

26 September

1948 (England) Forty-one-year-old prostitute Rachel Fennick (who was better known as either 'Red Rae' or 'Ginger Rae' on account of her auburn hair) was found on 26 September 1948 lying dead on the floor of her apartment in Soho's Broadwick Street.

From the wrecked state of the flat it was quite clear that Rachel had not given up her hold on life without a violent struggle; a battle that was lost as the knife blade tore repeatedly into her body. From the size and shape of the wounds the most likely weapon was a stiletto-type blade, although it had not been left at the scene of the murder.

The murders of prostitutes (and taxi-drivers for that matter) are notoriously difficult to solve. By the nature of their occupation they are constantly in the company of strangers. Whoever killed Ginger Rae might have been a client quarrelling over the price – or she might have been picking his pocket, who knows; or a psycho who liked hurting women. Or perhaps – and this is the possibility that was taken very seriously by detectives investigating the murder – she may have been murdered by her pimp; perhaps she had been holding back on his percentage. What makes this scenario plausible is that only a few weeks earlier another street girl, Helen Freedman (who also went by the *nom-de-guerre* 'Russian Dora'), had been discovered dead in her Long Acre flat. Russian Dora had also been stabbed to death, though in this instance the knife had been abandoned at the scene of the crime; she too had put up a spirited struggle against her assailant. The suggestion was that both women were working under the 'protection' of the same vice gang, and both women had been cheating on the proceeds. Their 'execution' would then be seen as a warning to other girls with the firm to toe the line. But these are just theories. The crimes were never solved, and it is unlikely they ever will be.

27 September

1927 (England) On 27 September 1927 the body of Police Constable George Gutteridge was found in a quiet country lane between Romford and Ongar, in Essex; he had been shot four times, twice through the left side of his face and once through each eye. The fact that PC Gutteridge was still clutching his notebook and pencil indicated that he had been in the middle of making inquiries – probably of a motorist he had stopped.

Local records showed that a car had been stolen at around 2.30 a.m. from Billericay, ten miles from the shooting, and it was later found abandoned in south London. Forensic examination revealed bloodstains on the running-board and a spent cartridge under one of the seats. It was not until some months later that any progress was made in the case, when a motorist in Sheffield saw a car being driven dangerously and took down the number and reported it to the police. It was the clue which eventually led to the Globe Garage, a business carried on by Frederick Guy Browne, a petty-crook specialising in car theft. It was on one of his regular spells in prison that Browne had met William Henry Kennedy. When Kennedy was released in 1927, he joined Browne at the Globe Garage. Three months later, stopped while driving a stolen car, they shot PC Gutteridge.

During the early part of 1928 police lay in wait at Browne's garage; they were not disappointed. Browne arrived at the wheel of another stolen car. He was arrested, and while he was in custody police searched the garage and Browne's home, where they found a veritable arsenal of handguns and ammunition including a Webley loaded with bullets of the type that had robbed PC Gutteridge of his life. Meanwhile, Kennedy had been apprehended in Liverpool.

According to Kennedy, they had been stopped by the policeman, and when he approached the car, Browne shot the officer twice in the head, then got out of the car and shot him through both eyes. A legend has grown up that Browne's purpose in this was connected with an old superstition that the last image a dying person sees is photographed on to his eyes. A more likely explanation is that Browne was a vicious thug with a reputation for hating policemen and was having a bit of revenge.

Frederick Browne and William Kennedy were convicted mainly on the ballistic evidence of master gunsmith Robert Churchill, who had scientifically matched the slug from the victim's body and the cartridge case from the stolen car with Browne's Webley. It was sufficient to send each of the killers to the gallows, Browne at Pentonville and Kennedy at Wandsworth, both on 31 May 1928.

28 September

1905 (USA) In September 1905, a white family comprising J. F. Conditt, his wife and their five children moved on to a small farm in the predominantly black district of Edna, Texas. Conditt appeared to alienate the locals not only by moving into the area, but by refusing to allow them to continue to use a water supply on his farm.

On 28 September, Monk Gibson and a friend, Felix Powell, were employed by J.F. to do some work around the farm during the rice harvest. Powell made sexual advances to Conditt's eldest daughter, twelve-year-old Mildred, and was not unnaturally rebuffed. Not long after, both Gibson and Powell returned to the farm where they raped Mildred and killed Mrs Lora Conditt and four of the children, Mildred,

Herschell, aged ten, Jesse, six, and three-year-old Joseph, with an axe and a knife. For some reason they spared the ten-month-old baby Lloyd.

At around noon on the same day, Gibson reported to neighbours that the Conditt family had been killed by two black men. The sheriff was called and started by questioning Gibson himself, who was evasive in his replies and unable to explain bloodstains found on his hands and clothes. Gibson and Powell were arrested and taken to the local jail, but because a lynch mob was forming, it was decided to move them. While the prisoners were being transferred Gibson escaped, and the Texas Rangers, accompanied by bloodhounds, started a manhunt. Gibson surrendered to the authorities on 5 October, and on 9 October Powell was indicted by the Jackson County grand jury for murder, and Gibson for being an accessory.

Felix Powell and Monk Gibson were tried separately; Powell was tried first, convicted, sentenced to death and hanged on 2 April 1907. Gibson's attorney asked for a change of venue in view of the unlikelihood of being able to find an impartial jury in Jackson County. Eventually, Gibson's trial was held in San Antonio where evidence was given that as a child he had attempted to hang a young girl. The hearing resulted in a mistrial, apparently because the judge had difficulty in apportioning guilt between Gibson and Powell. A second trial was held, with another change of venue, this time DeWitt County, and on this occasion the jury returned a verdict of guilty and Gibson, like his partner, was sentenced to hang. Gibson, aged nineteen at the time of his execution, maintained his innocence to the end.

29 September

1982 (USA) Within a single forty-eight-hour period seven people died in Chicago after taking the painkiller Tylenol. The first to die, on 29 September 1982, was schoolgirl Mary

Kellerman. Waking in the early hours of the morning with influenza, Mary asked her father for something to make her feel better. Mr Kellerman fished a Tylenol capsule out of the bathroom medicine cabinet and his daughter swallowed it; almost immediately she collapsed and was dead inside two hours. Postal worker Adam Janus took Tylenol because of a pain in his chest, and suffered a similar death. With a cruel irony, Janus's brother Stanley and his wife Theresa came to comfort the bereaved family, took twoTylenol, and quickly joined Adam in the mortuary. Mrs Mary Reiner had just left hospital with her three-day-old baby when she took Tylenol for a migraine, went into convulsions, followed by a coma and death. Later that same day, Mary McFarland developed a headache while working in a store; she took Tylenol as she always did in such cases, but this time she died. The final victim was thirty-five-year-old Paula Prince, who took two Tylenol after arriving home with a headache. Two days later worried friends found her body in the bathroom where it had fallen.

Police authorities and experts from the medical examiner's office established that the analgesic Tylenol had been taken by all the victims just before their untimely deaths, and an examination of the remaining capsules revealed that the Tylenol in the packs had been replaced by cyanide. The makers of Tylenol, McNeil Consumer Products, recalled every bottle sold in the state of Illinois and eight containers were found to have been tampered with containing a total of seventy-five contaminated capsules. Two weeks after the deaths, McNeil received a letter threatening that the killings would continue unless the company paid $1 million to a specified bank account, and a fingerprint on the blackmail letter led to the identification of James Lewis. Lewis was wanted for fraud in Missouri, and had already been acquitted of the murder of seventy-eight-year-old Raymond West in 1978.

A nationwide hunt for James Lewis was organised during which time he wrote to several newspapers emphatically denying that he was the 'Tylenol killer'; shortly afterwards he was arrested in New York. Lewis admitted that he held the McNeil Company responsible for the death after surgery of his five-year-old daughter in 1974. Following the operation she had been taking a McNeil-manufactured drug. However, he denied he was responsible for tampering with the capsules. Despite the obvious connections, the police were unable to find any direct evidence of murder against James Lewis, and he was tried only on charges of attempted blackmail and fraud for which he received consecutive prison sentences of eight and ten years.

30 September

1952 (England) Dennis Muldowney had one of the shortest Old Bailey trials on record – three minutes almost to the second – following which he was sentenced to death and, on 30 September 1952, hanged at Pentonville Prison.

It was back in June of the same year that staff at the Shelbourne Hotel in London's Earl's Court district were horrified to see one of their guests stabbed to death in the foyer. The killer made no attempt to escape and was still sitting moaning to himself when the police arrived. His first words were: 'I built all my dreams around her, but she was playing me for a fool.'

'She' was a woman known to the hotel staff simply as Christine Granville. In fact she was the Countess Krystyna Skarbek, and certainly no simple citizen – either of England or of her native Poland. But there, like it or not (and she made little of it), the Countess was a heroine of the type normally found only between the pages of spy novels. When her country was invaded by the Nazis in the preliminaries to the Second World War, Countess Krystyna made contact with British intelligence and, using the code-name 'Jacqueline

Armand', was active in occupied Europe throughout the conflict. The stories told about her are many, sometimes bordering on fantasy, but there are, nevertheless, any number which can be verified. In Italy, for example, she was stopped by a border patrol who wanted to arrest her as a spy. 'Jacqueline' raised both hands, as if in surrender; in the palm of each was a live grenade. She was allowed to pass. And there was the time in 1944 when she brought off her biggest bluff. It was her mission to try to save three allied officers who were due to be executed by firing squad in one of Germany's prison camps. Knowing that the American troops were advancing on the area, Krystyna walked in to the camp and simply told the commanding officer that 'If you shoot those men, I will see to it personally that when the Americans reach here you will be shot yourself.' Of course, Nazi intelligence also knew of the allied advance, and it was with great deference that the commandant escorted the three men and one heroine out of the camp gates. At the end of the war, Countess Krystyna Skarbek was awarded France's coveted Croix de Guerre, the Order of the British Empire and Britain's George Medal for Special Services.

Ironically, it was a life that the new Christine Granville wanted to leave far behind her. She was working as a stewardess on an ocean liner, which is where she had the misfortune to meet Dennis Muldowney. When they both left the ship and Muldowney took a job as night porter at the Reform Club, they continued to meet occasionally. Sadly, for Muldowney the friendship became obsessive. He resented her seeing her own friends, and when he heard she was travelling to Belgium to meet up with a wartime sweetheart, he became murderous; and was hanged. Some said later that heaven had gained another angel, and hell another demon; but perhaps that is too close to fiction.

October

1 October

1910 (USA) The atrocious bombing of the *Los Angeles Times* building had its origins in the deeply antagonistic attitude of its owner, General Harrison Gray Otis, towards the newly emerging strength and influence of the American trade union movement, and his regular use of the newspaper's columns to broadcast opposition to organised labour. On 1 October 1910, the *Times* headquarters was devastated by a single explosion. One wall of the building blew out and two floors crashed downwards into the basement carrying printing machines and workers with them. The gas main and heating plant were fractured causing a fire which was further fuelled by burning printing ink spilling from the damaged ink store, turning the broken shell of the building into a blazing inferno. In the aftermath it emerged that twenty members of the *LA Times* staff had died and the same number had been badly injured.

Shocked city fathers summoned William J. Burns of the celebrated Burns Detective Agency to lead the investigation, when it was discovered that three more bombs had been planted in different parts of the city on the same day, including one at the home of General Harrison G. Otis. These devices had failed to detonate, and William Burns was able to trace the source of the dynamite and to identify James B. McNamara, his brother John J. McNamara, a trade union secretary, and Ortie McManigal as its purchasers. After a nationwide hunt, the McNamara brothers and McManigal were arrested in Detroit in April 1911. Timing devices, similar in construction to those used in the Los Angeles bombs, were found in their possession. Burns finally persuaded Ortie McManigal to make a confession implicating the McNamaras; the brothers and McManigal were extradited to Los Angeles on 26 April.

Labour organisations sprang to the defence of the prisoners, staging national demonstrations and parades announcing that they had been framed. The American Federation of Labour engaged America's legendary defence lawyer Clarence Darrow. Burns, meanwhile, continued to gather evidence in support of the McNamaras' guilt and by the time they came to trial, Darrow was convinced they would be convicted. Faced with the choice of fighting a hopeless case as a defence of the union movement which would end with the defendants becoming martyrs for the cause, or pleading them guilty in the hope of avoiding a capital sentence, Darrow chose the second option. James McNamara was jailed for life; John received fifteen years' imprisonment for an earlier bombing, a charge brought in the absence of any direct evidence linking him to the *Times* bombing. McManigal as a state witness was freed.

It was Clarence Darrow's last case in defence of the trade union movement and his final appearance in a California court. Following the trial of the McNamara brothers, Darrow found himself in the embarrassing position of being indicted for allegedly attempting to suborn a juror; although after a long trial he was acquitted, it would not be the last time that 'America's defender' would have his credibility questioned by those who were opposed to his predisposition to champion the 'unpopular' causes of the poor and the left-wing.

2 October

1930 (USA) Mad or Bad? The question asked every day in courts throughout the world. Should this man, or woman, be held responsible for their actions and be judged on them; or should they be considered as having *not* been responsible for their actions? The case of Gordon Northcott posed a problem that accentuated the difficulty of insanity pleas; he was, nevertheless, executed for his crimes on 2 October 1930.

Northcott, along with his mother Sarah and a nephew called Stanford Clark, made a profitable business from abducting children and holding them at Northcott's isolated ranch in Riverside County, California, for the depraved pleasure of wealthy (and unidentified) clients from Los Angeles. And after Northcott himself had indulged a grope or two, the children were killed and their bodies buried in the surrounding desert. In February 1928, the headless body of a Mexican boy was found in a ditch near Puent. Less than two months later two brothers aged eight and ten went missing after being seen with Gordon Northcott at a boys' club. Inquiries at the ranch revealed that Gordon had already fled to Canada, and a search of the grounds turned up the missing head of the Mexican boy.

It was the teenage lad Clark who eventually spilled the beans, describing how Northcott had sexually abused his victims before beating them to death. Sarah Northcott had little option but to confess her part in the crimes, including actively participating in one of the murders. When police intelligence had eventually tracked down Gordon Northcott and extradited him back to California he was charged with just three murders. Although it was confidently believed that the total body count reached twenty, no further remains were found. Nor was the investigation helped by the contradictory statement made by Gordon Northcott himself, though he finally settled on a self-confessed total of seventeen. He also developed a habit of 'just remembering', and sending the police off on false trails to look for buried bodies.

During his court hearing Northcott dismissed his attorney and took over his own defence, in which he emphasised to the jury that he was *not* insane – a conclusion upheld by two independent psychiatrists. And if he was not mad, then he must be bad, so Gordon Northcott was sentenced to hang. While he was awaiting execution on San Quentin's Death Row, Northcott was taken ill, and firmly believing that he was about to die he made a full confession to Assistant Warden Clinton Duffy. This statement, which Duffy described as a catalogue of mass murder, torture and sodomy, was retained on his file when Northcott got over his far from fatal sickness. It was the sickness in his head that was the death of him. Gordon Northcott was executed on 2 October 1930, in a state of abject terror. Sarah Northcott was sentenced to life imprisonment for her part in the murder of the nine-year-old Mexican, and Stanford Clark had already turned state's evidence.

3 October

1922 (England) Edith Graydon, a manageress with a firm of milliners in the City of London, met Percy Thompson, a shipping clerk in the City, while travelling to Liverpool Street station one morning. They were married at the beginning of 1915 when she was twenty-two and he was twenty-six. Five years later they bought their own terraced house in Kensington Gardens, Ilford. By this time the marriage had already begun to prove a great disappointment to Edith, as, indeed, had her husband.

In June 1921 the Thompsons spent their summer holiday on the Isle of Wight with Edith's younger sister Avis and one of the Graydon family's friends, eighteen-year-old Freddie Bywaters. Bywaters had joined the merchant navy as a clerk, and at the time of the holiday had just returned from a voyage to Australia. Such adventures in foreign parts proved a great attraction to Edith, and before the vacation was half-way through, she had captured Freddie's attentions from Avis. This mutual attraction was fairly obvious, but all that complacent Percy Thompson seemed to notice was that his wife was happier and that Freddie Bywaters was a pleasant young fellow. In fact Edith had no difficulty in persuading her husband to take Bywaters on as a lodger. This arrangement was supplemented by secret meetings in town, and eventually even unobservant Percy began to notice that something was going on, and Freddie was asked to find alternative accommodation.

Not that this in any way spoilt Edith's new-found excitement, and when Bywaters went back to sea she inundated him with a stream of passionate letters, in all more than eighty in a single year, an outpouring of romantic fantasy which would eventually hang her. Unfortunately one of Edith's regular subjects concerned killing Percy by feeding him ground glass in his food.

On Saturday 23 September 1922 Frederick Bywaters arrived back in Tilbury determined to confront Percy Thompson with their love affair. The following Tuesday week, Edith and Percy had been to London to visit the theatre and were returning from Ilford station, when Bywaters leapt out of the darkness and stabbed Percy while yelling something about him separating from his wife. Then Bywaters ran off, leaving a horrified Edith to get help for her dying husband.

Bywaters and Mrs Thompson were jointly charged with Percy's murder, and tried in December 1922. Much was made of their illicit love affair and given the morality of the time it was no surprise that both were convicted and sentenced to death. Edith perished in Holloway Prison at the hands of executioner John Ellis, and Bywaters in Pentonville as a client of Thomas Pierrepoint.

4 October

1807 (England)

William Duncan was employed in the service of William Chivers Esq., as gardener. On the morning of 4 October, the niece of Mr Chivers went in his carriage to take an airing. Mr Chivers, who was between seventy and eighty years of age went into his garden to take a walk, as was his daily custom, inspecting the gardener at his work, and conversing with him. About eleven-thirty the gardener ran into the house in great agitation and terror, exclaiming to the servants: 'Lord, what have I done! I have struck my master, and he has fallen.' He then made off.

The footman went into the garden, where he found his master on the ground, apparently lifeless, and his face a most shocking spectacle. It appeared that the gardener had struck his master with a spade he was working with, the end of which entered the lower part of his nose, broke both his jaw-bones, and penetrated nearly to a line with his ears, so that his head was almost separated. The gardener had inflicted two deep wounds, one being about eight inches in length and three inches and a half in breadth.

Duncan was soon after apprehended, and the magistrates committed him to Horsemonger Lane Prison. The cause of the shocking act was a dispute between him and his master respecting the pruning of a vine. The jury, after having conferred for a considerable time, found the prisoner guilty of murder; and he was accordingly sentenced to be executed and then anatomised. The Privy Council, however, did not conceive that Duncan was guilty of wilful and premeditated murder, but admitted an immediate provocation on the part of the unfortunate old gentleman.

They therefore represented him as a subject for Royal clemency, in consequence whereof he was twice respited, and then ordered to be transported for the term of his natural life.

(*The Malefactors' Register*)

5 October

1974 (England) There is a spot on the north bank of the river Thames called Cold Harbour Point, near Rainham, in Essex; it is popular with bird-watchers. On 5 October 1974 one of those bird-watchers caught a glimpse of something quite terrible. It was the upper part of a man's torso, settled half in and half out of the water. Over the following week or so, several other dismembered parts of the same body were picked up along that stretch of the river. According to the pathologist whose job it was to examine the remains, they had been in the water for around five days. As there was no head, visual identification was impossible. However, detectives were privately convinced that the body was that of William Moseley, a small-time London crook, and blood samples taken from Moseley's wife and children proved a connection with the recovered torso. And that is as far as the investigation reached for almost a year.

On 7 September 1975, the bludgeoned and shot body of Michael Cornwall was unearthed in Chalkdell Wood, in Hertfordshire. It was known that he and Moseley had been close friends, so it seemed likely that the two violent deaths were connected. Police inquiries among the men's known associates yielded the information that two men had been heard discussing Moseley's death just before it happened – they were Reginald Dudley and Robert Maynard, and from the same source it was learned that Dudley had been in some disagreement with Moseley, who had given him a sound thrashing. Dudley, as might be expected, had vowed revenge

– and it looked as though he might have taken it. Michael Cornwall, in his turn, had set out to avenge the death of his friend.

The Old Bailey trial of Dudley and Maynard, along with five others, lasted seven months, and was the longest in British criminal history. At the end of it, Dudley and Maynard were convicted of the double murder and sentenced to life; their co-defendants were handed down various lighter sentences. It is only fair to mention that both Reginald Dudley and Robert Maynard have consistently protested their innocence, and have received considerable support in their demands for a review of their case.

Just six weeks after the trial ended, on 28 July 1977, a severed head wrapped in a woollen balaclava and sheets of newspaper was found in a public lavatory in north London. The first thing that the medical team noticed was that it was cold and damp – consistent, they decided, with thawing out after being in a deep-freezer. At last William Moseley's head could be reunited with the other parts of his body.

6 October

1909 (Australia) When Martha Rendall was convicted of murder and hanged in Freemantle Jail on 6 October 1909, she became the first and last woman to suffer capital punishment in Western Australia.

Three years earlier, Martha had gone to live with Thomas Morris, a carpenter, and his children, first as housekeeper and then as Morris's 'wife'. A vicious and spiteful woman, Martha never passed up an opportunity to punish the children, and soon the neighbours were remarking to each other how the formerly robust and well-nourished children were mere shadows of their former selves. In 1907 two of the children, Anne and Olive, had been suffering from colds and were prescribed throat swabs. Martha, of course, administered the swabs, a treatment which, if all the squealing and crying was anything to go by, was very painful. Anne Morris died of what was certificated as diphtheria on 28 July. Three months later Olive also fell victim to 'diphtheria'. When fourteen-year-old Arthur Morris complained of a sore throat some twelve months after the death of his sisters, out came the swabs and Martha got down to some enthusiastic swabbing. The result of which was that Arthur died.

In April 1909 George Morris made the mistake of drinking a cup of tea prepared by Martha, which seemed to scald his throat so badly that she was obliged to suggest a swab. George elected instead to run away from home. In trying to locate the fugitive boy the police began to question the neighbours, who had a lot to tell about the goings on in the Morris household.

An exhumation order was made on the three Morris children and post-mortem examinations established that their throats had been liberally washed with hydrochloric acid – little wonder they squealed; little wonder George took to his heels.

At Martha's trial the jury heard how first she laced the children's drinks with acid, and when they complained of a sore throat she swabbed them with more of the same. This 'treatment' naturally inflamed the mucous membrane of the throat – a symptom identical to that of diphtheria. Martha Rendall was quickly convicted of murder, and sentenced to death.

7 October

1984 (England) On the night of Friday 7 October 1984, Mrs Yianoulla Robertson reported finding the battered body of her husband Michael in the grounds of their home at Hayling Island.

Forty-one-year-old Robertson, an executive with the IBM company, was rushed to Southampton General Hospital suffering from severe head injuries from which he died on

9 October without regaining consciousness. The police investigation, led by Detective Chief Superintendent John Wright, the head of Hampshire CID, first concentrated on piecing together Mr Robertson's movements during the evening hours leading up to the attack. According to Greek-born Mrs Robertson, her husband went out earlier in the evening to collect a take-away meal, and police believed that the victim may have visited several public houses in the seafront area of Hayling Island; subsequently, an appeal was made for witnesses who saw Robertson on that evening.

Events began to move quickly then, and by the morning of 11 October a man was in custody and officers were about to arrest the victim's wife. At a brief sitting of the Havant magistrates court, thirty-seven-year-old Yianoulla Robertson was charged that 'on a date unknown, between 1 January and 10 October 1984, [she] solicited Timothy John Funge-Smith to murder her husband'. Mrs Robertson was remanded in custody. Funge-Smith, forty-one, appeared in court the following day, Wednesday, and was remanded in custody on the charge of murdering Michael Robertson, for whom he had worked as a gardener.

When Timothy Funge-Smith came to trial at the beginning of March 1985 it was in front of Mr Justice Tudor Evans at the Winchester Crown Court. The jury heard how when the prisoner had first been interviewed by the police he invented the alibi that he had been drinking in a local public house at the time of the attack on his former employer. But when he learnt that investigating officers had found the murder weapon – a three-foot galvanised pipe – and that it bore his palm-print, Funge-Smith telephoned the murder incident room and confessed to the crime. Also appearing in the dock was thirty-seven-year-old David Stacey, who admitted attempting to pervert the course of justice by giving the prisoner an alibi.

Sentencing Funge-Smith on 5 March, the judge told him:

'Whatever your motives, this was a brutal murder for which the sentence is prescribed by law.' That sentence was life imprisonment. One month later the Director of Public Prosecutions announced that the case against Mrs Robertson would not be pursued.

8 October

1871 (England) John Selby Watson represented a special kind of solid Victorian respectability, and that in its way was to prove his downfall. A scholarly man, Watson had specialised in a study of the classics and theology and in 1839 he was ordained as a cleric. He served his curacy in the rural peace of Somerset, before moving to the capital where he secured the headmaster's post at a well-regarded grammar school.

The year after his arrival in London, John Watson married Anne Armstrong, and over the succeeding years his scholarship reaped its own rewards in the form of a series of published translations, which were highly regarded by his peers. Trouble, however, was just around the corner. By 1870, through no fault of Watson's, the number of pupils at the school had begun to decline, and in an attempt to save money, the governors terminated their headmaster's contract. The problem was that John Selby Watson had reached the age of sixty-six, and after all the years' faithful service to one institution, his prospects of finding a new post were nil. Not entirely surprisingly, he began to slip into a black depression.

On the evening of 8 October 1871 when Ellen Pyne, the Watsons' servant, returned after her day off, she was told by the master of the house that Mrs Watson had 'gone out of town'; he added, rather enigmatically, that if she should find anything wrong with him on the following morning, to send for the local doctor, a man named Rugg. His cryptic prophecy came true and later Ellen Pyne found John Watson lying unconscious. On the bureau near his prostrate form there was a letter for Ellen enclosing her wages, and another addressed to 'The Surgeon', in which he had written: 'I have killed my wife in a fit of rage to which she provoked me.' Mrs Watson's body was later found in a locked bedroom; she had been bludgeoned to death with the butt end of a pistol which was found bloodstained in Watson's dressing-table drawer.

Although Watson had himself taken a large dose of prussic acid, he survived and was arrested and charged with Anne Watson's murder. His trial at the Old Bailey took place in January 1872, and his lawyers advanced a plea of insanity on his behalf. This clearly could not have hoped to succeed in view of the premeditation shown in leaving detailed instructions concerning the way in which his literary estate was to be handled. Accordingly, John Selby Watson, broken in spirit, was found guilty and sentenced to hang. However, this aged cleric was shown the mercy of having his capital sentence commuted to one of life imprisonment, and he died in Parkhurst Prison on 6 July 1884 at the age of eighty.

9 October

1942 (England) The murder of Ellen Ann Symes by Reginald Sidney Buckfield was as colourless and purposeless as could be, and were it not for Buckfield's attempt to rationalise his crime through literature, it would have been all but forgotten. Ellen was in her mid-thirties and married to Alfred James Symes, a joiner seconded to the night-shift of a local munitions factory. The couple had a four-year-old son, and Ellen was anticipating a second happy event. The Symeses lived in a house in the Brompton Farm Road, and to alleviate the inevitable loneliness of a 'night-work widow', Ellen Symes had slipped into the habit of spending Friday evenings with her parents at their home in not-too-distant

Dickens Terrace. The evening of 9 October 1942 was no exception, and after spending a few hours in quiet family pursuits Mrs Symes and her son accompanied the old couple to the Wainscott Workers Institute before turning off for home.

At about 9.40 p.m. the occupant of one of the houses along Brompton Farm Road was in his back garden when he heard what might have been an owl, or might have been a human cry; as he pondered this question the scream was succeeded by a thud, as though something heavy had fallen against the fence at the front of the house. To Mr Pattenden's horror, he found that the heavy something was the body of a woman, now lying on the ground bleeding profusely. The push-chair in which her child was being transported lay overturned, its occupant unhurt but frightened. Before help could be given, Mrs Symes had succumbed to a savage stab wound in the neck.

Mrs Symes's son had already told police that the attacker had been wearing army uniform, and it was on a routine check of the local military camp that PC Henry Giles learnt that a certain artillery gunner named Reginald Sidney Buckfield had gone absent without leave and was sleeping rough locally and supporting himself with casual fruit-picking. When he was tracked down 'Smiler' Buckfield (so called for his disarming physical characteristic of always appearing to be smiling) agreed that he had been around the district on the night of 9 October and gave a detailed itinerary of his movements between various public houses, but did not include the killing of Ellen Symes. Clearly suspicious of their guest, the police kept Buckfield in the cells while further inquiries were made. It was here that the little gunner penned an extraordinary story which he called 'The Mystery of Brompton Road'. It happened to be all about an artillery gunner named 'Smiler' (or sometimes Gunner X), who was suspected of murdering a woman. Although this version of events admitted no guilt on the part of the author, the story did contain a wealth of information about the circumstances of the killing that only the murderer would have known.

Reginald Buckfield was put on trial at the Old Bailey in January 1943, where his literary endeavour constituted a large part of the case against him. It also no doubt contributed heavily to the post-sentence inquiry into his sanity, when Gunner X was reprieved from the death sentence and instead committed to Broadmoor.

10 October

1923 (Scotland) The day on which Mrs Susan Newell became the first woman to be hanged in Scotland for fifty years (and in Glasgow for seventy). It had all begun the previous June when Mrs Newell, for reasons never adequately explained, took it into her head to murder paper-boy John Johnstone when he delivered to her home. On the following morning she had bundled the unlucky lad's body into a pram, covered it with a pile of old clothing and set off on foot steering the pram with one hand and pulling her eight-year-old daughter along with the other. Thus this strange caravan made its way through the soot-grimed suburbs of Glasgow in the early June light. When she had reached the New Road on her way to the city centre, Mrs Newell was offered a lift in the back of a lorry, which she accepted gratefully, being put down at Duke Street. With the child now atop the bundle in the pram Susan Newell continued her unsteady journey.

Here she attracted the attention of a woman looking through her kitchen window, who noticed, with a mixture of horror and disbelief, a small human foot which in response to a rather bumpy stretch of pavement, became dislodged from the bundle and hung over the edge of the pram. The poor woman was just telling herself that she must be imagining things, when a head popped out from its covering at the other end of the bundle. Enlisting the support of her sister, the horrified housewife followed the Newells at a distance, picking up a police constable on the way.

Mrs Newell had at this stage entered one of the many small courtyards off Duke Street and offloaded the bundle. She was just about to depart when she came face to face with the law. After a brief chase around the yard, during which she attempted to scale a six-foot wall, Susan Newell was taken firmly into custody. At the police station she told detectives that it was her husband who had killed the boy and she was thoughtfully getting rid of the evidence for him. Although John Newell was, for a short time, detained for questioning, he was able to prove an alibi for the day young Johnstone was murdered and Susan Newell found herself alone in the dock facing Lord Justice-Clerk Alness.

Susan Newell's defence of insanity was quickly disposed of by Professor John Glaister, who told the court that although the prisoner was of decidedly low intelligence, she exhibited no signs of insanity. The fact that she had committed an unspeakably cruel and callous killing did not in itself prove madness in the sense required by law to uphold a defence of insanity. After a retirement of thirty-seven minutes the jury returned a verdict of guilty by a majority, and with a strong recommendation to mercy. In the end Mrs Newell received the same mercy she showed John Johnstone – none.

11 October

1927 (England) The New Inn at Little Hayfield is still standing, though it is called the Lantern Pike now, and Little Hayfield has been absorbed into Hayfield itself. But not a lot more has changed in the past sixty-odd years there on the High Peak, an oasis between Sheffield and Greater Manchester.

In 1927 the licence of the pub was held by a man named Collinson, who with his wife Amy kept the business ticking over without too much strain. It was then, as now, a modest house – which is why, on the morning of 11 October, Mrs Collinson was alone in the pub. She was probably not much surprised by the visit of George Hayward; not, that is, until he began to bludgeon her with a piece of lead piping previously hacked from his own kitchen waste-pipe. Then, having dragged the poor woman across the parlour, he cut her throat with a carving knife.

George Hayward was a local, and his home, the White House, was near at hand. He had been a commercial traveller until very recently but was neither successful nor honest; which is why he was not only out of a job but being pressed by his former employers for money which he had collected from customers in the course of business and had failed to pay over. This debt amounted to some £70, but it was by no means the only debt clouding George Hayward's bleak financial horizon.

Murder, to be sure, is far less honest than embezzlement, but even George Hayward must have hoped that it would be more profitable. With the proceeds of ransacking the New Inn, Amy Collinson's murderer stood less than £40 better off. This is probably why he caught a bus to the neighbouring town of New Mills to draw his unemployment benefit from the Labour Exchange. From here he went to Manchester where he bought a money order for £4 to prevent his hire-purchase furniture from being repossessed.

The continually luckless George Hayward remained a free man for half a day longer; time enough to hide the rest of the proceeds of his killing in the flue of his bedroom chimney, where the police found it the next day when they arrested him.

In February 1928 the presiding judge at George Hayward's trial at Derby Assizes was Mr Justice Hawke; the following month, the presiding hangman at his execution was Thomas Pierrepoint.

12 October

1678 (England) In the summer of 1678 an odious perjurer and scoundrel named Titus Oates approached adherents of the Protestant cause with a list of fanciful allegations – the so-called Forty-three Articles – which claimed a conspiracy by Papists to assassinate the king and overthrow the Protestant religion in favour of his Roman Catholic brother James, Duke of York. Concerned that the document might be suppressed by the Council of State, an independently minded magistrate was sought to affirm the allegations. It was the lot of Sir Edmund Berry Godfrey to be chosen for the task. At the beginning of October 1678, he interviewed Oates and subsequently the infamous depositions were sworn. Now Sir Edmund, ever one of nature's gloomy men, began to offer dark hints that his life was in danger.

On Thursday 12 October, Sir Edmund left his lodgings in Hartshorn Lane, west London, at nine in the morning and was never seen alive again. His disappearance, though, was taken as menacing proof of the truth of the feared Popish conspiracy, and a full-blown hunt against suspected Catholics was in the air.

The body of Sir Edmund was found on Primrose Hill, in a spot called Barrow Hill, the following Tuesday 17 October. His sword had been thrust through him, he had been strangled, and his chest was covered with bruises; as if this were not enough, his neck was broken. The killers were assumed to be Papists. By the time of Sir Edmund's funeral on 31 October, rumours and accusations had become completely uncontrollable, and any person admitting to the

Catholic faith was in very real danger of imprisonment, or worse.

On 21 December, Miles Prance, a Catholic who was terrorised and cajoled into his treachery, came before Parliament with specific allegations that Robert Green, cushion man of the Queen's chapel, Lawrence Hill, a servant to the treasurer of the chapel and Henry Berry, a porter at Somerset House, had perpetrated the crime. The three men were arrested, Green being placed in the Gatehouse and the other two in Newgate. Their trial took place on 10 February 1679, and they were, with a sad inevitability, found guilty and sentenced to death.

Robert Green and Lawrence Hill were hanged from Tyburn Tree, and Henry Berry, a Protestant, was allowed a further week of life in the hope that he might confess to his sins. All three died protesting their innocence, but to superstitious observers their guilt was confirmed by a strange coincidence. Barrow Hill, where the body of the unfortunate magistrate had been discovered, had a more ancient name – 'Greenberry Hill'.

13 October

1972 (USA) In many ways, Herbert Mullin could be described as a stereotype 'visionary' psychotic killer. In other words, Mullin had been given a mission in life via voices in his head and 'telepathic messages'. His mission was to kill people in order to save the state of California from a cataclysmic earthquake and tidal wave. He understood from the voices that the 'small disaster' (murder) was justified by preventing the 'great disaster'.

The first time that Herbert Mullin responded to orders was on 13 October 1972. He had been driving along a deserted road in the Santa Cruz mountains when he passed a vagrant later identified as Lawrence White. Mullin stopped, got out of his car and beat the old man to death with a baseball bat. Just over a week later, on the 24th, he stabbed to death college student Mary Guilfoyle, cut her body open and pulled out the innards with his bare hands, leaving the resulting shambles to be picked over by vultures.

In December 1972, Herb Mullin began to hear a new set of voices; voices of people begging him to kill them. So he went out and bought a gun. At the end of the following month he shot five people dead in a single day.

Mullin was a certified paranoid schizophrenic, whose early mental problems had not been helped by his use of hallucinogenic drugs; this was the time at which he first began to hear the voices. One of the most worrying aspects of the case was the failure of any number of mental institutions to recognise the early danger signs and left him for so long without professional supervision. And had he not been stopped, like the vast majority of serial killers, he would have continued to murder. As it was, when the voices told Herb to shoot down Fred Perez as he worked in his garden, they forgot to tell him that Fred's neighbour was watching out of the window. Within minutes, Mullin was in custody confessing to thirteen murders.

Perversely, the jury at his trial decided that Herbert Mullin was not insane, but guilty of murder – two counts of first-degree and eight of second-degree. He is at present confined in San Quentin, where he will be eligible for parole in 2025, when he will be seventy-eight.

14 October

1826 (England)

An Affecting Account of a

CRUEL AND HORRIBLE MURDER

Committed on the Bodies of

JOHN AKEHURST and ELIZABETH HAINES

Here is a black and horrid deed,
Will fill you with affright,
Committed was near Leatherhead
Upon last Thursday night.
O weep for this poor aged pair,
Lament their cruel fate,
You need not blush to shed a tear
While I this deed relate.

John Akehurst and Elizabeth Haines
For them I now deplore,
He neared a hundred years of age
And she was seventy-four.
Confined to bed for many years
This aged man did lie:
O cruel fate that he beneath
A murderer's knife should die.

Last Thursday at the midnight hour
When all lay fast asleep,
Some murderous fiends by artful means,
Into the house did get.
Then to the room where Akehurst lay,
These monsters did repair,
Where he with feeble voice did pray
His aged life to spare.

But they intent on deeds of blood
Were deaf to all his cries,
None but a fiend could have withstood
His tears, his groans, his sighs.
He raised his hands to ward the blows
And mercy did implore.
The few grey hairs that crown'd his head
Were soaked in his gore.

With cut and wounds they mangled sure
His poor and aged frame,
His nurse this noise did overhear,
To his assistance came.
But O alas! With grief I tell,
What all must now deplore,
All bathed in blood, she quickly fell
A corpse upon the floor.

Next morning by the dawn of day
A lad who lived near,
Unto the cottage took his way –
He often worked there.
He found the door was open wide,
Which fill'd him with surprise,
On Mrs Haines he loudly cried
Then for assistance hies.

The neighbours came – O such a sight
They quickly did behold,
Their blood was chilled with affright
They could not tears withhold.
To see these bleeding aged frames,
In such a mangled state:
While crimson gore the bed-clothes stain'd,
Display'd their cruel fate.

O earth hide not their innocent blood –
To Heaven it loud doth cry,
For vengeance on the Murderer's head –
Where'er those blood-hounds fly.
May Justice soon them overtake,
And punished may they be,
All for the harmless couple's sake
They slew so cruelly.

15 October

1923 (USA) A fire broke out in the three-storey house at 9417 Nineteenth Avenue, Bensonhurst, Brooklyn, in the early hours of Monday 15 October 1923. The wood frame house had been turned into separate apartments on the three floors, and the flames spread rapidly through the building. In spite of the efforts of the New York fire brigade who rushed to the scene the house was gutted and six people died. Firefighters fought heroically to rescue survivors from the building and carried the bodies of the six who had perished to the street outside.

The dead were two boarders, George Keim and Francis P. Fowler; the seventeen-year-old son Charles, the daughter Marjorie, aged twelve, and the sister-in-law of the owner Lilian Andrews, and a maid, Rosina Weishert. Investigations led by the New York Fire Department soon found evidence of traces of gasoline in the charred remains of the building and the fire was officially classified as arson.

Police concentrated their inquiries on the background of those in the building at the time of the blaze, since the indications were that the fire was not the work of an irrational pyromaniac but, rather, of someone with a specific victim in mind and little regard as to who else died as a result. There seemed to be no evidence that anyone had a grudge against the Andrews family or Francis Fowler, so investigations centred on George Keim. Although at first nothing irregular was discovered in Mr Keim's past, as inquiries progressed, witnesses began to speak of trouble between Keim and his son-in-law William S. Ford. At one time Keim and Ford had been in business together, but the partnership had been dissolved by George Keim because, so he claimed, Ford's fondness for drink led to him neglecting the business.

Investigators also received a tip-off that a Brooklyn youth named Arthur Jones knew something about the fire, and he was detained for questioning. During the interrogation Jones confessed that he and another man had driven William Ford to the house at Bensonhurst where he poured petrol around the front and set it alight. Ford was taken into custody and later charged with murder and arson.

William S. Ford faced trial in March 1924, where his main defence was that Jones's testimony was uncorroborated and besides, he had been an accomplice. Despite these protestations the jury found Ford guilty after a retirement of less than an hour, and he was sentenced to die in the electric chair. While awaiting execution in Sing Sing Prison, William Ford committed suicide by hanging himself in his cell.

16 October

1991 (USA) At around 12.40 p.m. on 16 October 1991, thirty-five-year-old George Hennard drove his pick-up truck into the car park of Luby's cafeteria on Interstate 190 at Killeen, Texas. Hennard suddenly pushed his foot down on the accelerator and catapulted the pick-up through the plate-glass front window, showering diners with glass and debris and trapping one man underneath the truck. Hennard swung himself out of the driver's seat yelling: 'This is what Bell County has done to me!' As the terrified man trapped under the truck pulled himself free, Hennard raised a Glock-17 semi-automatic pistol. The first bullet tore through the man's skull, after which Hennard turned to the cowering diners, and began to cut them down with rapid fire, always on the move, always shooting. Choosing his victims apparently randomly and shooting at point-blank range, there is no telling how long the massacre would have continued if armed police had not arrived on the scene. Now Hennard's attention transferred to duelling with the police marksmen who were gradually closing in. It was a police bullet that finally stopped him, and bleeding from a wound he pumped a bullet through his own left eye and deep into his deranged brain. The killing spree lasted just ten minutes; amid the blood and wreckage lay twenty-two dead and eighteen wounded.

Meanwhile, a team of police officers had sealed off the elegant mansion which George Hennard had shared with his mother at Belton, just ten miles from the carnage at Killeen. Hennard's father had been a surgeon with the army, and like many other sons and daughters of military personnel, George had been uprooted frequently during his father's numerous postings. He got through school with neither academic nor sporting distinction. In the early part of 1979 George Hennard enlisted in the merchant marine. He had also picked up a drug habit, and after a particularly vicious brawl on board, he was dismissed and lost his seaman's licence. During George's absence, his father and his mother had separated and George took up residence with his mother. He began to acquire a reputation for unbalanced behaviour; he was sullen and abusive to the neighbours, and for no obvious reason would stand screaming and shouting on the front lawn. Nevertheless, Hennard had been trying, with increasing desperation, to gain back his seaman's ticket. At the beginning of 1991, the US Coast Guard tribunal finally refused to give George his licence back; days later he bought the Austrian-made Glock-17 which, come the autumn, would rob twenty-two people of their lives.

Quite what triggered the final rampage we are unlikely ever to know; still less what was going on in George Hennard's head as he stood like the angel of death amid the wreckage of Luby's cafeteria. Whatever the reason, nobody could ignore George Hennard now. As one correspondent reported from Killeen: 'Suddenly, the nobody from nowhere was the maniac behind the worst gun massacre in American history.'

17 October
1700 (England)

Sir Andrew Slanning, having made a temporary acquaintance with an orange-seller while in the pit of the Drury Lane playhouse, retired with her as soon as the play was ended, and was followed by Mr John Cowland, Gentleman, and some others. They had gone but a few yards before Mr Cowland put his arms round the woman's neck; on which Sir Andrew desired he would desist, as she was his wife. Cowland, knowing that Sir Andrew was married to a woman of honour, gave him the lie, and swords were drawn on both sides; but some gentlemen coming up at this juncture, no immediate ill consequences ensued.

They all now agreed to adjourn to the Rose Tavern, and Captain Waggett having there used his utmost endeavours to reconcile the offended parties, it appeared that his mediation was attended with success; but as they were going upstairs to drink a glass of wine, Mr Cowland drew his sword and stabbed Sir Andrew in the belly, who, finding himself wounded, cried out: 'Murder!'

Hereupon, one of Lord Warwick's servants and two other persons who were in the house ran up the stairs and disarmed Cowland of his sword, which was bloody to the depth of five inches, and took him into custody. Cowland now desired to see Sir Andrew, which being granted, he jumped down the stairs and endeavoured to make his escape, but was easily retaken.

He was instantly conducted before a Justice of the Peace, who committed him; and he was tried at the Old Bailey on three indictments – the first at common law, the second on the statute of stabbing, and the third on the coroner's inquest for the murder. These facts were fully proved, and among other things it was deposed that the deceased had possessed an estate of £20,000 a year, that his family became extinct by his death, and that he had been a gentleman of great good nature, and by no means disposed to quarrel.

Mr Cowland being found guilty on the clearest evidence received sentence of death, and, though great efforts were made to obtain a pardon for him, he was executed at Tyburn on 17 October 1700.

(*Old Bailey Records*)

18 October

1930 (England) Sarah Hearn had first moved to Cornwall with her aunt and sister in 1921, where they shared Trehorne House, in the small village of Lewannick. Towards the end of the decade, Mrs Hearn's aunt died, followed shortly afterwards by her invalid sister Minnie. Throughout this rather troubled time Sarah Hearn had found great comfort in the friendship of her neighbours William and Alice ('Annie') Thomas. When she was left alone in the house, the Thomases took to inviting Mrs Hearn on their regular outings in the family car. Mr Thomas had also made her a small loan to tide her over a difficult financial period.

Mr and Mrs Thomas decided to make the trip to Bude, a seaside resort, on 18 October 1930, and Sarah Hearn accompanied them. As she frequently did on such occasions, Mrs Hearn made some tinned salmon sandwiches for their afternoon tea which they took in a cafe. However, on their return journey to Lewannick Mrs Thomas became violently ill with stomach cramps and was confined to Plymouth Hospital, where she died on 4 November of arsenic poisoning. At Annie's funeral the village gossips were out in strength, and the general feeling was that Mrs Hearn was the poisoner – which was probably no surprise to her because immediately afterwards she left Lewannick. Just days later,

Mr Thomas received a letter from Sarah Hearn suggesting that she might take her own life.

In fact she did not, because when the police description of her was circulated, Mrs Hearn's new employer alerted the Devon constabulary. Meanwhile, the bodies of Mrs Hearn's aunt and sister had been exhumed, autopsied and found to contain traces of arsenic.

At the Bodmin Assizes in July 1931, Sarah Ann Hearn was defended by Mr Norman Birkett, one of the most successful attorneys of his day. He sought to prove first of all that it was possible for arsenic to be produced naturally in the salmon canning process and that there were attested cases where one person may succumb to such poisoning while others do not. As for the poison in the two exhumed bodies, this could be accounted for by naturally occurring arsenic in the soil in which they were buried – abnormally high in that spot according to the analyst.

After a sympathetic summing-up from Mr Justice Roche, in which he suggested that 'I do not suppose you have any doubt in your mind that the issue is down to two people – Mrs Hearn and Mr Thomas . . . If at the end of this case, you cannot say which it is, you ought to acquit Mrs Hearn.' Which the jury did, leaving the untimely demise of Annie Thomas a mystery.

19 October

1953 (England) The coroner's jury inquiring into the death of thirteen-year-old John Conroy listened in bewildered silence as, on 19 October 1953, Detective Superintendent Leslie Watts described finding the boy's body. He had been to the Conroys' family home in Denton Road, London, where he saw the corpse 'buried' in the base of a divan. The bed had been ripped open along the centre, forming two flaps. The child had been wrapped in a dark brown blanket, placed in among the upholstery of the bed and the flaps closed over it, but folded back in the area of the head rather like the lapels of a jacket. Two mattresses, four blankets, an eiderdown and sheets were piled in a heap on the floor. For obvious reasons the press had called this 'The Ritual Burial Murder'.

Circumstances related by the victim's father, Michael Conroy, were that on 25 September his wife Teresa had announced she intended to take the boy to visit a cousin on the following day. When Conroy got up (he did not sleep with his wife as she was nursing John) the family had already left; or so he supposed, because later in the morning he had found his son dead.

When Teresa Miriam Conroy was interviewed by detectives she claimed that John had suffered a fit and choked to death while she was nursing him. The pathologist, Dr Donald Teare was provisionally of the opinion that the symptoms of death were, indeed, consistent with asphyxia during an epileptic fit. However, the subsequent post-mortem told an altogether more sinister tale. Asphyxia it certainly was, but an examination of blood samples revealed from 45 to 60 per cent carbon monoxide saturation – fatal concentrations. John had also been fed barbiturates in too great a concentration for normal use.

Teresa Conroy appeared before the bench at the Old Bailey on 8 December 1953. Mr Christmas Humphries outlined the case for the prosecution, saying that John Conroy was an epileptic and his condition was worsening to the extent that he had to be nursed day and night, placing a quite intolerable burden on his mother; though there might also have been an element of 'mercy' in her actions. There was, however, another complication. John Conroy had a Post Office savings account with more than £600 in it. By dying without making a will his next of kin would get it. In Mrs Conroy's defence, Mr Elliott Gorst entered a plea of 'guilty but insane' on her behalf; and after a retirement of only twelve minutes, that is the verdict the jury returned. Teresa Conroy was ordered to be detained during Her Majesty's pleasure.

20 October

1946 (England) The body of the young woman had been found by two startled boys on the Sunday morning of 20 October 1946. They had been exploring one of the many war-damaged buildings in Manchester's Deansgate area when they made the discovery, and by 11.45 Detective Inspector Frank Stainton was in charge of what was clearly a case of murder. The woman's head had been brutally smashed, presumably with the bloodstained hammer which lay beside her body. An identity card in her handbag identified the victim as Olive Balchin.

The following morning the landlord of a public house close to the murder site reported that he had been walking his dog at around midnight on the Saturday and had seen a man and a woman arguing; he later identified Olive Balchin and her coat, and described the man who was with her. Within hours of this sighting a shopkeeper had identified the murder weapon as a tool which he had sold on the same day, 19 October, to a man matching the description given by the publican. Information had now been gathered which placed Olive Balchin, a prostitute, in the company of a young man of a similar description. It is at such times that local police officers come into their own; and one policeman couldn't get the name Walter Rowland out of his head. Rowland had already served a sentence for murdering his own baby, he was known to associate with Olive Balchin, and he fitted the descriptions. In fact, although he admitted all those details, Walter Graham Rowland was able to provide a fairly convincing alibi. Not that this prevented a jury from finding him guilty of murder, or a judge sentencing him to death.

It was while Rowland was awaiting execution that the governor of the nearby Liverpool Gaol received a note from one of his guests, a David John Ware. Ware was confessing to the murder of Olive Balchin, and later gave a detailed statement of the events to DI Frank Stainton. Walter Rowland's solicitor was understandably in seventh heaven, and immediately made an application to the Court of Appeal, and persuaded the Home Secretary to hold an inquiry. This was the point at which David Ware announced that he had been lying. Which in turn contributed to the Home Office announcement that they thought he was lying too.

On 27 February 1947 Walter Rowland was hanged. But that was not the last we heard of David Ware. On 10 July 1951, he bought a hammer and attempted to kill a woman in Bristol. After giving himself up to the police, Ware said: 'I have killed a woman. I don't know what is the matter with me. I keep having an urge to hit women on the head.' He was found insane and committed to Broadmoor where, in 1954, he hanged himself.

21 October

1969 (Canada) By 21 October it was all over, and another of Canada's most dangerously insane individuals had been removed to a place of confinement. The trial of Fred McCallum had opened before the Saskatchewan Queen's Bench on the fourteenth of the month, and he had pleaded not guilty to the two sample charges of non-capital murder on which he stood indicted. There was some confusion during the necessarily prolonged American-style process of jury selection, which extended it even further. McCallum, or at least his attorney, had objected that there were no Indians or Metis (people of mixed Indian/white ancestry) on the panel, so how could he be tried by 'a jury of his peers'. It was a point countered expertly by Mr Justice Walter Tucker who suggested that it would be even more 'outrageous' to start questioning potential jurors about their racial origins.

When the trial finally got under way the court was told that at around 3.20 a.m. on 30 January 1969 Father Andre Darsche, a Roman Catholic missionary working in Buffalo Narrows, Saskatchewan, had been woken from sleep by the insistent voice of nineteen-year-old Frederick Moses McCallum over the telephone. McCallum wanted the priest to 'see something'. Emphatic that he was going nowhere at that time of the night until he knew what the 'something' was, Father Darsche received the confidence that McCallum had killed somebody. According to McCallum he was at the Pederson house, a modest dwelling in the Buffalo Narrows community. And that is the address which Andre Darsche passed on to the police before he set off into the pre-dawn chill. In fact he and the police arrived at about the same time to find that Fred McCallum had not killed 'somebody', he had massacred most of the Pederson family, and a house-guest for good measure. All but the guest, Jean Baptiste Herman, had been attacked in their beds with a single-bladed fire-axe.

Within a half-hour of the discovery, Frederick McCallum had been arrested and charged with seven counts of non-capital murder. He appeared before a lower court on the following day and was remanded for psychiatric reports. Given the nature of the motiveless and bloody crimes, McCallum's attorney had little difficulty in persuading a jury that his client was guilty but insane.

In January 1970, a mental health panel indicated that Frederick McCallum was no longer mentally ill and no longer requiring treatment. He was transferred to a maximum security prison.

22 October
1738 (England)

GEORGE PRICE
Sentenced to Death for Murdering his Wife but Died of Gaol Fever on 22 October 1738

This malefactor was a native of Hay, though after seven years in service in that place he removed to London where he quickly married one Mary Chambers, later taking her to live in Brecknockshire. Here he told his relatives she was an officer's daughter and would soon become entitled to a large fortune. In this way, they were able to live off his family in some comfort. When suspicions became aroused the couple returned to London, where Mrs Price was delivered of twins. The children died mysteriously when Price gave them medicine, though he swore he had not poisoned them.

George Price now began to tire of his wife, and to pay court to several other women, eventually entertaining the notion of murdering her. Accordingly he took her out to Hounslow Heath in a chaise at ten o'clock at night. Suddenly he stopped the chaise and threw the lash of the whip round his wife's neck, but drawing it too hastily he made a violent mark on her chin. Immediately finding his mistake he placed it lower and pulled the ends with great force and such violence that it broke; but not till the poor woman was dead. Having stripped the body, he left it under a gibbet, having first disfigured it to such a degree that he presumed it could not be identified. Then he destroyed those clothes that belonged to his wife, and returned some garments she had borrowed from her landlady.

On the following day, there were so many inquiries

regarding the whereabouts of his wife, that Price fled to Portsmouth where he thought to sign on board a ship. While he was in an ale-house the crier was announcing him as a murderer and gave such an accurate description that he was obliged to flee again, this time returning to his native Hay and the house of his brother, whom he asked to buy a knife that he might commit suicide. This his brother refused. Eventually tiring of the life of a fugitive George Price returned to London and surrendered to justice. At the following sessions he was tried and found guilty, being sentenced to death. However he died of the pestilence called 'gaol fever' before the law could be executed on him.

(From a contemporary tract)

23 October

1929 (England) Sidney Harry Fox was born in 1899 to Rosalie Fox and her railwayman husband. It was not long before young Sidney had embarked on what was to be a lifetime of crime culminating in the murder of his own mother. Of course it started modestly enough, when he began to supplement his meagre income as a page boy with the richer pickings from other people's pockets and houses. Inevitably Sidney made a few youthful mistakes and was suitably punished with cautionary periods of incarceration. However, the Great War interrupted the young man's ambitions and he served King and Country in a most undistinguished way, collecting a term of imprisonment for forgery.

When Sidney Fox climbed back into civvies, he embarked on a new venture in collaboration with his mother Rosalie. The scheme was a simple one that consisted of the pair travelling the country from hotel to hotel, running up bills they had no intention of paying, and spreading bad cheques about like confetti. They did have one period of relative stability in 1928, when Sidney was milking a woman named Mrs Morse of everything he could get his hands on while he and Mrs Fox were living in her house. It ended when Mrs Morse woke up one night to find that Sidney had turned the gas tap on in her room, and was uncharitable enough to call the police.

When Sidney was released from prison he and Rosalie resumed their travels and found themselves, in October 1929 at the Metropole Hotel, Margate, with no more than the clothes they stood up in. But Sidney had a plan. He had already extended an insurance policy on his mother's life up to the midnight of 23 October. That is the night he lit a fire under the chair in which his mother had been snoozing before he strangled her, and under the bed on which he laid her body. He then closed the doors to give the flames a chance to take before raising the alarm and acting the part of the desolated son.

It was a desperate and cynical crime which Sidney Fox could not really have expected to get away with. The business of the insurance combined with his known poverty saw to that. Fox was found guilty of matricide and hanged at Maidstone Prison on 8 April 1930. He was thirty-one years old.

24 October

1975 (USA) The Puerto Rican Social Club in New York's Bronx was housed in one room with a single staircase leading down to the ground floor. Along one wall was a row of windows, while behind the bandstand there was a steel door leading to a fire escape. In the early hours of Sunday 24 October 1975, a fire broke out at the club which left twenty-five people dead and twenty-four seriously injured, two of whom died later in hospital.

Experts investigating the blaze concluded that the fire had

been started deliberately using a flammable liquid to accelerate the flames. It had been lit on the staircase, leaving no means of exit save the windows, and most of the survivors were people who had leapt into the street. Most of the dead had been found near the windows where they had been trapped trying to get out and had asphyxiated.

One witness was later found who had seen a green car double parked outside the building at about the time the club was set alight, but he could not remember the licence number. Although under hypnosis this witness still could not remember the registration plate, he did recall seeing three men getting into the vehicle.

The break in the case was a lucky one, when a man arrested in a stolen car offered to tell police who was behind the Puerto Rican Social Club fire in exchange for lenient treatment. The name he volunteered was Hector Lopez. Seventeen-year-old Lopez was taken into custody where he admitted that with another teenager, he had started the fire as a favour for an older man named Jose Antonio Cordero. Cordero was picked up and the other youth, Francisco Mendez, was arrested soon after in Puerto Rico. All three were charged with murder and arson.

At the pre-trial hearing Cordero was alleged to have instigated the plot because of his jealousy over a young girl who attended a dance at the club against his wishes. He claimed that this confession was forced out of him by physical abuse by the police investigators. However, at their trial in June 1977, Jose Cordero, Hector Lopez and Francisco Mendez pleaded guilty. Cordero was sentenced to life imprisonment; Lopez, who lit the fire, was also jailed for life, and Mendez received twenty-five years to life for spreading the fuel.

25 October

1849 (England) The trial of Frederick and Maria Manning was one of the sensations of the year, and opened on 25 October 1849, when they were charged with, and quite rightly convicted of, the murder of Patrick O'Connor – the Mannings' one-time lodger, and Mrs Manning's often-times lover. Poor O'Connor's body was found caked in quicklime beneath the flagstones of the Mannings' kitchen in Minver Street, south London. Frederick, it turned out, had bludgeoned O'Connor's head with a chisel after Maria had failed to dispatch him with a gun. At trial each of the prisoners sought to put the blame on to the other, but in the final judgement, both were found equally guilty and sentenced to the full rigour of the law.

Frederick and Maria Manning were executed on 13 November 1849 in front of the Horsemonger Lane Gaol in Southwark. A crowd of 50,000 spectators witnessed the hanging, including Charles Dickens, who complained to *The Times* about the levity of the crowd and the barbarity of the scene.

By the day of execution – which was set for eight o'clock in the morning – a crowd of 10,000 had congregated at the scene, with 800 policemen in attendance to maintain order. This gathering was serviced by all manner of hawkers, street traders and entertainers, pickpockets and prostitutes. Broadsides and ballad sheets about the crime sold in great numbers. In all, Henry Mayhew estimated that a quarter of a million copies of broadsides about the Mannings were produced. Many souvenir trinkets and china-ware pieces commemorating the impending event were also on sale.

At the appointed hour Frederick Manning was led out, head bowed and unsteady on his feet, accompanied by Calcraft, the executioner. The white hood was placed over his head and the rope positioned around his neck. Then it was Maria's turn to appear, dressed in respectable black satin, with a black silk veil and blindfolded, at her own request. Her demeanour was proud and steady as she was led to the scaffold and the preparations were made. A warder brought their two hands together [Frederick and Maria] as they stood over the trap-door, awaiting their fate. The chaplain asked the unrepentant Maria one last time if she had anything to say concerning her guilt. 'Nothing,' she said, 'but thank you for your kindness . . .' and two callous and calculating murderers were launched into eternity. Maria's wearing of a black satin dress on the scaffold is said to have put the material out of fashion for ladies' dresses for a period of at least twenty years.

26 October

1964 (Australia) One of the most enduring and bitter controversies in Australian legal history revolved around the confession of killer Eric Edgar Cooke to a murder for which another man had already been imprisoned. Cooke was executed on 26 October 1964, though the man he declared innocent remained in prison.

During the first nine months of 1963 the inhabitants of Perth were put in fear by a spate of brutal and apparently pointless murders. Despite assistance from London's Scotland Yard and the United States Federal Bureau of Investigation, it was a piece of gratuitous luck that led to the apprehension of the assassin. A young couple had found a rifle hidden behind a rock, which forensic ballistics identified as the weapon used in the last of the killings. When Eric Cooke, a Perth truck-driver and known burglar, went to retrieve the gun from its hiding place on 1 September he was arrested.

Rejecting a defence plea of insanity, the jury found Cooke guilty of murder and he was sentenced to death. While awaiting execution Cooke made a further confession and admitted to a murder for which a deaf mute named Beamish was already serving time. In a controversial decision, the authorities decided not to accept Cooke's unsolicited admission of guilt, and Beamish remained in prison until he was paroled in 1971. Eric Edgar Cooke was hanged at Freemantle.

27 October

1911 (England) This is the date on which Edith Bingham was brought to trial at the Lancaster Castle Assizes, on charges of murdering her father, William, her half-sister, Margaret, and her brother, James. Ironically, William Bingham was the resident custodian and guide to the castle and he and his family lived and died there.

The first casualty was William's daughter Annie, who died on 12 November 1910, and was certified to have succumbed to 'hysteria and cerebral congestion'. Victim number two was William himself, who died in January 1911 at the age of seventy-three; despite being a fit and energetic man, the cause of death was given as 'gastro-enteritis'. William's son James took over his father's job as the castle's keeper, and his stepsister Margaret left her job as the matron of a mental hospital to become his housekeeper. Within just a few days, on 23 July 1911, Margaret fell victim to, it was said, a brain tumour.

James now needed a new housekeeper, and it was with some misgivings that he asked his sister Edith to step into the breach. Poor Edith at twenty-nine was slightly mentally subnormal and practically illiterate, and she and her brother quarrelled constantly. In August, unable to stand Edith's far from smooth running of the house, James engaged a housekeeper from outside the family. Shortly before she arrived James was struck down with a violent sickness and, four days later, joined the dead. As a post-mortem on James Bingham's body revealed that he had died of arsenic poisoning, and as Edith had prepared the last meal he ate before becoming ill, the finger of suspicion began to point in her direction. Which is why she was in the familiar surroundings of the old assize court.

In fact the prosecution had been badly put together, and most of the evidence was purely circumstantial. In Edith's defence it was wondered quite why she would have wanted to kill, as well as James, her father and sister – both of whom had been exhumed and found to contain traces of arsenic. Indeed, by killing off her family she stood to lose her home and her livelihood. Besides, the murders were rather too well planned and executed to have been carried out by the simple-minded Edith. In short, had the Crown proved Edith Bingham's guilt beyond a reasonable doubt? The jury thought not, and returned verdicts of not guilty on all charges. So if Edith was innocent, who killed the Bingham family? The Lancaster Castle Mystery remains one.

28 October

1668 (England) Thomas Savage, described as a 'profligate apprentice' was convicted of the murder of a fellow-servant, was executed twice, and finally buried on 28 October 1668. Breaking the Sabbath (by his own confession, he having never once heard a whole sermon) was the first introduction to all his other vices, especially whoredom, drunkenness and theft, for he used commonly to pass the Sabbath at a bawdy-house in Ratcliff Highway with one Hannah Blay, a vile common strumpet, who was the cause of his ruin, and brought him to a shameful end.

He was first taken to drink there by an acquaintance, who afterwards went to sea; but having once found the way, he went after that alone, and would often carry a bottle of wine or two to junket with Blay. This, however, not satisfying her wicked desires, she told him frequently that if he would enjoy her company he must bring a good store of money with him.

To this he replied that he could bring none but his master's and that the servant-girl was always at home with him. 'Hang her,' said this limb of the devil; 'knock her brains out.'

Hereupon he went home and, seeing his master at the front door, climbed over the back fence unseen. When he had crept into the servant's room, the maid chided him with being in the bawdy-house, saying: 'You will never leave it till you are utterly ruined thereby.' This made him unaccountably angry, and he was so enraged that he determined to be her butcher. Soon after when the master and the rest of the household had gone to church, leaving Savage and the maid alone, he battered her to death with a hammer.

It was vain to think that he would not be taken, and despite an attempt at flight, the hue and cry was raised as soon as his master returned and saw his bloody deed . . .

Being brought to the place of execution Savage said a very pathetic prayer and was then turned off the cart, and struggled for a while. Upon this a friend struck him several blows upon his breast with all his strength to put him out of his misery. Wherefore, after he had hung for a considerable time and was to all appearance dead, the sheriff ordered him to be cut down. The body was taken to a nearby house where to the astonishment of all he began to breathe, and opened his eyes and mouth, but could not recover the use of his speech. However, hearing of his remarkable recovery, a sheriff's officer came to the house and carried Tom Savage back to the place of execution where he was hung up again until he was really dead. At the time of his death, he was in the seventeenth year of his age.

29 October

1901 (USA) It could almost have been the opening scene from a period play. In the dark of the night of 29 October

1901, Detective Whitney stood in the rain and knocked on the wooden door. When it opened he asked simply: 'Jane Toppan, the nurse?' 'Yes.' 'You are wanted in Massachusetts for questioning in connection with the deaths of Mrs Henry Gordon and Mrs Irving Gibbs.' Jane's nursing career was clearly over; as was her sideline in murder.

It all went back a long way, back to when little Nora Kelley was orphaned in 1859 and adopted by the Toppan family, who renamed her Jane. At the age of twenty-six, after the best education the Toppans could buy, Jane decided to be a nurse. The problems started when Jane's patients began, quite unexpectedly, to die. No charges were brought against her then, but she was dismissed without the usual references.

Between 1880 and 1901, Jane Toppan took a series of appointments as a 'private nurse', having forged a few letters of proficiency. And still the poor woman was plagued with patients who died. Whole families who, once healthy, had succumbed to Nurse Toppan's kind ministrations. People like Mrs Gordon and Mrs Gibbs, and the Davises. They had been treated by Jane during 1901, and the whole Davis clan was wiped out in just six weeks. Jane, jobless, simply packed her bags and moved on, hoping to start anew.

But that was to reckon without the interference of Captain Gibbs. Upon his return from sea Captain Gibbs found his wife had died and his distraught sister-in-law was complaining that the nurse had forbidden an autopsy – on the grounds that 'such practices are against the religious beliefs of the family'. The captain lost no time in conveying his suspicions to Detective John H. Whitney, and Whitney lost no time in obtaining orders for autopsies on some of the recently dead – whose remains were found to contain large traces of morphine.

In custody, Jane Toppan began a detailed inventory of her victims, but by the time she had reached thirty-one became a little confused. Despite her own strong allegation that 'I am not crazy', Jane Toppan was, nevertheless, confined to the Taunton State Asylum for the Criminally Insane, where she lived a long and healthy life, dying of old age at eighty-four.

30 October

1969 (Scotland) Twenty-nine-year-old Helen Puttock and her sister Jeannie were picked up at the popular Barrowland Ballroom in Glasgow on the evening of 30 October 1969. Both their dates were called John; Helen's John was polite, well-spoken and smartly dressed, with short hair. As the two couples left the ballroom Jeannie lost some money in a cigarette machine, and in trying to get a refund out of the manager, Helen's John became quite agitated; not aggressive, but forceful. As they left he turned and remarked, 'My father says these places are dens of iniquity.' Nobody paid much attention, except that on the taxi ride home, John boasted that at Hogmanay he did not drink, but prayed. He also made several references to Old Testament stories. The two couples separated, Jeannie at Kelso Street, the other John to take a bus. Helen and her John were set down at Earl Street; which is where Helen's body was found the next morning.

It was then that the police realised they were dealing with no ordinary killer. This was the third murder in eighteen months, all of young women leaving the Barrowland Ballroom. The first had been discovered on Friday 23 February 1968. Patricia Docker had been strangled and left where she fell dead in Carmichael Place, Glasgow. She had last been seen leaving the ballroom. On 17 August the following year, Jemima McDonald was strangled with her own tights in a derelict building in Mackeith Street. She had left the Barrowland at midnight the previous day.

The police may have had the problem of a serial killer on their hands, but at least now they had some clues to work with. For a start they had the description given by Helen Puttock's sister of 'John'. The Identikit portrait was to become the best-known face in Scotland; the problem was that quite a lot of people shared the same 'ordinary' features. And police had the killer's odd religious obsessions; and soon 'Bible John' was the name on everybody's lips.

However, despite massive manhunts and the untiring efforts of most of the Glasgow police force, Bible John was never caught, nor, as far as we know, did he kill again. Even the efforts of the celebrated Dutch 'psychic detective' Gerard Croiset were not able to shed light on the enigma. Although the crimes remain unsolved there is one possibility that has gained some credibility over the years; and that is that each of the three murders was committed by a different person – that there never was a Bible John.

31 October

1946 (England) It could fairly be said that when the noose tightened around Harold Hagger's neck, the thing that really hanged him was a yellow string bag. It was on 31 October 1946 that the body of forty-eight-year-old Dagmar Petrzywalski (known as Dagmar Peters) was found in a clump of bushes off the A20 on the ominously named Labour-in-Vain Hill at Wrotham, in Kent. Absence of any signs of a struggle led police to believe – correctly as it turned out – that she had been strangled elsewhere and dumped from a motor vehicle.

Information from Miss Peters' mother indicated that she had been hitch-hiking her way to London at dawn on the morning of her death – a regular trip she made to meet her brother. On these occasions she was accustomed to carry her few necessaries – mostly sandwiches – in a yellow bag crocheted by a sister-in-law and a battered attaché case. Neither the bag nor the case was found near Dagmar Peters' body.

The murder investigation was under the control of Scotland Yard's almost legendary Chief-Inspector Robert Fabian, who was to more than live up to his reputation for inventiveness. Fabian asked the victim's sister-in-law to knit another, identical yellow bag, a photograph of which was published in that evening's newspapers. The picture was recognised by young Peter Nash, the son of a farmer at West Malling, who had found the original bag in Clare Park Lake whence, it was later established, it had drifted from a near-by cider-making factory, via an old mill stream.

Among the lorry drivers visiting the cider works on the day of Miss Peters' death was an old lag named Harold Hagger, who already had one conviction for assaulting a woman. Under interrogation he admitted picking Dagmar Peters up on the road where she was thumbing a lift. She had, according to his story, tried to steal the wallet out of his jacket pocket; a struggle ensued in which, unluckily, Miss Peters became entangled in her own scarf and was asphyxiated. Where was that jacket, Fabian wanted to know. 'Hung up in the cab of the lorry,' Hagger replied. Well, a bitterly cold early morning at the end of October, and there was Hagger driving along in an unheated cab in his shirtsleeves. The jury didn't believe it any more than Robert Fabian had; and they showed their disbelief by consigning Harold Hagger to the hangman.

November

1 November

1909 (England) Gorse Hall was a large private residence in its own extensive grounds just outside Dukinfield, Cheshire. In 1909 it was occupied by Mr George Henry Storrs, a wealthy building contractor. On 1 November, Storrs was relaxing at home with his family in the dining-room, while the servants were below stairs and the coachman and his family were in their quarters above the stables.

At about 9.20 p.m. Mary Evans, the cook, went down to the cellars, and when she returned was surprised by a gunman pointing a revolver at her. With commendable pluck, Mary broke free and raised the alarm. George Storrs rushed out of the dining room and closed with the intruder, much to the disadvantage of the other. Until, that is, the intruder pulled a knife and fatally stabbed Storrs before fleeing leaving his gun behind.

Although the vague description offered by George Storrs and Mary Evans could have fitted half the local male population, it was one Cornelius Howard, a thirty-one-year-old petty crook, whom the police pulled in. It was a very shaky case from the start, because nobody could make a positive identification (Mrs Storrs could be of no help at the identity parade because 'they all look so untidy'), and there was no way of connecting Howard with the abandoned, and incidentally defective, gun. He also had a supportable alibi. Nevertheless, Cornelius Howard was put on trial at the Chester Assizes in March 1910. His alibi was proved watertight and he was declared innocent of the murder of

George Storrs – which he was. And there the case rested, unsolved, until July of that same year.

Seemingly determined to compound the errors of the Howard fiasco, the police arrested Mark Wilde, a native of nearby Stalybridge, on a charge of wounding a young man with a knife. For good measure they put him in an identity parade where Mary Evans declared that he looked 'even more like the murderer than Howard' – whatever that meant. No matter, it was sufficient to have Wilde charged with the murder of George Henry Storrs, and he appeared before Mr Justice Horridge at the assizes on 24 October 1910. In a vague attempt at proving identity, Cornelius Howard was brought back to court and stood in the dock alongside Wilde so that the jury might compare features. Then Home Office analyst Sir Herbert Willcox testified that blood found on Wilde's clothing was human (though at the time there was no test for blood grouping, and Wilde's explanation that he had become bloodied in a fight in a pub was as good as any). The jury thought so, anyway, because Mark Wilde was acquitted.

The police did not try for the proverbially lucky third time, and the Gorse Hall Murder became the Gorse Hall Mystery. The culprit was never caught, and it may be unwise to attach any importance to the fact that Storrs's coachman committed suicide shortly after Cornelius Howard's arrest. R. W. James, in his short history of the Cheshire Constabulary, declared: 'The case of the Gorse Hall murder was not a good example of police work. No motive for the murder could be found except in the imagination of the press and public.'

2 November

1952 (England) On the late Sunday afternoon of 2 November 1952 sixteen-year-old Christopher Craig and nineteen-year-old Derek Bentley were on the roof of Barlow and

Parker, wholesale confectioners, of Croydon. They were looking for a way in to burgle the premises when they were spied by a woman in a house opposite who called the police. During the police siege of the building Police Constable Sidney Miles was hit by a bullet and killed. Craig was armed with a handgun at the time and had exchanged several shots with the police when Bentley, who was already under arrest, was heard to shout out 'Let him have it, Chris', just before the officer was killed. One of the most controversial cases in British legal history would turn on those five words. In the opinion of the police (and later the Crown prosecutor) this was a direct incitement to shoot officer Miles. According to the defence it was a plea for Bentley to hand over his gun.

The subsequent Old Bailey trial before the Lord Chief Justice, Lord Goddard, opened on Tuesday 9 December 1952. Christopher Craig and Derek Bentley stood jointly accused of murder, though Craig was supposed to have fired the fatal shot. This was the era of that first youth 'culture', the 'Teddy Boys' – and the official atmosphere in court was very prejudicial to a trial unbiased by feelings of revenge against violent youth. In fact, even Mr F. H. Cassels who undertook Bentley's defence was open in his belief that 'both the little bastards ought to swing'. In fact, only one of the defendants would stand on the gallows.

The trial lasted three days and concluded with a none too unbiased summing-up by Lord Goddard, during which he took great delight in wielding Bentley's knuckle-duster: 'Have you ever seen a more horrible weapon?' The jury were at their deliberations for only seventy-five minutes before returning with a verdict of guilty on both young men. It was with undisguised glee that the judge passed sentence of death on Derek Bentley, and with some irritation that, because he was only sixteen years of age, he could only sentence Christopher Craig to be detained during Her Majesty's pleasure.

Derek Bentley, after the rejection of numerous pleas for a reprieve, was hanged at Wandsworth Prison on 28 January 1953 by executioner Albert Pierrepoint. Christopher Craig spent ten and a half years in prison. Since the date of his execution, a tireless campaign led by Bentley's sister Iris has been calling for a posthumous pardon, only to be met with mealy-mouthed refusals by a succession of Home Secretaries.

3 November

1697 (England) Francis Salisbury and Thomas Houghton were executed at Tyburn on 3 November 1679, for the uncommon crime of forging a sixpenny die-stamp. As this stamp was a form of state revenue, the crime was considered treason, and punished accordingly.

> These two were indicted in the Old Bailey, 15 October 1697, in forging a sixpenny stamp to stamp vellum, paper and parchment; and that after 12 September they did stamp five hundred sheets of paper with the said stamp, and did utter and sell a hundred sheets of the said paper, knowing it to be false and counterfeit.
>
> A witness declared that he met Dr Salisbury in the Physic Garden at Westminster, who said he could put him in the way of making up his losses, and that was by stamped paper; that he (the witness) waited for the doctor the next day at the Fountain Tavern in High Holborn; from whence the doctor took him to a stable, and in a hole from under the manger he took out five quires, and gave them to him, and asked whether it was well done. And then he let him out the back door. That he met with him at another time after that, and he

delivered him fifteen quires more, which made it up to a ream, and that he gave him five pounds for it.

Another witness deposed that he met Dr Salisbury at the Thatched House, by Charing Cross, to buy some counterfeit stamped paper of him; and he gave Salisbury six pounds for it; and that they were to get him some more for the next night, at the Goat Tavern, where they would meet; and Houghton told him they could not get so much done by that time, for the old man was sick. Telling him likewise that the old man was as ingenious a man as any in England; and that if they were to put down thirty shillings apiece, they would make such a die as Captain Harris, who made the true die, should not tell the difference. And that afterwards they went to Houghton's lodgings in Westminster, where they found in a chest a quantity of counterfeit stamped paper.

Salisbury altogether denied the fact, and Houghton said he had taken the paper for a debt; but the fact being plainly proved upon them, the jury found them both guilty of the indictment.

On the day of his execution at Tyburn, after the other criminals who then suffered were tied up, Dr Salisbury came in a mourning coach attended by two ministers, and being brought into the cart, he fell upon his knees, and, praying a considerable time by himself, he afterwards joined with the ordinary in the usual offices performed on such melancholy occasions, and then was turned off.

(*Old Bailey Records*)

4 November

1950 (USA) It was as horrible a death as anybody could imagine – trapped in a burning circus tent with a crowd of hundreds; unable to get to the exit as the fumes choked and the strips of burning canvas cascaded down. That was the fire set by Robert Dale Seegee. Despite the fact that he admitted this, and several other similar offences, on 4 November 1950 he was sentenced to a derisory two-to-twenty years.

In July 1944 the famous Ringling Brothers circus arrived in the small town of Hartford, Connecticut, and the big top mushroomed as if by magic. The first show was scheduled for 6 July. By early afternoon queues were forming, and soon the families were settling into their seats in anticipation of the spectacle to come. At around 2.30, after the orchestra had blasted out the overture and the eyes of the audience were straining upwards to catch every daring and dangerous movement of the high-trapeze act, a sinister figure huddled in the shadows was starting a fire against the canvas wall of the big top. The heavy material might have proved difficult to ignite, but in compliance with local regulations it had been coated with paraffin wax to ensure it was waterproof. A few moments later there was a shrill cry of 'Fire! Fire!', and the audience, circus hands and performers watched with amazement as they saw a flame flickering upwards near the main entrance. At first there was little concern, it seemed to be a small enough fire, and surely somebody was attending to it . . . Suddenly there was a strong gust of wind, a fury that set the big top billowing and flapping, and fanned the fire into a sudden burst, igniting the wax coating and sending blazing canvas snaking down on to the shrieking audience. Now the crowd was on its feet, scurrying blindly for the steel runway which served as the exit; on the runway the panicking mass of desperate bodies jammed itself to a standstill, a crowd so dense it was impossible to move, impossible now even to breathe. Flaming debris continued to rain down, setting alight hair and clothing . . .

Within five minutes of the fire being lit 169 people were

dead, either as a direct result of the inferno or by crush asphyxia in the attempt to escape it. More than 250 more were ferried to hospital for emergency treatment, many of them suffering from serious injuries.

It was not until six years later, when detectives were running a cross-check on all suspected cases of arson in which circus hands employed on the fateful day at Hartford appeared, that they came up with a name – Robert Dale Seegee, called 'Little Bob'. In June 1950 he was traced to Ohio and taken in for questioning. Seegee admitted he was responsible for the circus fire and that he had also started a few more. And just for good measure Little Bob laid claim to an impressive list of other homicides. Under questioning, he said that for years he had been haunted by nightmares in which he was told he must start fires. Although there was little enough evidence on which to indict Robert Seegee on any of the crimes to which he was prepared to admit, he was eventually charged with ten counts of arson. Seegee pleaded guilty and was sentenced to two separate terms of imprisonment.

5 November

1949 (England) Comparatively few killers who are acquitted commit murder a second time. One of the exceptions was a young Irish labourer named Anthony O'Rourke.

On 5 November 1949, the tranquillity of the small market town of Pickering was disturbed by the discovery of the body of a resident (with the singularly appropriate name of Pickering) lying on the floor of his cottage at 10 Willowgate. He was still alive, but suffering from severe head wounds. Thomas Pickering was rushed to hospital where, after a protracted battle, he succumbed to his injuries on 15 December. Meanwhile, investigations had revealed that until recently Anthony O'Rourke, his wife and children had been lodgers with Mr Pickering, having departed on

5 November. They were now living with Miss Rose Harper at Westgate.

At his trial, O'Rourke was identified as the man seen entering 10 Willowgate at noon and leaving an hour later. He had also cashed Mr Pickering's tobacco coupons. In his defence, O'Rourke admitted going to the house, claiming that Mr Pickering had said some very uncomplimentary things about his, O'Rourke's, mistress Florrie, and had been taught a lesson in manners; that Pickering died as a result of this education was a tragic mistake. Surprisingly, Anthony O'Rourke was acquitted of the charge of murder, *and* of the admitted manslaughter. (It no doubt helped that the jury was unaware of O'Rourke's previous record for bigamy, theft and child cruelty.)

Anthony O'Rourke might well have thanked heaven for a merciful release, and returned to his family at Castlegate a wiser and better man. But in the late evening of 4 June 1951, worried neighbours who had noticed a lack of activity at 129 Westgate, broke in to find the place ransacked and uninhabited. On the following morning, Anthony O'Rourke walked into the local police station and confessed to killing fifty-five-year-old Rose Harper; the body, strangled with a black stocking, was later found wrapped in a rug under the table. O'Rourke's story was that Miss Harper had been pestering him for sex, and when he declined she, like Tom Pickering, had insulted Florrie. To add insult to injury, Miss Harper had then dealt him a painful blow to the testicles. In a rage, O'Rourke had struck back, but again misfortune had guided his hand, and Miss Harper had died. It was not much of a defence, and when O'Rourke asked to be represented again by Mr John Parris (who had been so successful on his behalf in the Pickering case) the attorney is recorded as commenting: 'This is getting somewhat monotonous.' Nevertheless, he managed once again to sway the jury, and his client's charge was reduced to manslaughter. On his early release from prison (during which time his wife had divorced him), Anthony O'Rourke married Florrie and settled down.

6 November

1946 (England) On the night of 6 November 1946, Mrs Olive Nixon was walking home to her house in Park-village East, in London's Regent's Park, and had got within fifty yards of her front door when she was savagely attacked from behind. Her assailant battered Mrs Nixon to death with a heavy object and made off into the dark, making no attempt at robbery. This apparent lack of motive did nothing to help the police inquiry, and despite a painstaking investigation, the murder team was wound down and the case file left open. And so it remained for ten years.

In the early hours of the morning of 10 August 1956, a thirty-two-year-old labourer walked into the Albany Street police station and announced: 'I killed Mrs Nixon. I hit her on the head with a brick. I have given myself up because I have been afraid that sooner or later I will kill another woman. Last Wednesday I met a girl at Hampstead. We walked to the woods and I had a terrible urge to kill her . . .'

It is not uncommon for the police to receive such visits; usually they are from unbalanced individuals craving a moment of notoriety. However, it is very unusual for a crank to 'confess' ten years after the crime has been big news. Besides, Adam Ogilvie was in possession of information about the death of Mrs Nixon that had never been released to the media. He clearly had to be taken seriously.

The following November, Ogilvie stood before Mr Justice Gorman at the Old Bailey. By this time he had retracted his confession, and explained: 'I made it to prove my innocence to my wife; to get her back. I pretended to her that I did the killing, and told her that I would murder her, too, if she did not stop quarrelling with me. I thought if I was acquitted she would come back.' As to the fine details of the case which he was in possession of, Ogilvie told the court that they had been told to him by 'a coloured man'.

The jury did not acquit Adam Ogilvie; they were convinced by his original confession, and he was sentenced to death on 20 November 1956. It happened that Parliament was, at that time, engaged in discussions on the new Homicide Bill, and during the period that it was making its passage into law, capital punishment was unofficially suspended; in other words, the Home Secretary was advising the exercise of the Royal Prerogative in cases of murder. Adam Ogilvie's sentence was commuted to life imprisonment.

7 November

1839 (England) Banks, though periodically raided, are rarely the scenes of cold, calculated murder; least of all are their managers cast in the role of cold, calculating murderers. Except when they are . . .

On the night of 7 November 1839, an alarm was raised which brought firefighters and police to the premises of the Newcastle Savings Bank. In an office from which the fire appeared to have originated lay the body of the bank's assistant chief cashier, a Mr Millie. He had died of a fractured skull, and, incongruously, his pockets were laden with lumps of coal. In the adjoining office another body was stretched out on the floor – that of Archibald Bolam, the bank's manager, bleeding from wounds to the throat, but a long way from death. Bolam's story was that he had, over the previous several months, received a number of threatening letters – all anonymous and, inconveniently, now destroyed. On the evening of the 7th, a man with a blackened face had come into the bank, killed Millie, tried to kill him, and made off with the contents of the till, pausing, presumably, to set fire to the building.

When the manager was examined more carefully, it was found that the wounds to his throat were only superficial, and furthermore, the direction in which the blood had run down his coat suggested that he had been either sitting or standing at the time they were inflicted, and he had then laid down on the floor – in short, it looked as though Bolam had murdered his clerk, set fire to his office after making the body more combustible by the addition of some house-coal, and then inflicted his own injuries. This conclusion seemed confirmed when a number of the account books and gold coin missing from the bank were subsequently found at Bolam's home.

Despite the apparent strength of the case against Archibald Bolam, it was suggested at his trial (by the judge!) that the bank manager might, after all, only be guilty of manslaughter if Millie had received an accidentally fatal blow during an argument – possibly resulting from the clerk's disapproval of his superior's appropriation of the bank's funds. At any rate, this is the way that the jury chose to interpret the events, and Alexander Bolam, saved from the gallows, was sentenced to transportation for life – in those days, perhaps a fate even worse than death.

8 November

1980 (England) What happened over the night of 8 November, they didn't yet know, but when police officers were dispatched to the council flat in Harris Street, Camberwell, at four o'clock the next morning they were expecting to be unpleasantly surprised. That would have been an understatement. The floors, walls and furniture in most of the rooms were soaked in blood; but what turned their stomachs was that in the midst of this gory shambles four people were sleeping as peacefully as if they had been in a three-star hotel suite, the remains of a Chinese take-away meal sharing table space with pools of congealing blood. The three men and one woman were taken back to the police station, leaving detectives to solve the riddle of the source of the spilt blood. The solution came sooner than they could have hoped.

A little later that morning several parts of a man's dismembered body were found in black plastic rubbish bags on waste ground not far from Harris Street. Other bits of the same body were discovered over the following days, and on 11 November the head was found in Harris Street itself, and was identified as having belonged to former boxer Donald Ryan. By this time the four people picked up at the flat in Harris Street had been identified as Shirley Brindle, Michael Ward, John Bowden and David Begley, and they were charged with Ryan's murder.

According to the Crown prosecutor at their subsequent trial, the four defendants and Ryan had been sitting around for most of the day of 8 November drinking large quantities of cider. Then Bowden and Begley had bludgeoned Ryan with one of the empty bottles and robbed his pockets of a measly £20. Afterwards they had submerged the unconscious man's body in a bath of boiling water, before dismembering him alive with a saw, machete and electric carving-knife.

While the men got on with bagging up the pieces of Donald Ryan's body, Shirley Brindle had popped out to get them all a meal from the nearby Chinese restaurant. This they ate at the flat before setting off for a night's drinking at the Red Bull. Then they made a nocturnal sortie to dispose of the packaged remains of Don Ryan. It was a disturbed neighbour who called the police.

On 26 November 1981, Bowden, Ward and Begley were convicted of Ryan's murder and Shirley Brindle of unlawful disposal of his body.

9 November

1808 (Ireland) At the Clonmell Assizes in the year 1808 John Ryan and Mathew Kearinge were indicted for the murder of David Bourke; in a second count, with the murder of John Dougherty; in a third, with setting fire to the house of Laurence Bourke; and in a fourth, with maliciously firing at Laurence Bourke, with an intent to kill him.

After the Solicitor-General had opened the case he called Laurence Bourke, who stated that on the night of 9 November he was informed by his servant that there were a number of men in arms advancing towards the house. From the window he could see the prisoners in the dock and several others surrounding the house. They demanded that he open the door, but he refused. Then they fired several shots in through the different windows. In the house were Dougherty, the deceased, a servant and Bourke's wife and child. They were alarmed, but had no ammunition save what the guns were loaded with. The prisoners and their party, finding they could not get into the house, set it on fire. Mrs Bourke and her child then went to the window and called out to Ryan (who was a relation) not to burn the house, but he replied with an oath that he would; and a shot was fired at her, which frightened her so much that she and the child fell out of the window and were seized by the prisoner Kearinge; but afterwards they made their escape.

The house was now falling in flames about Bourke's head, and he opened the door and ran out. Several shots were fired at him, but he escaped to the house of his father. In his flight he fired his piece once and killed one of Ryan's party. When he reached his father's house, Laurence Bourke found that the good man had already gone to his assistance, so he returned to his burning house where he found Ryan's gang departed and his father, David Bourke, lying just yards from the smoking ruin.

Winifred Kennedy and other witnesses were examined and corroborated the testimony of Bourke proving that the deceased John Dougherty was burnt in the house. It was also proved that the whole of Ryan's party were entertained at dinner by him that day, and they all left the house armed, for the purpose of attacking Bourke.

On the part of the prisoner Ryan an alibi was attempted to be proved by a woman who lived with him, which entirely failed; and, after a very minute charge from the learned judge, the jury brought in a verdict of guilty against both prisoners. They were executed accordingly.

10 November

1902 (England) Twenty-four-year-old Kitty Byron was one of those lady killers for whom we might entertain rather more pity than for her objectionable victim. Although murder can never be justified, that of Arthur Reginald Baker can be understood better than most.

Kitty had been living with Baker at his lodgings in London for several months. He was already married, though he promised Kitty divorce; he was also a violent alcoholic – violent, that is, towards Kitty. To top it all, Baker was utterly disloyal, and it was this graceless trait which led to his untimely death.

It was the year 1902, an altogether more prudish time than our own, and Baker's landlady at Duke Street had never been too keen on the 'goings on' upstairs. She might have been able to swallow the 'Mr and Mrs' charade had it not been complicated by the frequent ferocious rows. In the end, this good lady put peace and quiet above rent and Baker was asked to leave. He, being the way he was, made a mealy-mouthed apology, confessed that Kitty was not really his wife, and promised to throw her out if he could keep his room. Unfortunately, Kitty got to hear of this arrangement through a loose-tongued housemaid.

That was on the morning of 10 November. Feeling bitter and betrayed, Kitty Byron followed her treacherous partner to work in the City, stopping only to purchase a spring-bladed knife. When she reached Lombard Street post office, Kitty sent Baker a telegram at his office demanding to see him there and then. What was said on the steps of the post office we will never know; all we know is that Kitty, in full view of passers-by, stabbed Arthur Baker in the chest and, as he fell to the ground, the back.

Later, in a statement to the police, Kitty Byron said: 'I killed him willingly, and he deserved it.' Whatever the morality of that, it earned Kitty the death sentence. However, acknowledging the great strength of public feeling in her favour, not least through a 15,000-signature petition, the Home Secretary first commuted Kitty's sentence to life imprisonment and then to ten years. After serving six years of her sentence, she was placed in a benevolent institution for women.

11 November

1805 (England)

Elizabeth Barber was born in King Street, Deptford, and married an honest waterman by whom she bore children. Barber's good conduct obtained him an excellent situation in a custom-house, while his wife was ruining him by her flagitious conduct. She was soon beyond all control. Once she stabbed a man for which she was indicted and imprisoned at Maidstone for one year. This, however, proved no check to her behaviour, for having formed an intimacy with John Dennis Daly, she murdered him on 11 November 1805, stabbing him in the breast with a knife. Again she was sent to Maidstone Gaol.

In evidence against her, a neighbour testified that she had heard people scuffling in the room upstairs and shortly afterwards heard the cry of 'Murder!' Then she heard Mrs Barber shout: 'I'll do it; I'll do it! I will not put up with it!' About half an hour later, Elizabeth Barber opened the door of her room and yelled down: 'Murder! Bloody murder! My husband has stabbed himself and is dead. Will nobody come to my assistance?' The witness then called the woman who lived underneath her, and both of them went up to Barber's room. When they got there they found John Daly sitting up in a chair with his head hanging on his left shoulder; the front of his shirt was open, and the wound in his breast was washed very clean. Elizabeth Barber was sitting close by smoking a pipe, and observed, unconcernedly, that Daly had stabbed himself.

Barber was found guilty of murder, and the learned judge immediately passed sentence of death. She then begged the judge that her children might afterwards have her body. Her dress on the day of execution (which took place on Pennenden Heath) was very decent; and from the time of her being led from the prison to the fatal drop she never uttered a sentence. Before leaving jail, however, Elizabeth Barber made a full confession of her guilt.

(*The Malefactors' Register*)

12 November

1867 (England) In 1867, Todmorden was a small manufacturing town on the river Calder, and its vicar was the Reverend Anthony John Plow. The other members of his household were Mrs Plow, the vicar's wife, Jane Smith, a nursery maid, a servant named Sarah Bell and a third servant. Miles Wetherill, the sixth character in this drama, was a smart, not unhandsome lad of twenty years. When he first fell in love with Sarah Bell, Miles followed the accustomed practice of the time by seeking permission from her employers to pay her suit. For reasons not immediately clear, the Rev. Mr Plow expressed very strong objections. However, Miles Wetherill was not to be discouraged, and for six months the artful couple met clandestinely without the knowledge of Mr and Mrs Plow. Their luck was not to last, and finally Sarah was discovered and given a vehement lecture by her employer, resulting in the girl tendering her notice.

Sarah Bell left the vicarage on the morning of 12 November 1867 to return home. On her journey she was accompanied by the faithful Miles. During this time Sarah acquainted her lover with the fact that it was Jane Smith who was at the root of their troubles, because she had betrayed their secret to Mrs Plow, and she to her husband.

At eleven o'clock on the night of the murders, the Rev. Mr Plow was preparing to go to bed when he heard a heavy banging at the back door. Suspecting that Wetherill was the cause of the disturbance (having staged similar stunts before), the vicar left the house by the front door and stole round to the back of the house to confront the manic figure of Miles Wetherill. The young man pulled out a pistol and pressed the trigger, the cap of which refused to ignite. Enraged, Wetherill struck at Plow with an axe, and dragged the vicar back into the lobby where he continued to slash brutally at him. Meanwhile, the servants had awoken and joined the fray, grabbing Wetherill until their master was able to make his escape. The attacker then turned his attention on Jane Smith, whom he struck so viciously that the blow nearly severed her hand from her wrist; Wetherill finally cornered her and put a fatal shot through her body.

Taking up a heavy poker, Miles sought out Mrs Plow in

her bedroom and was lambasting her about the head with his weapon when he was interrupted by the help summoned by the surviving servant. Had they not stepped in, Mrs Plow would certainly have joined Miss Smith in an early grave.

Miles Wetherill was placed on trial at Manchester Assizes charged with the murder of Jane Smith (in fact, the Rev. Anthony Plow also died on the day before the trial began). In a summing-up which could be seen as slightly biased, the judge stated that he failed to see anything in the case which could obviate a verdict of guilty being given. Miles was accordingly convicted and suffered death outside the New Bailey Prison before a crowd of about 25,000 spectators.

13 November

1970 (South Africa) According to superstition, Friday the thirteenth is a most unlucky day; certainly for Maria Groesbeek it was the unluckiest day of her life. On Friday 13 November 1970, she was hanged.

Slightly less unlucky, but unfortunate enough, was 28 March 1969, also a Friday; that was the day Christiaan Buys died; and at the time Maria was Mrs Buys. The couple had been married in 1953 and had spent many years of absolute hell with each other. According to Maria's account, she had been subjected to continual deprivations and beatings. In 1969 she became involved with a man of just twenty named Gerhard Groesbeek, the Buys' lodger.

It was in the following month that Christiaan Buys, a railway worker hailing from the Orange Free State, died in the Voortrekker Hospital after several weeks' illness. Although Buys had been treated for pneumonia, a subsequent post-mortem examination revealed a high deposit of arsenic in his internal organs. The inevitable suspicion that was bound to attach to Martha was in no way lessened by the fact that she immediately got married to Gerhard Groesbeek. Not long after their wedding, Maria and Gerhard were taken in and questioned by the police. Under interrogation, Maria Groesbeek admitted feeding her late husband on food laced with arsenic-based ant poison, but only after he refused to allow a divorce. She claimed she just wanted revenge for the way he had treated her: 'I wanted to make him thoroughly sick so he would give me permission to divorce him.' Maria was immediately charged with murder and Groesbeek with being an accessory.

Although Maria had painted a picture of a broken marriage and a cruel husband, things would soon be seen in a quite different light. The fact was, as any number of witnesses would testify, Christiaan Buys had been a singularly mild and sensitive man, generous to a fault, and kindness itself to his wife and children. Besides, more than one person was to recall Maria saying she was fed up with her husband and if he would not agree to a divorce she would poison him. All these witnesses appeared against Maria Groesbeek during her trial at the Bloemfontein Criminal Sessions, where the judge and two assessors later found her guilty of premeditated murder. As for Gerhard Groesbeek he was tried separately, but evidence of his awareness of Maria's plans was not conclusive enough to convict him beyond a reasonable doubt, and he was acquitted.

Meanwhile, sustaining herself on a diet of prayer and self-pity, Maria Groesbeek languished in Pretoria jail awaiting her appointment with the hangman.

John Muckett
Who was Executed at Chelmsford for the Murder of his Wife, with whom he quarrelled because he had no Potatoes for Dinner
14 November 1801

John Muckett was in the first battalion of the 4th Regiment of Foot, quartered at Colchester, Essex. At his trial, Thomas King and his wife stated that the prisoner and his wife and themselves lodged in the same room. About five o'clock, the prisoner came home and said he would have some dinner. His wife said she would put the kettle on and get him some tea. He replied he would not have tea, he would have some bacon. His wife accordingly gave him some bacon, and lay it on a stool near the bed where he was lying. He then grumbled because he had no potatoes. She immediately set about preparing some, and he damned her for not making more haste. She replied that she could not handle the dirty kettle and iron his linen at the same time. He said he would have no grumbling at him, and immediately knocked her off the stool. She gave him a small blow in return, on the shins, with the nozzle of the bellows, upon which he kicked her and threw her across the room.

King then interfered, and said the prisoner should not beat her any more. He said he would: she was his own wife and he would do as he pleased with her, and he would kill her as soon as not. He again gave her several violent blows to the head. The poor woman attempted to walk across the room, but was very lame, and was obliged to lie down. She was very sick in the evening, and Muckett appeared sorry for his conduct.

The deceased was put to bed; and nothing more occurred until the prisoner was heard calling out in the night: 'Betty! Betty!' Mrs King got up and found her dead. The prisoner then, in a state of remorse, went down on his knees, exclaiming he was a wretched man, for he had murdered her.

The Lord Chief Baron told the jury that this was a clear case of murder, and having been found guilty he was sentenced to be hanged. At the place of execution he addressed the spectators, acknowledging the justice of his sentence; and he earnestly exhorted them to bear in mind the dreadful example they had before them of the consequence of suffering a sudden impulse of anger to get the better of their understanding.

(A contemporary broadsheet)

15 November

1991 (USA) On 15 November Thomas McIlvane walked through the unlocked employees' entrance at the Royal Oak, Michigan, postal depot and into the sorting room where he opened fire with a sawn-off Ruger semi-automatic carbine. As the workers dived for cover, some even making the jump to safety from the second-storey windows, McIlvane singled out the supervisors, shooting three dead; in the brief six-minute shooting spree a further six victims fell wounded. McIlvane then turned the rifle on himself and put a single shot through his own head. Thomas McIlvane was still alive when he arrived at the William Beaumont Hospital at Royal Oak, but died early the following day.

Sudden, yes. But with some knowledge of McIlvane's past and his personality, it was not entirely surprising. After serving with the US Marines (from which he was dishonourably discharged after deliberately driving a tank over a car), thirty-one-year old McIlvane joined the ranks of the US Postal Services as a postal deliverer attached to the regional office at Royal Oak. A prickly character by nature, McIlvane was popular neither with his supervisors, nor, it appears, the customers along his delivery route with whom he frequently argued and occasionally fought. This latter problem had already led to one suspension from duty, and in 1990, after a series of disagreements with managers, Tom McIlvane was dismissed. That said, it is only fair to mention that McIlvane was not the only employee at the office to have problems with its supervisors, and the postal workers union supported his appeal against dismissal. The court of arbitration finally ruled against McIlvane on 8 November 1991.

McIlvane was very much the stereotypical mass killer. Like the majority he was either serving, ex-, or quasi-military and had a passion for guns. He was also deeply involved in the macho world of martial arts (McIlvane was a black-belt kick boxer). Almost a psychological profile for a spree killer. Which must also have occurred to the office of the United States Postmaster General which, on the day after the Royal Oak shootings announced a systematic check of all personnel records in order to identify staff who had a history of violent or threatening behaviour. In addition, a telephone hot-line was promised, to coordinate information from employees who had been threatened in the course of their work. Ironically, as the announcement was being made, the William Beaumont Hospital released a bulletin stating that one of the six victims wounded at Royal Oak, a female supervisor, had died of her injuries.

16 November

1949 (England) Around ten o'clock on the bleak morning of 16 November, two young men, their raincoats belted against the icy wind, entered the little jewellery store. The elderly Jewish proprietor looked up, and his eyes registered danger; paying customers these were not, paying customers rarely carry pistols. Their only words confirmed his suspicions: 'Give us the money!' With unexpected agility old Abraham Levine leapt round the counter and grabbed hold of one of the robbers; as he did so the second man began to rain down blow after blow on the old man's head with the butt of his gun. Still old Abe kept fighting. Twice the gun burst into life, and in an instant the two men were across the shop, leaving behind them one more statistic on Leeds city's crime list. In another instant they were out into the crowd of shoppers, shooting wildly to scatter the terrified pedestrians, each scrambling for cover; women screaming. Some public spirited citizens gave chase; more shots, and in the panic and confusion two fugitives were created. In the uncanny silence that followed, the old jeweller, bleeding from his head and body, stumbled out of his shop and collapsed on to the pavement. He died in hospital the following night.

Within hours of the abortive raid, a thousand police officers were on the streets of Leeds, hunting for information on the whereabouts of the two killers. Two days after the shooting twenty-year-old Walter Sharpe and seventeen-year-old Gordon Lannen were taken into custody in Southport. On a March morning in 1950 they stood their trial at the Leeds Assizes. Despite a defence that Sharpe and Lannen carried a gun because of the influence of 'these wretched gangster films', and had fired it by accident, the verdict was a foregone conclusion.

In passing sentence on Gordon Lannen, Mr Justice Sreatfield told him: 'The jury have very properly convicted you of a most shocking and disgraceful murder. You come under the protection of the Children and Young Persons Act, and, because you are under the age of eighteen, you cannot suffer the supreme penalty of the law. The Act protects even young gangsters.' In an atmosphere of gravity such as no other occasion could produce, the black cap was placed over the judge's wig and he sentenced Walter Sharpe: 'For your part in this most shocking crime it is my duty to pass upon you, young though you are, the sentence which is prescribed by law for this offence.' Sharpe was hanged at Armley Gaol on 30 March 1950.

The murder of Abraham Levine is not a great classic, not a classic of any degree, simply a pointless crime of greed and stupidity. But it deserves recalling if only to remind ourselves of this simple truth: wherever guns are available, there will be gangsters ready to use them.

17 November

1981 (England) The duty officer at the Ailsworth village police station, in Cambridgeshire, took the early-morning call from a woman who gave her name as Mrs Muriel McCullough, and claimed that on the previous night, 17 November 1981, her house had been burgled. She said she had been visiting friends in Cheshire and had just arrived home.

It fell to the lot of PC Alan Gregory to go out to the McCullough residence and have a look. When he arrived he found the lady of the house in such an agitated state that she was unwilling to go upstairs with him to investigate. When the officer reached the main bedroom, he could understand why – lying on the bed was Bill McCullough, Muriel's second husband. He had been shot through the head. PC Gregory's suspicions were naturally aroused, especially when Mrs McCullough declined to go up to the bedroom to see if any of her jewellery was missing. The constable decided to play a hunch of his own. He told the reluctant lady that he had found her husband upstairs, but that he was ill in bed. Still Mrs McCullough remained firmly in her chair; indeed, she seemed quite unconcerned about Bill's well-being. Then Gregory spilled the beans and told her that he was more than ill, he was dead. This provoked a silence, followed by: 'Bill! Oh, my Bill! I want my Bill!'

Police Constable Gregory reported his suspicions back at the station, but as fifty-two-year-old former beauty-queen Muriel McCullough had a cast-iron alibi, all the police could do was to keep a close watch on her. An investigation into Mrs McCullough's recent activities was rewarded by the information that she had been dealing with a couple of Liverpool gangsters named Collingwood and Kay; they had been introduced by a mutual friend, Joe Scanlon. Scanlon later made a statement accusing Muriel McCullough of hiring the two thugs to beat up her husband, though James Collingwood confessed that she had in fact offered him and Alan Kay £8,000 to kill him. They had gone to the house on the night their 'employer' was away in Cheshire and carried out the hit.

A further interview with Mrs McCullough confirmed this story. She told detectives that her husband of eleven months had proved to be a drunken bully and she had hired Collingwood to teach him a lesson: 'I wanted him to know what it was like on the receiving end.'

Mrs McCullough, James Collingwood and Alan Kay were jointly charged with murder at the Birmingham Crown Court in November 1982, and all three were convicted and sentenced to life imprisonment.

18 November

1943 (England) The first anybody knew about Bertie Manton's over-enthusiastic chastisement of his wife was on the following day, when two sewer-men were measuring the water level of the river Lea where it flows through Luton. It was the gloomy afternoon of 19 November 1943, and a heavy fog had settled over London and the Home Counties. Lying in six inches of water the men found a bundle; inside was the naked body of a woman.

In any homicide investigation the vital first clue is the identity of the victim; in the case of the Luton sack murder, the job was made doubly difficult, because her killer had not only removed every identifiable accessory, but had so battered the woman's face that it was unrecognisable. Then the investigating team had a lucky break. A trawl was being made of second-hand clothes shops and rubbish dumps for clothes that might have belonged to the victim. On 21 February 1944 a strip of black cloth was found bearing the dyer's tag 'V2247'; it had been allocated to a coat deposited by Mrs Caroline Manton of 14 Regent Street, Luton.

Chief Inspector William Chapman called at the address in person, and interviewed Horace 'Bertie' Manton, a former boxer. Manton's story seemed plausible enough: after a violent quarrel Mrs Manton had packed her bags and left. Bertie even produced a letter from her – addressed from 'Hamstead'. But Chapman was by no means entirely happy, and called in Scotland Yard's leading fingerprint expert, Frederick Cherrill.

Fred Cherrill's first impression of 14 Regent Street was how spotless it was. Not just clean, like most homes, but spotless. *It had been completely wiped of fingerprints.* This was particularly noticeable in the cellar where, grimy as the walls were, the rows of bottles stacked on shelves had been scrupulously cleaned. Why? Then, in a remote corner of the cellar, the fingerprint-man discovered why. On the only jar that had escaped cleaning he found a clear print. Without needing to check, he knew it was the thumb-print of Mrs Caroline Manton.

Detective Inspector Chapman now looked afresh at the letters supposed to have come from Manton's 'estranged' wife; and noticed again the spelling of 'Hamstead'. He asked Bertie Manton to write out the text of the letters and true to expectation Manton left out the 'p' in Hampstead. In the end Manton confessed that he and his wife had been engaged in one of their familiar rows when he had got fed up and battered her to death with a wooden stool – a crime for which he was sentenced to life imprisonment. He died three years later in Parkhurst Prison.

19 November

1944 (England) It was a familiar, if sad, story of the effect of war on human relationships. November 1944 saw Leonard Holmes back from the conflict in Europe to an altogether quieter pattern of life – and a wife whom he suspected may not have been preparing a home fit for a hero. In short, she had become, at least in Leonard's mind, just a tad too familiar with any number of other uniformed men to be found hanging around the local pubs. That was what it was like when they went out for a quiet drink together on the evening of 19 November. He and his wife Peggy were sitting in one corner of the bar in their New Ollerton local, when those damned RAF men stormed in; and Peggy's eyes began to wander. It developed into a quarrel; as it always did. The quarrel became more and more belligerent; as it always did. Then, when they got home, Peggy Holmes dropped the bombshell: 'All right,' she yelled, 'if it makes you happy, I *have* been untrue to you!'

Quite why Leonard Holmes had a hammer in the living room we will never know. What we do know is that he used it to deadly effect on Mrs Holmes's head. Then, for good measure, he strangled her.

Leonard Holmes came up for trial at the Nottingham Assizes in February 1945. On the face of it, the case was an open and shut one. The only question was what degree of culpability Holmes could be said to have. In other words, was this a matter of murder, or did circumstances mitigate towards manslaughter? According to the trial judge, Mr Justice Charles, it was not open to the jury to find a verdict of manslaughter. Which did not please Holmes's attorney. However, at appeal, Mr Justice Wrottesley upheld the original ruling, declaring that suspected, or even proven infidelity does not amount to sufficient provocation to reduce a crime from murder to manslaughter.

And that, perhaps, should have been that. But Leonard Holmes decided to take his case as far as the House of Lords. Here the same ground was painstakingly explored yet again. Was a verbal confession of adultery sufficient provocation? According to their Lordships it was not. Lord Simon, speaking on behalf of the panel of judges, upheld the ruling of the Court of Criminal Appeal and the trial judge. Adultery, the panel was convinced, did not provide a licence to kill. Indeed, it was their Lordships' opinion that the doctrine of provocation rarely applied in cases where there was a deliberate intention to kill (as Holmes had admitted). Where it did, it was necessary for a husband to discover his wife *in the act* of adultery.

Having exhausted every avenue of appeal, Leonard Holmes was obliged to keep his appointment with the hangman, on 28 May 1945.

20 November

1836 (England) At the Central Criminal Court session on this date, Robert Salmon, a medicine vendor in Farringdon Street, London, was indicted for killing John McKenzie by administering to him excessive quantities of pills composed of gamboge, cream of tartar and other noxious and deleterious ingredients.

The deceased was a ship's master living in the neighbourhood of Commercial Road. He was persuaded to take some

'Morison's Pills' as a purgative by a Mrs Lane, a woman employed by his wife as a seamstress, and who sold the Hygeian medicines. Subsequently Mr Salmon's assistance was called upon after Mr McKenzie began to suffer from rheumatism in his knee. Salmon recommended ever-increasing doses of the pills, until at length the mariner's life was put in jeopardy. Medical advice was sought, but too late, and death soon put an end to the poor man's sufferings. A post-mortem examination left no doubt that the medicine prescribed by Mr Salmon had been the cause of death in this case, and he was indicted.

In Robert Salmon's defence, a great many people were summoned from all parts of the country, who stated that they had themselves taken large quantities of the self-same pills with most efficacious results. Indeed, they appeared to be a cure for almost every species of malady to which the human frame was subject. One witness said that he had taken no fewer than 20,000 Morison's Pills over two years, and had gained infinite relief from swallowing them in very large doses.

Mr Justice Patteson then left it to the jury to decide whether the facts had been adequately proved, and after a retirement of about half an hour they found the prisoner guilty of manslaughter with a recommendation to mercy. This last was because Salmon was not the manufacturer of the medicine, only their vendor.

On the following Saturday, Robert Salmon was brought to the bar to receive judgement. Mr Justice Patteson ordered him to pay a fine of £200, adding: 'I think it right to caution you that, in the event of your being again found guilty of conduct of a similar description, the character of your offence will be materially altered [a thinly disguised threat of a murder charge]. I hope that the punishment which is now inflicted on you will deter others from rashly administering medicines, with the nature of which they are unacquainted, in large quantities, as the result may be fatal.'

21 November

1931 (Scotland) At around three o'clock on the morning of Saturday 21 November 1931, Peter Queen rushed into a Glasgow police station and told the duty officer: 'Go to 539 Dumbarton Road, I think you will find my wife dead.' He added: 'Don't think I have killed her.' At least, that is what Queen claimed to have said. A lot different from '*I* think I have killed her', which is what the police would later claim he said.

At the age of eighteen, Peter Queen had made an unfortunate marriage to a girl who turned out to be an alcoholic. Two years later she was confined to a home. With unbelievable bad luck, Queen then got attached to a young woman named Chrissie Gall, who also became an alcoholic. When Chrissie had to leave her father's house because he went to live with another daughter, Peter arranged for her to live with a couple of his friends, James and Fay Burns. In December 1930 Peter Queen moved in as well. By this time Chrissie, who was calling herself 'Mrs Queen' was irredeemably addicted to alcohol and alternated between defiance, when she would become violent, and penitence, when she would become suicidal, saying such things as 'some day you will come in and find me strung up'. As things turned out this was no idle threat, and Chrissie made several half-hearted attempts on her own life. Wisely, perhaps, because the Burnses were getting a mite fed up, Queen rented a place on the other side of town. On 20 November Chrissie became so drunk that Peter tried to call a doctor. As one was not immediately available he arranged for a house-call the following morning. According to his subsequent statement, Peter had put Chrissie to bed and when he went into the room a couple of hours later he found her dead, with a thin cord tied around her neck. The post-mortem showed she had died from asphyxia. The problem was: who could say whether it was murder, or suicide? So a lot rested on what Peter Queen really did say in the police station.

The case of HM Advocate *v.* Peter Queen opened in Glasgow on 5 January 1932, and there was no shortage of witnesses to Queen's love, patience and understanding towards his wife. Sir Bernard Spilsbury supported the suicide theory, and even the judge summed up the prosecution case as 'scanty and unconvincing in so far as it supports the theory of homicide by the accused'. The main evidence was the police contention that Queen had told them '*I* think I have killed my wife'. And that, perversely perhaps, is what the jury believed. Peter Queen, an unlikely killer if ever there was one, was given a death sentence which was later commuted to life imprisonment.

22 November

1855 (England) It says something for William Palmer's innate intelligence that, having been a petty criminal from an early age, he eventually qualified as a doctor, at Saint Bartholomew's Hospital, London. It must be added, though, that he had already been dismissed from one apprenticeship, with a druggist, for embezzlement, and had to flee from another after grossly abusing his surgeon master's hospitality.

Palmer set up a modest practice in Rugeley, Staffordshire, and married. But it seems that, as a leopard is said not to be able to change its spots, so William Palmer found it impossible to settle to a life of domesticity and honest labour. At home there was constant friction – not least about the illegitimate child that he fathered on one of the servants. Business suffered, perhaps on account of his preference for gambling and horse racing over medicine.

To finance ever increasing debts, Palmer did away with

his mother-in-law in order to inherit her fortune. As his gambling losses and racing-stable debts increased, so others mysteriously died; such as his wife, who had been insured for £13,000, and his brother, insured for a similar amount. Along the line four of Palmer's children also perished. None of these 'windfalls' ever did more than satisfy the smallest part of his financial needs, and by 1855 Palmer was not only in debt, but in the clutches of the money-lenders. Then, in November of that year, he visited Shrewsbury races with a gambling companion named John Parsons Cook. Cook won; Palmer, not unusually, lost. Cook's celebration party proved to be Palmer's golden opportunity. Cook was taken ill, and Palmer generously offered to collect his winnings – which he used to pay off his own debts. Meanwhile, John Cook, in his room at the Talbot Arms Hotel deteriorated under Dr Palmer's ministrations, and died. The following day, 22 November, Cook's stepfather demanded a post-mortem examination, which revealed traces of antimony.

Palmer was put on trial at the Old Bailey in London in May 1856. An interesting side-issue of the case is that, because of the unlikelihood of Palmer getting a fair trial in Staffordshire, so great was the public disapprobation, it was necessary to pass a special Act of Parliament to get the trial transferred to London. Found guilty of murder and sentenced to death, William Palmer was publicly executed outside Stafford Gaol on 14 June 1856.

23 November

1839 (England) Francis Hastings Medhurst was a highly respectable young man, who was found guilty of the manslaughter, on 23 November 1839, of Joseph Alsop, a fellow scholar. The crime took place at the Rectory House Academy, at Hayes, Middlesex, an educational establishment run by the Rev. Mr Sturmer, a clergyman of the Established Church and minister of the parish of Hayes.

Joseph Alsop and Francis Medhurst were the Rev. Sturmer's pupils, the former being twenty-one years of age and the latter twenty-two. On the day in question, Rev. Sturmer was in his study with Joseph Alsop and a pupil named Bunney, when Francis Medhurst entered the room and complained to the old clergyman that Dalison, another pupil, whom he called 'a blackguard', had broken the glass of his, Medhurst's, watch. Alsop, who was a close and constant companion of the said Dalison, was most indignant at the language used to describe his friend, and told Medhurst: 'You are a liar and a blackguard yourself for saying so!' Whereupon Francis Medhurst lifted the stick which he was carrying in his hand and rained a number of severe blows down on his accuser's head and arms with it. This led to a general scuffle, during the course of which young Alsop wrested the stick from his attacker and made as if to give Medhurst some of the same treatment. The latter, however, pre-empted the blows by swiftly drawing out a clasp-knife and sticking it in Alsop's stomach. Despite surgical assistance being quickly administered, it proved of no avail, and after lingering between life and death for a few days the unfortunate young man died.

It was not until the following week that Francis Medhurst was arrested. This was around the time that the inquest was being heard on the death of his victim. The coroner's jury returned an unsurprising verdict of wilful murder against Medhurst, and he was instantly conveyed to Newgate Prison. Despite the charge originally brought against him, Francis Medhurst was found guilty at his trial at the Central Criminal Court of the lesser offence of manslaughter, and on this conviction he was sentenced to a comparatively lenient three years in the house of correction.

An interesting postscript to this case is that Francis Medhurst's grandfather had also been tried for murder, though he escaped the full penalty of the law because of his clear insanity. The victim had been his wife, whom he stabbed to death, and for this alleged murder he was tried at the York Assizes in the year 1804.

24 November

1929 (England) Irrationally jealous of his 'wife's' supposed infidelities, James Achew cut her throat in their Notting Hill, London, lodging house on 24 November 1929. Having taken Sybil de Costa's life, Achew then attempted to cut his own throat with the same weapon, and when this failed, put his head in the gas oven – which also failed to rob him of his life. At his trial the following January, the deciding issue was whether this level of jealousy amounted to delusionary insanity. Dr Watson, Senior Medical Officer at Brixton Prison, argued that Achew was suffering from melancholia and delusional insanity, provoking this series of questions from the Crown prosecutor and the judge:

MR EUSTACE FULTON: Many men are extravagantly and foolishly jealous about women without being insane?

DR WATSON: Yes.

MR JUSTICE AVORY: In other words, jealousy without cause is not of itself evidence of insanity?

DR WATSON: No.

MR JUSTICE AVORY: Apart from this delusion of infidelity on the part of the woman is the prisoner otherwise, as far as you can judge, sane?

DR WATSON: He has no other delusion, but I do not think the one he had could be entertained by a perfectly sane man.

As a result of this questioning Mr Justice Avory, in his summing-up to the jury, advised them that the fact that

Achew was under the delusion that Sybil de Costa had been unfaithful did not alone justify the verdict of 'Guilty but insane'. He was accordingly convicted of wilful murder and sentenced to death. However, a subsequent examination declared that James Achew was not entirely responsible for his actions and he was reprieved and committed to Broadmoor. This is by no means the only case that underlines the chasm of difference between legal insanity and medical insanity.

25 November

1939 (USA) Shortly after eight o'clock on the morning of 25 November 1939, a waitress employed at the Old Barn Inn, Salt Lake City, Utah arrived for work at what she expected to be an empty building. The thirty-three-year-old proprietor, Grant F. Wentz, had left a message at the woman's home warning her that he and his family would be away for the day but that she should report in for work as usual. Entering the building, she was immediately aware of a strong smell of gas. Puzzled, the waitress hurried upstairs to the owner's living quarters and was horrified on entering the living room to see the bloodstained body of five-year-old Marie Wentz lying on a settee. The woman ran screaming from the building. An autopsy later revealed the child had been bludgeoned with a heavy object and that her throat bore marks consistent with strangulation with a cord or wire.

In a front bedroom of the apartment lay the body of Mrs Afton Wentz, the wife of the owner, incongruously tucked up in bed. As in the case of the child, her head had been battered and her throat bore marks of a thin ligature which had been removed. In each of the rooms and the hallway the gas jets had been fully turned on. Further tragedy waited in a second bedroom where the bludgeoned and strangled bodies of the two other Wentz children, Darlene, aged six, and Barth, four, were found. The grisly search continued through into the kitchen which revealed the body of Grant Wentz, a .22-calibre rifle lying beside him.

To the experienced eyes of the detective team this looked like a classic case of murder followed by suicide; a diagnosis confirmed when the pathologist reported that Wentz had been dead for a much shorter time than the rest of the family. With such a clue it was not difficult for officers to piece together the motive behind so barbarous an act of mass murder; it was established that Grant Wentz had recently been depressed over the Old Barn's lack of success, and his inability to pay outstanding bills. A bloodstained hammer and pieces of heavy wire cut from a radio aerial were found close to the restaurant, and tests proved them to be the murder weapons. The official verdict on the tragedy was murder and suicide. However, it remains a mystery why Wentz, and we must assume it was Wentz, took the trouble of turning on all the gas taps before killing himself.

26 November

1969 (England) On 26 November 1969 Stanley Wrenn, a nineteen-year-old vagrant from Liverpool, picked up an iron gas-ring and brought it down savagely on the sleeping head of Colin George Saunders, and then stabbed him to death. Thirty-five-year-old Saunders, a homosexual who was working as a chauffeur for a hire-car company, had been sharing his bed-sitting room in Bromley with Wrenn for the previous five weeks. During this time he had managed to infect Wrenn with gonorrhoea – which was, in part, the reason for the attack; the other part was theft.

Having dispatched his 'benefactor', Wrenn plundered the room of anything valuable, and clutching a suitcase containing his victim's best shirts in his hand, and with Saunders' car keys and driving licence in his pocket, he climbed behind the wheel of the Humber hire-car parked outside the house. Partly due to panic, and partly due to inexperience with large limousines, Wrenn backed the vehicle at speed into another car; much to the driver's understandable annoyance. Stanley Wrenn, on the pretence of calling the police, went back into the house he had just left, waited a few moments, and then announced that the police were on their way.

Meanwhile, a colleague of Saunders, who worked for the same company, arrived and was puzzled to find Stanley Wrenn 'taking the car round for Colin'. The new arrival helped Wrenn park the hire-car and went back to the firm's office. Needless to say, the aggrieved driver, who had been waiting patiently for the police to arrive, was both bewildered and, by now, rather angry. In fact he was so frustrated that he went in search of the man who owned the limousine. He knocked on the door of the house and in company with a sympathetic tenant who had opened it, made his way to Colin Saunders' room. And found him dead.

Stanley Wrenn, wisely, had disappeared. However, after the charade of the previous morning, he must have realised that there was unlikely to be any competition for the identity of Colin Saunders' killer, and he turned himself in to the police.

Following his Old Bailey trial, Stanley Wrenn spent just ten years of a life sentence in prison. He was released in June 1980, at the age of thirty.

27 November

1875 (England) The trial of Henry Wainwright opened at the Old Bailey on 27 November 1875, and the grisly story that unfolded, the story of the two bullets found in Harriet Lane's severed head, led Henry to the scaffold and his brother Thomas to prison as an accessory.

In 1871, Henry Wainwright, a married brush manufacturer with his business at Whitechapel, in London's East End, took Harriet Lane as his mistress and set her up in some comfort in a house at nearby Mile End. Miss Lane, an attractive and well-educated young woman of twenty was in receipt of a weekly stipend of £5 from Wainwright as well as the clothes, jewellery and costly gifts with which he showered her. In August 1872, Henry and Harriet became the proud parents of a baby daughter; an event which was repeated in December of the following year.

Inevitably, perhaps, the situation of supporting two homes and a business, of living two domestic lives, began to sour for Henry. This was complicated by his brother Thomas leaving the business after some disagreement over the amount of the profits which was being used to finance Henry's liaison. As the business began to hit hard times, so Harriet's allowance began to shrink and she was moved to a less elegant address. This did not please her – a fact which she voiced often and loudly. Then in June 1874 she disappeared – according to Henry, to the continent with a new lover.

However, even this did not improve Henry's brush-making operation, and he was eventually forced to give up the Whitechapel premises. To this end he hired a youth named Stokes to help carry some heavy packages from the building. While Wainwright went off to hail a cab, the lad took a peek into one of the bundles and saw a mass of decomposing flesh which was subsequently identified as the late Harriet Lane's leg.

Stokes, after some difficulty, persuaded two policemen of what he had seen and Wainwright was followed and taken into custody as he was lifting the assorted parts of Harriet's body from the cab into his brother Thomas's house near London Bridge. As Henry Wainwright looked from the scaffold over the sea of faces waiting outside Newgate for the drop to open, he snarled: 'Come to see a man die have you, you curs?' They were his last words.

28 November

1984 (England) That a killing can be, and sometimes is, excused, can be seen as an essential requisite of any compassionate legal system. Because it is only when a person's life reaches the open forum of a public court that the full background – perhaps of unendurable provocation – can be fully appreciated, and the clemency of the law mobilised to the task of protecting the 'innocent'.

On 28 November 1984, Police Constable Pat Durkin of the South Yorkshire force was shot dead by his wife Diana Jade Durkin; it was just one week after their wedding-day. Neighbours were startled awake at dawn by the sound of a shot, followed by what one witness described as 'a cry, a death cry'. Then there was silence.

On the face of it, the couple's relationship was stable enough. They had met in rather romantic circumstances when Diana accidentally locked herself out of her flat, and Pat Durkin in his panda car, responded to her SOS call. Twenty-five-year-old Diana, a clerk with the Department of Health and Social Security, had moved into Durkin's house in Sivilla Road, Kilnhurst, six months before their wedding at the register office in Rotherham, Yorkshire – a ceremony which was interrupted so that the bride and groom could go out on to the street and find two people to act as witnesses.

Eight days later, Mrs Durkin was in another of Rotherham's official buildings – the magistrates' court – where she was remanded in custody charged with the murder of her husband.

When Diana Durkin appeared before Mr Justice Hodgson at the Crown Court in Sheffield in July 1985, a quite different kind of relationship was exposed to public scrutiny – a relationship dominated by Pat Durkin's extreme sexual demands, traversing the border into perversion.

Mr George Tierney, speaking in Mrs Durkin's defence, told the court that her husband exercised a 'Svengali-like' hold over her, which was strengthened by her intense love for him. Mr Tierney went on to say: 'There is reference in her statement to the police of pornographic films, allegations of bestiality and sickening perversions.' Many of the allegations were translated into this kind of innocuous description – 'perverse', 'pornographic', 'kinky' – so that it became difficult to know the true extent of Diana Durkin's 'nightmare'.

Mr Justice Hodgson actually refused to read out in court statements relating to the case, defending his action with the words: 'I could hardly accept it until I saw the things found in their house' (presumably a coy reference to the paraphernalia of sexual sado-masochism), and in deciding not to jail Mrs Durkin, he said: 'There seems no reason to blacken anyone's name by going into details of their marriage. One doesn't want to be seen covering up, but it is encapsulated in the phrase, that she was subjected to sadistic behaviour over a lengthy period of time, which she accepted because she was in love with him.' Mrs Diana Durkin was put on probation for three years on condition that she remained an in-patient at a psychiatric hospital.

29 November

1989 (USA) One of America's most odious – and most prolific – serial killers was sentenced to death on 29 November 1989 after being convicted on sixteen charges of murder, nine of sexual mutilation and three of sodomy. A peripatetic killer, Randolph Kraft murdered his way around the states of Michigan, Oregon, Ohio, Washington and

New York between 1972 and 1983. Although he was eventually only charged with sixteen, it is confidently believed that Kraft was responsible for a total of sixty-seven murders, most of which involved torture and mutilation.

The first established victim was a twenty-year-old marine named Edward Daniel Moore, whose body was found in the Seal Beach area of California in December 1972. He had been sexually assaulted and strangled. In 1975, three more young men were found dead in similar circumstances. Another man disappeared in 1976, and was later found strangled and castrated. Four more cases were associated with the same killer in 1978, and two in 1980. There seemed to be a break in the series until 1983, when in the first two months of the year three marines were found emasculated and strangled.

Highway Patrol officers were chasing an erratically driven car on 14 May 1983, and flagged it down on the freeway. The driver got out of the car and identified himself as Randolph Kraft, a thirty-eight-year-old computer programmer. So far it was all routine. Then the officers looked into Kraft's car and saw the dead body of Terry Lee Gambrel, another marine. He had died from an overdose of a stupefying drug. Randy Kraft said nothing at the time, nor has he ever offered a single word of confession or explanation.

Investigations established that Kraft was a homosexual, and suggestions were offered that it was his feelings of guilt over his sexual preferences that caused him to kill his partners. The frequent acts of emasculation could be seen as an extension of this shame, in that by removing his victims' 'maleness' he normalised his sex acts by making his partners more like women. That is the complicated explanation. It is equally possible that Randy Kraft was simply a sexual sadist who derived his gratification from the torture and mutilation of his live victims. Whatever the answer is, the authorities seem unlikely to get any help from Kraft himself as he waits on Death Row for his appointment in San Quentin's execution chamber.

30 November

1774 (England) The execution of John Rann on 30 November 1774 for highway robbery and murder deprived England of one of its most colourful villains, a man cast from the same mould as Jack Shepherd and 'Blueskin'.

Rann was described by a contemporary as 'an impudent and arrogant self-created gentleman', and it was his boast to have worked in the service of some of the most well-connected masters and mistresses in the country. About four years before his execution, John Rann was coachman to a gentleman of fortune near Portman Square, London, and it was at this period that he dressed in the manner which gave rise to his nickname of 'Sixteen-string Jack', for he wore breeches with eight strings at each knee. After living in the service of several noblemen, he is said to have 'lost his character' and turned pickpocket, along with several others – Jones, Clayton and Colledge, the latter being known as 'Eight-string Jack'.

On 30 May, Rann was taken into custody and brought to Bow Street charged with robbery, and happened to come before the magistrate/novelist Henry Fielding. It is written that Jack stood before his Lordship 'wearing a bundle of flowers in the breast of his coat as large as a broom, and his irons were tied up with a number of blue ribbons'. He was tried and acquitted . . . 'Soon afterwards,' so it was written in a contemporary account, 'Rann appeared at Barnet Races, dressed in a most elegant sporting style, his waistcoat being blue satin trimmed with silver; and he was followed by hundreds of people, who were eager to gratify their curiosity by the sight of a man who had been so much the subject of public conversation.'

A very short time before Jack was capitally convicted he attended a public execution at Tyburn, and, getting within the ring formed by the constables round the gallows, desired that he might be permitted to stay there. 'For,' he said, 'perhaps it is very proper that I should be a spectator on this occasion.' And so he was well prepared when, after several exploits in company with William Collier, the 'second most notorious highwayman', he should be identified in the act of robbing Dr William Bell, chaplain to the Princess Amelia, close to Ealing. On that very evening he was taken, with his mistress, and, after trial – where, it is written, 'he was dressed in a new suit of pea-green clothes, and his hat was bound around with silver strings' – Jack Rann was 'left for execution'.

After conviction the behaviour of this malefactor was for some time very improper for one in his unhappy circumstances. On Sunday 23 October, he had seven girls to dine with him. The company was remarkably cheerful; nor was Jack Rann less joyous than his companions . . .

December

1 December

1906 (England) The memory had never left him; he could still remember himself, little Joe Jones, walking home from school when he saw the two men in uniforms pushing a frail, pathetic creature into the back of a horse-drawn cart. Joe never saw his grandfather again. Later in life he learnt that the old man had died within weeks of being thrown into the feared Wordsley workhouse. And he made this resolve – that they would never, ever take him the way they had taken his grandfather.

The child grew up, and the man had a child of his own, a beloved daughter named Ethel, the joy of whose birth was marred by the death of Joe's wife in giving it. Now that child had grown up, and was herself now courting, with a young chain-maker named Edmund Clarke. After three years the couple wed, and Joseph blessed the match by asking them to share his house at Quarry Bank, near Stafford. There could not have been a happier family in the district; until the autumn of 1905, when old Joe lost his job at the steel-mill. The change was almost frightening. Joe Jones, with more time on his hands than he could cope with, took to gambling and drinking heavily. Soon he had squandered his way through what savings he had put by over the years, and was relying on young Edmund to support his habits. Then in a generous but ultimately unwise gesture, Edmund bought their communal home from Joe. So the pattern repeated itself, until old Joe Jones was penniless once more, relying on handouts again to pay for his beer. Finally, realising the mistake of his generosity, Edmund politely but firmly refused to underwrite his father-in-law's drinks bill. This merely served to bring down Joe Jones's wrathful abuse, and spine-chilling threats of violence.

When Ethel Clarke arrived home from shopping on Saturday 1 December 1906, she was struck motionless with horror as she gazed on what, just two hours before, had been her loving, beloved husband. There on the couch lay Edmund Clarke, his skull so badly smashed that his brain was exposed, his throat cut through to the spine; the room awash with his blood. Old Joseph Jones simply got out of his chair, went to the door, and took the short walk to Brierly Hill police station. The bloody poker, and the cut-throat razors which had so barbarously cut short Edmund Clarke's life were quickly recovered by detectives and marked for presentation at Joseph Jones's trial at Stafford Assizes.

The trial took place in March 1907 and barely occupied the day's sitting before old Joe was remanded to the death cell at Stafford Gaol. It is said that when Joseph Jones came face to face with executioner Henry Pierrepoint he was heard to mutter: 'This is a damned sight better than the workhouse!'

2 December

1988 (South Africa) Trust Feed is a small black community on the outskirts of Greytown in the Natal Midlands; thirty-four-year-old Brian Mitchell was in charge of the local police station. During the tense and often violent times before and during the transition to a new constitution, it was part of the job of officers such as Mitchell to keep an eye on gatherings of politically active groups that could undermine security and stability. One of these groups was the United Democratic Front, sympathetic to the then banned African National Congress. Under cover of dark on the night of 2 December 1988, Lieutenant Brian Mitchell led a group of four black

African special policemen in an attack on a house in Trust Feed. It was Mitchell's belief, and there is no reason to doubt the truth of that conviction, that the house was occupied by UDF activists. From outside, Mitchell fired two shots in the direction of the house and then sent his specials in, guns blazing. A total of eleven people lost their lives.

The massacre itself was bad enough, but it was not even the right house. The building stormed by Mitchell's officers was occupied by supporters of Inkatha, who were gathering for a family funeral; one of the victims was the dead man's sixty-eight-year-old widow. Even so the situation might have been saved had Lieutenant Mitchell confessed his error and offered to resign. As it was, he tried the cover-up approach, first ordering his specials to set fire to the death-house and then sending the officers away on extended leave. Unfortunately, when matters did come to light, the higher police authorities sent to investigate the case proved obstructive and uncooperative. In the end it was only the persistence and courage of Captain Frank Dutton that, despite threats to his own life, exposed the whole ugly story, and brought Brian Mitchell to court. Meanwhile, Mitchell had been *promoted* to captain.

Captain Mitchell appeared before Mr Justice Andrew Wilson at the Supreme Court in Pietermaritzburg in the spring of 1992. There was little doubt that Mitchell would be convicted, what was in doubt was whether, against expectation, the judge would exercise the full right of punishment. He did; Captain Brian Mitchell became the first white policeman to be sentenced to death for a quasi-political crime. In fact he was given eleven death sentences. More surprising still, was Mr Justice Wilson's undisguised distaste for the manner in which the police had handled the investigation and he called for a public inquiry into the cover-up. It was a brave stand, and without doubt a genuine one; but the fact is, Mitchell's capital sentence will never be carried out, and as for the inquiry, all that law and order minister Hernus Kriel would offer was a departmental inquiry. When the four special policemen involved in the Trust Feed shooting appeared before him, Judge Wilson took a more lenient view; bearing in mind that they were acting under orders given by a superior officer, he sentenced them to fifteen years' imprisonment.

3 December

1612 (England) The indictment charged the prisoner, as an accessory before the fact, of the murder of John Turner, fencing-master, on 3 December in the year 1612.

Robert Creighton, Baron of Sanquire (or Sanchar, in Scotland), while playing at foils with John Turner about five years before the murder, had an eye thrust out by one of Turner's foils; whereupon the Baron, resolving to be revenged, sought help from several assassins to murder Turner.

He had not an opportunity of effecting it till the year 1612, when he prevailed upon Gilbert Grey, one of his servants, and Robert Carliel, both Scotsmen, to undertake it; but Gray afterwards declined the attempt, and Robert Carliel associated himself with one James Irweng, another Scotsman, and these two, on 3 December, about seven in the evening, went to a public-house in the Friars, which Turner frequented as he came from his school, and finding Turner there, they saluted him, and fell into conversation with him; when Carliel, on a sudden, fired a pistol at Turner, and shot him in the breast; and he dropped immediately to the ground dead, saying only 'Lord have mercy upon me, I am killed.'

After this Carliel fled to Scotland, Lord Sanquire absconded, but Irweng and Gray were taken while endeavouring to make their escape; and Gray was later made an evidence against the rest.

At length, Lord Sanquire surrendering himself, and Carliel, the principal assassin, being brought back from Scotland, Carliel and Irweng were tried at the Old Bailey, and being convicted of the murder, they were executed in Fleet Street, near the Friars; and Lord Sanquire being afterwards arraigned at the King's Bench bar as accessory before the fact, confessed the indictment, and was thereupon condemned, and executed in Palace Yard.

4 December

1723 (England) It is not often that an individual criminal case will make any lasting mark on legal history. On the one hand, the law tends to be a ponderous process noticeably resistant to change; on the other, criminals tend to be, as a category, an unimaginative section of humankind, rarely necessitating the law to be rewritten for their benefit. One of the few exceptions was a law enacted in 1723 in response to the misdeeds of a gang of ruffians operating in the county of Hampshire, and called the Waltham Black Act, the effect of which was to increase the number of capital offences on the statute from around thirty-six to over 150. The first to fall victim to the act were Richard Parvin, Edward Elliot, Robert Kingshell, Henry Marshall, Edward Pink, John Pink and James Ansell. All of whom were executed at Tyburn on 4 December 1723, for murder and deer-stealing.

These men belonged to a gang of daring plunderers, who carried on their depredations with such effrontery that it was necessary to enact a law to bring them to punishment. Having blackened their faces they went in daytime to the parks of the nobility and gentry, whence they repeatedly stole deer, and at length murdered the Bishop of Winchester's keeper on Waltham Chase; and from the name of the place, and their blacking of their faces, they obtained the name of the 'Waltham Blacks'.

The following is the substance of the Act of Parliament on which they were convicted: 'After the first day of June 1723, any person appearing in the forest, chase, park, etc., or in any high road, open heath, common or down, with offensive weapon, and having his face blackened, or otherwise disguised, or unlawfully and wilfully hunting, wounding, killing or stealing any red or fallow deer, or unlawfully robbing any warren, etc., or stealing any fish out of any river or pond, or (whether armed or disguised or not) breaking down the head or mound of any fishpond, whereby the fish may be lost or destroyed; or unlawfully and maliciously killing, maiming or wounding any cattle, or cutting down or otherwise destroying any trees planted in any avenue, or growing in any garden, orchard or plantation, for ornament, shelter or profit; or setting fire to any house, barn or outhouse, hovel, cock-mow or stack of corn, straw, hay, or wood; or maliciously shooting at any person in any dwelling-house or other place; or knowingly sending any letter without any name, or signed with a fictitious name, demanding money, venison or other valuable thing, or forcibly rescuing any person being in custody for any of the offences before mentioned, or procuring any person by gift, or promise of money, or other reward, to join in any such unlawful act, or concealing or succouring such offenders when, by Order of Council, etc., required to surrender – Shall Suffer Death.'

Thus under these blanket laws the original 'Blacks of Waltham' were held in Newgate until their trial on 13 November 1723, where they were found guilty and sentenced to die on 4 December of the same year. One circumstance was very remarkable on this occasion: the judge had no sooner pronounced sentence, than Henry Marshall, who shot the keeper, was immediately struck dumb; nor did he recover his speech till the day before his death.

5 December

1831 (England) Although the crime of 'Burking' more properly relates to the iniquitous activities of the body-snatchers William Hare and William Burke (from whose name the term derives) it did, in a modified form, transfer to villains nationwide. Indeed, some turned the crime of 'Burking' into a trade mark; such a pair were John Bishop and Thomas Williams; and on 5 December 1831, they were hanged for it.

It was on Tuesday 8 November that Bishop and Williams, along with James May and Michael Shield were taken up on the charge and examined at Bow Street police station; the specific charge was the murder of an unnamed Italian youth. It appeared that May (for some reason known as 'Jack Stirabout' and a regular 'resurrection man') and Bishop, also well established in the trade of body-snatching, offered a subject for sale at King's College. Shield and Williams remained outside with the corpse in a hamper. The price was twelve guineas, and Mr Partridge, a lecturer in anatomy, offered nine. However, he was also struck with the freshness of the merchandise and let his fears be known to the police. Eventually Shield was discharged and the remaining three were committed for trial.

As early as eight o'clock on the morning of Friday 2 December the court was crowded to capacity. At nine the Deputy Recorder heard the prisoners' pleas of 'not guilty'. In his defence, Bishop admitted that, having failed in his occupation of carrier, he turned to the sale of corpses; he was, however, emphatic that he had never sold a body that had not died a natural death. It was, he said, a coincidence that on the day they were arrested he had merely met his co-defendants in a public-house. With the prisoners' reputations clearly in mind, the jury had no hesitation in finding all four men guilty of murder. The Recorder then passed sentence: 'That each of you be hanged, and your bodies delivered over for dissection and anatomisation.'

The following is a contemporary account of the execution:

> At half-past twelve o'clock the gallows was brought out from Newgate yard and pulled to its usual position opposite the Debtor's door. The unhappy convicts were then led from their cells and pinioned on the scaffold. All Williams's bold confidence had entirely forsaken him and he looked the most miserable wretch it is possible to conceive. The moment Bishop made his appearance he was greeted with the most dreadful yells and hootings by the crowd. The fateful preparations were completed, and in less than five minutes after the wretched men appeared on the scaffold the usual sign was given, the drop fell, and they were launched into eternity. Bishop appeared to die very soon, but Williams struggled hard. Thus died the dreadful Burkers of 1831.

6 December

1985 (USA) According to Carroll Cole, he had killed thirty-five women; 'loose women' he called them. And he thought it was because they reminded him of his mother: 'I think I kill her through them.' At any rate he wanted to die for his crimes. He demanded a non-jury hearing because he thought that judges were more likely to impose a capital penalty; and he was right. When Cole was sentenced to death for the murder of Marnie Cushman, he smiled and said, 'Thanks, judge.' He refused to appeal against sentence and was executed by lethal injection in Carson City, Nevada, on 6 December 1985.

The first of the killings was probably in San Diego in 1971 when Carroll Cole strangled Essie Louie Buck; although he was questioned about the incident at the time, no charges were ever brought. Then in Las Vegas in 1977 he strangled Kathlyn Blum in a parking lot. And in the summer of 1979 he strangled Bonnie O'Neil on the street. In both the latter cases Cole had undressed and sexually assaulted his victims after death.

On a return visit to Vegas in 1979, Carroll Cole murdered fifty-one-year-old Marnie Cushman in a hotel room; then on into Texas, where, on 11 November 1980, he strangled Dorothy King in her own home. On the following night Wanda Faye Roberts was strangled in a parking lot before Cole returned to Dorothy King's home and slept with her corpse.

This time Carroll Cole was identified as the man seen in a bar with Wanda Roberts just before her murder. Later in the month of November he strangled thirty-nine-year-old Sally Thompson, but neighbours in her apartment block heard noises and called the police. Incredibly, Cole was detained by the officers, but then released. It was only later, when he had been re-arrested, that Carroll Cole confessed to his horrific series of killings. He did apologise, though, for his vagueness of recollection; he was, he said, drunk most of the time.

In April 1981, Carroll Cole went on trial in Dallas for the three Texas killings. He pleaded insanity, and, perhaps to emphasise this defence, claimed that he had cannibalised one of the Oklahoma victims while dismembering her body. Cole was convicted on all counts of murder, but a penalty hearing jury voted against the death sentence.

It was when he was extradited to Nevada to face a second trial in Las Vegas that Carroll Cole asked for the big one. Pleaded that he wanted to die . . . And he did.

7 December

1811 (England) Two of London's most notorious murders were committed on 7 and 19 December 1811, and involved the virtual decimation of two families by an assassin named John Williams. They enjoyed celebrity not only for the sheer awfulness of the crimes, and for the manner of Williams' disposal, but because Thomas de Quincey, that *aficionado* of opium and the English murder, praised them in his essay 'On Murder as a Fine Art'.

The first of the killing sprees took place on a Saturday night in the Ratcliff Highway, then and now a seedy part of east London, which was the home of the family of John Marr. Marr kept a small hosier's shop in which he had invested what meagre savings he had, and with Mrs Marr and their baby lived in cramped quarters below the business. There was also an apprentice to Marr's trade living in, an enthusiastic boy of thirteen from Devon, and a servant named Mary, who was also companion to Mrs Marr. On the night in question, Mary had been sent on an errand to buy oysters for the family's supper, but when she returned, could gain no admittance to the house. Worried, the girl called a neighbour who entered by a back way and passed into the shop, 'and there beheld the carnage of the night stretched out on the floor'; the whole family including the baby had been battered, slashed and stabbed to death in an orgy of bloodletting beyond comparison.

The next infamy was committed on the nineteenth of the same month when the elderly publican of the King's Arms, Gravel Lane, his wife and their ageing maidservant were similarly dispatched by the same hand. However, this time the killer had been careless and left behind him a sailor's maul, or mallet, which was traced to the Pear Tree tavern and thence to one of its habitués, John Williams.

Williams aroused sufficient suspicion that he was taken into custody and remanded in Coldbath Fields Prison where he cheated justice and the executioner by hanging himself from a beam in his cell. On the last day of 1811 the remains of Williams were, according to the custom with suicides, carried in a cart to the crossroads at Cannon Street where, between twelve o'clock and one, he was cast into the grave, and a stake driven through his heart before the pit was covered.

8 December

1987 (Australia) At 4.20 p.m. on Tuesday 8 December 1987, a man dressed in blue jeans and an army-style jacket drove a red station wagon into the side street beside Melbourne's Australian Telecom tower; there was nothing strange in that, except that the man was cradling a high-powered rifle as he ran five floors up a fire escape to the offices of a credit union company. Entering the offices, the gunman began by arguing with a male office worker; then, quite suddenly and without any warning, he raised the rifle and began firing indiscriminately around the room. Terrified office staff threw themselves in the direction of whatever shelter they could find, behind filing cabinets, under desks. One woman said later: 'He was screaming at everyone to lie flat on the ground.' The gunman then ran from floor to floor shooting wildly at anyone he saw. On one landing, he stopped as a lift opened and shot dead four people inside. A woman survivor in the lift told police: 'He shot down four of my friends right in front of me. He looked at me and I thought he was going to kill me, too. It was awful.' Awful indeed.

Eventually, on the tenth floor, the wild assassin was tackled and disarmed by the concerted efforts of a security officer and one of the male clerks. However, in a final desperate bid for self-destruction, the gunman hurled himself through a window but was saved from instant death on the street below by the quick-thinking security guard who grabbed his legs. With the strength of desperation the struggling killer kicked out and broke free, still shouting and cursing as he plummeted 130 feet to his death. An eyewitness said: 'He obviously wanted to die. Half of his body was dangling below the railing and somebody was trying to hold him by the ankles. Suddenly he hollered and fell to the ground.'

Eight office workers, including five women, died at the hands of the gunman, who was identified as Frank Vitkovic, a twenty-two-year-old student. It had been the second mass killing in the city of Melbourne within a few months.

9 December

1932 (Australia) This was the day on which Eric Roland Craig picked up thirty-year-old prostitute May Miller in a car that he had earlier stolen from Sydney's city centre. The woman directed him to a 'lovers' lane' near to the Centennial Park in the suburb of Paddington, where she demanded five shillings and started to take her clothes off. Craig, unemployed at the time, replied that he did not have five shillings. Miss Miller, after a spirited bout of cursing, attacked him. In response Craig picked up the broken branch of a fig tree lying nearby, and beat her head to a pulp. He then stripped the body and dragged it into the bushes before gathering up the victim's clothes, knotting them together in a bundle and dumping them on the roadside.

Five days later Eric Craig stole another car and picked up sixteen-year-old Bessie O'Connor, a well-known New South Wales swimming champion, and drove her to the Sydney National Park. The next morning Bessie was found naked and almost dead from a series of terrible head wounds, thought to have been inflicted with an axe. As in the case of May Miller, her clothes were later found knotted together in a clump of bushes close to the scene of the killing. Bessie O'Connor died in hospital without regaining consciousness, and a special murder squad was assembled. An observant detective on the team noticed that the knot used to tie up the clothes was the same as that used in the May Miller case; it was a knot familiar to artillerymen. The first obvious step was to make a check of serving soldiers at the large barracks in Victoria district, close to where the two stolen cars had been abandoned. When these inquiries proved negative, the search was widened to include former soldiers; it was then that witnesses identified Eric Craig as the man seen with the victims shortly before the killings.

Under interrogation, Craig admitted the murder of May Miller, but denied responsibility for the death of Bessie O'Connor. He was tried first for the Miller murder, found guilty on the lesser charge of manslaughter on grounds of provocation, and sentenced to twenty years.

Craig then faced three further trials, all arising from the killing of Bessie O'Connor. Twice the jury failed to agree on a verdict, and on the third occasion Eric Craig was found guilty and sentenced to death. On 19 September 1933, the capital sentence was commuted to life imprisonment without the possibility of remission.

Although Eric Craig never admitted any crime other than the murder of May Miller, police recalled that in 1932 another prostitute, named Hilda White, had been found dead in a park in Paddington; she had been strangled and stripped, and some of her clothing had been tied together with a now familiar knot . . .

10 December

1913 (England) The evening of 10 December 1913 was as cold, dark and windy as that winter month can be, and for ship's steward Walter Eaves it must have seemed even colder standing waiting for his dilatory lady-friend on Liverpool's Oldhall Street. Suddenly his thoughts were interrupted by a sharp rap on the head. From the door of John Bradfield's tarpaulin shop a wooden shutter had detached itself, fallen, and struck Mr Eaves on the head as it descended. It was his bowler hat that saved Eaves's head, but nothing had saved the bowler hat, and when a youth darted out of the shop to recover the shutter, an indignant Eaves spared no words in defence of the luckless hat. The youth ran back into the shop and in his place an older young man emerged, sympathised and pressed two shillings into Mr Eaves's hand by way of compensation. Shortly afterwards the ship's steward saw both men emerge from the shop pushing a heavily laden hand-cart. They all exchanged polite words again – mainly concerning the 'dinted' hat – and all parties returned to their own business.

On the following morning John Bradfield, Tarpaulins, was still closed after its customary opening time of 8.30. In fact it had been a matter of pride that John's sister Christina always opened on the dot. Miss Venables the typist arrived to find the two shop boys in charge – Samuel Elltoft and George Ball.

At midday in another part of town, a barge-master had just hooked a tarpaulin bundle out of a lock. It contained half a hundredweight of old iron, a corset, sundry other female garments, a battered umbrella and the even more battered body of Christina Bradfield.

It did not take the police long to connect Elltoft and Ball with the crime. Sam Elltoft was immediately apprehended, and a photograph of his accomplice was published in the press along with a description. On Saturday 20 December, George Ball found he could not resist the Everton versus Chelsea football match at Goodison Park. Football mania? Bravado? Just sheer stupidity? He never said, but it must have crossed even George's mind that somebody among the thousands of spectators would recognise him. And they did; and it eventually cost George Ball his life – on the scaffold at Walton Prison. The jury simply did not believe in the mysterious stranger who had broken into the shop, killed Miss Bradfield and forced the shop boys to dispose of her body. And why should they have? As for Sam Elltoft, he was convicted as an accessory and served four years in prison.

11 December

1759 (England) In which it will be learnt that on this date a gentleman in his seventy-fifth year was hanged for the murder of a child twenty-five years before.

We will not dwell on the profligate life led by William Andrew Horne prior to his having criminal connection with his own sister. This sister was delivered of a boy in February 1724, and Horne persuaded his brother Charles to take a ride with him three days after the birth, when they put the new-born babe in a bag and carried it in turns on the ride to Annesley, in Nottinghamshire, where William dismounted and took the child into a field where he placed it behind a haystack and covered it with hay. On the following morning the child was found dead, through severity of the weather.

It so happened that these brothers were somewhat quarrelsome, and following one incident brother Charles confided his dreadful secret to their father. The latter, perhaps wisely, advised against mentioning the subject again. Whereupon Charles Horne ignored his father's advice and acquainted a magistrate with the facts of the matter; he too hesitated to take notice and, as it had happened so long ago, advised that it might remain a secret. Thus no more was said until the year 1754, when Charles, being seized with a violent fit of illness, and presuming that he should live but a short time, said he could not die in peace without disclosing his secret; thus he summoned a Mr White of Ripley and told his tale. Mr White, like those before him, said that it was not proper for him to interfere in the affair. It happened that Charles Horne recovered most remarkably – which he attributed to his easing his mind of its dread secret.

Some considerable time after this, William Horne got into

a quarrel with another gentleman, named Roe, at a public-house, during which Horne was called an 'incestuous old dog'. Whereupon Horne successfully prosecuted him, and made a great enemy. Roe, after questioning Charles Horne went himself to a magistrate and had a warrant sworn, on the understanding that Charles Horne would give evidence against his brother. Charles approached his brother and suggested a pact that in exchange for five pounds he would go to Liverpool and be silent. William, greedy as he was, refused.

Before long the man Roe with a constable went to the house of William Horne in search of him. Although it appeared that he was not home, Roe became suspicious of a large linen trunk – which was found to contain William Horne. Thereupon he was taken into custody and committed by the magistrates to appear before the next assizes. On 10 August 1759, Horne was brought to trial before Lord Chief Baron Parker, and after a hearing of nine hours, the jury found him guilty, and sentence of death was passed. On the day appointed for his execution he had just completed his seventy-fourth year.

12 December

1913 (England) Charles Burnham could hardly believe his eyes when he saw the account of an inquest reported in the *News of the World*. A certain Mrs Margaret Lloyd had died very unexpectedly in her bath shortly after her wedding. That was exactly what had happened to Burnham's daughter Alice, on 12 December 1913. And if Mr Burnham had not noticed this story, or had not acted on it, then one of England's most heartless, most cynical killers may have remained at large to strike again. As it was, George Joseph Smith, the notorious 'Brides in the Bath' killer, disposed of three unwanted spouses in watery graves, and plundered the worldly goods of a further four bigamously married 'wives'.

Smith's first murder victim (as far as we know) was Bessie Mundy, whom he married using the name Henry Williams, at Weymouth in 1910. They separated after Smith had relieved her of £2,500, but got together again at Herne Bay in 1912. Bessie must have come into some money by then, because Smith (or 'Williams') thought it was worthwhile drowning her for it. The autopsy verdict was one of drowning during an epileptic fit. Then there was poor Alice Burnham; this time Smith married in his own name, at Blackpool. The murder, again in the bath, gained Smith £140 plus life insurance of £500. Cause of death was attributed to accidental drowning.

George Joseph Smith (or John Lloyd as he was calling himself now) married Margaret Lofty on 17 December 1914 – at Bath! They immediately returned to London, where Smith first dragged Margaret to the local doctor and told some cock and bull story about her having blackouts, then drowned her in the bath and attributed it to one of her fainting fits. After the inquest had found that Mrs Lloyd's death was due to a tragic accident, Smith collected the life insurance, emptied her savings account and slipped quietly away. Unfortunately for Smith (or whatever name he was using at the time) Mr Burnham was already making his suspicions known to the police.

Because at his trial Smith offered a defence of accidental death it was, under English law, permissible for the Crown to introduce evidence of the other drownings in order to prove what is called in legal terms 'system'. In other words, the first time a new bride drowns in her bath it is tragic; the second time it is suspicious; the third time it begins to look like murder. It certainly did to the jury, because it took them only twenty-two minutes to convict him. Friday the thirteenth proved a very unlucky day for George Joseph Smith – on that date in August 1915 they hanged him.

13 December

1867 (England) In England the 1860s saw an increase in the activities of a vociferous Irish Republican movement spearheaded by the secret Fenian Brotherhood. They had already been successful in rescuing two Fenian prisoners from a police van in Manchester. This gave them the confidence to attempt an even bigger coup, the rescue of Richard O'Sullivan Burke and Joseph Casey from Clerkenwell Prison in London.

At 3.45 on the afternoon of 13 December 1867, dynamite was placed against the wall of the prison. An attempt had been made the previous day, but the fuse failed to take. A wagon brought a large cask of explosive up to the wall, a white ball was thrown into the air to warn the prisoners in the exercise yard, and the fuse was lit. Unfortunately for the would-be rescuers the police had got wind of the plot and the two prisoners had been moved elsewhere. A huge explosion pierced the wall, but also devastated a block of tenements opposite. Six people were killed instantly, six more died later and 120 were injured. Because of the time of day all the victims were women and children.

Five men and one woman were quickly arrested and brought for trial before Lord Chief Justice Cockburn and Baron Bramwell at the Old Bailey. They were tried on a sample charge of the murder of Sarah Ann Hodgkinson, one of the victims. The main defendant was Michael Barrett, who was accused of actually lighting the fuse; two of the other defendants turned Queen's evidence against him. The woman who had been arrested tried to hang herself in her cell and was acquitted for lack of evidence. Barratt continued to maintain his innocence, and took the opportunity to treat the court to a polemic on Irish liberty: 'If it is murder to love Ireland more deeply than life, then indeed I am a murderer . . .'

The outcome of the trial was a foregone conclusion, and

the execution of Michael Barrett was set for 26 May 1868 at Newgate Prison. Large crowds gathered to witness the spectacle. Barrett's proud and noble demeanour in the face of death earned hushed respect from the spectators, and when the trap-door fell Barrett's body did not so much as shudder.

The hanging of Michael Barrett was the last public execution to be carried out in Britain. Three days after Barrett suffered the ultimate sanction the Capital Punishment Act was given royal assent. Henceforth executions in Britain would be carried out within the privacy of prison walls.

14 December

1987 (USA) In what was called the 'Christmas tree massacre', Virgil Knight, of Oklahoma, having lost the custody battle for his three children went on a rampage during which he shot dead five people, including his ex-wife and two of his children. Knight then turned the gun on himself, and when police officers arrived they found him lying beneath the Christmas tree surrounded by the bodies of his family.

15 December

1882 (Ireland) On Friday 15 December 1882, three men, Patrick and Myles Joyce and Patrick Casey fell victim to the public hangman William Marwood at Galway Prison. It was not one of Marwood's more conspicuous successes, and resulted in Myles Joyce (who was probably innocent anyway) dying from slow strangulation.

The case that had brought these men to such a tragic end began in the early hours of 18 August 1882, when John Joyce, his wife Bridget, mother Margaret, daughter Margaret and sons Michael and Patrick were attacked in their home at Maamtrasna in the West of Ireland. Joyce, his wife, mother and daughter were already dead when villagers entered the house on the following morning. The two boys were still alive although seriously injured, and Michael died not long afterwards in hospital. Two of the victims had been shot and four had been savagely beaten with blunt instruments and horribly disfigured.

Before dying, young Michael was able to give detectives descriptions of the murderers. A neighbouring farmer also recalled seeing a party of men, all known to him, heading along the road to Maamtrasna on the night of the murders. This information led to thirteen arrests. In the end ten men were charged with murder, four of whom were cousins of the victims from a branch of the family with whom they had been feuding for some time.

On Wednesday 1 November, all ten men stood before Mr Justice Barry and pleaded not guilty. The hearing was adjourned until 13 November, when it was announced that the defendants would be tried separately, and the first case to be heard was that against Patrick Joyce. Meanwhile, two men had elected to turn Queen's evidence and testify against the others; what were known as 'approvers'. At the end of the trial, after a retirement of just eight minutes, the jury returned a verdict of guilty and Patrick Joyce was sentenced to death. Following Patrick Joyce into the dock was Patrick Casey, and a similar case followed resulting in a verdict of guilty after only twelve minutes' deliberation; Casey was also sentenced to death. The third trial, that of Myles Joyce, commenced on Friday 17 November, the jury returning after a record six minutes with another verdict of guilty. The remaining defendants decided to change their pleas to guilty, and as in the other cases all five were sentenced to death.

It was (indeed it still is) an unwritten understanding that defendants who plead guilty and thus save court time, effort and expense, will be treated more leniently; so it was that three Joyces and two Caseys had their sentences commuted to penal servitude for life. Of the three remaining men, both Patrick Joyce and Patrick Casey made statements insisting that Myles Joyce was innocent of any part in the murders – not that it made any difference.

16 December

1924 (England) This was the night on which James Doyle, a young miner, was out with his fiancée on the edge of Doncaster cricket ground, a popular place for young couples to go to do the sort of things young couples do. Which made it the ideal spot for peeping toms to do the sort of things peeping toms do. Albert Needham, a collier, and his pal Wilfred Thrussle were peeping toms. In fact it was by way of being a hobby with them, equipped with flashlamps and rubber knee pads – so that they could creep about more quietly. It so happened that Albert and Wilf were pursuing their hobby on the same night and in the same place that Jimmy Doyle and his companion were pursuing theirs.

In mid-embrace, young James heard a scuffling movement from behind the boundary wall. Guessing that they were peeping toms, but fearing the worst, Doyle leapt to his feet and took out the knife he carried with him for just such emergencies. In the scuffle which followed he managed to push that knife twice into Albert Needham's body. Needham, fatally wounded, staggered back crying: 'My God Wilf, he's done it!' He then collapsed to the ground and died.

Such was the sympathy for young Doyle in his predicament at being charged with murder, that his workmates and other well-wishers subscribed to a fund for his defence. It is perhaps a measure of that support, that the sum gathered was sufficient to retain the services of the most eminent criminal lawyer of his day, Sir Edward Marshall Hall KC. At James Doyle's trial before Mr Justice Branson at the Leeds Assizes on 25 March 1925, he pleaded self-defence. Marshall Hall, with his usual silver tongue, described to the jury in graphic terms, how this young man, angry at the vulgar activities of Needham and Thrussle, and finding himself outnumbered, had drawn his weapon because he feared for the safety of himself and his fiancée. It is a fitting tribute to the eloquence of the master, that Jimmy Doyle was acquitted of both murder *and* manslaughter, and was, to general public approval, discharged.

17 December

1708 (England) Madam Churchill, convicted along with three men of a foul murder, nevertheless faced the hangman alone, on 17 December 1708.

> Deborah Churchill, though born of honest parents who gave her a good education and brought her up in the ways of religion and good manners, decided to throw off these things and abandon herself to all manner of filthiness and uncleanliness, which afterwards proved her shame and ruin. She had been married twice – once to an army ensign, and again to a man she met in the Fleet Prison – when she began to keep the company of Bully Hunt, a Lifeguardsman. The couple lived for seven years together in a lascivious and adulterous manner; she also keeping company with one Thomas Smith, a cooper, who was eventually hanged at Tyburn for housebreaking.
>
> Deborah Churchill was committed to New Prison for picking a gentleman's pocket of a purse wherein there was a hundred and four guineas. Whilst she was there she seemed full of piety. She at last got out of this mansion of sorrow, but soon forgetting her afflictions she pursued her wickedness continually, till she had been sent no less than twenty times to Clerkenwell Bridewell, where she was whipped and kept beating

hemp from morning to night for a small allowance of bread and water, which just kept life and soul together. Yet let what punishment would light on this common strumpet, she was no changeling, for as soon as she was out of jail she ran into still greater evils.

One night, along Drury Lane, in company with Richard Hunt, William Lewis and John Boy, they fell out with one Martin Were, and she bidding her companions sacrifice the man, they killed him in Vinegar Yard. The three men who committed this murder made their escape, but she, being apprehended as an accessory was condemned for it on 26 February 1708. However, she was given a respite on account of her being thought to be with child; which she only pretended to be to put off her death for some time. But when she had lain under sentence of death for ten months and was found not to be with child, she was called to her former judgement. Then, being conveyed in a coach to Tyburn, on Friday 17 December 1708, she was there hanged, in the thirty-first year of her age.

(*The Newgate Calendar*)

18 December

1974 (USA) Jealousy had been the motivating force in the Housdens' marriage since the occasion of their wedding. It had got steadily worse until, in 1974, Charles Housden could stand it no more. He had had more than enough of the suspicion, the persistent accusations, and the spying on him while he worked driving one of Detroit's city buses. It would not have been so bad if there had been even a grain of truth in it, but it would have been all but impossible to find a more loyal, more faithful husband than Charlie Housden. So he moved out and filed for divorce. The worm, which is what a lot of people thought Charlie had become, had turned. His wife Nina turned too; she turned even more spiteful, even more resentful. Of course, she *knew* he had flown into the arms of another woman – or at least she thought she did – and if Nina couldn't have him for a punch-bag, then no other little schemer was going to.

On 18 December 1974, just days before the divorce was due to be made absolute, Nina Housden invited her husband back to their former matrimonial home at Highland Park; just a drink, for old times' sake. Then having got Charlie incapably drunk (in fact he was unconscious), Nina strangled him with a length of washing line. After carefully rolling back the carpet and covering the floor with a thick layer of newspaper, she began to chop his body into manageable portions with a meat cleaver. Then she wrapped the bits up in cheerful Christmas paper and loaded them on to the back seat of her car.

It was Nina Housden's bad luck that the car, previously so reliable, chose to break down outside Toledo, Texas. When she took it to a garage, the mechanic reckoned it should be fixed in a couple of days; and if he was surprised that Nina insisted on camping out on the front seat till the job was done, then he said nothing. What did upset him, though, was the smell coming from the back of the vehicle. In fact he did say something about that, something about it stinking out his repair shop. Nina sweetly explained that she was taking some parcels of venison to her family for Christmas; and that if it was beginning to go off, then it was his fault for taking so damned long over fixing the car. Late that night, while Nina was grunting and snoring across the front seats, the mechanic took a peek into one of the gaily wrapped parcels. Then wished that he hadn't. The dismembered human leg was decomposing rapidly.

Incorrigible to the last, following her conviction and sentence to life imprisonment, Nina Housden is said to have told newsmen: 'Charlie wasn't a bad egg. He just made the mistake of running around with other women.'

19 December

1765 (Ireland) On 19 December 1765 Peter McKinlie, George Gridley, Richard St Quentin and Andrew Zekerman were executed and their bodies later hung in chains as a grim reminder to all who passed through Dublin's fair city of the wages of sin; in this case mutiny and piracy.

In many ways there was a kind of justice in the crimes, for the ship involved was a privateer – one of those heavily armoured vessels manned by government-licensed pirates to plunder foreign ships on the high seas. Captain Glass was one of the most successful privateers and this ship had been chartered to take his ill-gotten treasure back to England. What he did not know was that a plot was being hatched by members of the crew to murder everybody on board except each other and snatch the treasure.

McKinlie, Gridley, St Quentin and Zekerman made their bid for the ship on 13 November when the vessel reached the mouth of the Bristol Channel. At around midnight the master was attacked and killed; two seamen hearing the commotion came up on the quarter-deck and were swiftly murdered and their bodies thrown overboard. The swash-buckling Captain Glass, meanwhile, had taken up his sword and engaged the conspirators in spirited combat, though by sheer strength of numbers they overpowered and slew him with his own sword. As to Mrs Glass and her innocent daughter, they were simply tossed into the sea. These black-hearted villains then set sail for the Irish coast. On 3 December the vessel lay at the mouth of the river Ross, where they loaded the longboat with their spoils, and after scuttling the ship rowed for shore, leaving two apprentice boys on board to drown. One of the lads swam out to the longboat but was struck by Zekerman with such force that the unhappy boy sank straight below the waves.

These murderous mariners landed on Ireland's shore and in the town of Ross sold off some of their ill-gotten booty before travelling on in the direction of Dublin. Meantime the wreck had washed up off Fishertown where suspicion had already been aroused by the behaviour of McKinlie and his crew as they passed noisily through, and a message was sent ahead to Dublin to have them detained. McKinlie and Zekerman were arrested together and interrogated until they confessed and obligingly implicated Gridley and St Quentin, who had left Dublin for Cork where they meant to seek passage on a craft bound for England. They were arrested at an inn near Cork and with a little persuasion made their own confessions.

20 December

1946 (USA) Joe Medley didn't like redheads; which need not have been a problem, a lot of people aren't keen. But Joe *did* have a problem, he *really* didn't like them; and on 20 December 1946, it cost him his life. Medley was a professional criminal of a very versatile kind, able to turn his hand to most forms of dishonesty, though robbery he found the most rewarding. In fact it was for armed robbery that he came to be in prison, and had he not escaped, he would have been looking at between thirty and sixty years there.

When Joe emerged into the world again he was a changed man; not in that normal sense that prison hardens and desensitises, but in that he had a deep-seated neurosis – he simply could not stand redheaded women. In fact he built an entirely new reputation on killing them.

It was in New Orleans that Medley met twenty-eight-year-old redhead Laura Fischer. On Christmas Eve 1944, Laura's body was found in a hotel bathtub. She had drowned, but a subsequent post-mortem examination failed to discover any signs of violence that might have indicated foul play. By this time Joe Medley was long gone, heading towards Chicago – where he checked into a hotel with another redhead, Blanche Zimmerman. Blanche was found on 17 February 1945. Like

Laura Fischer, Blanche was dead in a tub of water. The fact that her body contained no small quantity of drugs and alcohol at the time contributed to the coroner's jury returning a verdict of accidental death.

In Washington next, Medley became acquainted with fifty-year-old redhead Nancy Boyer. No baths this time; Nancy was found shot dead on the floor of the kitchen in her apartment. It was March 1945, and Joe Medley would soon be no further threat to redheads.

The FBI had traced Joe to St Louis, where he was arrested in possession of some of Mrs Boyer's belongings. Extradited back to Washington, he was charged with her first-degree murder, and on 7 June 1945, he was sentenced to death. On the morning of 3 April 1946, while still patiently waiting his turn on the corridors of Death Row, Joe Medley and a fellow-prisoner, Earl McFarland, broke out. Joe Medley was on the loose again. But not for long. Perhaps he had lost his touch; perhaps he was unlucky, because a brief eight hours later he was picked up almost in view of the prison. McFarland was also rearrested a week later and brought back to jail just in time to keep his appointment with the executioner.

Joe Medley didn't have long to wait either; he died in the electric chair on 20 December 1946.

21 December

1908 (Scotland) In the year 1908, the first-floor apartment at 15 Queen's Terrace, Glasgow, was occupied by a maiden lady named Marion Gilchrist and her servant, Helen Lambie. Miss Gilchrist had been a tenant there for thirty years, and Helen had been with her for three. It was customary for Helen Lambie to go out each evening at about seven o'clock to fetch the evening newspaper and any shopping that was needed. On 21 December there was no variation to this pattern until Helen returned to find that the front door was open and standing on the landing outside Miss Gilchrist's door was Mr Adams, a neighbour from the flat below. Adams had apparently heard a noise and, as he had arranged some time ago had come to check that everything was in order. As Helen Lambie was opening the flat door a man rushed past them and down the stairs into the street. In the living room Miss Gilchrist lay dead in front of the fireplace, her head and face savagely battered.

Although a description based on the man seen by Mr Arthur Adams and Helen Lambie was circulated, it was not until the evening of Christmas Day that there was any definite clue to work on. It had been brought to the notice of the police that a German Jew calling himself Oscar Slater was endeavouring to dispose of a pawn ticket for a crescent-shaped diamond brooch. The brooch exactly matched one stolen from Miss Gilchrist. To add to their suspicions, when police visited Slater's lodgings he had already left Glasgow for New York aboard the *Lusitania*. On his arrival, Oscar Slater was arrested, his baggage was impounded, and he agreed to return voluntarily to Glasgow.

On 3 May 1909, he stood trial at the Edinburgh High Court charged with Miss Marion Gilchrist's murder. But the bottom had already fallen out of the case against Slater. For a start, although the crescent brooch was like that stolen from Marion Gilchrist's flat, it was one that Oscar Slater had owned for many years – and had pawned many times over those years. And as for his 'sudden guilty flight' to America, it was proved that his immigration papers had been arranged long before the murder. But that did not stop a jury convicting this patently innocent man and a judge sentencing him to death. Thankfully Scottish justice was saved the ultimate shame of hanging an innocent man, though Oscar Slater spent the next eighteen years in Peterhead Gaol. It was only due to the tireless campaign launched by Sir Arthur Conan Doyle that eventually a court of appeal quashed the sentence, and Oscar Slater was awarded £6,000 for wrongful imprisonment and the anguish suffered while under sentence of death. He died in 1948.

22 December

1697 (England)

Executed on 22 December 1697, was a highwayman named John Shorter, of about thirty years of age. Whilst this fellow was in Newgate, about two years before, he had designed, with some other malefactors to have seized on the waiters at Newgate, and to have burned Mr Tofield's papers, the notary then in the lodge of the prison; withall designing to wrest the officers' arms from them, and to fire upon them if they opposed. They further designed to have bound the officers as they came one day from the chapel, and if they made the least opposition to have cut their throats; and that after their escape they would go on the highways, take travellers' horses and, mounting them, would ride off. Moreover they had agreed that if anyone knocked at the lodge under the gate they would let them in and bind them also, and then lock them up with the officers in the dungeon or condemned hold.

One of these confederates being a smith, he was to have been employed in knocking off the others' fetters; and if the turnkeys had any money in their pockets they would take it from them, to carry themselves off and buy provisions. And if the trained bands, or the mob, should come to seize them, they would fire upon them with the officers' blunderbusses, and would be masters of the prison till the King should send them a pardon, or else they would be starved or shot to death.

Shorter not only confessed this crime, but also owned he knew of the murderer of one Lorimer, in Newgate, but was prevailed upon by one Tokefield, and John Hart, not to discover it; he further said that the latter of these persons carried the bloody knife three days in his pocket; and he verily believed that the day before he suffered death himself at the gallows he saw Lorimer's ghost as he was at prayers in the chapel of Newgate, which put him into a great consternation, as was visibly observed by Mr Smith, the ordinary.

Thomas Randol was one of the persons concerned with Shorter in this conspiracy. This offender was executed on Wednesday 22 January 1695, for the murder of Robert Stevens, a Quaker. He was conveyed in a cart to the deceased's door, in Whitechapel, and from thence to Stone Bridge, by Kingsland, where, after he was dead, his body hanged in chains on the gibbet he suffered on, and continued there till it was consumed by the weather.'

(*The Malefactors' Register*)

23 December

1900 (England) It was all to do with that damned pig! Here he was facing trial for murder, and it was all the pig's fault. Why couldn't they let him forget it? John Edward Casey was standing in the dock at the Norwich Assizes, charged that, on the night of 23 December 1900, he murdered Mrs Thirza Isabella Kelly, a young widow whose husband had lost his life during the Boer War. After the tragedy, she had gone to live at Stokesby, just outside the herring port of Great Yarmouth. Seventeen-year-old Casey lived in the village with his parents, and from the first time he saw her, John Edward became infatuated with Mrs Kelly, though they had never spoken to each other.

On the evening of 23 December, Casey had been drinking with friends in the local pub, the Horse Shoes. In fact they had been drinking rather more than perhaps they should, because his companions began to tease Casey about the pig. It turned out not to have been wise to mention the pig, and after bursting into a fit of uncontrollable sobbing, John Casey left the Horse Shoes and headed for Mrs Kelly's cottage. He broke in through a window and went up to where Mrs Kelly was sleeping with her baby. When Casey crept into the room, the terrified woman woke suddenly and jumped out of bed. A struggle followed in which Mrs Kelly was stabbed no fewer than seven times; barely alive, she managed to crawl back on to the bed where she was found on the following morning, still just this side of death, by her mother. Mrs Kelly only had time to describe the attack to the police before she died.

And that is how John Casey comes to be facing a jury. A jury who is at this very moment being told by Casey's medical witness about the pig. It seems that a couple of years before the murder, Casey had broken into his employer's home and stolen some women's underwear. He had dressed in the garments and then dragged a pig in from the yard and slaughtered it, scattering bits of the carcase around the house. What was left of the animal, Casey dressed in the underwear he had worn, and suspended it from the living-room ceiling. It was the belief of the Superintendent of the Norfolk Lunatic Asylum that Casey's perversion demonstrated 'an intense sensual pleasure in killing creatures and shedding blood'. And the jury agreed that this was exactly what had happened to Mrs Kelly; however, they would not accept the claim that he was insane at the time. Convicted of murder, John Edward Casey was sentenced to death by the Lord Chief Justice, Lord Alverstone. In consideration of his youth, Casey was later reprieved and sentenced to penal servitude for life.

24 December

1975 (USA) It was around 9.15 p.m. on Christmas Eve 1975 when Theodore Van Deventer, a West Orange County,

Florida, judge was sharing a Christmas drink with chief of police Don Ficke that the telephone rang. 'It's Tommy Zeigler,' a voice said. 'I'm hurt.' When Ficke took over the call, Zeigler told him he was at the family store and had been shot. The police chief summoned a team of officers and they drove straight to the Zeigler furniture store at 1010 South Dillard Street where they found the shop in darkness and Zeigler wounded. Before he was removed to hospital in an ambulance, William 'Tommy' Zeigler told Chief Ficke: 'It was Charlie Mays.' By this time the police had restored the power supply which had been turned off at the main switch. The light revealed blood everywhere and four bodies.

Zeigler's mother-in-law, Virginia Edwards, was lying near the front of the shop, shot in the chest and head. His wife Eunice had been shot in the back of the head. Father-in-law Perry Edwards' body lay by some linoleum racks, battered and shot through the head. Finally there was Charlie Mays, a local black community leader; he had also been shot and bludgeoned.

At first, the police thought the motive for the killings was robbery. William Zeigler's wound was less serious than it looked, and police were able to interview him in hospital on the following day. According to his statement, Zeigler returned to the store in the evening and found Ed Williams, who did part-time carpentry for the business, waiting outside; they had gone in together by the back entrance. Suddenly he was attacked from behind by at least two men, one of whom was bigger than himself, and black. During the fight which followed Zeigler pulled out a gun and tried to fire it at his assailant. Then he himself was shot.

Police put out a call for the apprehension of Ed Williams, but before he could be brought in he surrendered himself. Williams agreed that he had been at the store with Zeigler; they had met outside as his boss had said, but Zeigler had gone in through the front entrance while Williams was told to make his way around the back. When Williams got into the back of the shop Zeigler had tried to shoot him; luckily the gun had jammed and the handyman had made off.

Forensic tests later established that the bullets which killed Mr and Mrs Edwards had come from a .38 recently bought by Zeigler, and all twenty bullets fired during the incident that night had come from one or other of the eight guns later found there – all of them owned by William Zeigler. For good measure it was discovered that two months previously, Tommy Zeigler had taken out two insurance policies on his wife's life each for $520,000.

On 29 December William Zeigler was charged with two counts of first-degree murder relating to the deaths of Eunice Zeigler and Charles Mays, and two counts of second-degree murder in the deaths of Perry and Virginia Edwards. At the trial a reconstruction of the crime convinced the jury sufficiently to return a verdict of guilty. Although a penalty hearing jury recommended a life sentence, Circuit Judge Maurice M. Paul felt less benevolent, and sentenced Zeigler to death. The Florida Supreme Court dismissed his appeal, and on 22 March 1982 the United States Supreme Court also refused his appeal. At the time of writing William 'Tommy' Zeigler is still on Death Row in Florida State Prison.

25 December

1980 (Canada) It was on Christmas Day that the first of serial killer Clifford Olson's victims was found. The badly mutilated body of twelve-year-old Christine Weller was discovered in Vancouver; in spring the following year a thirteen-year-old went missing from the same area, and another body, that of Darren Johnsrud was found in some woodland. In the end, Olson would claim the lives of eleven young people before he was arrested. Most bizarre of all was that he demanded $10,000 per corpse to identify the last resting places of four of his victims – stranger still, the Attorney-General authorised the payment.

26 December

1948 (England) Harry Michaelson was one of the last of that breed of 'variety' entertainers who were so popular in the latter days of the music hall, but never quite survived the change from live entertainment to television. His stage name was 'One Minute Michaelson', and he was a lightning cartoonist.

In the early hours of 26 December 1948, Harry was found fatally injured at the door of his basement flat in London's Paddington district. The door was open and it later became clear that Harry Michaelson had been attacked inside the apartment, in the bedroom, and had managed to stagger out in search of help (Mrs Michaelson was spending a few days with family). He died in hospital without regaining consciousness.

Police later found an open window through which it was assumed the intruder entered, woke Harry Michaelson, who confronted him in the dark and was attacked. The weapon that had been used was a tubular steel chair, on which a single fingerprint was discovered. It was at a time when the identification of single prints was a relatively new science, and it was several weeks before Scotland Yard got the break they so desperately needed. A twenty-one-year-old Welshman named Harry Lewis, a thief by trade, was seen acting suspiciously in St John's Wood, and was taken in for questioning. He was routinely fingerprinted, and one of those prints was seen to match the single print on the chair that killed Harry Michaelson.

Confronted with this indisputable evidence, Harry Lewis made a full confession. According to his statement he had been wandering the streets, homeless and penniless, when he saw an open window and decided to climb in and help himself. Lewis managed to creep into the bedroom, and was in the act of dipping his hand into the pocket of Harry Michaelson's trousers, when their owner awoke and startled him. In panic, the intruder set about him with the heaviest object to hand – the chair. Net gain: £5 8*s* 9*d*.

Harry Lewis was tried at the Old Bailey on 7 March 1949. His defence was that it was not the beating that he gave Harry Michaelson that killed him, but the hospital treatment that he received! It was a suggestion refuted scientifically by a senior pathologist, but it is probably true to say that the jury had made up their own minds about that story. Harry Lewis was found guilty; the recommendation to mercy was not endorsed by the Home Secretary, and Harry Lewis was executed at Pentonville Prison on 21 April 1949.

27 December

1865 (New Zealand) In the same way that John Tawell had been trapped by the use of the newly installed telegraph system in England in 1845 (see 1 January), and the fugitive Dr Crippen was waylaid at sea thanks to the wireless telegraph in 1910 (see 31 July), so New Zealand was having its own success with the wonders of its new telegraph network in snaring one of its own brutal killers. It was in December 1865 that a description of James Stack was sent around the country and, supported by a government reward of £50, was instrumental in Stack's arrest at Kaipara on 27 December of the same year.

James Stack was a former soldier and current bully-boy, never far from trouble. Following the death of his wife in 1865, he moved in with his mother-in-law Mrs Mary Finnigan at her cottage at Otahuhu. Also living in the house were Mary Finnigan's three youngest sons: seventeen-year-old James, fourteen-year-old Benjamin and ten-year-old John.

On the first day of the Auckland Races, towards the end of

September 1865, Mrs Finnigan and her three sons disappeared. Inquiries were instigated by Mary's eldest son, Alexander, who had been away serving in the army, but no trace could be found of his mother or his siblings. All James Stack could suggest, preposterous as it might sound, was that they had suddenly upped and left for the gold diggings at Hokitika.

There the matter rested, but persistent rumour, and perhaps a guilty conscience, resulted in James Stack taking to his heels. This would have been just a few days before Christmas. Now the local constable made a move. A thorough search of the cottage revealed nothing more incriminating than some partially burnt clothing, so it was decided to dig up the ground around the house. It was by the side of the boundary fence that searchers found the body of James Finnigan; Benjamin's remains were uncovered in the same area, and Mary Finnigan's last resting place was beneath the vegetable garden. There was no trace of the body of John Finnigan. Medical examination proved that the three victims had died from massive fracturing of the skull; and in Benjamin's case his throat had been cut as well.

When he was apprehended, James Stack was returned to Auckland to be charged with murder. At his trial, he was convicted and sentenced to death. Just before his execution Stack received a visit from Alexander Finnigan who implored him to reveal the burial place of his brother John. Stack, however, stubbornly continued to deny any part in the murders, and once more protested his innocence. It was not until some years later that the skeleton of ten-year-old John Finnigan was recovered, not far from the place where his mother and brothers had lain.

28 December

1836 (England) On 28 December 1836, a bricklayer passing some new building works in London's Kilburn district noticed a package wrapped up in sacking hidden behind a paving stone which had been leant up against the wall. When he removed the stone for a closer look, the labourer was appalled to see that the package rested in a pool of frozen blood. After the superintendent of works and other witnesses had assembled, the bundle was opened to reveal the trunk of a woman later estimated to have been about fifty years of age. Of the head and limbs there was no trace.

On 6 January of the following year, 1837, Matthias Rolfe, a lock-keeper at Stepney, was closing one of the canal gates when he fished out a human head. The flesh, it was recorded, was 'quite perfect, but the jawbone was broken and protruded through the skin, and one of the eyes seemed to have been knocked out by means of a blunt instrument. One ear was split, and an ear-ring hole was pierced above it; it looked as if the ear-rings had been torn from the ears. The skull had been fractured by a heavy blow, and the surgeon estimated that the grisly relic had been in the water for four or five days. The head belonged to the dismembered trunk.

It was 2 February before the legs came to light, being the unwelcome find of a man cutting osiers in Coldharbour Lane. The very decomposed limbs were matched with the exhumed torso and found to correspond perfectly.

After the finding of the head in the canal lock-gate, a man who had reported his sister missing viewed the body and identified it as Hannah Brown. It was not difficult then to associate this luckless individual with a man named James Greenacre. When he was arrested, Greenacre had in his possession pawn tickets from Hannah Brown's silk dresses and shoes, and his lodgings revealed the four locked trunks which testified to his imminent departure for America. In an adjoining room there were remnants of bloodstained cloth of the same type that was found near the sack containing the body. Although he attempted suicide, Greenacre recovered to stand his trial, be convicted of Hannah Brown's murder and be sentenced to death. He was executed at Newgate on 2 May 1837.

29 December

1908 (England) 'I have just shot somebody!' Not a customary opening on a visit to the local GP, but on this freezing night of 29 December that was it: 'I have just shot somebody!'

The man speaking was Edward Lawrence, a wealthy brewer based in Wolverhampton; the doctor's name was Galbraith. It was, to say the least, a strange situation, and Dr Galbraith invited a colleague at the surgery to accompany him back to Lawrence's home. When the three men arrived, they found Ruth Hadley shot in the head and dying. In fact she departed this life shortly afterwards and before reaching hospital.

As the inquiry into Ruth's death evolved, it was clear that Lawrence had been having an affair with her; and an affair that was serious enough for him to have left his wife and children. It was also established that Lawrence the brewer was uncommonly fond of his own produce; in short, he was a drunkard, and a violent drunkard at that. It was not a good start for a defence against a charge of murder; less so when it was learnt that Mrs Lawrence had recently filed for divorce on grounds of cruelty.

Edward Lawrence stood his trial at Stafford, where even more facts came before the jury. Such as Edward threatening to kill Ruth – often! In fact Miss Hadley had left him once, only to return in the midst of his affair with another mistress. On the night of Ruth Hadley's death, the court was told, a servant had interrupted a row in which the victim was throwing cutlery at the accused. And it was on this point that Edward Marshall Hall could elaborate in Lawrence's defence. Ruth, it seemed, was both as fond of alcohol as her lover, and as violent in her cups. This particular night, Lawrence had run upstairs to fetch his revolver and fired it in order to frighten Miss Hadley. Afterwards he hid it under the mattress. Ruth had retrieved the weapon and a struggle ensued during which she was shot – accidentally of course.

Well, it must have said something for the persuasive tongue of one of the country's leading defence advocates that Marshall Hall convinced the jury. He must have convinced the judge too, because after the jury had acquitted Lawrence, the judge told him: 'If you will turn over a new page in your life you may yet have a happy time . . . then, perhaps, God will forgive you for the life you have led.'

30 December

1932 (South Africa) It might have been expected that Daisy De Melker – for being a woman if nothing else – might have been reprieved from her death sentence. But poisoners have always been just that bit more vilified than other killers. Perhaps it is the slow, cruel deliberation with which they take life that has caused the English Crown Prosecution Service always to field one of the Law Officers of the Crown – the Attorney-General or the Solicitor-General – in poisoning trials. And why in South Africa the death sentence of a poisoner was never commuted.

Alfred Sproat's attention was attracted by the obituary commemorating the death of Rhodes Cecil Cowle published in the *Rand Daily Mail* in March 1932. Cowle was the only surviving child of Daisy De Melker, Sproat's former sister-in-law. And because he was puzzled, Alfred wrote to the police authorities drawing attention to the other unfortunate losses in Daisy's immediate family. Alfred's own brother, Robert, had been her second husband and had died five years previously. Her first husband, William Cowle, had also died suddenly too, in 1923. As well as that, and counting Rhodes, all five of their children had also died long before their time.

The Johannesburg police discovered that Rhodes Cowle

and his mother quarrelled frequently, usually over matters of money. He was, by all accounts a surly and unpleasant youth, fond of threatening suicide when it seemed he might not get his own way. He was also not beyond landing his mother a few blows to the head when aroused. All in all the police felt it might be a good idea to exhume the bodies of Rhodes, William Cowle and Robert Sproat. Arsenic was found in Rhodes' remains, strychnine in those of the two others.

The problem was in linking Mrs De Melker with the poisons; a matter quickly solved when the attendant press publicity jogged the memory of a chemist named Spilkin, who came forward to report that Daisy De Melker had bought arsenic from him just days before the death of Rhodes Cowle. Daisy was taken in for questioning and eventually found herself before a bench consisting of Mr Justice Greenberg and two assessors. The trial lasted thirty days (then the longest trial of a European in the legal history of the Union of South Africa), and Daisy spent a total of eighteen hours in the witness box. At the end of the process, the charges of poisoning her husbands remained unproved, but Mrs De Melker was convicted of the murder of her son. Sufficient to earn her the capital sentence, which was carried out on 30 December 1932.

31 December

1975 (England) The first attack took place on the evening of 31 December 1975. The victim was Mrs Grace Adamson, who had opened her front door to a man posing as a policeman. He forced his way in, stabbed Mrs Adamson seven times, left her for dead and went to get a beer in the local pub. For those who are unfamiliar with English serial murders, 1975 was the time of the reign of terror of the 'Yorkshire Ripper'. Mrs Adamson was murdered in Bingley, Yorkshire – as it turned out, the town where Peter Sutcliffe had heard voices in the graveyard telling him to kill. But as if the Ripper were not enough to cope with, the Yorkshire police would soon find out that they had another serial killer on their hands.

Three days after the Bingley killing, sixteen-year-old Stephen Wilson was stabbed to death while he was waiting at a bus-stop in Wastburn. Stephen did not die immediately and he was able to give the police this description of his attacker: about twenty-two years old, with black shoulder-length hair, wearing a black jacket and carrying a shoulder-bag. As Stephen Wilson lay dying in hospital his killer was in full flight, swimming across a freezing river before taking a cab home. It was the taxi-driver who eventually led the police to Mark Rowntree's address. But not before he had killed twice more.

Mrs Barbara Booth described herself as a 'model', and it is in one of those publications known as 'contact magazines' that Mark Rowntree first became aware of her services. On the night of 7 January 1976, he visited her house in Leeds and stabbed her to death; for good measure he also killed Mrs Booth's three-year-old son.

Following the taxi-driver's directions, detectives were waiting for Rowntree when he arrived home. While making a statement in custody, his only regret seems to be that he fell one victim short of the death toll of his hero the 'Black Panther' (see 14 January) – five.

A comparative rarity among serial killers, Rowntree, although he had been adopted as a baby, enjoyed all the love and privilege of a secure middle-class family. He was educated at a public school and was competent enough to be offered a place at university. He chose instead to become a bus-driver. Sadly, Mark also suffered from schizophrenia, which in part was responsible for an unreasonable belief that women despised him.

At his trial at Leeds Crown Court in June 1976, Mark Rowntree pleaded guilty to manslaughter on grounds of diminished responsibility. The plea was accepted by the Crown, and Rowntree was ordered to be confined to Rampton top-security psychiatric hospital without limit of time.

Index

More True Crime from Headline

THE 1995 MURDER YEARBOOK

BRIAN LANE

THE MOST UP-TO-DATE ACCOUNT OF THE YEAR'S HORRIFYING CRIMES

Following a year characterised by crimes of unparalleled violence and sensational trials, *The 1995 Murder Yearbook* focuses on the key areas of current concern: the increasing numbers of children who kill, as in the tragic death of James Bulger; the scandalous escalation of the incidence of police officers being slain on duty by ever more desperate criminals; and the parallel scourges of the spread of firearms and the rise of the professional contract killer.

As well as notable British trials, including those of child killer Robert Black; Colin Ireland, the gay serial killer; and those responsible for the sadistic murder of Manchester teenager Suzanne Capper, Brian Lane covers celebrated court cases from all over the world. *The 1995 Murder Yearbook* also includes the investigation into the horrifying murders at Cromwell Street, Gloucester.

NON-FICTION / TRUE CRIME 0 7472 4537 1

More True Crime from Headline

ENCYCLOPEDIA OF WOMEN KILLERS

BRIAN LANE

From Lizzie Borden to Aileen Wuornos . . . a chilling catalogue of the world's most deadly females

Women who kill are neither a new nor a common phenomenon. But it is their comparative rarity which makes the motivations of those women who do turn to murder the focus of massive public speculation.

In *The Encyclopedia of Women Killers*, true-crime historian Brian Lane has assembled the most comprehensive international collection of cases on the subject yet published. From more than 200 individual profiles a pattern emerges of two main categories of these deadly females: those who murder willingly for the all-too-familiar motives of greed, jealousy and revenge, and those for whom killing is the last resort in their flight from male aggression.

INCLUDES: BEVERLEY ALLITT • MARY BLANDY
AMELIA DYER • SHEILA GARVIE • BELLE GUNNESS
HÉLÈNE JEGADO • CHRISTINE & LEA PAPIN
PAMELA SMART • CAROLYN WARMUS
SIMONE WEBER • and many more

NON-FICTION / TRUE CRIME 0 7472 4205 4